KT-237-172

THE MODERN MOTOR ENGINEER

A PRACTICAL WORK ON THE MAINTENANCE, RUNNING, ADJUSTMENT, AND REPAIR OF AUTOMOBILES OF ALL TYPES, AND ON THE MANAGEMENT OF GARAGES

BY

ARTHUR W. JUDGE

WHITWORTH SCHOLAR, A.R.C.Sc.; D.I.C.; A.M.I.A.E.
AUTHOR OF "HIGH-SPEED INTERNAL COMBUSTION ENGINES"
"MODERN MOTOR CARS AND COMMERCIAL VEHICLES," ETC., ETC.

WITH SPECIAL CONTRIBUTIONS BY EXPERTS

VOLUME II

THE CAXTON PUBLISHING COMPANY, LIMITED
CLUN HOUSE, SURREY STREET, LONDON, W.C.2

The Publishers guarantee that the Binding, Printing, Paper and Blocks for Illustrations used in this book are the products of British workers.

Made and Printed in Great Britain by
Hazell, Watson & Viney, Ltd., London and Aylesbury.

M.E. 3

CONTENTS OF VOL. II

CHAPTER I

SERVICING HIGH-SPEED OIL ENGINES

CHAPTER II

THE GARAGE AND ITS EQUIPMENT

CHAPTER III

THE EQUIPMENT OF LARGER GARAGES

CHAPTER IV

BREAKDOWN EQUIPMENT

CHAPTER V

CAR ELEVATING FOR INSPECTION AND REPAIR

CHAPTER VI

THE FUEL SYSTEM AND CARBURETTOR

CHAPTER VII

THE CLUTCH

CHAPTER VIII

THE GEAR BOX

FULL-PAGE PLATES

VOL. II

THE MODERN MOTOR ENGINEER

VOL. II

CHAPTER I

SERVICING HIGH-SPEED OIL ENGINES

In view of the fact that the high-speed oil engine has to a large extent replaced the petrol engine for commercial- and passenger-vehicle purposes, the modern motor engineer must be familiar not only with the principle of this type of engine, but also with its maintenance, possible faults and their remedies, and also with the servicing of these engines.

The oil engine, as we shall term it in the following considerations, is also known as the *Diesel* and the compression-ignition engine. It operates on a heavier and generally cheaper fuel than petrol and, owing to its appreciably higher heat efficiency, it gives a greater power output for a given quantity of fuel consumed. The fuel employed is known as Diesel, Gas Oil, Solar Oil, Diesoleum, etc., and it weighs from $8\frac{1}{4}$ to 9 lb. per gallon as against $7\frac{1}{4}$ to $7\frac{3}{4}$ lb. for ordinary petrols.

The general design of the oil engine follows that of high-speed petrol-engine practice. In this connection, the arrangement and cooling of the cylinders, the lay-out of the pistons, inlet and exhaust valves, camshaft, timing gear, connecting rods, crankshaft, and lubrication system are similar to those of the petrol engine; moreover, the same metals are employed. Where the oil engine differs from the petrol engine is in the design of the combustion chamber and in the method of introducing and igniting the fuel. The oil engine, therefore, is provided with entirely different shapes of combustion chambers (and sometimes piston heads), with a much higher compression ratio, and with a special pump and nozzle for injecting the fuel direct into the combustion chamber. It does not, therefore, require a carburettor, magneto (or coil) ignition, and sparking plugs. Some engines, however, are fitted with special plugs, known as *heater* or *glow* plugs, containing an electric resistance element which is heated to redness by means of the battery current. These plugs are only used for warming the combustion chamber when the engine is cold, for starting purposes; they are not used for ignition purposes as with ordinary sparking plugs, but are switched off immediately the engine has started up.

HOW THE FOUR-CYCLE OIL ENGINE OPERATES

The following outline of the operation of a modern oil engine is given for the benefit of those readers who may not be familiar with this type.

It is not possible, however, to consider at any greater length the theory or the descriptions of the various types of oil engines now in common use. Those who wish to obtain a fuller knowledge concerning the theory and practice of the high-speed oil engine and the various designs employed for road, rail, and marine purposes should consult the work given in the footnote.[1]

The principle of the four-cycle oil engine is illustrated in Fig. 1, which shows the cycle of operations that is employed in this type. Referring to Diagram (A), this shows the cylinder, piston, and valves of the

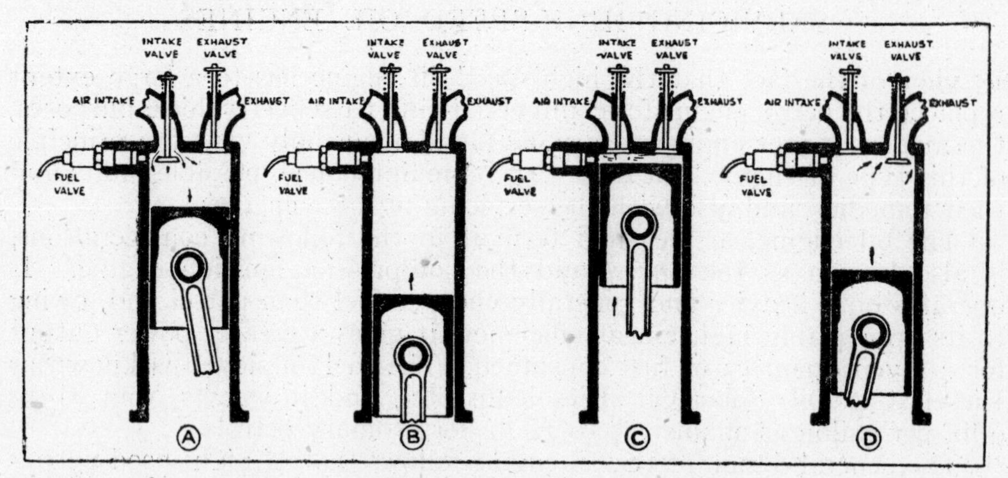

Fig. 1.—Illustrating Principle of Four-cycle Oil Engine.

oil engine. There are two valves, namely, an inlet valve for admitting pure air from the outside atmosphere and an exhaust valve for the outlet of the burnt products of combustion of the air and the fuel ; these valves operate with practically the same valve timing as those of petrol engines.

As shown, the piston is descending on its induction, or suction stroke, the air-inlet valve being opened by its overhead rocker arm and push rod from the camshaft below ; the latter—as in petrol-engine practice—runs at one-half engine speed. When the piston reaches the lowest part of its downward travel the air-inlet valve closes ; the exhaust valve, it will be observed, has remained closed during the whole of the suction stroke.

On the subsequent upward stroke [Diagram (B)] of the piston, both valves remain closed so that the charge of air within the cylinder is compressed. In the case of the high-speed oil engine, a much higher compression ratio, namely, from about 14 : 1 to 17 : 1 is employed, so that a much higher compression pressure occurs when the piston completes its upward stroke. The value of this pressure is from 450 to 550 lb. per sq. in., according to the compression ratio used and, to some extent, upon the

[1] *High-speed Diesel Engines.* A. W. Judge. (Chapman & Hall, Ltd., Henrietta Street, London, W.C.2.)

design of the combustion chamber. Owing to this high pressure, the air becomes heated to a relatively high temperature, namely, to about 500° to 550° C.; this temperature is above the ignition or burning temperature of the fuel used.

Just before the piston reaches the top of its compression stroke a small quantity of fuel is sprayed across the cylinder clearance space from the fuel valve shown on the left-hand side. The fine particles of fuel are almost immediately burnt in the compressed-air charge, since, as previously stated, the temperature of the latter is above that of the ignition-point of the fuel. The pressure of the burning fuel and the air rises during ignition to about 700 to 850 lb. per sq. in., and the piston is forced downwards. Diagram (C) shows the piston near the top of its compression stroke at the moment of the fuel injection.

The expansion stroke follows, and as the piston moves downwards the heated combustion products expand so that both their pressure and temperature fall, until, when the exhaust valve opens, the pressure falls to atmospheric value (14·7 lb. per sq. in.).

In most designs of oil engine, the exhaust valve is timed to open when the crank is at 40° to 50° from its bottom dead centre. The exhaust valve remains open during the next upward stroke of the piston—as shown in Diagram (D)—so that the burnt gases are forced out through the exhaust valve. When the piston arrives at the top of the exhaust stroke, or thereabouts, the inlet valve commences to open once more, and the cycle of operations, which has taken two complete revolutions of the crankshaft, is complete.

SOME FACTS CONCERNING OIL ENGINES

The high-speed oil engine, as used on most commercial vehicles, does not operate on the original Diesel or constant-pressure principle, but rather on an intermediate cycle between that of the Diesel and the petrol engine, or Otto cycle. By advancing the moment of commencement of the fuel injection sufficiently, namely, to 20° to 30° before top dead centre on the compression stroke, it is possible to obtain petrol-engine conditions of combustion. It is not advisable, however, to do this in many cases, as with this amount of injection advance the cylinder pressures become excessive and the engine is apt to work with a pronounced "knock." *For this reason, oil-engine operators should not attempt to advance the injection beyond the setting recommended by the manufacturers.*

Apart from the development of excessive pressures, too much injection advance causes increased fuel consumption and wear of the cylinder walls and bearings.

The *method of regulating the speed* and the load, in the case of oil engines, is by increasing or reducing the period over which fuel injection occurs. When the engine is idling, the injection period may be as short as 10° of crank angle, so that if injection occurs when the crank of the particular cylinder is 10° before its top dead centre, it will cease when the crank (and piston) are on the top dead centre. For full-power output the injection period is usually from 25° to 35° of crank angle.

It is usual with most motor-vehicle oil engines to fit *a speed-control governor*. This is usually built as part of the fuel-injection pump, and it serves to regulate both the idling speed and also the maximum engine speed. The driver's accelerator pedal is arranged to over-ride the governor control between these two extreme limits of speed.

It is inadvisable to run an oil engine at higher speeds than those recommended by the makers, since not only does the fuel consumption per horse-power hour increase, but the engine generally works with a smoky exhaust and may develop "Diesel knock."

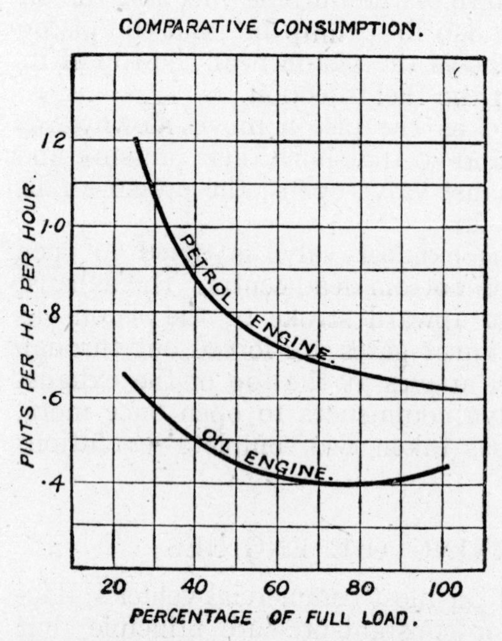

Fig. 2.—Comparative Fuel-consumption Curves.

The usual fuel consumptions obtained with the better designs of oil engines range from ·35 to ·45 lb. of fuel per b.h.p. hour.

Fig. 2 illustrates a typical fuel-consumption curve for the complete speed range of a motor-vehicle oil engine. It will be observed that the lowest consumption occurs at about 75 per cent. full load. At the lowest and the highest engine speeds the fuel consumptions are appreciably higher. The upper curve shows the corresponding petrol consumption of a petrol engine of similar power output; the consumptions at all loads are considerably higher than for the oil engine. It will be observed that the fuel consumption at 75 per cent. full load is ·4 lb. per b.h.p. hour for the oil engine and ·67 for the petrol engine, so that the latter type uses about 67 per cent. more fuel under similar load conditions. It is mainly on account of its much lower fuel consumption that the oil engine has largely replaced the petrol engine in heavy vehicles.

The oil engine has the important advantage over the petrol engine of giving a better pulling effort, or torque, over the lower engine-speed range, so that the top-gear performance at these speeds is much better.

A further advantage of the oil engine is its easy starting and the ability to take up its load very shortly after starting from the cold. Unlike the petrol engine, which requires a preliminary warming-up period of several minutes before it will "pull" satisfactorily, the oil engine can be put under load almost at once; it is advisable, however, to run it for a short time before starting off.

Although the modern motor-vehicle oil engine is necessarily somewhat heavier than the corresponding type of petrol engine, the difference in the weights has been brought down to a low figure, due to the use of light aluminium and magnesium alloys and to careful attention to design details.

PRACTICAL WORKING CONSIDERATIONS

Although the operation of all four-cycle oil engines is basically the same, the various designs of commercial engines differ considerably in their combustion chamber and fuel-injection arrangements. In order, however, to understand some of the most widely used oil engines, it is best to study, first, the general operation of the simplest type, namely, the *direct-injection* or *open-combustion chamber* engine.

The principle of operation of this engine is illustrated diagrammatically in Fig. 3. This type of oil engine has a plain cylinder head and a special shape of piston crown, which is designed from combustion considerations; several alternative shapes of piston crown are possible, however. The piston *h* is shown near the top of its compression stroke, both valves being closed, and fuel injection is taking place.

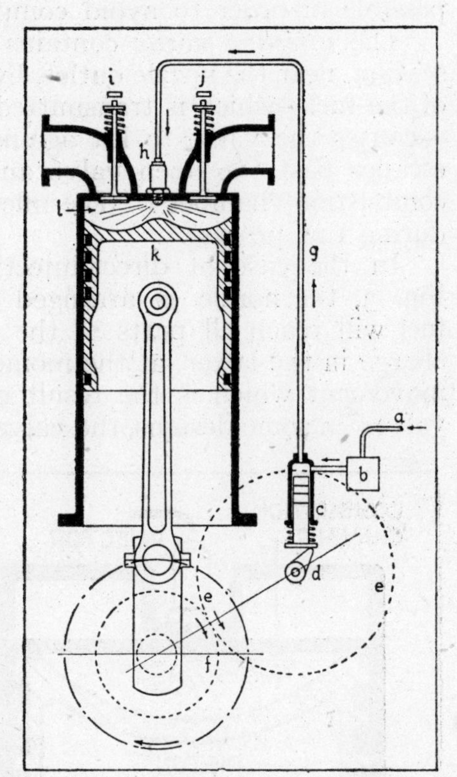

Fig. 3.—Principle of Direct-injection Engine.

Fuel from the main supply tank is pumped or fed by gravity (or vacuum feed) to the fuel pipe *a*, and through a fuel-straining filter *b*, to the fuel-injection pump *c*. This pump has a small well-fitting plunger working in an accurately ground and lapped barrel. In common with other forms of plunger pump, it has a non-return inlet valve, or its equivalent, which allows fuel to be drawn into the barrel as the plunger moves down, but will not allow fuel to pass back again into the inlet pipe as the plunger moves upwards. It has also a non-return valve on the delivery-pipe side, which allows fuel to be pumped past it into the latter pipe, but will not permit any fuel to flow back from this pipe into the barrel when the plunger moves downwards again, for the ball or cone valve then returns on to its seating. The fuel pump delivers only a very small quantity of fuel into the delivery pipe at each stroke. The usual quantity for a six-cylinder engine of about 100 b.h.p. is of the order of $\frac{1}{1000}$ cu. in. at light loads and $\frac{1}{200}$ to $\frac{1}{250}$ cu. in. at normal loads.

Since the fuel must be delivered at a pressure well above the compression pressure (450 to 550 lb. per sq. in.) and combustion pressure (750 to 900 lb. per sq. in.), the whole of the fuel pump and fuel-delivery-pipe system must be of strong construction. The usual fuel delivery pressures range from about 900 to 1,500 lb. per sq. in., although in special cases pressures up to 3,000 lb. per sq. in. are employed.

The plunger of the fuel pump is lifted by means of a small cam *d*, which is driven by a shaft from the timing wheel *e*; this, in turn, is driven from another gear wheel *f* on the crankshaft. Since the latter wheel has only one-half the number of teeth of the former, the cam *d* rotates at one-half engine speed.

The fuel delivered by the pump is forced, under the high pressure previously mentioned, through a narrow-bore strong steel pipe *g* to the fuel-injection valve *h*, situated in the head of the cylinders. The fuel pipe *g* usually has a bore of 1½ to 3 mm., this bore being kept as small as possible in order to avoid compression and also pressure-wave effects.

The *injection nozzle* contains a conically seated valve held on to its seating, near the nozzle outlet, by means of a strong spring. The pressure of the fuel—which is transmitted to part of the conical face of the valve—causes the valve to lift against the spring pressure, so that the fuel escapes past the open valve and through the nozzle opening into the combustion chamber *l*. The inlet valve *i* and exhaust valve *j* are closed during this process.

In the case of direct-injection engines of the type illustrated in Fig. 3, the nozzle is arranged to give a wide-angle spray so that the fuel will reach all parts of the combustion space. The compressed-air charge in the latter, at the moment of injection, has a certain amount of movement which is the result of its one-sided entry through the inlet valve; in some designs, the valve is provided with a deflector or "mask" to give the air a certain degree of swirl, or turbulence. The latter persists during the subsequent compression stroke and greatly assists the combustion of the fuel particles sprayed from the nozzle.

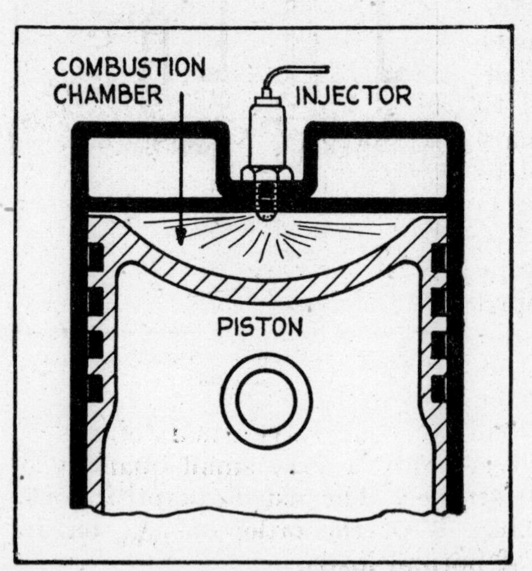

Fig. 4.—Direct-injection, or Open Combustion-chamber Engine.

OTHER TYPES OF DIRECT-INJECTION ENGINE

The direct-injection engine is made in a number of different designs. In practically all cases, however, the cylinder head is flat, whilst the piston crown is given a special shape. The fuel-injection nozzle is always designed to give an appropriate shape and penetration to the fuel injected so that the furthermost portions of the combustion space are reached. The basic principle of this and other types of engine is to ensure the thorough mixing of the fuel particles with the air in the combustion space.

The direct-injection engine is one of the most efficient of the various types, since it has no auxiliary combustion chamber and therefore no additional passages or surfaces where the heat of compression and combustion can be absorbed.

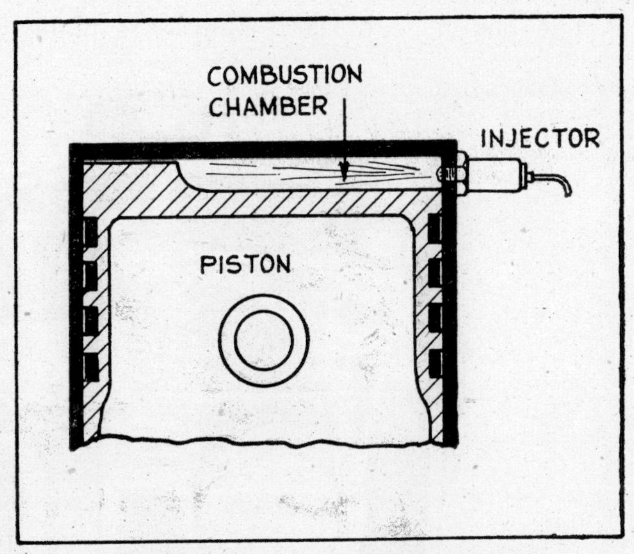

Fig. 5.—Another Design of Direct-injection Engine.

In consequence, this type is much easier to start from the cold, and as a general rule it is not necessary, nor usual, to fit glow plugs for starting purposes.

Two other well-known designs of direct-injection engines are illustrated, diagrammatically, in Figs. 4 and 5. The former diagram shows a cylinder fitted with a concave-headed piston, the surface of the piston crown being part of a sphere. To obtain equal penetration in all directions, the injection orifices should be at the centre of this spherical surface when injection is occurring. Fig. 5 shows another variation of the direct-injection engine, with shallow cavity piston.

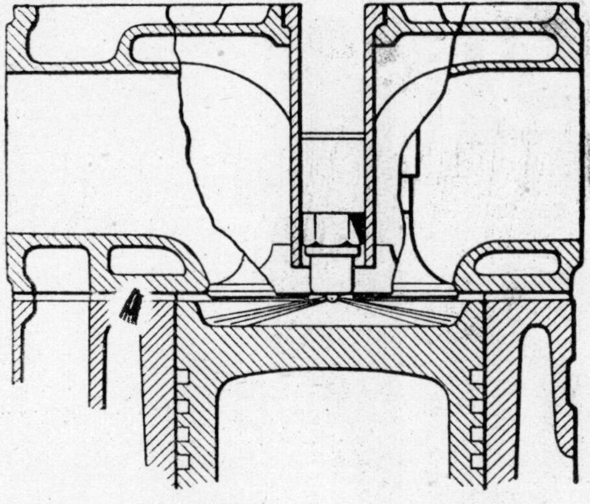

Fig. 6.—Actual Design of Cavity-piston Direct-injection Cylinder Head.

The design shown in Fig. 5 has a cut-away piston head and the injector on the side of the combustion chamber. The cut-away portion does not extend right across the piston, but forms a kind of fan-shaped cavity in the piston head. The injection nozzle is arranged to give a flat type of spray of approximately the same angle as the fan-shaped cavity. It will be observed that the piston comes fairly close to the cylinder head, on the left, so that during the latter stages of the compression stroke the air is forced from this region into the piston cavity; this motion of the air assists in the combustion of the fuel.

THE LEYLAND CAVITY-PISTON ENGINE

The Leyland oil engine illustrated in Fig. 7 is widely used in this country, so that the motor engineer should be familiar with its design and construction.

The piston *b*, in this example, is made with a deep cavity *a*, but,

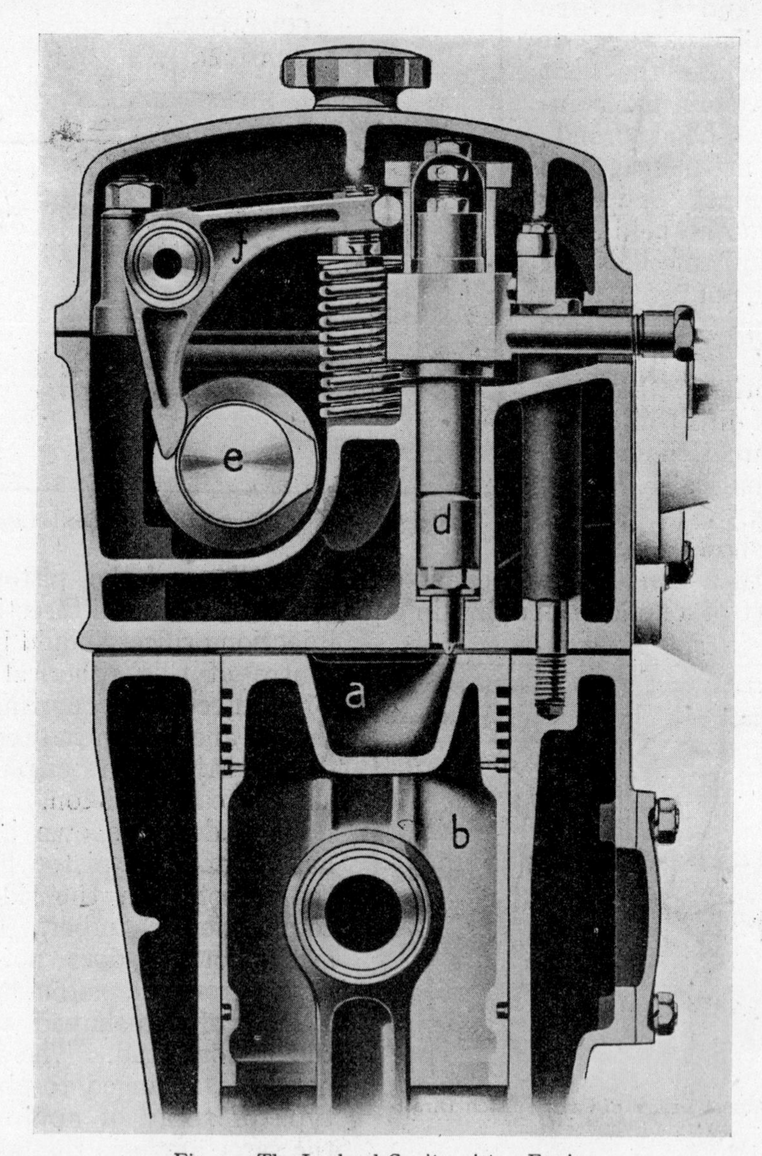

Fig. 7.—The Leyland Cavity-piston Engine.

instead of this cavity being central it is offset in the direction of the fuel-injection nozzle *d*. When the piston is approaching the top of its compression stroke the air between the flat portion of the piston crown and the cylinder head is forced into the cavity so that on this account it acquires a turbulent motion. In addition, the air is given a swirling movement during the suction stroke, by means of the masked inlet valve (Fig. 8). As this swirl persists throughout the compression stroke the air in the piston cavity is in a state of turbulence when the fuel is injected, so that the air flows rapidly past the fuel-injection nozzle and picks up the fuel particles, thus enabling them to burn in the most efficient manner. This type of engine requires no glow plugs for starting and it has a very low fuel consumption.

The engine has overhead inlet and exhaust valves operated from an overhead camshaft *e* and rocker arms such as *f*. The piston is of a strong aluminium alloy, known as " Y-alloy," and has six piston rings, the upper four being compression rings and the two lower ones oil control or scraper rings.

The engine is of the six-cylinder type, of $4\frac{3}{8}$-in. bore and $5\frac{1}{2}$-in. stroke, giving a cylinder capacity of 496 cu. in. (or 8·1 litres). It develops 55 b.h.p. at 1,000 r.p.m., and 93 b.h.p. at the higher governed speed of 1,800 r.p.m. A four-cylinder engine of similar design is also made. It has a bore of $4\frac{1}{2}$ in. and stroke of $5\frac{1}{2}$ in., and gives 70 b.h.p. at 1,800 r.p.m.

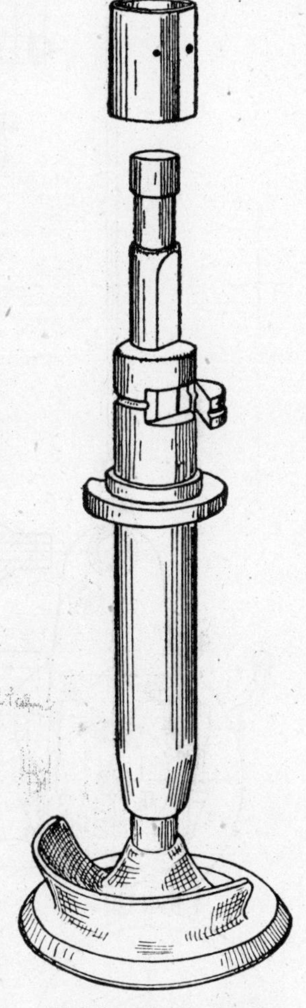

Fig. 8.—The Leyland Masked Inlet Valve.

ARMSTRONG-SAURER ENGINE

The more recent Armstrong-Saurer vehicles are fitted with the type of direct-injection turbulent cylinder arrangement shown in Fig. 9. The cylinder head is flat and the fuel-injection nozzle is at the centre of the head.

A special design of cavity piston (shown in Fig. 12) is employed, the cavity being in the form of a symmetrical double lobe. Two inlet and two exhaust valves are employed for each cylinder.

The piston, at the top of its stroke, approaches very closely to the cylinder head. The particular design of cavity combustion chamber has been adopted in order to obtain a type of air-charge movement, known as the *dual-turbulence* one, to ensure complete combustion of the fuel.

Referring to the diagrams shown in Fig. 10, these depict the air movements and the deflection of the fuel spray. The upper left-hand view shows the direction of the horizontal stream from the valves A and C, which are both of the masked type. The path of the fuel spray in still air is shown at B, in the upper right-hand diagram, whilst C in-

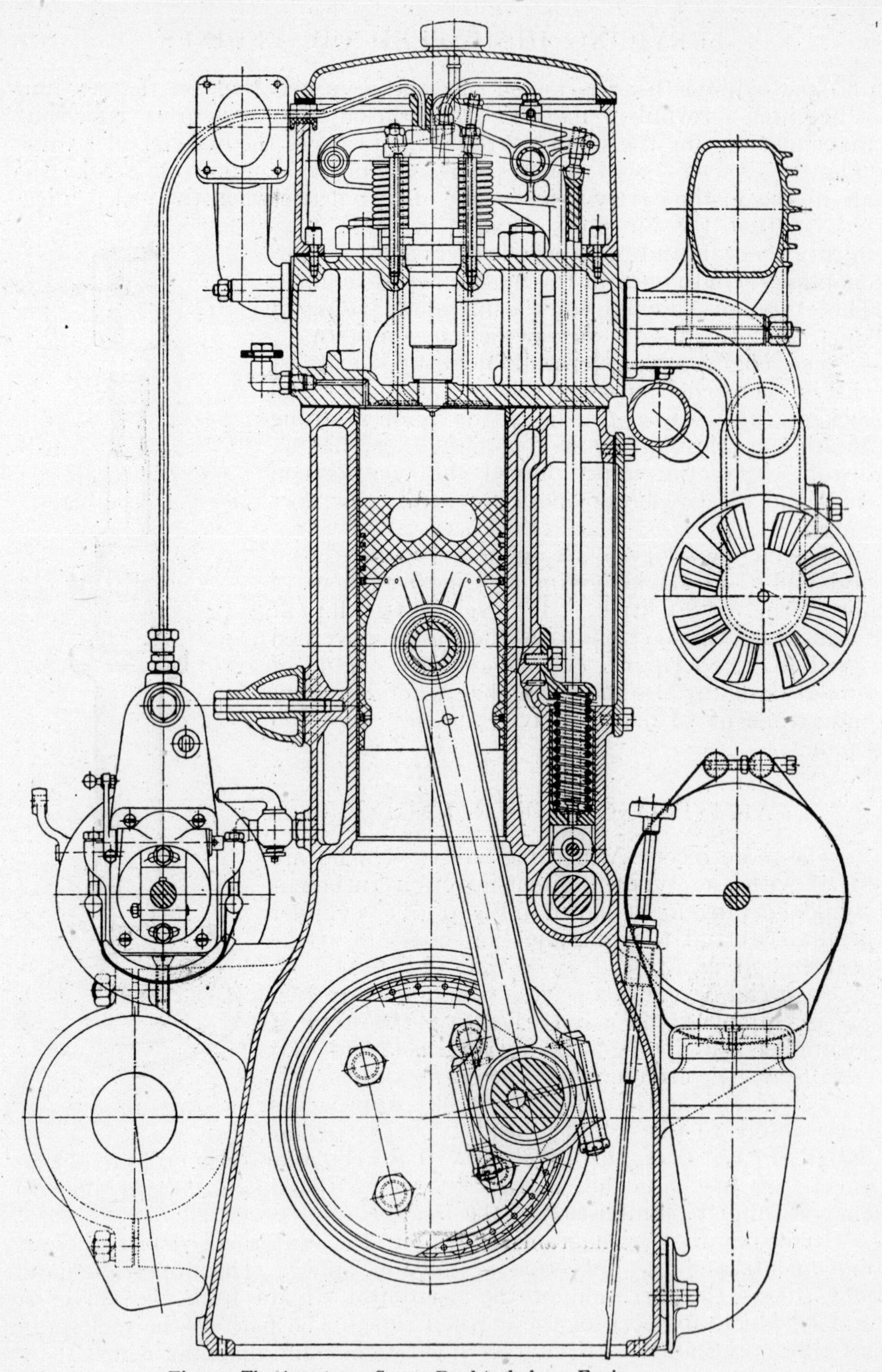

Fig. 9.—The Armstrong-Saurer Dual-turbulence Engine.

dicates the effect of the rotary swirl upon this path. At D is shown the horizontal air stream in combination with the vertical air swirl caused by the air being trapped by the piston during its ascent. At E is shown the superimposed air swirl acting on the path of the fuel spray F. The vertical air movement is obtained by means of the special shape of combustion engine used. It will be observed that the air movements obtained by this dual turbulence give a very intimate mixing of the fuel with the air during the combustion process.

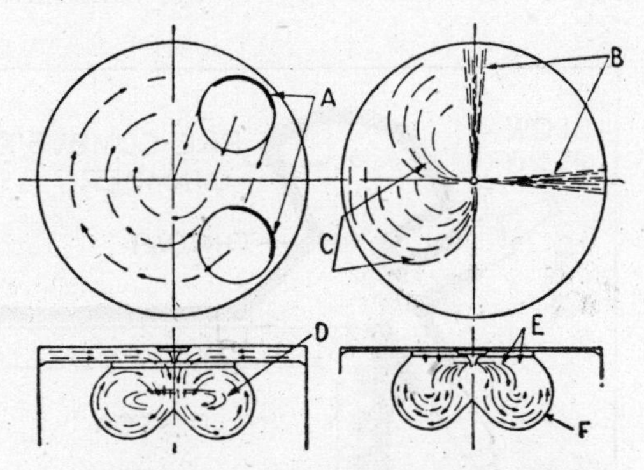

Fig. 10.—Principle of Dual Turbulence Engine.

The Armstrong-Saurer engines built in this country are made in the four- and six-cylinder models giving maximum b.h.p.'s of 80 and 120 respectively, at 1,800 r.p.m. These engines have a bore of 110 mm.

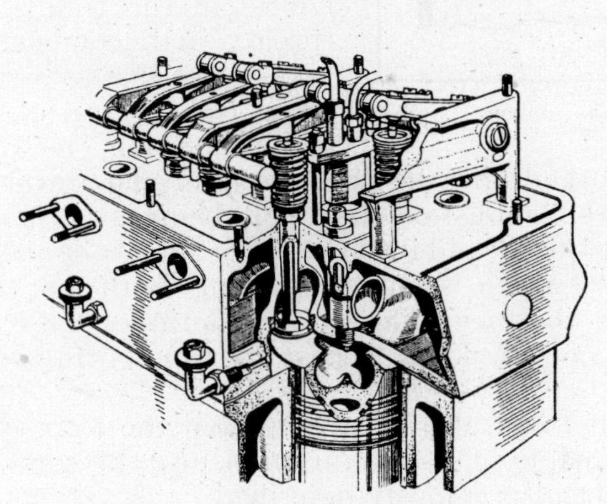
Fig. 11.—Cut-away View of Part of Armstrong-Saurer Engine.

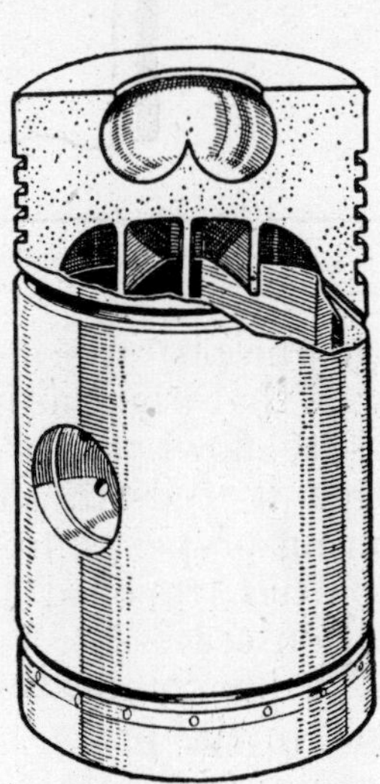
Fig. 12.—Cavity Piston of Armstrong-Saurer Engine.

and stroke of 150 mm.; compression ratio of 15 : 1; weights of 1,350 and 1,720 lb., and fuel consumptions of ·385 lb. per b.h.p. hour.

PRE-COMBUSTION CHAMBER ENGINES

At one time the pre-combustion chamber engine was the most widely employed of any, for motor-vehicle purposes. It is still used on recent Continental engines imported into this country and there is an appreciable number of British engines still in service having this form of combustion chamber.

Referring to the diagrammatic sketch shown in Fig. 13 of a typical pre-combustion chamber engine of the well-known Acro design, it will be observed that there is an auxiliary chamber communicating with the cylinder by means of a fairly narrow throat, or venturi. The fuel injector is fitted in such a position that it sprays its fuel into this throat. The action of the pre-combustion chamber engine is, briefly, as follows:

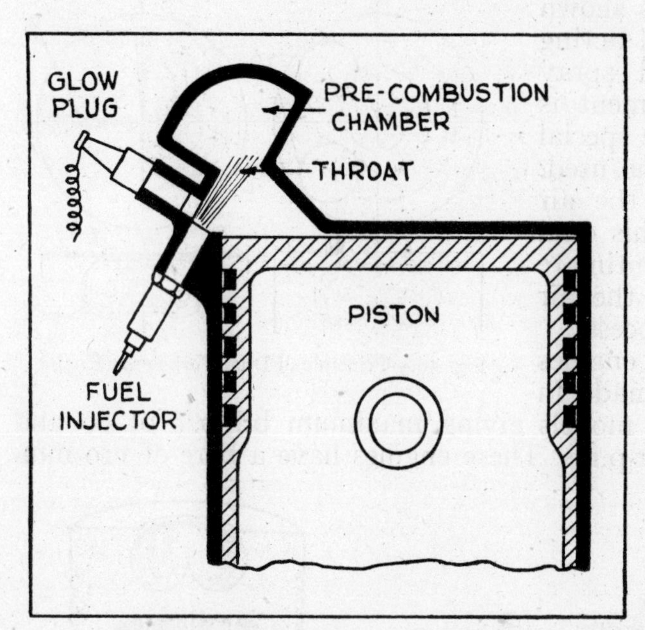

Fig. 13.—Pre-combustion Chamber Engine.

As the piston approaches the top of the compression stroke, the air charge is forced into the auxiliary chamber. Fuel is then injected just before the piston reaches its top dead centre and ignites in the tunnel, or throat, and combustion takes place in this region. Upon the reversal of the piston's motion, the space above the piston becomes enlarged and the pressure falls. The result of this is that the air in the pre-combustion chamber, being at a higher pressure, flows out through the throat and into the space above the piston so that it feeds the fuel spray (which is still proceeding) with air, thus ensuring proper combustion of the fuel. This action continues until the piston has travelled about 15° of crank angle past its top centre, when injection ceases.

The pre-combustion chamber can also be arranged in the form of a cavity in the piston; the principle of its operation is just the same as for the external type of Acro head previously described.

Fig. 14 shows a sectional view of a high-speed oil engine of the pre-combustion type similar to that employed on motor vehicles such as the earlier Armstrong-Saurer models and the A.E.C. motor omnibuses. The piston *A* is shown at the top of its compression stroke. *D* denotes the auxiliary chamber; *C* the communicating throat; *E* the fuel-injection nozzle, which receives its supply of fuel from the fuel-injector pump shown; *F* the heater or glow plug for starting purposes and *B* the inlet valve. The valves are operated by push rods and rocker arms from the camshaft shown to the right of the connecting rod. Special features of the engine include a crankshaft with large-diameter ball-bearings for the main journals, a five-ring piston of aluminium alloy, and full pressure-fed lubrication system.

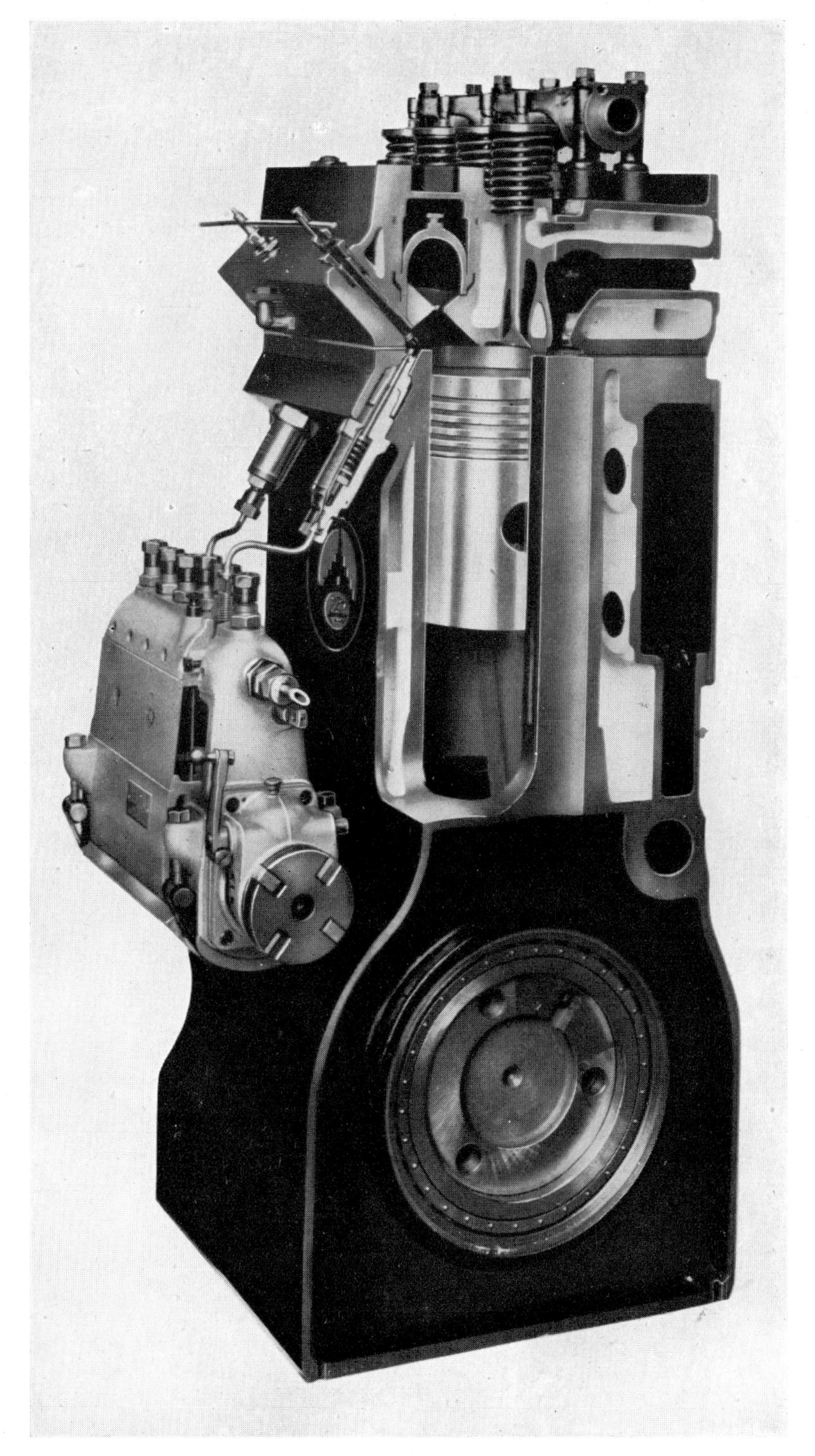

THE ARMSTRONG-SAURER ENGINE WITH "ACRO" HEAD.

A part-sectional photographic view of the same engine (Armstrong Saurer) is given in Plate facing p. 12. The six-cylinder fuel-injection pump is shown connected to two injection nozzles only. The pre-combustion chamber, five-ring piston, water jackets, valves and rocker-arms, and ball-bearing crankshaft are clearly shown in the photograph.

The pre-combustion chamber engine, when correctly adjusted and the fuel-injection system timed properly, runs smoothly within a speed range of about 400 and 3,000 r.p.m., with a smokeless exhaust. It is not so efficient as the previously described direct-injection engine, and therefore has not such a low fuel consumption. It is necessary to employ glow plugs for starting purposes.

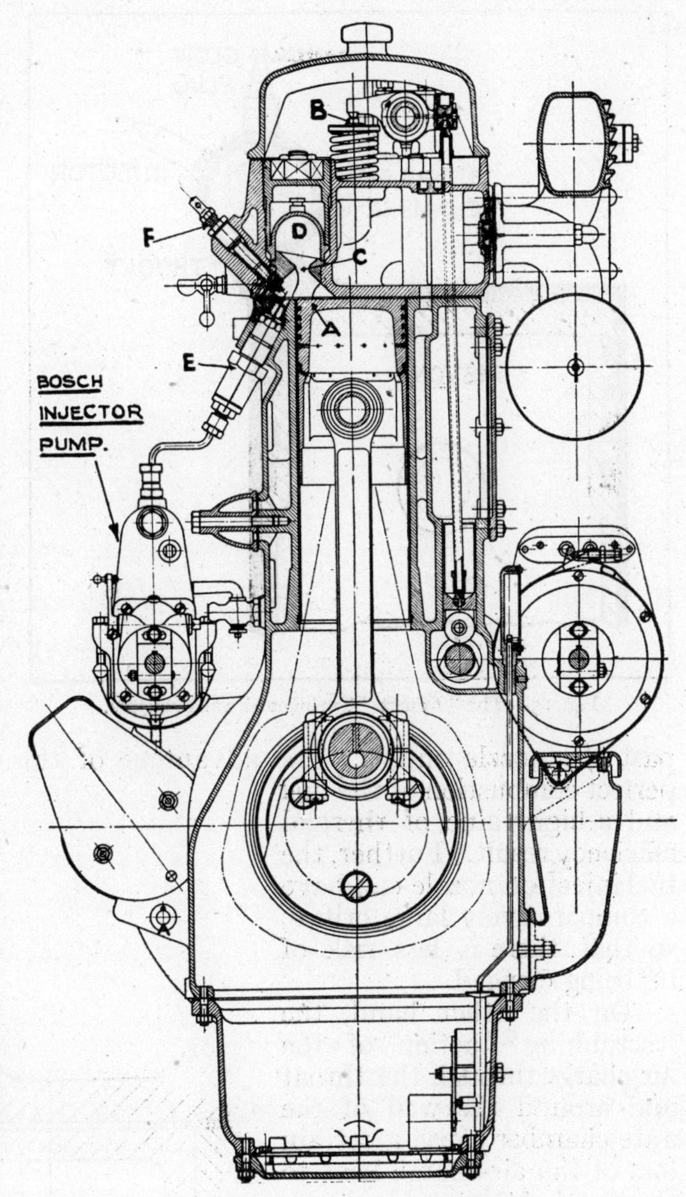

Fig. 14.—Sectional View of Pre-combustion Chamber Engine.

THE TURBULENT-TYPE OIL ENGINE

Although the compressed-air charge in most designs of oil engine has always a certain amount of movement or turbulence at the moment of fuel injection, certain types are designed especially to give a considerable amount of turbulence of a definite directional nature. Some of the direct-injection engines possess such turbulence—mainly as a result of employing masked inlet valves, but the class of oil engines known as the *turbulent* type generally obtain the desired degree of turbulence by means of an ante-chamber into which the air is forced during compression, with a swirling movement.

Fig. 15 illustrates the principle of the widely used " Comet " oil-engine combustion system. In this design the piston at the end of its compression stroke comes within a very short distance of the cylinder head, so that practically the whole of the air charge is forced through the throat shown into the spherical combustion chamber. Since the throat is tangential to the sphere, the charge is made to circulate around with an approximately circular rotation. The single-hole fuel nozzle directs the fuel spray at right angles to the air stream, the latter picking up the fuel particles as it sweeps past the nozzle outlet. The advantage of this method is that almost perfect combustion of the fuel and a high value of thermal efficiency result. Further, the fuel injection nozzle can have a comparatively large orifice, so that there is less risk of its being clogged.

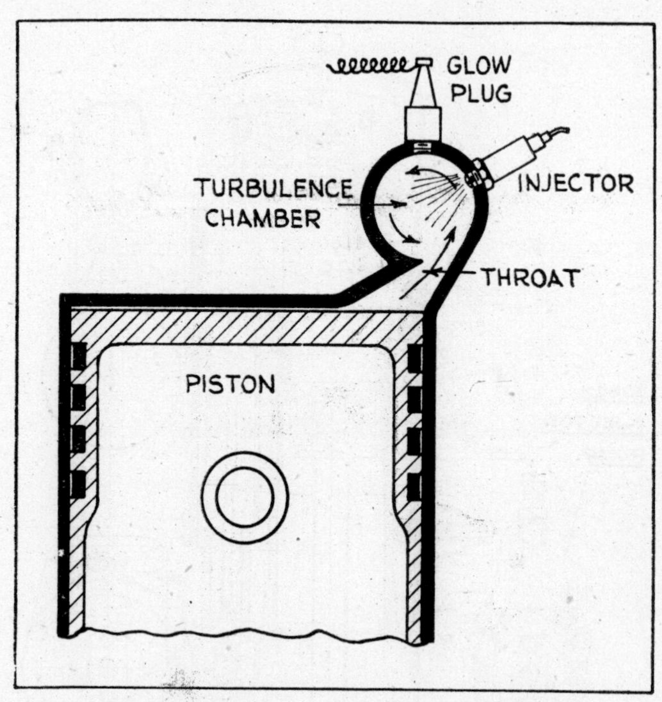

Fig. 15.—The " Comet " Turbulent-head Principle.

On the other hand, the " scrubbing " action of the air charge through the throat and around the wall of the ante-chamber cause a certain loss of the air-charge heat to the metal of the cylinder head, so that a loss of efficiency occurs on this account. The engine, also, is more difficult to start from the cold, so that glow plugs have to be used.

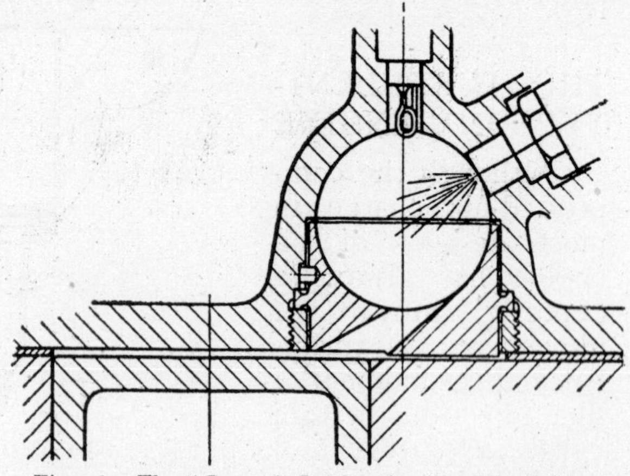

Fig. 16.—The " Comet " Combustion Head (A.E.C.).

The " Comet " type of head is employed in nearly forty different makes

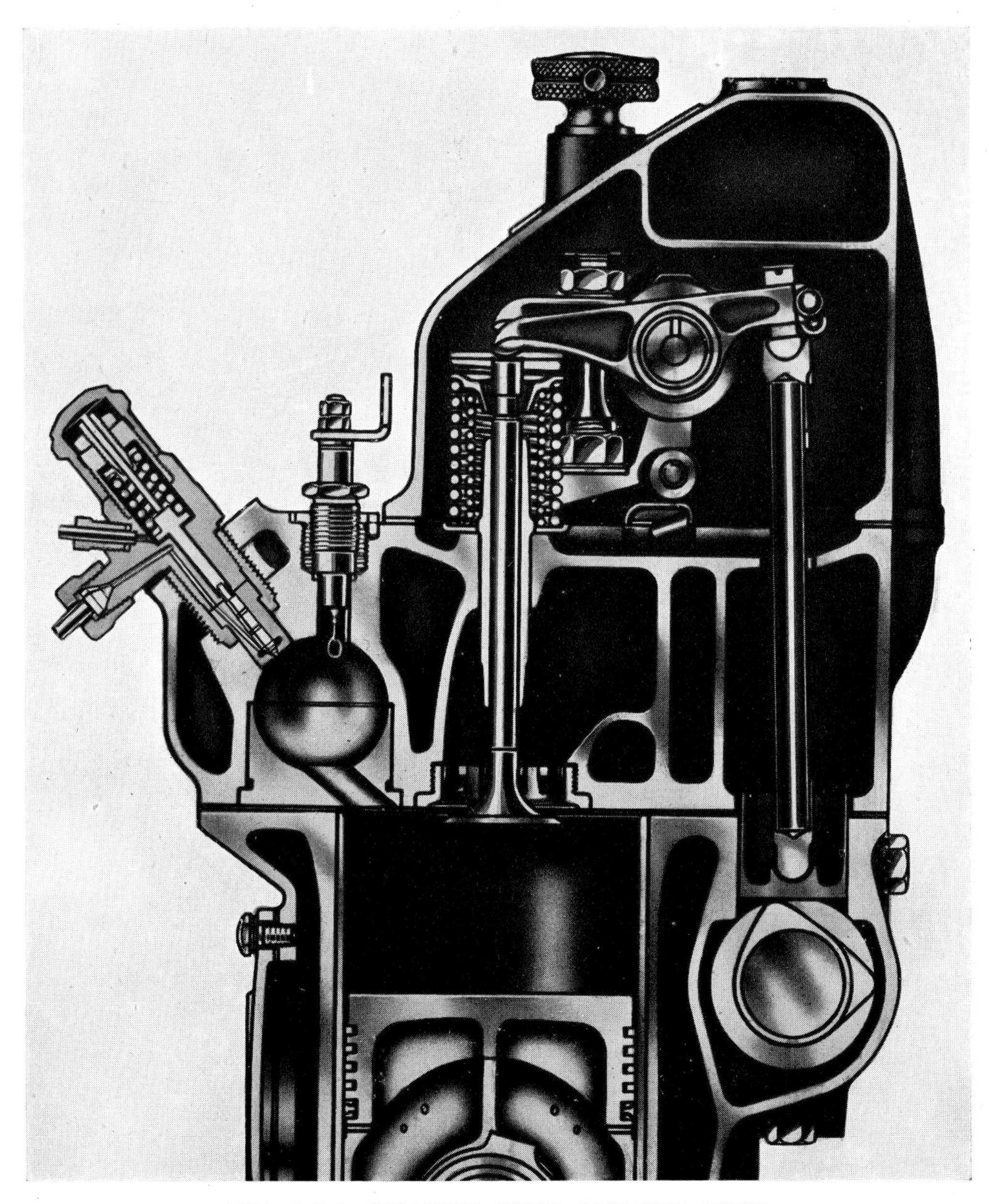

THE A.E.C. CYLINDER WITH "COMET" HEAD.

of British and foreign oil engines, on account of the high average (or mean) working pressures and speeds obtainable with it. Mean pressures up to 115 lb. per sq. in. and speeds of over 3,000 r.p.m. can be obtained without a smoky exhaust.

There is one important feature which contributes to the successful operation of this type, namely, the making of the lower half of the spherical chamber in the form of a heat-insulated part or "hot plug." Fig. 16 shows the actual design of the "Comet" head as used on the A.E.C. motor-'bus engines. The lower half of the spherical chamber is made of a heat-resisting nickel-chrome steel and is heat-insulated from the rest of the cylinder head over the greater part of its surface. Further, the axis of the fuel nozzle is directed radially inwards, not to the throat but some distance above the latter, as if to impinge on the hot plug. The object of the latter is to prevent the pungent exhaust which would otherwise occur when the engine is idling and the temperature of the combustion chamber had fallen to the point where the objectionable combustion products are created. By maintaining the hot plug above this critical temperature, the exhaust gases can be kept clear and comparatively odourless. The hot plug, it will be noted, is held in position by means of a screwed ring. When overhauling this type of engine, it is important to ensure that when this ring is screwed home *it should be approximately* $\frac{1}{32}$ in. *below the cylinder face.*

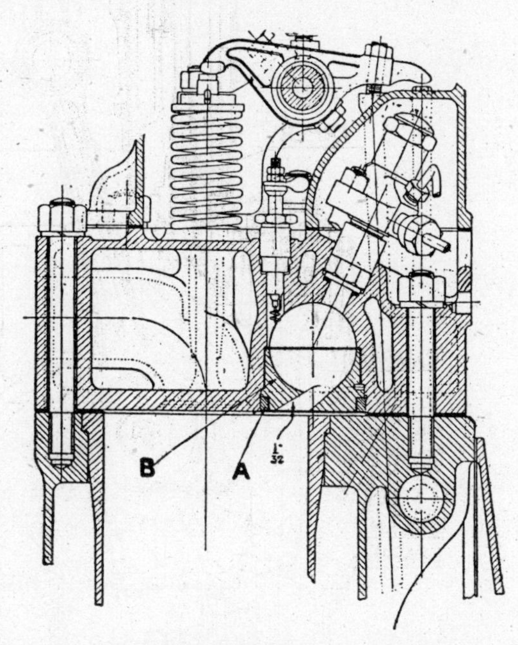

Fig. 17.—Cylinder Head of Crossley Engine.

Fig. 17 shows the cylinder head of the Crossley engine, which is fitted with the "Comet" type of combustion chamber. The lower half, or hot plug A, is secured in position by means of the nut or screwed ring A. The glow plug, it will be noticed, is in a tangential recess on the left. The overhead valve gear and the cylinder head holding-down studs and nuts are clearly shown in this illustration.

Plate facing p. 14 shows a photographic sectional view of the A.E.C. cylinder, which employs the "Comet" combustion chamber.

THE PERKINS ENGINE

The Perkins series of four-cylinder oil engines of low horse-power used on light commercial vehicles, and on certain experimental cars, have a spherical combustion chamber, somewhat similar to that of the "Comet"

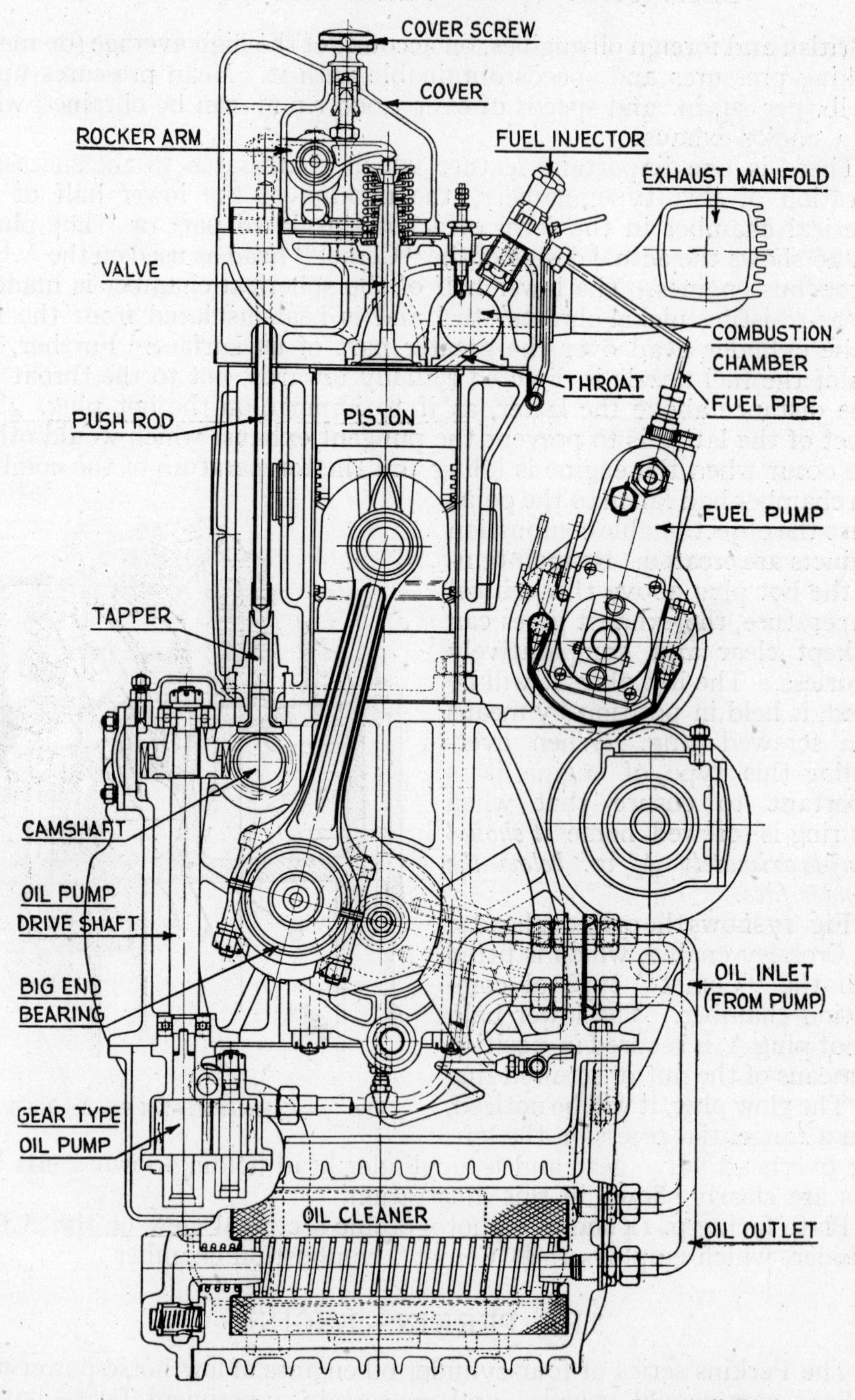

Fig. 18.—Sectional View of A.E.C. Oil Engine, fitted with the "Comet" Head.

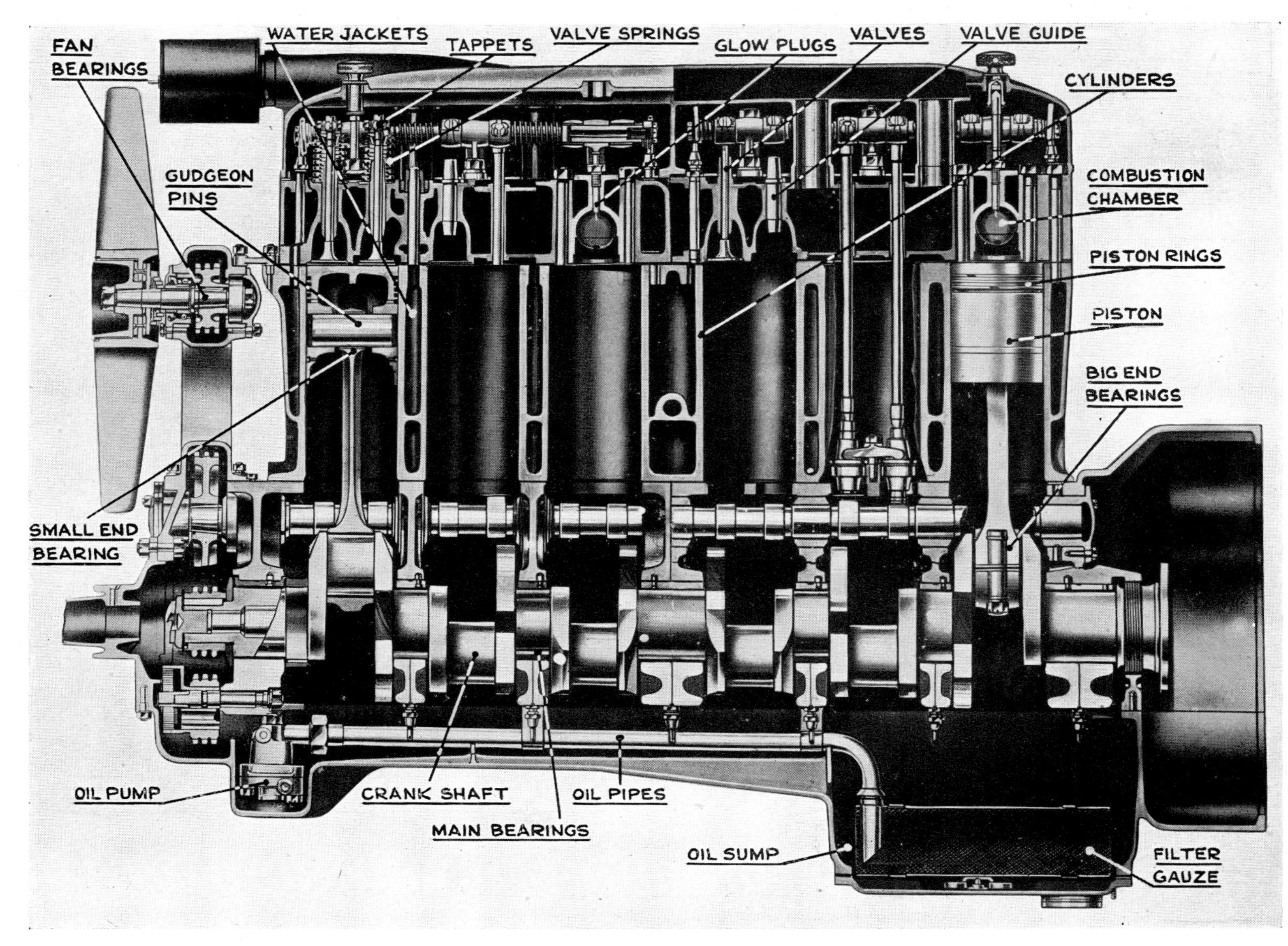

A SECTIONAL VIEW THROUGH THE A.E.C. 130-H.P. SIX-CYLINDER HIGH-SPEED OIL ENGINE, SHOWING PRINCIPAL ITEMS OF MAINTENANCE ATTENTION.

design, but the fuel injector E, Fig. 19, is placed in the parallel throat connecting the spherical chamber with the cylinder. The fuel is injected into this throat, the fuel injector having two outlet holes which are arranged so that part of the fuel is sprayed upwards into the air cell, thus becoming entrained in the air stream, while the remainder is forced down the passage against the air stream. The combined advantages of the turbulent air cell and direct-injection systems are claimed for this design. Starting from the cold is easy, no glow plugs being required. The engines of this type run smoothly, without "Diesel knock," and maintain speeds—in certain cases—of over 4,000 r.p.m.

Fig. 19.—Principle of the Perkins Combustion System.

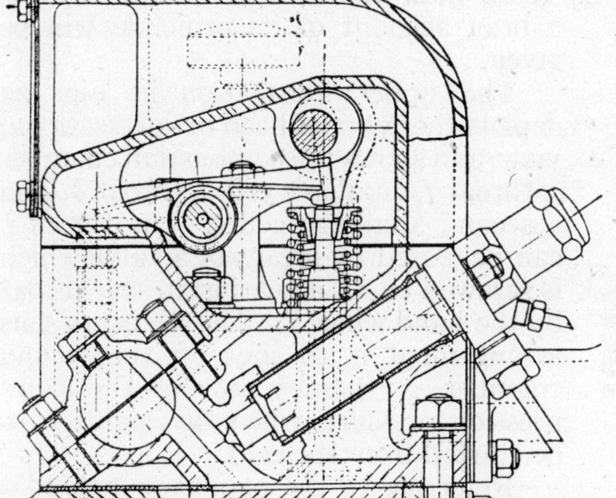

Fig. 20.—Actual Lay-out of the Perkins Cylinder Head.

THE CLERESTORY-HEAD TYPE

Another fairly widely used method of obtaining turbulence is shown in Fig. 21. In this example, the combustion chamber is in the form of a short cylinder placed centrally above the cylinder proper. The inlet and exhaust valves are arranged to seat in the flat ends of the combustion chamber, as shown in the illustration. The piston has a spigot above which almost but not entirely fills the entrance to the combustion chamber. It will be observed that, in the left-hand diagram, this spigot practically touches the edge of the combustion chamber on the left but leaves a clear passage on the right. In consequence, as the piston nears the top of the compression stroke the displaced air charge enters the combustion chamber from the right with a tangential movement, so that when the fuel is injected from the central injection nozzle above, the fuel sprays across the direction of movement of the air stream, where it readily finds all the air it requires for rapid combustion. This compact and symmetrical design gives efficient combustion combined with easy cold-starting without the use of glow plugs.

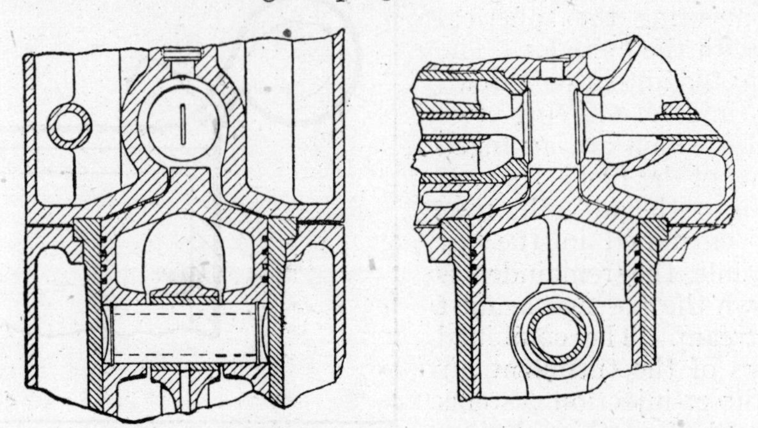

Fig. 21.—The Clerestory-head Combustion Chamber.

THE LANOVA COMBUSTION HEAD

In view of the fact that this Continental type of oil engine is made under licence in this country by more than one firm of manufacturers, a brief account of its principle will be given.

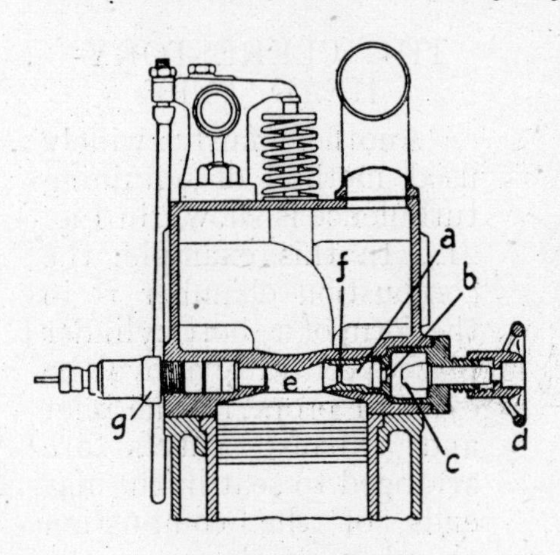

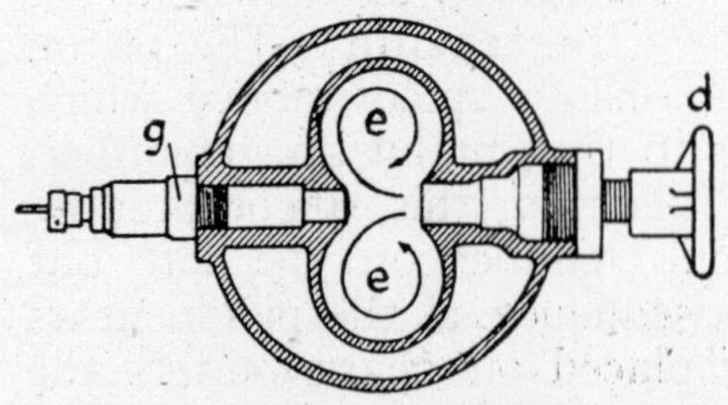

Fig. 22.—The Lanova Combustion System.

The upper illustration in Fig. 22 depicts the cylinder head in side-sectional view, and shows the combustion chamber *e*, throat *f*, auxiliary cell *a*, throat *b*, and a second auxiliary cell *c*. The throat *b* can be closed by means of a valve which is screwed on to a seating in the throat by the hand wheel *d*. The object of this arrangement is to shut off the second chamber *c*, thereby raising the compression pressure, when the engine is to be started from the cold.

Referring to the plan view below, it will be observed that the main combustion chamber *e* is of double-lobe shape. The fuel injector *g* is located so as to direct its fuel spray towards the opening *f* in the first auxiliary chamber.

When the piston is almost at the top of its compression stroke, the fuel stream is injected across the space between the two main combustion-chamber lobes, towards the throat *f*. By the time the spray reaches this entrance it has become heated, so that ignition commences before

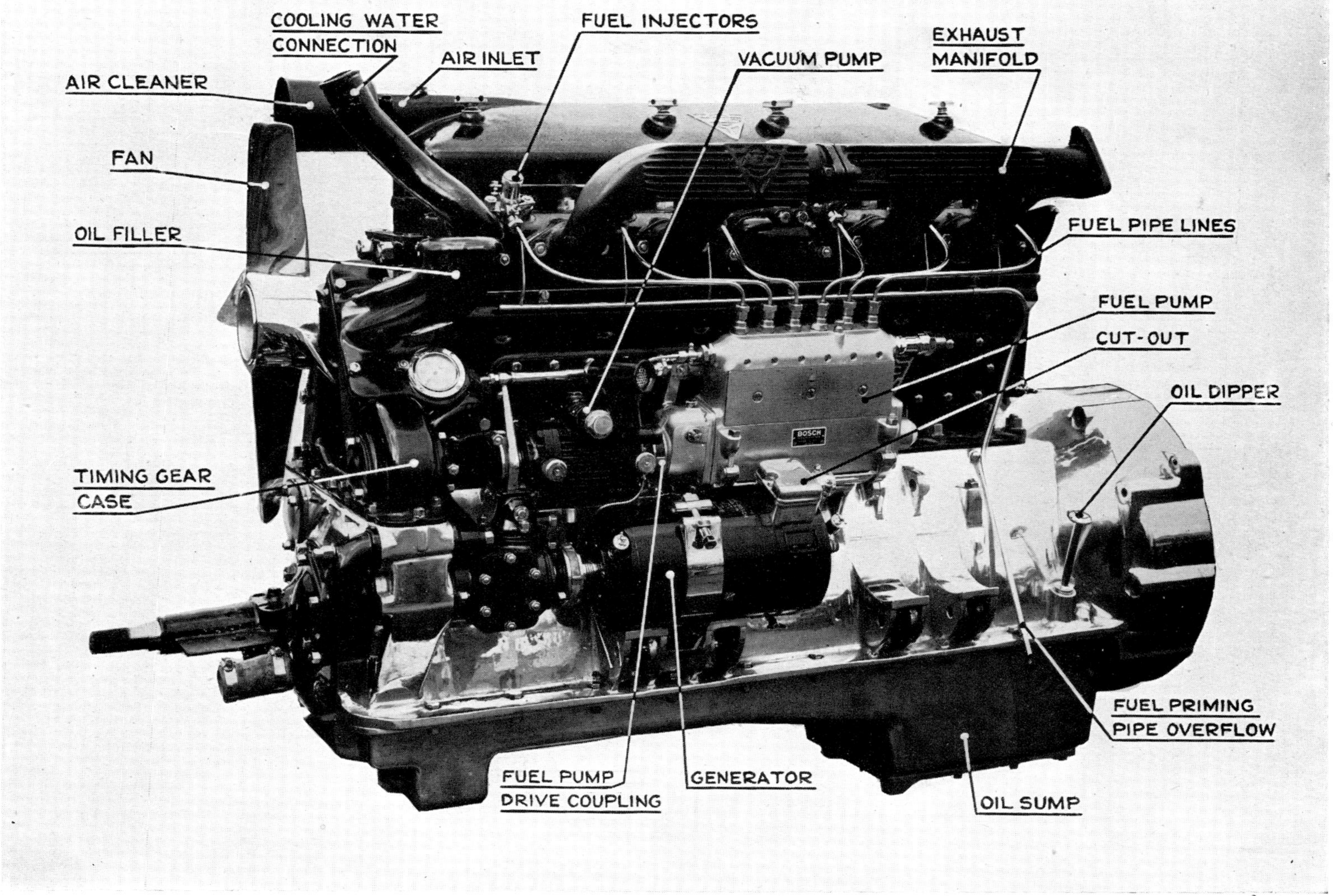

COOLING WATER CONNECTION
FUEL INJECTORS
EXHAUST MANIFOLD
AIR INLET
VACUUM PUMP
AIR CLEANER
FAN
OIL FILLER
FUEL PIPE LINES
FUEL PUMP
CUT-OUT
OIL DIPPER
TIMING GEAR CASE
FUEL PRIMING PIPE OVERFLOW
FUEL PUMP DRIVE COUPLING
GENERATOR
OIL SUMP

EXTERNAL VIEW OF THE A.E.C. 130-H.P. SIX-CYLINDER HIGH-SPEED OIL ENGINE, SHOWING PRINCIPAL POINTS OF ATTENTION.

the fuel enters the air cell *a*. As soon as the piston begins to descend, the pressure in the combustion chamber becomes less than that in the air cell *a*, with the result that the air rushes out in the opposite direction to that of the fuel spray, thus atomising the latter and carrying it around in the two lobe-shaped combustion chambers *e*, so that an intimate mixing of the fuel particles with the air is ensured. The rate of pressure rise when ignition commences is relatively low, since only a portion of the air is available for combustion.

The compression pressures used are 380 to 440 lb. per sq. in., while the combustion pressures rise to 550 to 650 lb. per sq. in.—values which are comparatively low for high-speed oil engines. As a result, the engine runs smoothly and it also yields high values of the mean effective pressure, namely, from 115 to 120 lb. per sq. in. The fuel-injection pressure is about 1,200 lb. per sq. in.

THE VICTOR ENGINE

The "Victor" horizontally opposed two-cylinder engine of 80 mm. bore by 100 mm. stroke is the smallest British oil engine. It has a cylinder capacity of 1,000 cu. cms., is water-cooled, and develops 20 b.h.p. at 3,000 r.p.m. Its overall dimensions are 19 × 30 × 17 in. and it weighs 280 lb., thus giving 14 lb. per h.p.; the fuel consumption is about ·4 lb. of crude oil per b.h.p. per hour. At full power the engine uses 8 lb. of oil per hour, or slightly less than one gallon.

The cylinder head is shown in Fig. 23. It employs a spherical air cell with horizontal venturi or throat. The fuel is sprayed vertically downwards across the main direction of the air stream. No glow plug is fitted, since the engine starts readily from the cold.

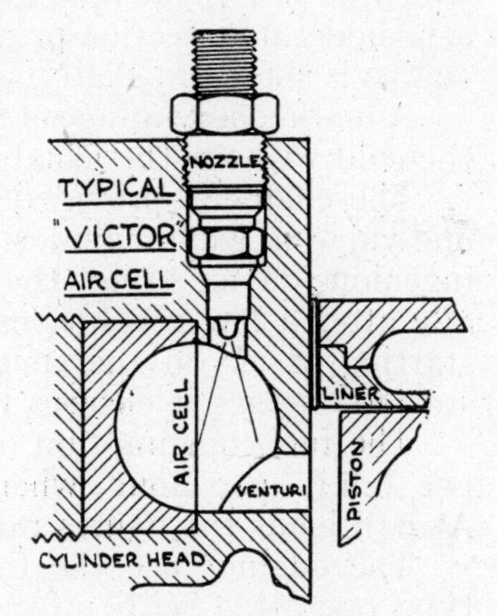

Fig. 23.—The Combustion Head of the "Victor" Engine.

THE FOWLER-SANDERS ENGINE

This design of engine employs a turbulent type of auxiliary combustion chamber, but, unlike the "Comet" engine, it has a relatively large communicating throat, so that the frictional and heat losses of the air charge and combustion products in moving through the connecting passage are appreciably less. This engine, which is employed on the Fowler motor vehicle, tractor, rail-car, and stationary engines, works on the principle illustrated in Fig. 24 (A) and (B). The object of the cylinder head design is to produce a high degree of turbulence, so that during injection the fuel is atomised and mixed intimately with the air. Diagram (A) shows the piston moving upwards at the beginning of the compression stroke. As the air in the cylinder is displaced by the piston, it flows *upwards* through a large opening at the side of the cylinder, into the dome-shaped combustion chamber. The shape of this chamber causes the air to whirl round in an anti-clockwise direction.

Diagram (B) shows the piston near the top of the compression stroke when the air in the combustion chamber is hot and when the injector has just commenced to admit fuel. The air whirl indicated by the arrows is now opposite to that shown in Diagram (A), due to the piston displacing the air in a *sideways* direction. This two-way swirl causes very rapid and thorough mixing of the air and fuel, resulting in perfect combustion throughout the speed and load range of the engine. It ensures easy starting from cold, silent and smooth running, and low fuel and oil consumption. The injectors employed are of the single large-hole type which do not choke up and are easily cleaned, while the fuel pump works at a moderate injection pressure. A sectional view of the Fowler-Sanders engine is shown in Plate facing p. 20.

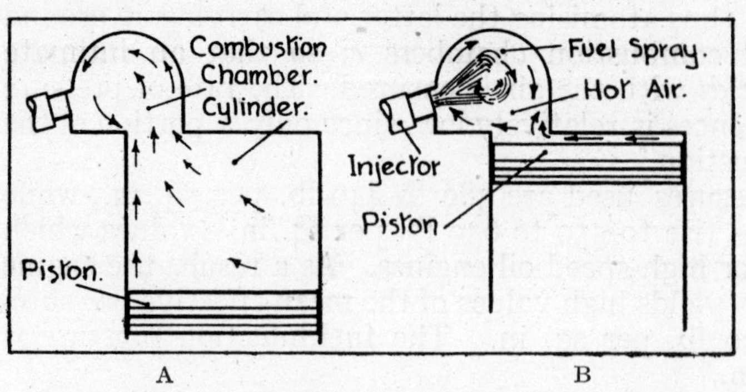

Fig. 24.—Illustrating Principle of the Fowler-Sanders Engine.

A marked advantage of the system described is the ease of starting from the cold without the usual aid of heating plugs or starting cartridges.

The engine is provided with a patent decompression gear which lifts one valve in each cylinder so that the engine can be cranked freely. An ingenious device brings the engine back on to full compression *automatically* after a few revolutions of the crankshaft. This device makes hand starting easier on the smaller engines, whilst on the larger electrically started engines it ensures that no undue load is put on to the battery.

The fuel consumption of the engines is of the order of ·39 to ·41 lb. per b.h.p. per hour when operating on three-quarter to full load. At half-loads the figures range from ·42 to ·48.

The engines use the C.A.V.-Bosch fuel injectors of the single-hole type operating with injection pressures of about 2,000 lb. per sq. in. The maximum speed of these essentially heavy-duty engines is from 900 to 1,100 r.p.m.

The four-cylinder engine has a bore of $4\frac{1}{4}$ in. and stroke of $6\frac{1}{2}$ in., giving a cylinder volume of 5,812 cu. in. It develops 56·8 b.h.p. at 1,100 r.p.m., and has a brake mean pressure of 115 lb. per sq. in. at maximum power. The compression ratio is 15·2 and compression pressure 450 lb. per sq. in. The maximum cylinder pressure is 780 lb. per sq. in.

Although it has only been possible to describe the principles of a limited number of successful British makes of high-speed oil engines here, the reader should not now find it difficult to understand practically any other type of commercial-vehicle engine.

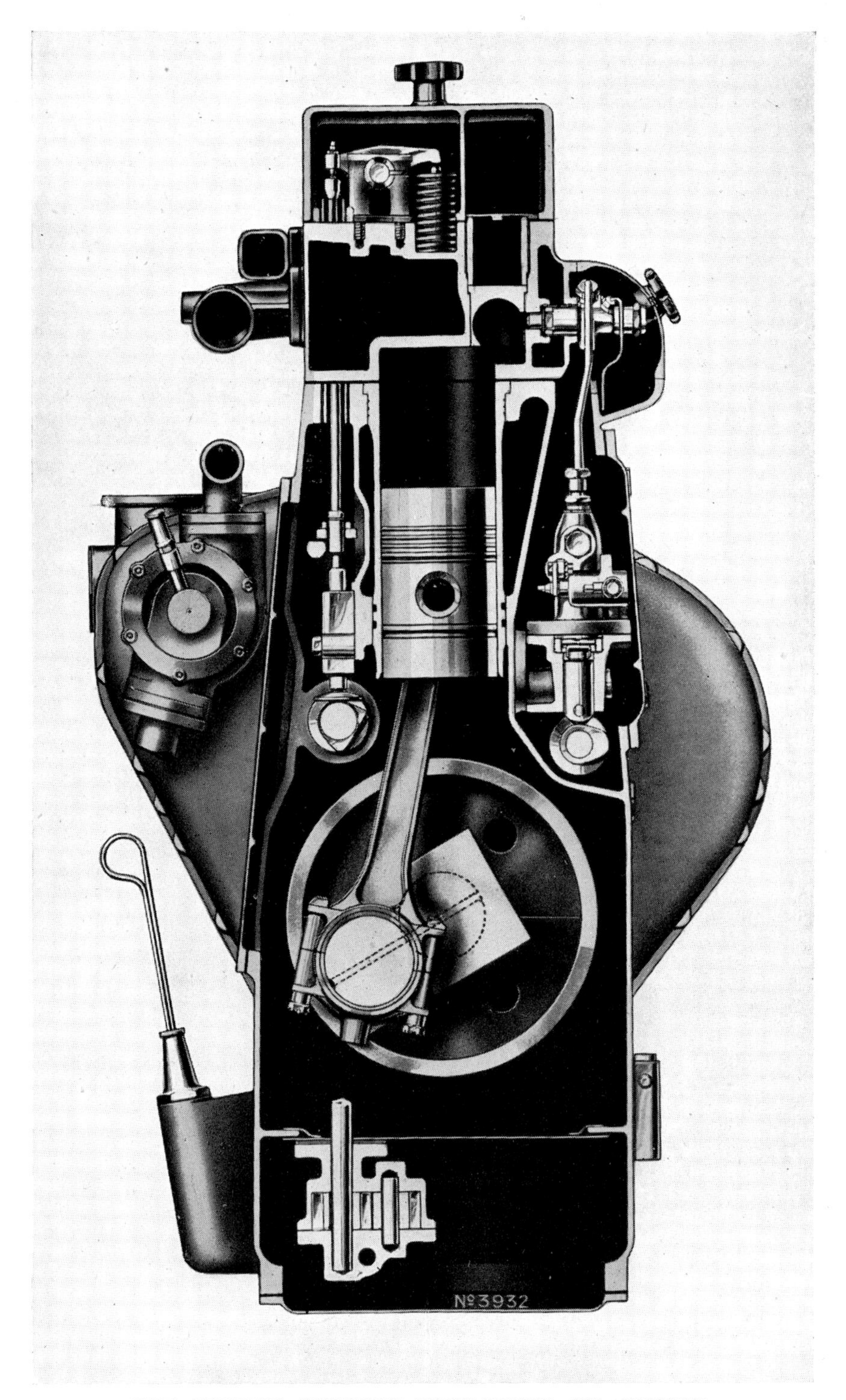

THE FOWLER-SANDERS HIGH-SPEED OIL ENGINE.

THE FUEL-INJECTION SYSTEM

The fuel-injection system of an oil engine takes the place of the carburettor and electric ignition system of the petrol engine. It consists of the fuel-feed system with its fuel filters, the fuel-injection pump, fuel-feed tubing, and the fuel-injection nozzle or valve.

The fuel-feed system delivers the Diesel oil from the main storage tank to the fuel-pump suction pipe, in the same way that the petrol-feed system (vacuum, gravity, or mechanical pump) ensures the supply of petrol from the main tank to the carburettor. In some cases the fuel is fed by gravity from a dashboard tank, but more frequently either the vacuum feed or mechanical pump is employed for this purpose. The same types are used as in petrol-engine practice, for Diesel oil, although about 15 to 20 per cent. heavier than petrol, is not very viscous and therefore flows readily in the usual sizes of fuel-feed pipes.

A special design of fuel-feed pump, devised by the Bosch firm, is particularly convenient, since it is attached to the fuel-injection pump and is operated by the latter's camshaft. The principle of the Bosch fuel feed pump is shown in Fig. 25, whilst the method of mounting the unit on a four-cylinder fuel-injection pump is shown in Fig. 26; in the latter diagram it will be noted that the fuel-pipe system and fuel filter are also shown.

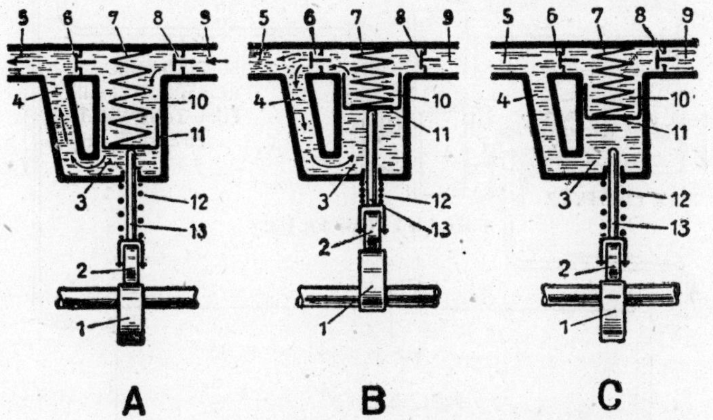

Fig. 25.—Illustrating the Action of the Bosch Fuel-feed Pump.

1, Cam.
2, Tappet Roller.
3, Outer Chamber.
4, Connecting Channel.
5, Fuel Outlet.
6, Delivery Valve.
7, Plunger Spring.
8, Suction Valve.
9, Fuel Inlet.
10, Inner Chamber.
11, Plunger.
12, Tappet Spring.
13, Tappet Spindle.

Referring to Fig. 25, Diagram A, when the pump operating cam 1 is in the position shown the plunger 11 is forced down by the spring 7 so that the fuel is driven up from the tank to the suction valve 8 into the inner pressure chamber 10. At the same time the outside of the plunger 11 forces fuel from the outer pressure chamber 3 through the channel 4 to the outlet 5. As the cam again rotates, the plunger 11 commences its inward stroke through the medium of the roller 2 and tappet spindle 13, thus displacing fuel through the delivery valve 6, along the channel 4, to the outer pressure chamber 3 (Diagram B).

Upon the next outward stroke of the plunger, fuel is delivered to the outlet 5, provided that the fuel-injection pump requires a further supply of fuel. If, however, the injection pump has enough fuel for the moment, the plunger 11 will only move outward sufficiently to balance the pressure between the outlet 5 and the spring 7 (Diagram C) and the tappet spindle 13 will leave the plunger 11 and will not re-engage with it until its next inward stroke. It follows that the next plunger stroke will depend upon the pressure in the outlet 5 which, in turn, is dependent upon the amount of fuel the engine is using. Further, as the outer pressure chamber 3 which surrounds the tappet spindle 13 is continually under pressure, no air can possibly enter with the fuel from the tank.

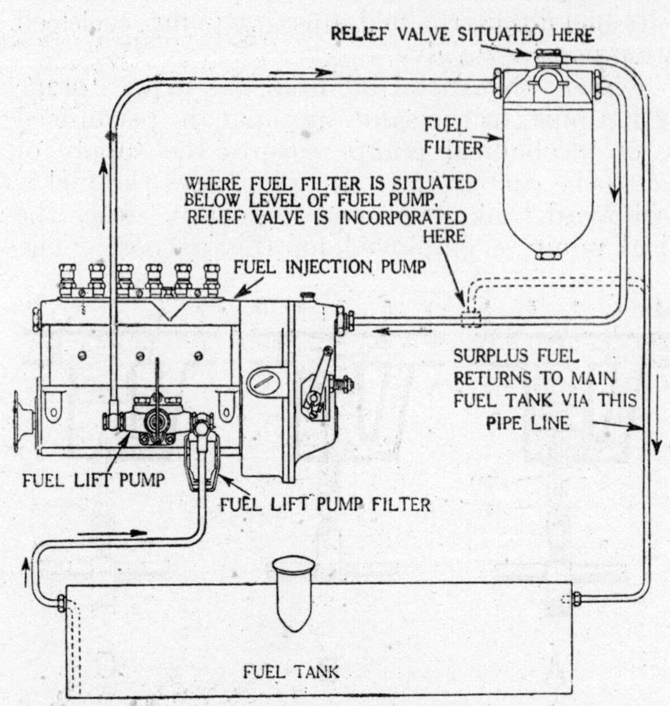

Fig. 26.—A Typical Fuel-feed System showing Fuel Injection and Feed Pumps and Filter.

FUEL-INJECTION NOZZLES

The fuel-injection nozzle supplies the fuel to the cylinders in the form of a finely divided spray of a certain predetermined shape, depending upon the type of combustion chamber. If the latter is of the turbulent kind, a single-hole sprayer is satisfactory, since the rapid swirl of the air charge gives the proper degree of mixing of the fuel and air.

On the other hand, the direct-injection engine generally requires a wide-angle spray or a series of conical sprays provided by a number of holes, as with the Gardner or Armstrong-Saurer types.

The majority of British oil engines employ the *Closed Type* of nozzle, whereby the exit orifice of the nozzle is closed by a spring-loaded valve ; the hydraulic pressure of the fuel delivered by the fuel pump overcomes this spring pressure and lifts the valve, thus opening the outlet orifice or orifices.

There is another type of injection nozzle, known as the *Open Type,* which has no controlling valve ; in this case the fuel delivered is controlled entirely by the fuel pump.

There is also a class of injection nozzle having its controlling valve opened and closed mechanically, by means of an engine-driven cam or similar device.

DIESEL ENGINE FAULT-FINDING CHART

The chart given on the next page will enable most of the faults experienced with high-speed Diesel engines to be readily located.

It will be observed that there are four main types of fault likely to occur, as follows:

(1) *Engine Stops, or Refuses to Start.*
(2) *Engine Fires Intermittently.*
(3) *Engine Loses Power or Gives Poor Acceleration and*
(4) *Smoky Exhaust.*

Having found by superficial examination to which of these classes the fault belongs, the various probable causes given in the right-hand column should be studied, one by one, until the actual cause of the trouble is found. The most probable cause of "Misfiring" is a choked fuel injection valve in one of the cylinders. To ascertain which particular injection valve is at fault, cut-out each of the cylinders in turn by stopping its fuel supply. Usually a special device is provided on the valve for this purpose; otherwise the fuel-pipe union should be disconnected from the valve, when the fuel will ooze out.

If each cylinder be tested in this manner, the effect of cutting out a correctly firing cylinder will be to cause an appreciable drop in engine speed, whereas in the case of the faulty cylinder there will be no perceptible difference in the running of the engine as a whole when the fuel supply of this cylinder is shut off.

DIESEL ENGINE FAULT-FINDING CHART

SYMPTOM	*PROBABLE CAUSE*
ENGINE STOPS OR REFUSES TO START	*FUEL SUPPLY TO PUMP EXHAUSTED* *FUEL PUMP OUT OF ACTION* *FUEL LEAKAGE FROM PUMP* *AIR LOCK IN MAIN FUEL LINE TO PUMP* *FUEL INJECTION TIMING INCORRECT* *FUEL PUMP WRONGLY CONNECTED TO ENGINE DRIVE SHAFT* *CHOKED FUEL FILTER* *GOVERNOR "NO LOAD" STOP REQUIRES ADJUSTMENT*
ENGINE FIRES INTERMITTENTLY	*CHOKED INJECTION VALVE* *DIRT ON INJECTION VALVE SEATING* *PARTLY CHOKED FUEL FILTER* *LEAKAGE OF FUEL FROM ONE OR MORE PIPE LINES BETWEEN PUMP AND CYLINDER* *STICKING INJECTION VALVE* *BROKEN VALVE SPRING IN FUEL PUMP PLUNGER* *FAULTY OR WORN PLUNGER* *SHORTAGE OF FUEL SUPPLY TO PUMP* *BROKEN PUMP TAPPET ROLLER* *INCORRECT INJECTION TIMING ADVANCE* *INLET OR EXHAUST VALVE OF ENGINE STUCK UP* *BROKEN INLET OR EXHAUST VALVE* *BROKEN INLET OR EXHAUST VALVE SPRING* *AIR LOCK IN FUEL SUPPLY PIPE* *LEAKAGE AT FUEL PIPE UNIONS ON PUMP OR INJECTION VALVES* *DISTORTED FUEL INJECTION VALVE*
ENGINE LOSES POWER OR GIVES POOR ACCELERATION	*INTERMITTENT FIRING* (see above) *INCORRECT INJECTION TIMING* *INCORRECT INJECTION PERIOD* *POOR ENGINE COMPRESSION* *INCORRECT INLET OR EXHAUST VALVE TIMING* *LUBRICATION TROUBLE* *UNSUITABLE FUEL* *SHORTAGE OF FUEL DUE TO PARTIALLY CHOKED FILTER, OR INSUFFICIENT SUPPLY* *WORN INJECTION VALVES* *EXCESSIVE CARBON IN COMBUSTION CHAMBER* *DECOMPRESSOR GEAR NOT FULLY INOPERATIVE*
SMOKY EXHAUST	*DEFECTIVE FUEL INJECTION VALVE CAUSING DRIBBLING AT NOZZLE* *INJECTION TIMING TOO FAR RETARDED* *INJECTION PERIOD TOO LONG* *UNSATISFACTORY NATURE OF FUEL* *LOSS OF COMPRESSION (CAUSING DELAYED COMBUSTION)* *WRONG SIZE OF FUEL PUMP OR INJECTION NOZZLE* *GOVERNOR "FULL LOAD" STOP REQUIRES ADJUSTMENT*

TYPES OF CLOSED INJECTION NOZZLE

The widely used Bosch fuel-injection nozzles are supplied in two distinct classes of closed nozzle, known respectively as the *Pintle* and *Hole Nozzles*.

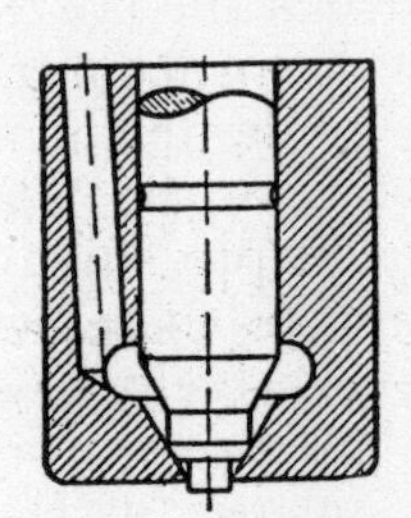

Fig. 27.—The Pintle-type Nozzle, Closed.

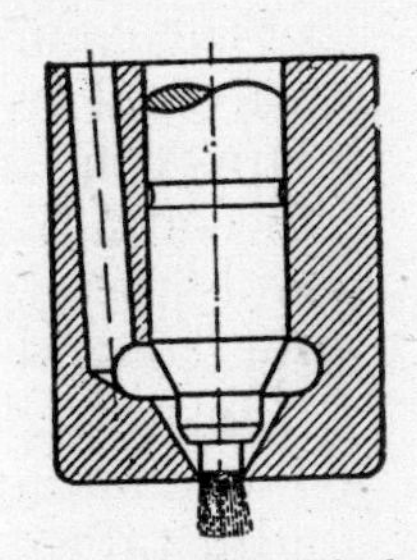

Fig. 28.—The Pintle Nozzle, Open.

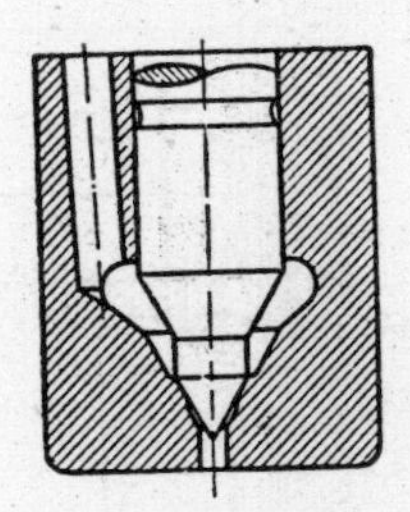

Fig. 29.—The Single-hole Nozzle, Closed.

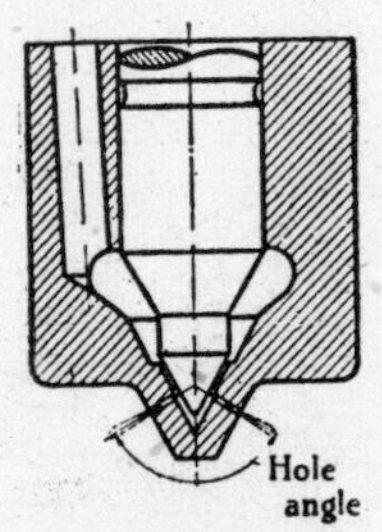

Fig. 30.—The Multiple hole Nozzle, Open.

Figs. 27 and 28 show the pintle nozzle in the " closed " and " open " positions, respectively.

Fig. 29 shows a single-hole nozzle in the " closed " position and Fig. 30 shows a multi-hole one in the " open " position.

The two latter types of nozzle differ from the pintle ones in the form of spray produced. The single-hole nozzle can be fitted with its axis perpendicular or inclined to the walls of the combustion chamber. The single-hole nozzle is less liable to choking with carbon or dirt than the multiple-hole type, but it gives a smaller spray angle and greater penetration of air change, for similar fuel-injection pressures.

THE NOZZLE HOLDER

The nozzles previously described are mounted in nozzle holders, and it is so arranged that the nozzles can readily be detached from the holders for cleaning purposes.

Fig. 31 shows the nozzle-holder unit employed on

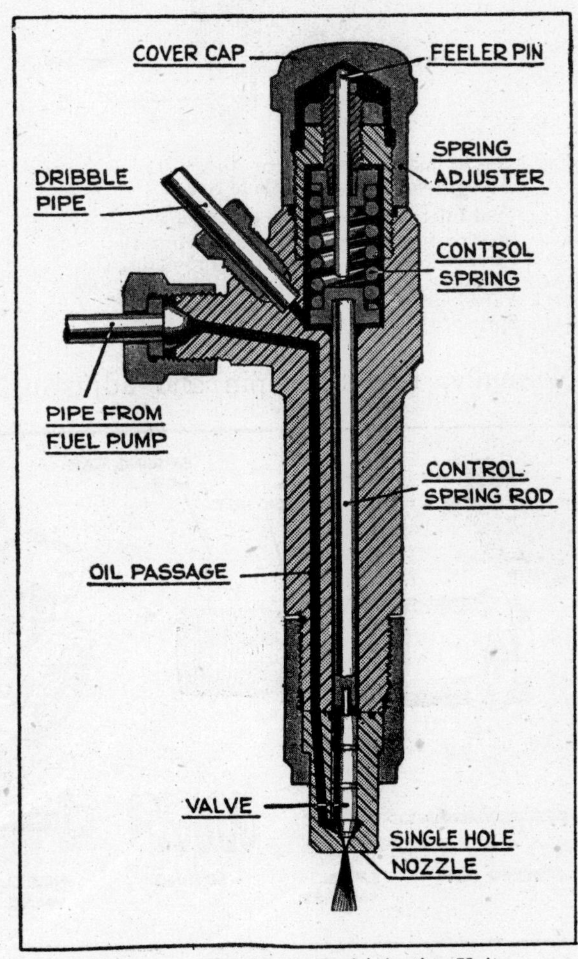

Fig. 31.—The A.E.C. Fuel-injection Unit.

A.E.C. oil engines. It is of the single-hole nozzle pattern, and fuel from the fuel-injection pump is fed through the pipe shown on the left, to the fuel or oil passage (shown in black) which leads to the lower side of the conical face of the nozzle valve. This valve is an accurate lapped fit in its guide and it is in contact above with the control-spring rod. The pressure of the control spring is therefore transmitted to the valve below. The amount of this pressure is adjustable by means of the spring-tensioning screw shown, so that the valve may be regulated so as to lift at any predetermined value. The small rod which passes through the adjusting screw cap is known as the *Feeler Pin*. When the injection valve is operating satisfactorily, this pin experiences a series of "kicks," which can readily be felt by placing the finger on the feeler pin; the latter is therefore a useful means of testing the working of the nozzle valve. Normally, the feeler pin and adjusting screw are covered by means

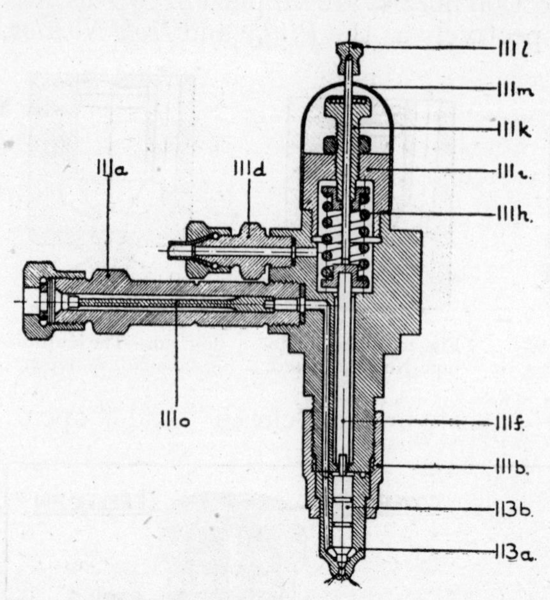

Fig. 32.—Sectional Drawing of C.A.V.-Bosch Nozzle Holder with Multi-hole Nozzle.

111*a*, Fuel Inlet Connection.
111*b*, Nozzle-cap Nut.
111*d*, Leak-off Nipple Stud.
111*f*, Spindle.
111*h*, Valve Spring.
111*i*, Spring-cap Nut.
111*k*, Compression Screw.
111*l*, Feeling Pin.
111*m*, Protecting Cap.
111*o*, Edge-type Filter.
113*a*, Nozzle Body.
113*b*, Nozzle Valve.

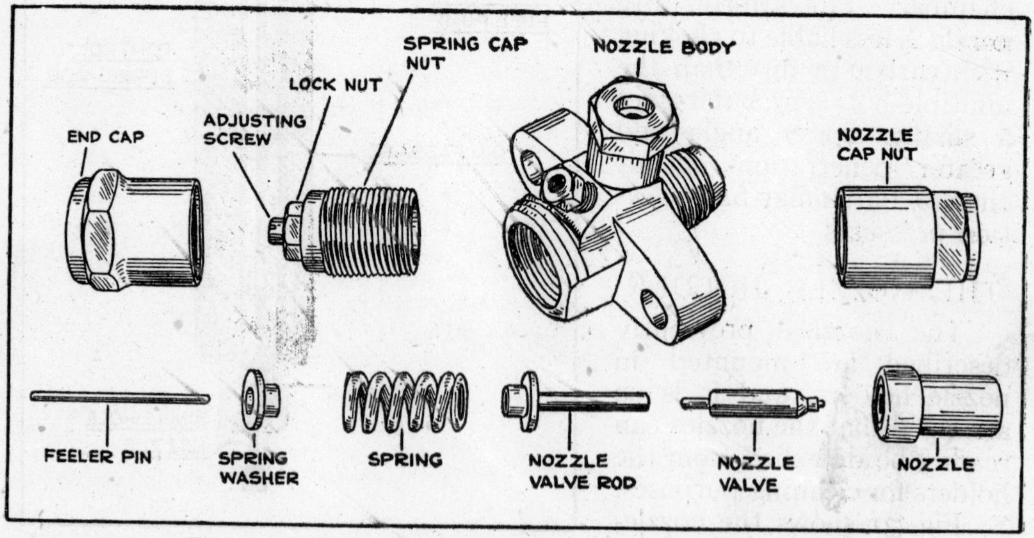

Fig. 33.—Components of C.A.V.-Bosch Fuel-injection Nozzle Unit.

of the cap shown, but the latter is readily removable for access to these parts.

The *Dribble Pipe* shown on the upper left side is to take off any fuel that may leak past the nozzle valve and control-spring rod.

Fig. 32 shows a sectional view of a C.A.V.-Bosch nozzle holder fitted with a multi-hole nozzle. The various components are given in the key below the illustration. Fig. 33 shows the complete set of components of an A.E.C. nozzle holder.

FITTING NOZZLE HOLDERS

When preparing to fit the nozzle holder into place in the cylinder head, care should be taken to see that a suitable soft solid copper joint ring (or one of the *special* copper asbestos washers supplied by the makers) is provided to make the joint between the nozzle-cap nut end and the cylinder head metal (see Fig. 31). The metal of the cylinder head, the faces of the copper joint ring, and the face of the nozzle-cap nut should then be " cleaned " in order to facilitate a leak-proof joint.

The joint washer should be an easy, but not loose, fit for the nozzle body, and as this is quite an important feature, the special washers for the purpose should be obtained from the makers. On no account should normal sparking-plug type washers be used.

The nozzle holder can now be fitted in place, all care being taken to see that it is an easy fit in the cylinder-head tunnel and on the holding-down studs, so that it can be placed down on the copper joint *without force of any kind*. The nuts on the flange should then be tightened down evenly in order to prevent the nozzle being canted and so "nipped" in the cylinder head. This is very important, since any unevenness in tightening down may cause distortion of the nozzle, resulting in its failure.

THE ARMSTRONG-SAURER NOZZLE

The Armstrong-Saurer dual-turbulence engine employs the multi-hole nozzle illustrated in Fig. 34. This injector has four equally spaced holes, each of 0·25 mm. diameter, i.e. about $\frac{1}{100}$ in. diameter. The opening pressure of the nozzle valve is adjustable by means of the spring shown. Fuel is led to the lower side of the valve from the left-hand passage leading down from the top screwed connection.

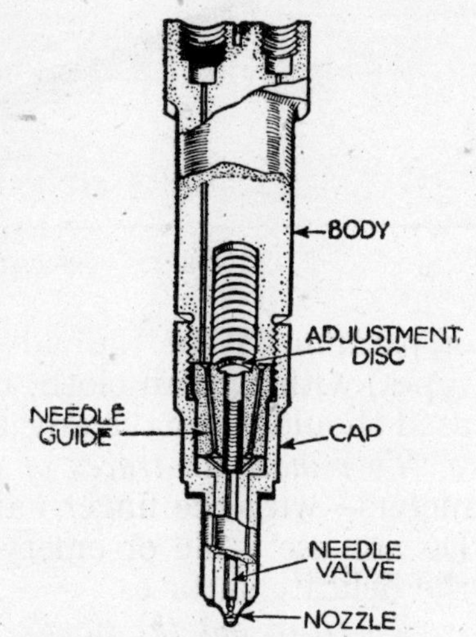

Fig. 34.—Armstrong-Saurer Nozzle.

THE CARE OF INJECTION NOZZLES

Injection nozzles, like sparking plugs, require periodic attention, but they seldom give any trouble provided the fuel delivered from the fuel-injection pump is perfectly clean, i.e. well filtered, and the nozzle holder is adequately cooled; the latter factor depends upon the design of the cylinder head.

Normally, *injection nozzles should be cleaned every* 2,000 to 3,000 *miles* of road service. They should be taken from the engine and the end of each nozzle first cleared of any carbon deposit by scraping. The open end of the fuel pipe from the pump should be covered over to prevent entry of dust.

The nozzle should then be dismantled in a dust-free room; the various components of a typical injector are shown in Fig. 35. After dismantling the nozzle parts, they should be washed thoroughly in petrol

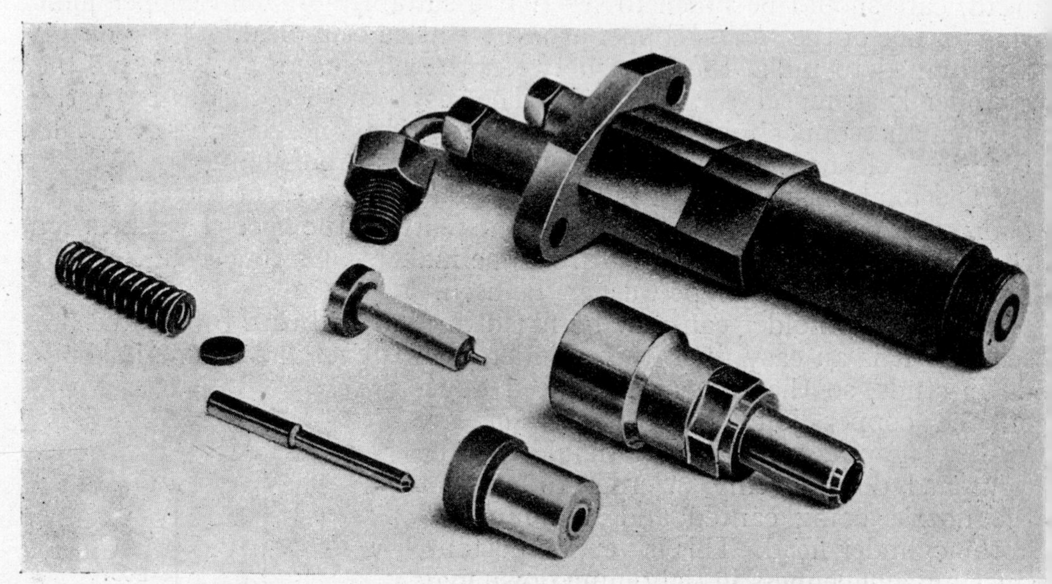

Fig. 35.—Components of Typical Fuel-injection Nozzle Unit.

or paraffin. Wipe the valve face and the pintle of the valve (for pintle types) with a clean cloth, using a fair degree of hand pressure; the cloth used should not have any traces of fluff or loose fibres.

To remove all traces of carbon, scrape the pintle—which has two diameters—with the finger-nail or, very carefully, with the blade of a knife. Do not use a file or emery cloth or any other abrasive, as this will ruin the delicate surfaces.

To clean out the nozzle orifice, sharpen a match-stick to a point and use this to ream out the hole. Do not use a metal object for this purpose.

Next, immerse the nozzle body in paraffin and, placing the valve in position, pump the valve up and down rapidly a few times. The valve seat in the body may be wiped by wrapping a piece of thin rag around a match-stick and inserting it into the nozzle body. Another good scheme is to use compressed air to blow through the nozzle body. If the valve and seating are properly cleaned, the valve, when snapped smartly back on its seating, will produce a metallic click. If the valve gives a soft noise or feels sticky, this indicates that there is dirt on the seating.

Before assembling the nozzle valve it should be immersed in clear Diesel oil, so that the valve slides freely in its guide. After the nozzle has been cleaned it should be tested on a nozzle-testing apparatus, or it can be connected to its fuel pipe on the engine, but without screwing it into the cylinder head. The spray effect can then be observed in the open air as the engine is rotated by hand, with the compression released.

It is most important to observe, when cleaning injection nozzles, that *scrupulous cleanliness is essential* and that *no abrasives or metal tools* should be used on the valves or nozzles.

DETAILED CLEANING INSTRUCTIONS

The following are detailed instructions for cleaning C.A.V.-Bosch fuel-injection nozzles (Fig. 36).

Assuming, however, that the nozzle valve has been soaking and the two surfaces A and B on the top of the nozzle-body flange already mentioned are clean and free from damage, the inside of the nozzle body should be examined. For this purpose, the collection of tools shown at Fig. 37 is recommended. These can be obtained from a service station. The three small borings G (Fig. 36) should be explored to see that they are clean and clear, followed by examination of the valve-stem boring in which the nozzle valve slides. This surface should be clean and bright and free from high spots or scratches or dull patches. The valve seating J (Fig. 36)

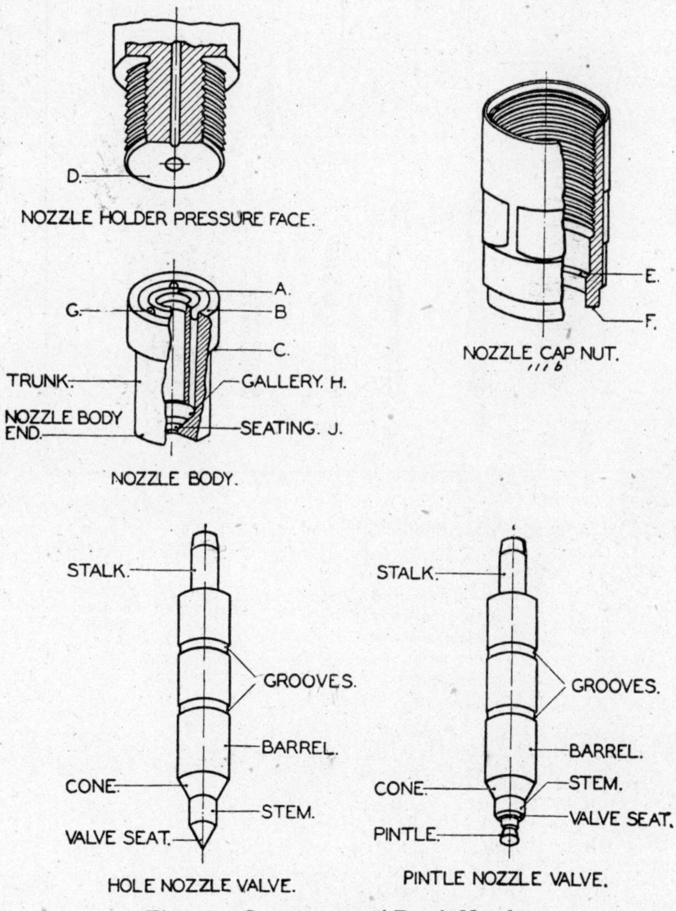

Fig. 36.—Components of Bosch Nozzles.

should now come under observation under a strong light to ensure that it is free from dirt or carbon. If this is not so, and indeed, in any case, it is advisable to use the soft brass seat scraper *h* to remove any carbon or particles that may be imprisoned on the seat. The gallery H (Fig. 36) should now be examined with the aid of the special soft brass groove scraper *i* to ensure that it is also clean and free from dirt or carbon.

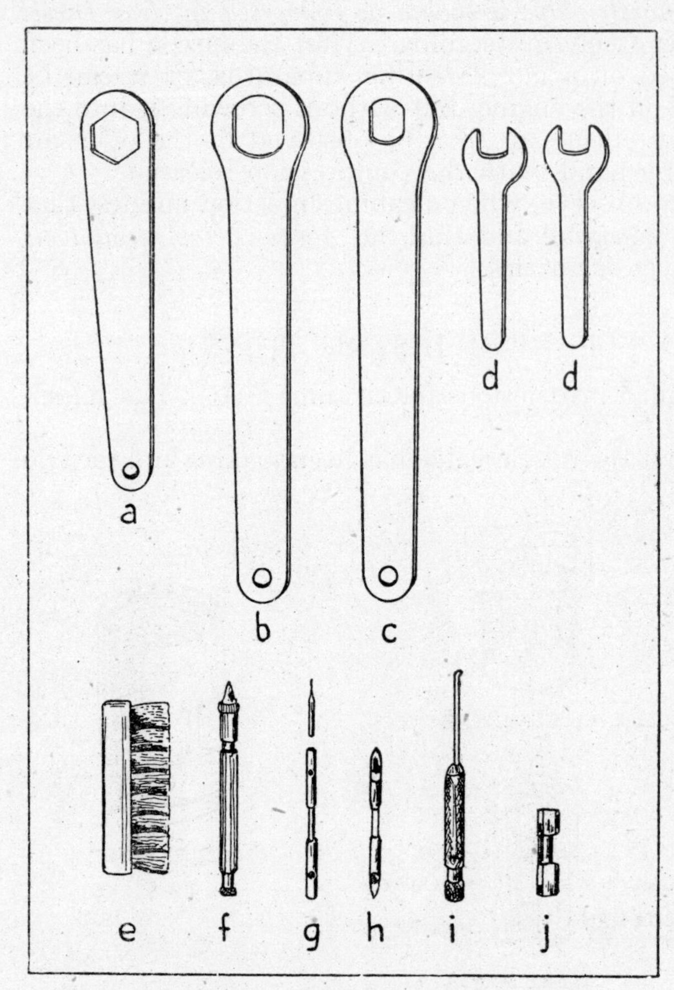

Fig. 37.—Set of Tools for Servicing Bosch Injection Nozzles.

a, Nozzle-holder Cap-nut Spanner.
b and *c*, Nozzle-holder Spring Cap-nut Spanners.
d, Compression-screw Spanners.
e, Brass Wire Nozzle-cleaning Brush.
f, Nozzle-probing Tool.
g, Nozzle-body Pintle-hole Cleaner.
h, Nozzle-body Seat Scraper.
i, Nozzle-body Groove Scraper.
j, Nozzle-stem Cleaner.

The foregoing cleaning process applies to each of the hole types, multi-hole and pintle-type nozzles. In the case of the hole or multi-hole nozzles, the spray hole or holes in the nozzle end should be probed with the special tool *f*. Reference to the leaflet describing the use of this tool should be made where any difficulty is met in clearing the holes satisfactorily. In cases where success cannot be achieved in clearing the holes, the complete nozzle should be returned, securely wrapped and packed, to the nearest service depot for attention. Assuming that the spray holes have been cleaned satisfactorily, then the nozzle body can be placed into the container to soak in paraffin.

Where pintle-type nozzles are concerned, the orifice in the nozzle-body end should be cleaned with the special soft brass pintle-hole cleaner *e*, taking care that the appropriate size cleaner insert is used in the holder provided.

The nozzle valve should now be taken up and polished by rubbing with an absolutely clean cloth—a piece of used boiled cotton cloth is best—upon which there is no suggestion of fluff. Particular attention should be given to the valve seat. This and the smaller cylindrical portion above it, called the "stem" and "cone" in Fig. 36, can be cleaned with the fine brass-wire brush. To ensure that the stem and cone are free from any particles, the soft brass stem cleaner *j* should be applied with a rotary action, pressing the nozzle valve into the cleaning tool with the finger. In the case of pintle-type nozzle valves, the pintle projection should be cleaned carefully with the brass-wire brush *e*. A piece of *soft* wood is also very useful for this purpose, pressing the nozzle-valve pintle into the wood and turning with a rotary action by the fingers.

It is important that the greatest care be taken with the nozzle valve and the pintle to prevent any damage to either, which may result in valve leakage or spray distortion, with consequent bad engine running.

After ensuring that the exterior of the nozzle is clean and free from carbon, the valve and body may be assembled together. This should be done after the two parts have been washed thoroughly in clean paraffin or fuel oil and placed together, preferably with the fingers whilst immersed in the clean oil.

The nozzle holder should now receive attention and the highly ground face D should be clean and free from scratches. It should be washed carefully in clean paraffin, and whilst being handled, protected from receiving any damage. This face must register with the nozzle flange cleanly and squarely to form a high-pressure joint, and so must be in perfect condition. The exterior of the nozzle holder, of course, should be cleaned thoroughly from dirt and grease in the usual manner. At infrequent periods, it is advisable to dismantle the interior of the nozzle holder to examine the spring 111*h* (Fig. 32), spring plate 111*g*, and nozzle spindle 111*f*. When dismantling, the special spanner *d* (see Fig. 37) should be applied for the removal of the nozzle-holder spring cap 111*i* (Fig. 32), which is revealed after removal of the covering protection cap. The interior of the nozzle holder and the parts removed should be washed carefully to remove any dirt or moisture. Care should be taken when dissembling these parts that the spring-adjusting screw 111*k* (Fig. 32) is not altered in any way and is firmly secured with its lock nut. If the spring and the parts are in good condition, they should be reassembled carefully, and preferably after having been slightly coated with, say, lubricating oil. The cap nut 111*i* should be screwed home securely with the special spanner so that it will not loosen with subsequent use.

The nozzle holder and nozzle may now be assembled carefully, after having immersed the pressure faces of each in clean paraffin or fuel oil, to ensure that they are free from any particles. The nozzle-cap nut 111*b* should be screwed on to the nozzle holder by the use of the special spanner.

The nozzle holder with nozzle should be tested always on the nozzle-testing outfit, as previously described, after cleaning. If the pressure at which the spray breaks is not that recommended by the engine-maker, then it can be adjusted by the spring-adjusting screw and lock nut, using spanner *b*.

NOZZLE-TESTING APPARATUS

When a number of injection nozzles have to be given routine tests before refitting, it is advisable to employ a special nozzle-testing apparatus as shown in Fig. 38.

The principle of this device is that of employing a hand pump to give the desired fuel pressure (by means of a differential piston) and to apply the fuel at this pressure to the nozzle in order to observe its spraying effect in air; the value of the pressure is read off a pressure gauge.

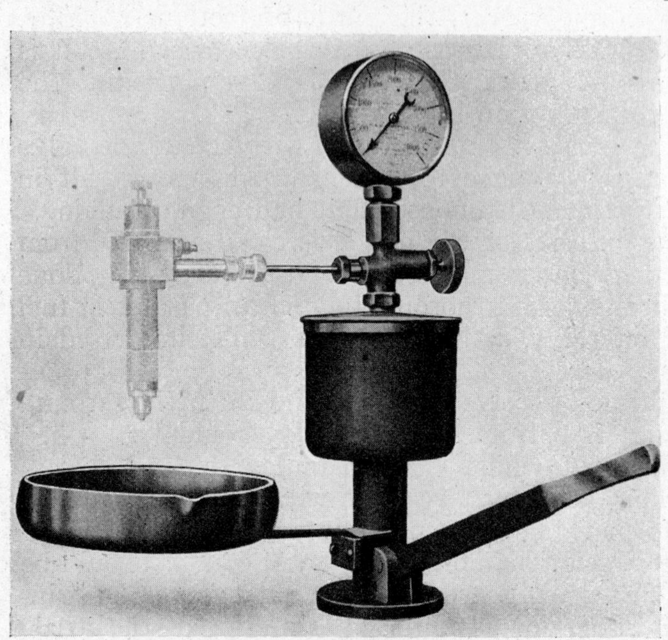

Fig. 38.—The Armstrong Injection-nozzle Testing Apparatus.

Referring to the line diagram, which shows another type of nozzle tester, Fig. 39, fuel oil is contained in the small reservoir 1, whence, if the tap is open, it flows by gravity to the hand-pump 4 suction pipe. Pressure is applied by means of the handle 5 and the fuel under pressure is forced to the pipe 7. The pressure gauge 6 communicates with this pipe, but a shut-off valve operated by the wheel 2 enables the gauge to be shut off from the nozzle during spraying tests; the gauge reads up to 300 atmospheres (about 4,410 lb. per sq. in.). An air-release screw is provided for getting rid of any air in the system. It is left open whilst hand pumping until fuel begins to flow, when it is tightened down. The pump is then used again until fuel flows from the pressure pipe 7. The apparatus is then ready for use and the nozzle holder is connected to the pipe union of 7. The nozzle pressure is adjusted by means of the adjusting screw 8 after releasing the locking nut 9 and its value is read off the gauge.

When using this tester, if the nozzle does not " buzz " with its usual characteristic noise while injecting this indicates that the needle valve is either too tight, is bent or untrue, or is binding on its seating.

If the nozzle pressure for spraying is too high, either the adjusting spring pressure of the nozzle is too high, the nozzle orifices are partly blocked, or the valve is dirty or sticking.

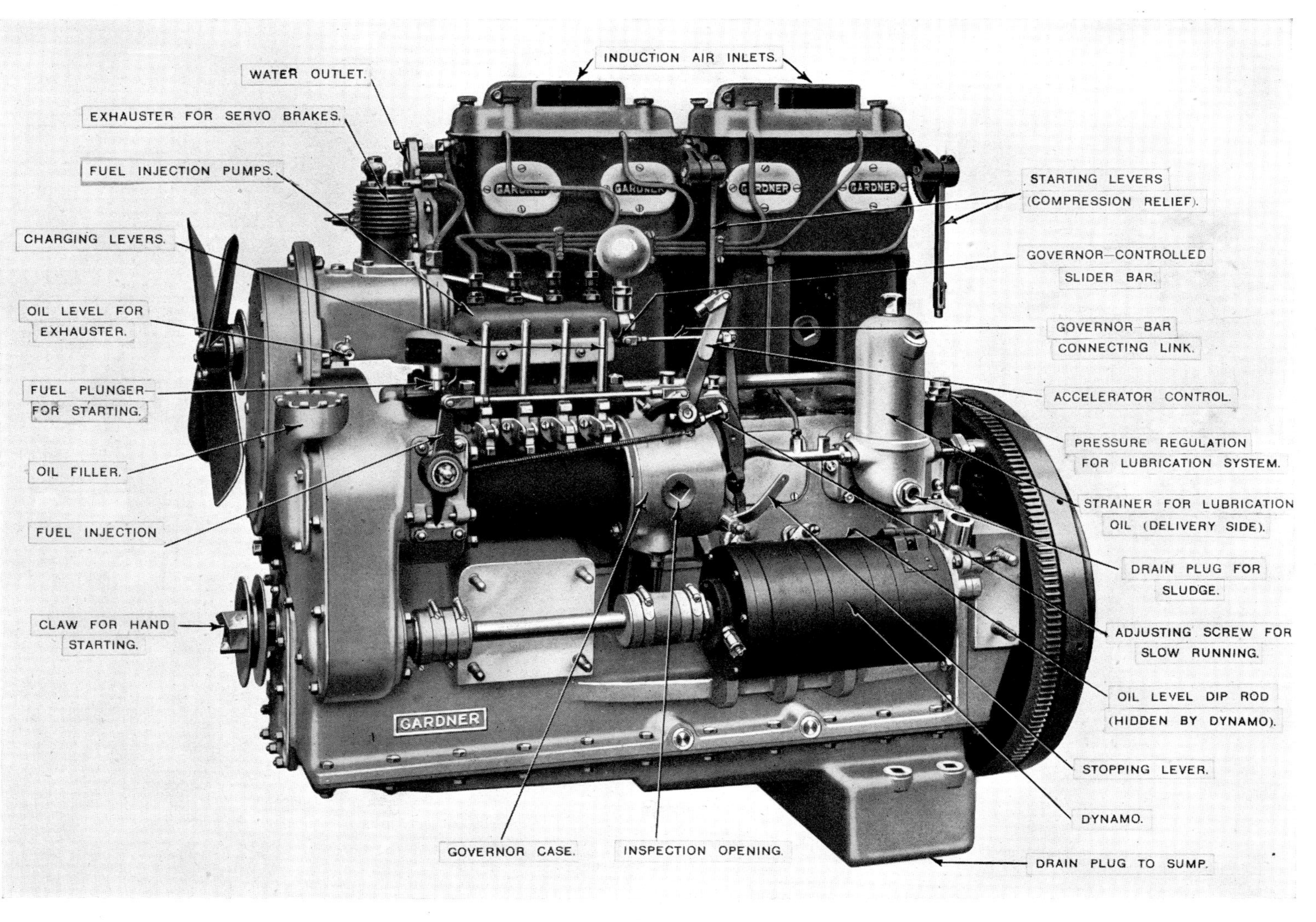

THE GARDNER FOUR-CYLINDER HIGH-SPEED OIL ENGINE.

If, on the other hand, the gauge *pressure is lower* than the maker's recommended value, there may be some dirt on the seating, the valve may be stuck open, or the controlling spring either broken or not adjusted to the correct tension.

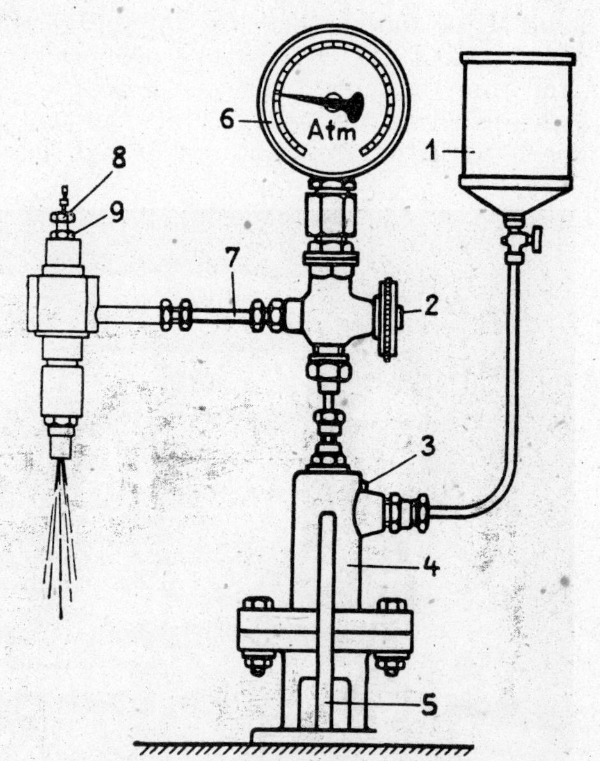

Fig. 39.—The C.A.V.-Bosch Nozzle-testing Apparatus.

MAINTENANCE OF GARDNER ENGINE NOZZLES

The fuel-injector nozzle of the Gardner oil engines is of the multi-hole non-adjustable tension type.

The makers recommend that the nozzles should be removed from the engine and cleaned every 3,000 to 4,000 miles. Any carbon deposit around the outlet orifices should carefully be scraped off and the needle valves examined for leakages. The outlet orifices should be quite clear and each hole, when the nozzle is tested on a testing apparatus or on the fuel pump, should give the same type and size of spray.

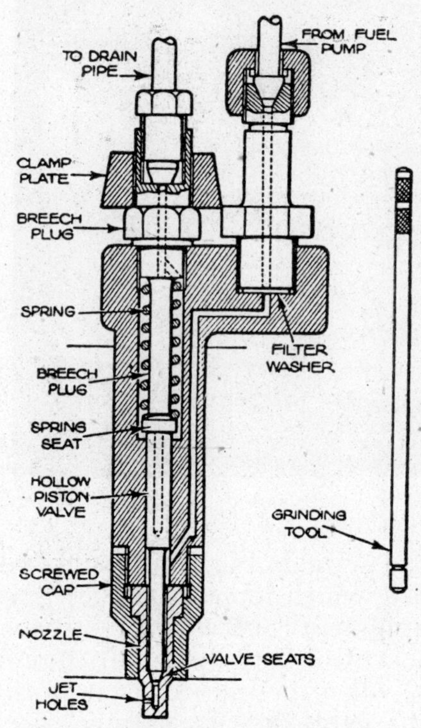

Fig. 40.—The Gardner Fuel-injection Nozzle.

The Gardner spraying nozzle is shown in Fig. 40, the tool shown on the right-hand side being supplied for guiding purposes. The principal items of attention are *the piston valve and its seating*, *the jet holes*, and *the injection-pressure valve*.

The sprayer should be tested for any jet choking by removing it from the cylinder and connecting it again in the open air where the spray may be observed whilst the hand lever of the pump is worked (Plate facing p. 32). If the sprays from each jet are not of the same shape and of equal size, the sprayer should be dismantled and the jet holes pricked with the correct size of pricker supplied by the makers. At the same time the central bore of the nozzle should be cleared out, as any particles dislodged naturally fall into this central bore. The method of clearing the latter is by forcing liquid through the jet holes *from the outside of the*

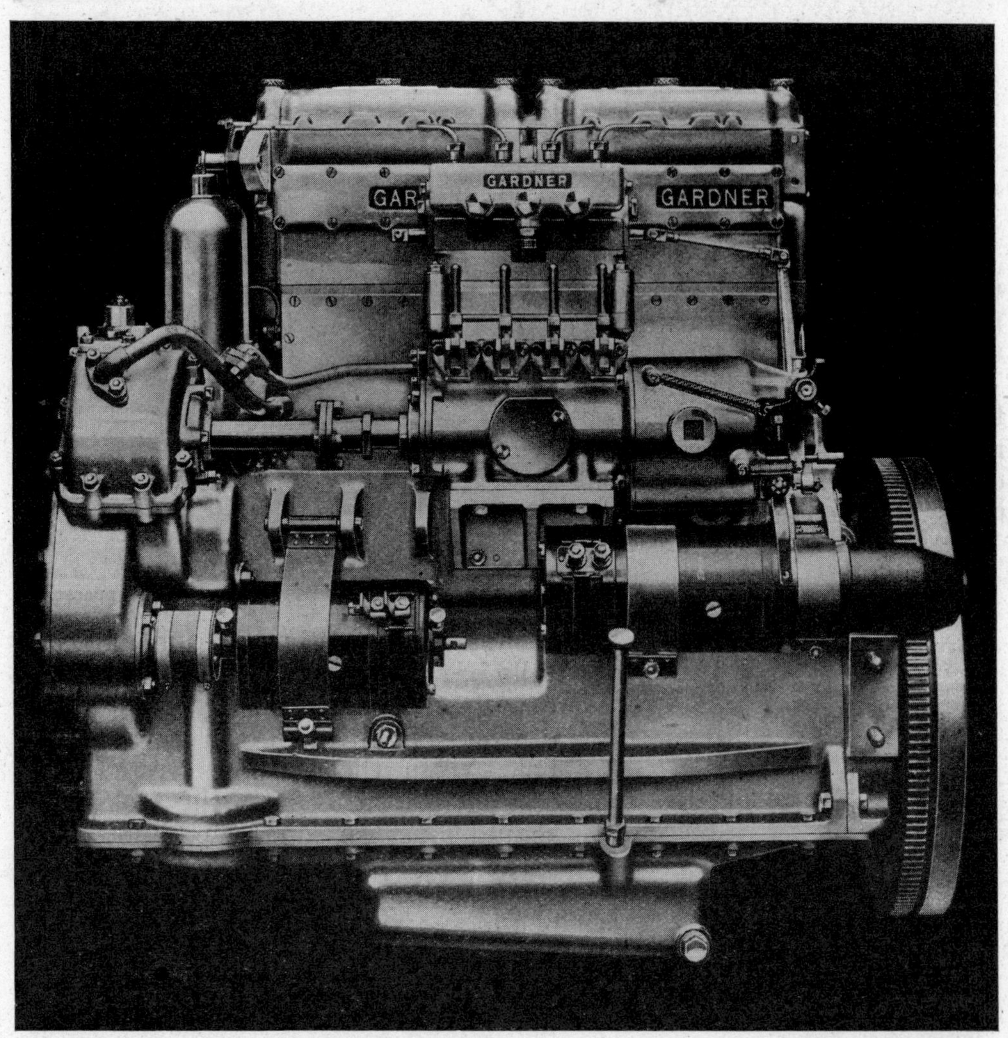

Fig. 40A.—The Gardner Four-cylinder Type 4 L.K. High-speed Oil Engine.

nozzle to the inside. For this purpose a special syringe (Fig. 41) is supplied for use in conjunction with a special nozzle which replaces the injector nozzle during the operation. The extra equipment is necessary by reason of the futility of any attempts to clear the central bore by forcing liquid in the same direction as the flow of the fuel when the injector is at work.

If any leakage is discovered between the valve and its seating, a new injector should be fitted. While it is sometimes possible to restore the

METHOD OF TESTING THE GARDNER FUEL-INJECTION NOZZLE

defective seals with the aid of the special nozzle-grinding tool, shown on the right in Fig. 40, this is only an emergency procedure ; it is better in most cases to return the unit to the makers, who will clean it at a very low charge.

It is useful to remember that a pressure of 60 lb. per sq. in. will compress the spring to a length of exactly $1\frac{5}{16}$ in.

An important point to observe when fuel injectors are dismantled is that of *keeping every one of the component parts of each separate injector*

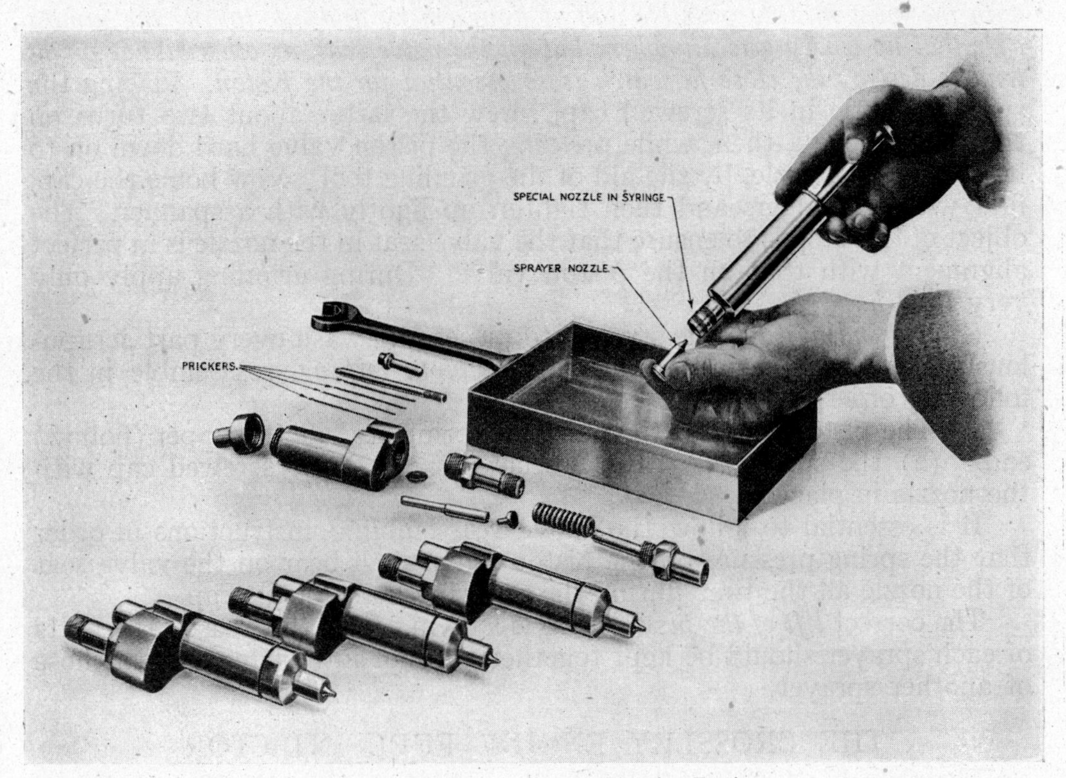

Fig. 41.—The Gardner Nozzle-cleaning Device.

together, since these parts are lapped together at the makers' works, and a part from one injector may, therefore, not operate satisfactorily if fitted to another injector.

The injection valve should be tested for leakage by the outside testing method previously described. The fuel pump of the Gardner oil engine is provided with a handle for priming purposes. This should be given a few strokes in order to expel all air from the fuel. The pump handle should then be pressed with a force just short of that required to lift the sprayer valve from its seating. If *the valve is unsound*, fuel will emerge from the jet holes and run down the nozzle. If more than two drops per minute leak out, the valve seating should be examined for dirt or wear effects. In any case the valve and its seating should be washed with clean paraffin. If, on further trial, the valve still leaks, the seating may require grinding-in.

The method of grinding-in a sprayer-valve seat is as follows :

Take the sprayer to pieces in the following order : (1) the screwed cap and the nozzle ; (2) the breech plug and spring ; (3) the hollow piston valve with the small spring seat.

Remove the spring seat from the hollow end of the piston valve and screw into the hollow the knurled grinding tool supplied with the engine and replace the piston valve in the sprayer. Then smear the valve seat *with the most minute possible dab of flour emery and oil, taking the utmost care that no emery gets anywhere but on the valve seat, as otherwise it might tend to destroy the close fit which is so essential for the piston.* Placing the sprayer nozzle in its screwed cap, screw the latter about two turns on the sprayer body, then, while pressing the piston valve hard down on to its seat in the nozzle, by the aid of the grinding tool, screw home the cap, first with the fingers and then tighten up lightly with a spanner. The object of this step is to ensure that the valve seat in the nozzle is in perfect alignment with that on the piston valve. During grinding apply only very *light hand pressure.*

After grinding take the sprayer to pieces and wash every part scrupulously clean with clean paraffin, and, *without wiping*, reassemble in the following order :

(1) The piston valve with the small spring seat at the upper (hollow) end : (2) the spring ; (3) the breech plug ; (4) the screwed cap with the nozzle in place.

It is essential to follow the above reassembling instructions in order that the spring pressure on the piston valve shall bear on the valve seat of the nozzle all the time during the screwing home of the cap.

The correct *lift of the piston valve* is ·008 in. For this reason the parts of each sprayer should be kept together and not interchanged with those of another sprayer.

THE CROSSLEY ENGINE FUEL INJECTOR

The Crossley " Comet " head oil engine employs the C.A.V.-Bosch fuel-injection system, with pintle-type fuel-injection nozzle. The nozzle-holder spring is set at the maker's works so that the valve opens at 1,500 lb. per sq. in. As this pressure has been arrived at after a good deal of experiment and is best for the engine operating under all conditions, this setting should be adhered to. If the nozzle holder has been dismantled, the correct setting may be found by connecting the nozzle holder to a testing outfit, similar to the one previously described, and the compression-spring adjusting screw turned until the nozzle valve sprays at 1,500 lb. per sq. in. This setting should be " locked " by means of the lock nut provided.

FUEL-INJECTOR TROUBLES AND THEIR CURES

The injection nozzle should always be removed from the cylinder head and its spraying action observed in the open air, using either the fuel pump or a nozzle-testing apparatus for this purpose.

The nozzle should have a characteristic "buzz" if it is working correctly.

The following table gives in a convenient form the most probable injection-nozzle faults, causes, and suggested remedies.

NOZZLE FAULTS, CAUSES, AND REMEDIES

Difficulty.	Probable Cause.	Suggested Remedy.
1. Injection pressure too high.	(*a*) Interference with compression screw.	(*a*) Readjust compression screw, set, and lock.
	(*b*) The nozzle valve "sticks" or is "seized" in the nozzle body.	(*b*) If thorough cleansing with petrol or paraffin does not rectify, the nozzle complete should be scrapped and replaced from stock.
2. Injection pressure too low.	(*a*) Interference with compression screw.	(*a*) Readjust compression screw, set, and lock.
	(*b*) Nozzle-holder spring broken or nozzle needle sticking.	(*b*) Replace spring from spares or clean nozzle as above.
3. Nozzle dribbles.	Nozzle valve damaged or "sticks" open.	As 1 (*b*).
4. Spray from the nozzle is deformed.	Nozzle valve damaged or affected by carbon deposit.	As 1 (*b*).
5. Fuel dribbles from leak off connection.	(*a*) The nozzle valve is a slack fit in the nozzle body.	(*a*) Replace complete nozzle from spares.
	(*b*) Nozzle-cap nut not tightened.	(*b*) Tighten nut with special ring spanner.
	(*c*) Damaged face or foreign matter between the pressure faces of the nozzle and nozzle holder.	(*c*) Remove nozzle to examine faces, clean and replace.

FINDING THE FAULTY INJECTION NOZZLE

In the case of a multi-cylinder oil engine misfiring the fault will usually be found to be that of a defective injection nozzle—assuming that the inlet and exhaust valves are in satisfactory order and have the proper clearances.

The faulty nozzle can be located by disconnecting each nozzle fuel-pipe supply in turn. In the case of the cylinders which are "firing" properly the effect of shutting off the fuel supply of each of these cylinders will be to cause a marked drop in the engine speed. On the other hand, if the faulty nozzle is treated in a similar manner there will be *no effect upon the engine speed.*

This method is similar in principle to that of short-circuiting, with the blade of a screw-driver, each sparking plug of a multi-cylinder petrol engine, in turn, in order to ascertain the faulty plug.

The fuel supply to the injection nozzle may be stopped either by disconnecting its fuel-pipe union or by means of the hand control which is sometimes provided for this purpose. If the fuel-pipe union is unscrewed, the fuel delivered from the fuel pump to this pipe will ooze out into the air instead of going into the nozzle.

THE FUEL-INJECTION PUMP

Having dealt with the fuel-injection nozzle the fuel pump itself will now be considered. In this connection, since the large majority of British and Continental oil engines are fitted with the Bosch make of fuel pump, we shall confine our attention to this design. Since, however, certain other makes of fuel pump not in wide use follow the same general operation principles as the Bosch pattern, a good deal of the general information given will be found applicable to these types.

Before the motor engineer or mechanic can be in the position to regulate, maintain, or service a fuel-injection pump satisfactorily he must fully understand its method of operation, so that it is proposed to give a brief account of the principles and working of the fuel pump previously mentioned.

THE FUEL-PUMP PRINCIPLE

There are two principal kinds of fuel pump in present use, known respectively as *The Constant Pressure* or *Common Rail* and *The Jerk Pump* or *Timed Pump Systems.*

In the former system, the fuel pump is employed to supply fuel at a constant pressure to a fuel reservoir, or storage chamber. From this chamber the fuel is admitted to the combustion chamber by means of a mechanically operated valve—usually mounted in the injection-nozzle unit. The lift of this valve is made variable, in order to admit more or less fuel for altering the power output. The American Cummings oil engine employs the *Storage* or *Common Rail* system.

In the *Jerk Pump* system, which is much more widely used, the fuel pump itself " times " the fuel-injection period, the control of the fuel supply being on the pump plunger. The injection nozzle has a spring-loaded valve which is opened by the hydraulic pressure of the fuel from the fuel pump. The C.A.V.-Bosch fuel pumps and injection nozzles operate on this principle. Other examples of such injection systems are the Bryce, Simms, Benes, Deutz, and B.E.H. ones.

The principle of the jerk pump is illustrated diagrammatically in Fig. 42, which shows on the left a plunger-type fuel pump having non-return fuel-inlet and delivery valves. The plunger is forced upwards by means of the cam shown; this is driven at one-half engine speed in the case of four-cycle engines and at engine speed for two-cycle engines. The plunger is returned, or kept in contact with the cam, by means of the compression spring. Fuel is drawn into the plunger barrel through the inlet valve on the down-stroke of the plunger, and on the up-stroke it is forced out through the delivery valve into the fuel pipe. It then enters the passage, shown by the arrow, leading to the underside of the injection-nozzle valve, and, lifting this valve, issues in the form of a conical spray. The compression spring indicated by the helical lines above controls the opening pressure of the valve, as previously explained.

In the case of multi-cylinder engines there is a separate plunger unit and cam for each cylinder, but for convenience, all of these units are arranged side by side in a single casing and are operated by a single camshaft, having the cams set at angles corresponding to those of the main engine crankshaft. Sometimes, however, a single plunger unit is arranged to feed a pair of cylinders.

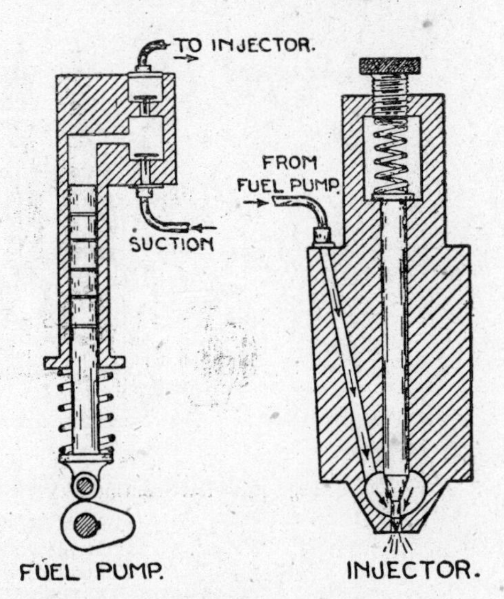

Fig. 42.—Showing Principle of the Jerk Pump.

THE C.A.V.-BOSCH FUEL PUMP

This fuel pump, as previously mentioned, belongs to the jerk-pump class. It has a constant plunger stroke, and this stroke for the 1, 2, 3, 4, and 6-cylinder B.P.E. models is 10 mm. The plunger diameters are between 5 and 10 mm., the former giving an output per stroke of ·0041 cu. in. (65 cu. mm.) and the latter ·0171 cu. in. (280 cu. mm.).

Each pumping unit comprises a pump element, consisting of the plunger and its barrel and the delivery valve with its seating. Fuel from the main fuel tank, after suitable filtering, flows to the fuel-inlet connection 101*g* of the pump (Fig. 43), and keeps the common suction chamber in the pump casing full of clean fuel oil, which can then be drawn readily into the pumping chambers of the various elements through two small lateral ports provided. The plunger 105*a* moves vertically in the barrel with a constant stroke of 10 mm. To enable the pump to vary the quantity of fuel delivered per stroke, the plunger is provided with a vertical channel (see Fig. 44) extending from its top edge A to an annular groove, the upper edge of which is cut in the form of a helix. External means 107*a* and *d* (Fig. 43) are provided whereby the plunger can be rotated in its barrel whilst working.

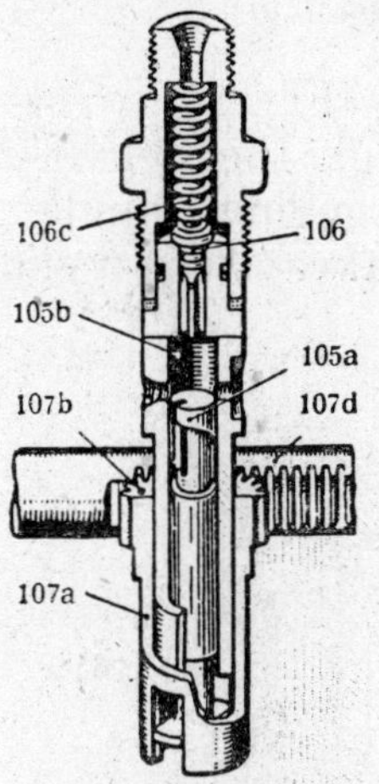

Fig. 43.—A Complete Pump Element in Sectional View.

105*a*, Pump Plunger.
105*b*, Pump Barrel.
106, Delivery Valve and Seat.
106*c*, Valve Spring.
107*a*, Control Sleeve.
107*b*, Toothed Quadrant.
107*d*, Control Rod.

OPERATION OF THE PUMP

Fig. 45 shows a fuel pump similar to that popularly used on 6-cylinder commercial-vehicle oil engines.

The pump element 1 (Fig. 45) is shown at the bottom of its suction stroke, two small ports being open and the pump barrel filled with fuel oil. On the next up, or delivery, stroke (see pump element 2) the plunger displaces

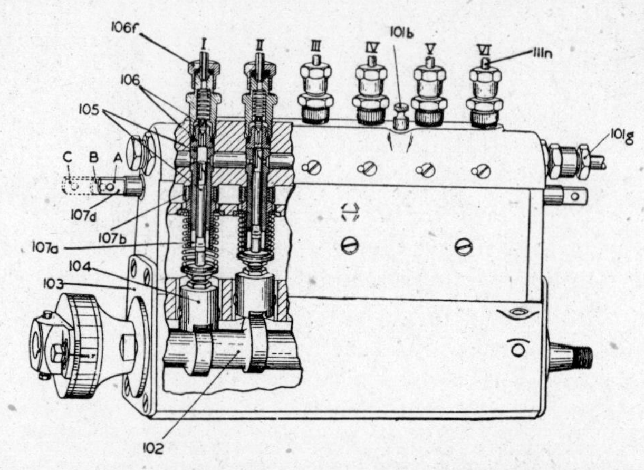

Fig. 44.—Part-sectional View of Bosch Six-cylinder Fuel Pump.

Control Rod 107*d* at (A), Engine in Starting Position.
Control Rod 107*d* at (B), Engine at Normal Load.
Control Rod 107*d* at (C), Engine Stopped.

101*b*,	Lubricating Oil Gauge Rod.	106*a* & *b*,	Delivery Valve and Seating.
101*g*,	Fuel-inlet Connection.	106*f*,	Delivery-nipple Nut.
102,	Camshaft.	107*a*,	Control Sleeve.
103,	Bearing End Plate.	107*b*,	Regulating Toothed Quadrant.
104,	Plunger Guide and Tappet Roller.	107*d*,	Control Rod.
105*a* & *b*,	Pump Barrel and Plunger.	111*n*,	Delivery Pipe.

fuel back through the two small ports until its top edge A (Fig. 45) covers them, so that the remaining fuel is pressed out through the delivery valve 106 via the pressure pipe 111*n* to the nozzle in the engine cylinder. Since the plunger is of constant stroke this top edge will always cover the

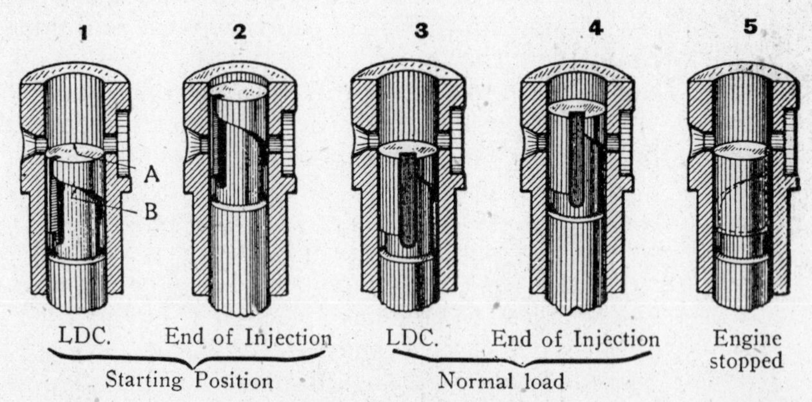

Fig. 45.—Showing the Bosch Fuel-pump Plunger and Barrel, the Plunger being shown in various positions during its strokes.

ports in the pump barrel in the same position of the cam rotation, so that injection at the nozzle will always commence at the same moment relative to the position of the engine crank. So long as the ports are kept covered by the plunger, the pump will continue to inject fuel through the nozzle, but reference to 2 (Fig. 45) will show that before the plunger reaches the top of its stroke, the helical edge B of its annular groove (see Fig. 45) has uncovered the right-hand port, which enables the enclosed fuel to take the path of least resistance (via the vertical channel and annular groove) back through the port in the barrel to the common suction chamber. The position of the plunger stroke at which the helical edge B will uncover the port is adjustable by rotating the plunger axially by means of a toothed quadrant 107*b* (see Fig. 43) which is clamped to a sleeve 107*a*, having slots engaging the lugs of the plunger at its lower end.

The toothed quadrant 107*b* meshes with a rack provided on the control rod 107*d*, which similarly actuates all the pump elements in the unit, and is externally connected either to the governor or other controls by suitable linkage.

ANTI-DRIBBLE DEVICE

When the helical edge B of the pump plunger uncovers the port in the pump barrel near the end of the delivery stroke, the pressure of fuel is immediately reduced so that the delivery valve at once drops on its seating, thus cutting off communication between the pump and the nozzle until the next delivery stroke takes place. In coming to its seat to act as a non-return valve, the delivery valve is, however, made to perform the other highly important function of pressure-pipe release. This double function is obtained by means of the novel but entirely simple construction of the delivery-valve unit, and reference to Fig. 46 will show that it is an ordinary mitre-faced valve with a guide which has a circular groove cut in it, dividing the guide into two parts. The lower part has four longitudinal grooves communicating with the circular groove.

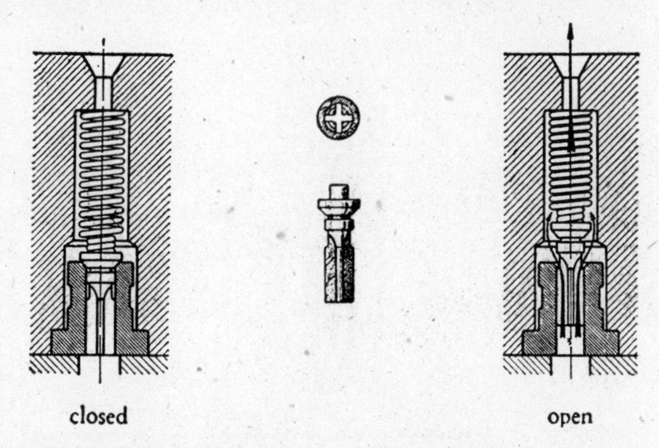

Fig. 46.—The Plunger-unit Delivery Valve, between Plunger and Fuel-delivery Pipe to Injection Nozzle.

The upper part of the guide forms a small piston which is a highly ground plunger fit for the valve seating, and is also internally ground. When the pump is on its delivery stroke, as the pressure of the fuel rises, the delivery valve is pushed up until the pressure fuel can escape through the longitudinal grooves over the valve face to the nozzle. Immediately the pump plunger releases the pressure in its barrel, the delivery valve (under influence of its spring and the great difference between the pump barrel and the delivery pipe) resumes its seat, causing the small piston parts of the guide to sweep down the valve seating with a plunger action, thus increasing the space in the delivery pipe (by an amount equal to the volume of the small piston part of the valve guide) before the valve actually seats itself. The effect of this increase of volume in the delivery-pipe system is, of course, that of suddenly reducing the pressure of the fuel therein so that the nozzle valve in the nozzle can " snap " to its seat, thus instantaneously terminating the spray of fuel in the cylinder entirely without " dribble."

HOW THE OUTPUT IS REGULATED

The word " Stop " and an arrow engraved on one end of the pump casing in line with the control rod 107*d* (Fig. 43) indicate which way the control rod should be removed to stop the engine. A pump element at no output or " Engine Stopped " position is shown at 4 (Fig. 45) when the

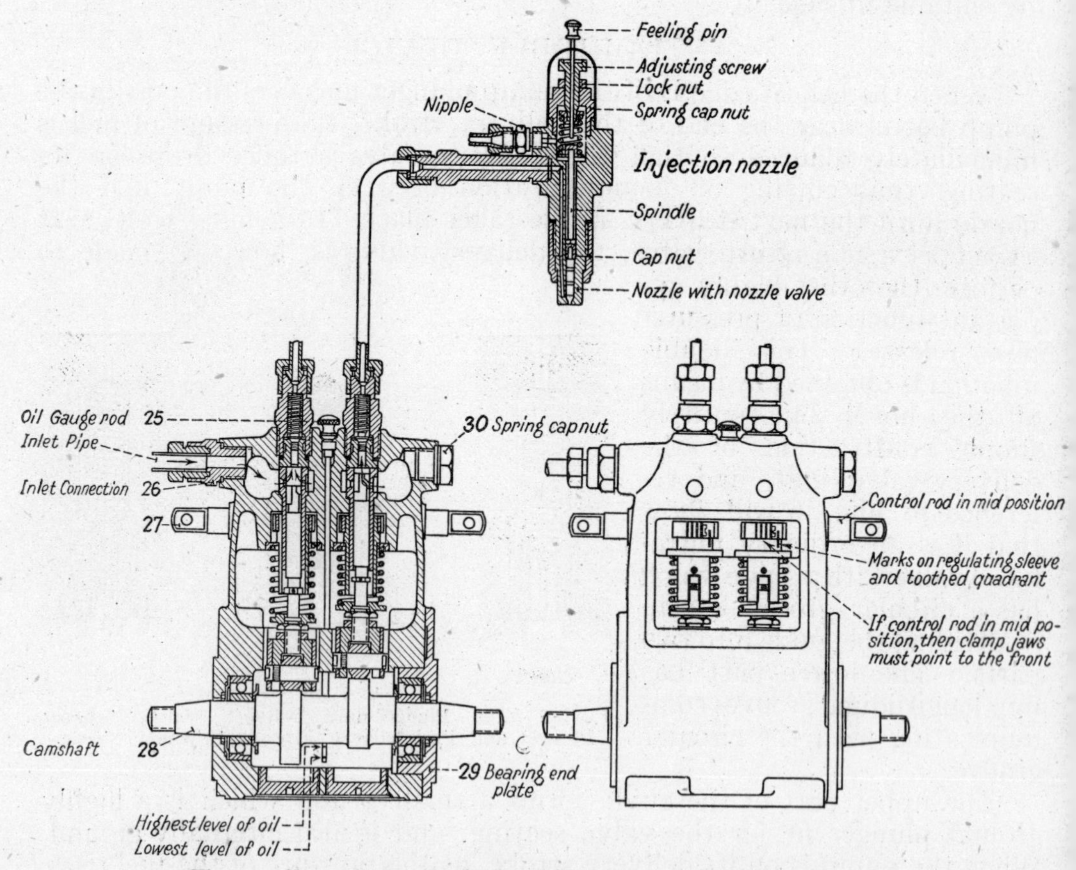

Fig. 47.—Two-cylinder C.A.V.-Bosch Fuel Pump and Injection Nozzle.

control rod will be at *c*, and the vertical channel of the pump plunger will be opposite the right-hand port in its pump barrel, as at 5 (Fig. 45), so that no fuel is delivered even when the engine is turned.

To start the engine the control rod 107*d* should be moved over to the "starting" position from "stop" so that the plungers will be in the positions shown in 1 and 2, Fig. 45. At this point the plungers are actually delivering more fuel than is required by the engine at full load, which condition is necessary to obtain easy starting. When the engine starts, the control rod should be released to the position giving the desired engine speed. It is important that the excess fuel delivery is only obtainable for starting the engine, and to ensure that this is so *when the engine is operating at full speed,* a trip collar is often provided by the engine manufacturer; otherwise the exhaust will be dense and smoky, and heavy carbon deposits will be formed in the engine. When moving the control rod to its starting position, this collar must be temporarily "tripped" out of use, but should automatically come into operation again immediately the engine starts.

At 3 and 4 (Fig. 45) the pump element is shown at normal output, in which position the engine will be operating at normal load. The actual position of the control rod in these conditions can always be found only by experiment on the particular engine concerned. The control rod 107*d* can be connected to the governor at one end and to the hand control or accelerator at the other. In lining these, however, care should be taken that no transverse or rotational forces are transmitted to the control rod which may result in the latter either jamming or becoming stiff in action, with consequent faulty control of the engine.

A complete fuel pump, fuel-delivery pipe, and injection nozzle of C.A.V.-Bosch design is given in Fig. 47; the various components can readily be traced from this illustration.

ALTERING THE INJECTION TIMING

In some types of high-speed oil engine it is advantageous to be able to advance or retard the moment of injection, to facilitate starting or to suit the higher speeds; in other cases—notably in turbulent-head engines—the timing of the injection should be kept constant.

The Bosch fuel pump is supplied with an injection-advance device which is available in two models, giving respectively 8° and 12° of rotation on the pump shaft, i.e. 16° to 24° on the crankshaft. Fig. 48 illustrates the injection-advance device, the various parts being described in the caption below.

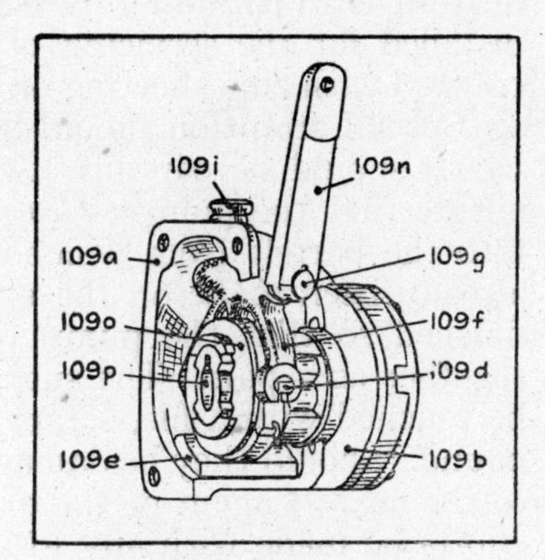

Fig. 48.—Illustrating the Bosch Injection-advance Device.

109*a*, Housing.
109*b*, Half-coupling Paws.
109*d*, Clamp for Splined Bush.
109*e*, Felt Pad.
109*f*, Adjusting Stirrup.
109*g*, Spindle.
109*i*, Lubricating Oil Cup.
109*n*, Adjusting Lever.
109*o*, Splined Bush.
109*p*, Splined Cone.

The adjusting lever 109*n* is connected by a small shaft and fulcrum with the stirrup 109*f* carrying a loose clamp 109*d* which is located between the collars of a female splined bush 109*o*. This bush engages with the two paws of the half-coupling and the inclined spline on the inner cone 109*p* in which the pump camshaft is fitted. It will be seen that the splined bush 109*o* can be made to slide longitudinally along the paws of the half-coupling by movement of the adjusting lever 109*n*, the action of the inclined splines on the inner splined cone causing an angular displacement between the pump camshaft and the engine driving shaft.

The advance device should be lubricated with engine oil at the end of every 500 to 600 miles, oil being applied through the oil cup 109*i*.

DISMANTLING THE FUEL PUMP

The fuel pump is a high-precision mechanism and its dismantling should not be lightly undertaken, as only mechanics specially trained can be expected to carry it out successfully. Strict cleanliness should be observed when preparing to dismantle fuel-injection pumps, care being taken that all iron filings, dirt, grit, dust, etc., have been removed from the bench on which the work has to be done. The bench should then be covered with a sheet of clean grease-proof paper and a number of small clean containers provided for the various parts removed. It is also advisable to have a thoroughly clean covered vessel available containing a supply of fresh clean paraffin for washing these parts. If permanent facilities are installed for the servicing of injection equipment, the bench should be covered with zinc sheeting or linoleum or a similar easily cleaned material.

Special attention should be paid to the pump plunger and barrel unit, which should be carefully isolated, a specially important point being to ensure that the plungers are never laid down separately or fitted except into the barrels from which they were originally taken. Comment has already been made on the extremely fine limits to which these parts are finished so that the pump plunger and its barrel should always work together as a pair. The surface of these parts should never at any time be touched with a file, scraper, or other hard tool or any abrasive compound. Should they be damaged, the entire injection pump should be sent to the nearest agent of the makers for attention, rather than preliminary efforts be made with any form of grinding paste, powder, or stone.

The delivery valve and seating should be treated in the same way, as these are similarly matched, and if trouble is experienced after they have been cleaned and rubbed together, the pair should be replaced from spare parts stock.

In the case of multi-cylinder injection pumps, if it is considered necessary to dismantle the pump elements, control sleeves and control rod, it is important that this work should be referred to the nearest agent of the makers in whose shops will be found the necessary apparatus for ensuring that the controls are again assembled and adjusted to give the uniformity of delivery required. The importance of accuracy in this respect cannot be exaggerated, and a special power-driven machine has been devised to enable the calibration to be performed at high speed.

(A) To change the plunger (referring to Figs. 43, 44, and 49) spring 105*d*, examine plunger 105*a* and camshaft 102.

(1) Remove inspection cover plate.

(2) Remove bearing-end plate 103, after rotating camshaft 102 to

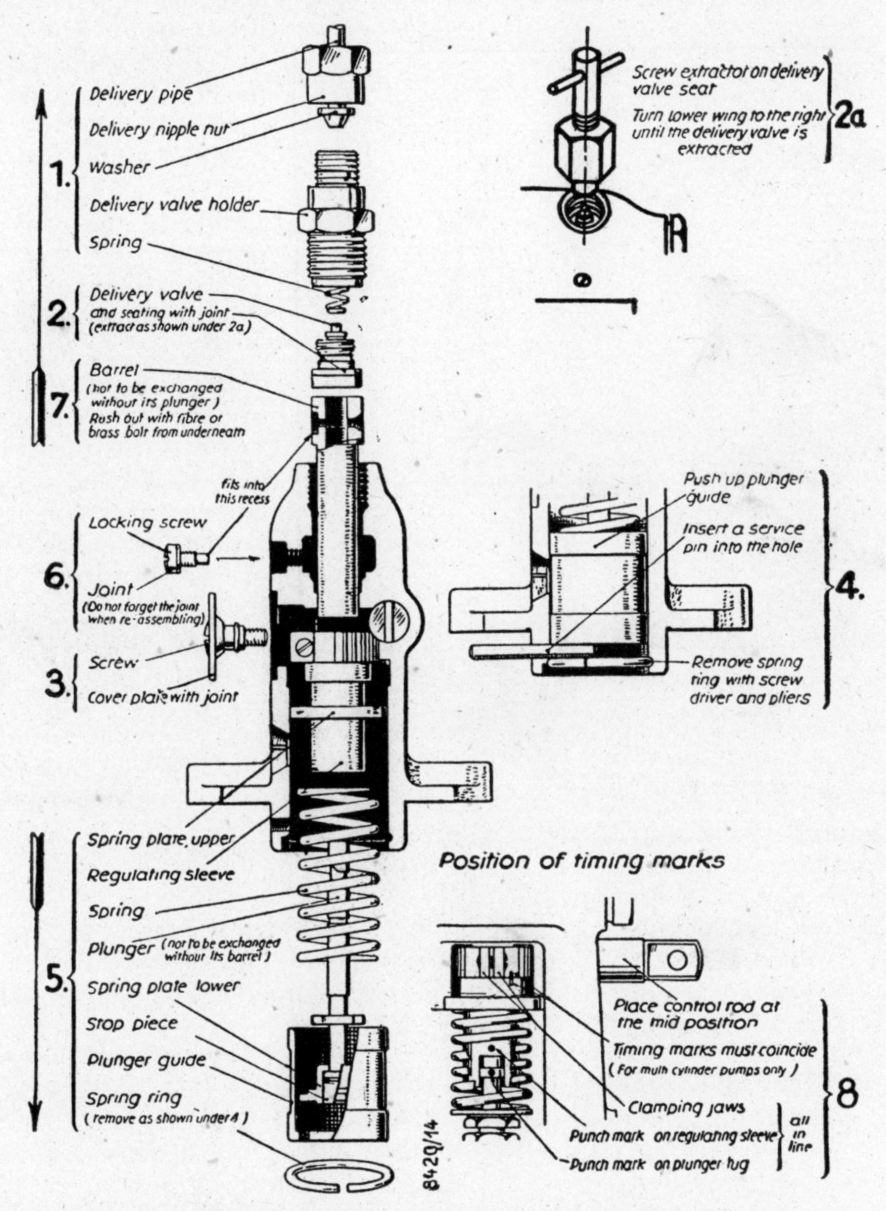

Fig. 49.—Showing all the Components of C.A.V.-Bosch Fuel-pump Unit.

bring the plunger guide 104 to its top dead centre position and inserting the tappet holder *a* under the head of the tappet-adjusting screw. This should be repeated for each element, when the camshaft 102 can be easily withdrawn. The pump half-coupling (or advance device) need only be removed from the camshaft if it is fitted at the opposite end to the bearing-end plate. Should this be done, care should be taken that the shaft position is marked so that on reassembling the pump the firing sequence will be correct. The removal of the advance device, or the coupling, from the cone of the camshaft should never at any time be done with the use of a hammer; a properly fitting extractor *c* should be used for this purpose.

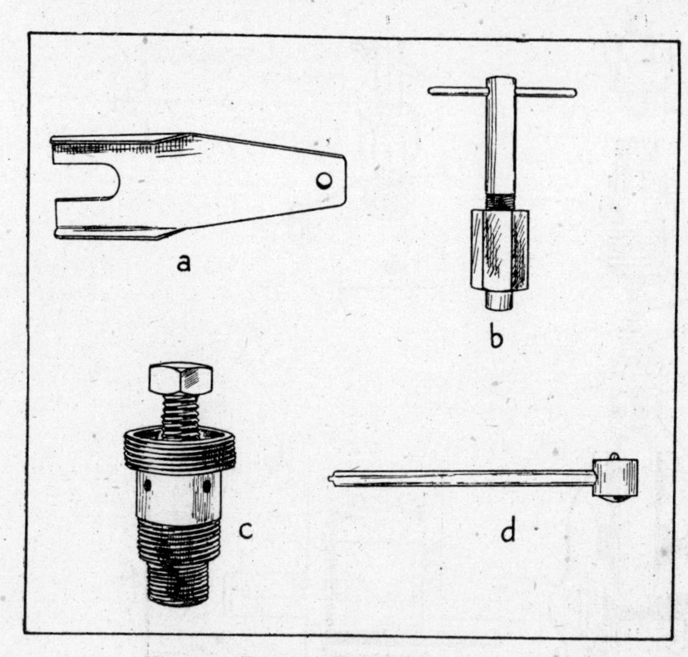

Fig. 50.—Tools for Fuel-pump Servicing.

a, Tappet-bridge Holder.
b, Delivery Valve-seat Extractor.
c, Coupling and Advance Device Extractor.
d, Closing-plug Spanner.

(3) Unscrew the closing plugs (with tool *d,* Fig. 50), at the base of the housing and push up the plunger guide 14 until it is possible to withdraw the tappet holder, after which the tappet assembly 104, the lower spring plate, the plunger spring, and plunger may be withdrawn through the holes.

(B) To change delivery valve and seating.

Unscrew delivery-valve holder, withdraw spring and delivery valve 106*b*. The valve seating 106*a* and its joint can now be removed by means of the extractor tool *b* (Fig. 50).

(C) To remove the pump barrel.

Unscrew the locking screw and push barrel from below by means of fibre or soft brass bolt. As this process involves complete readjustment to the delivery of the injection pump it is recommended that it be placed in the hands of a C.A.V.-Bosch service agent.

REASSEMBLING THE FUEL PUMP

In reassembling the pumps great care should be taken that all joints and other parts are entirely clean. They should be (1) rinsed in clean paraffin; (2) allowed to drip; (3) smeared with a lubricating oil, and finally brought together entirely without the use of cotton waste, rags, or cloth wipers of any kind.

(1) Refit the barrel of the element carefully, observing that the slot in it is opposite the hole for the locking screw. Tighten down locking screw after making sure that its joint is in place.

(2) Refit valve seating and joint; place cleanly and securely in position. Replace delivery valve and its spring and finally fit delivery-valve holder with its joint in position, and screw down tightly.

(3) Insert plunger with spring and lower spring plate into the barrel, taking care that the lug on the lower edge of the plunger fits into the slot in the control sleeve, for which it is marked.

(4) Insert tappet assembly, and press against the spring until the tappet holder *a* (Fig. 50) can be inserted between the tappet-adjusting screw and the pump housing.

(5) Refit camshaft in its bearing in the pump housing, taking care that the coupling (or advance device) is fitted so that the correct firing order will be maintained.

(*Note.*—The camshaft gives different firing orders according to the position in which it is placed in the pump. For instance, a 4-cylinder camshaft firing 1-3-4-2 when reversed in the housing gives a firing order of 1-2-4-3. This similarly affects a 6-cylinder pump. Refit the bearing end plate 103 and tighten securing screws.)

(6) Refit inlet-connection union nut, inlet closing plugs, and lubricating oil gauge rod 101*b*.

(7) Smear the mitre-joint face of the closing plug 101*a* with white lead or other securing compound and tighten up hard.

(8) Fill the camshaft chamber with lubricating oil to the prescribed level with best-quality engine oil.

(9) Replace inspection cover plate.

FUEL-PUMP GOVERNORS AND CONTROLS

Most commercial-vehicle oil engines are now fitted with governors for controlling both the idling and maximum speeds; the driver's foot accelerator controls the intermediate speeds for varying the engine's output to suit the road conditions, acceleration, or speed requirements.

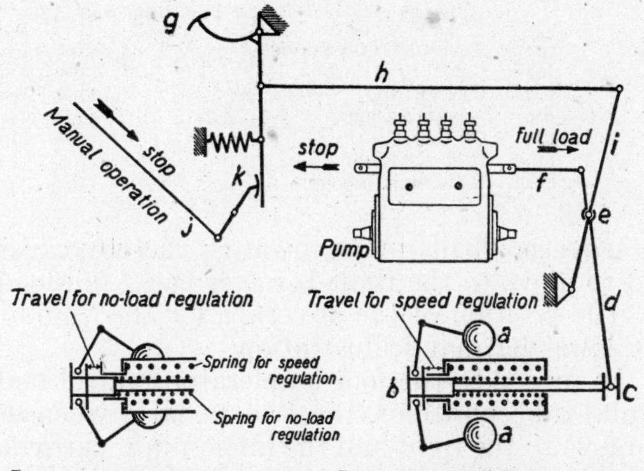

Fig. 51.—Illustrating Principle of Fuel-pump Governor.

Fig. 51 illustrates the principle of the control system mentioned. A centrifugal type of governor is shown at the lower right-hand side. This has two weighted and hinged levers, the ball weights *a* on which move outwards as the speed increases, causing a collar *b* on the governor shaft to move to the right. The same movement on the extreme right-hand collar *c* moves the pivoted lever *d* about its hinge pin *e*, and causes the fuel-pump control rod *f* to move to the left, towards the "stop" position, thereby shutting down the fuel supply. Should, however, the speed fall

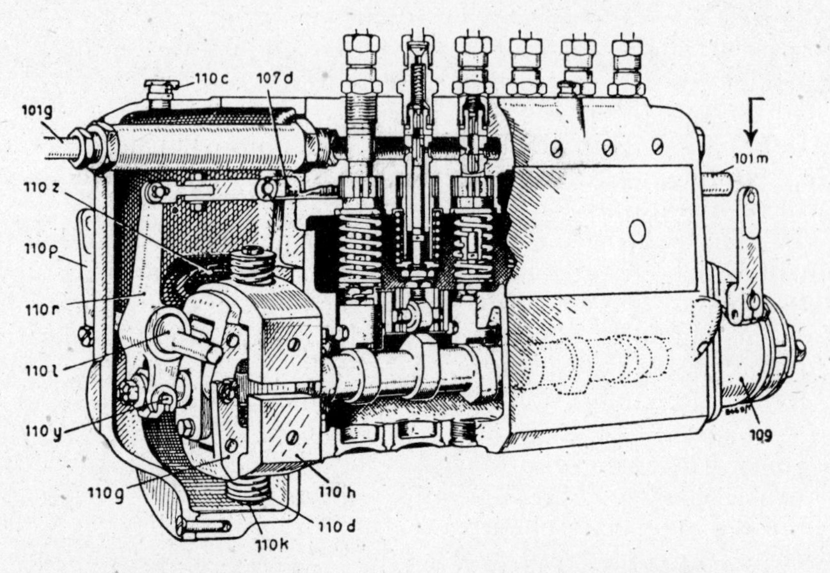

Fig. 52.—C.A.V.-Bosch Fuel-injection Pump, with Governor.

101*g*, Fuel-inlet Connection.
101*m*, Control-rod Stop.
107*d*, Control Rod.
109, Advance Device.
110*c*, Oil Cup.
110*d*, E. & F. Spring.
110*g*, Bell-crank Levers.
110*h*, Fly Weights.
110*k*, Adjusting Nut.
110*l*, Eccentric.
110*p*, Control Lever.
110*r*, Floating Lever.
110*y*, Coupling Crosshead Pin.
110*x*, Access Plug.

the governor balls move inwards, thereby causing the fuel-pump control rod to move to the right towards the "full-load" position.

The position of the governor for the "no-load" position is shown in the lower left-hand illustration.

In regard to the foot-accelerator control between the "no-load" and "full-load" positions, the foot pedal *g* when depressed causes the rod *h* to move to the right and the hinge-pin *e*, carried on the lever *i*, is therefore moved to the right; this causes the fuel-pump control rod to move to the right also, so that more fuel is supplied to the engine and its output is therefore increased. The manual operation lever *j* operates a movable stop *k* which fixes the return position of the hinge pin *e* and therefore the speed of the engine.

Fig. 52 illustrates the C.A.V.-Bosch six-cylinder type fuel pump with the governor gear incorporated in the same casing (on the left-hand side). The various parts are identified in the caption below the illustration, and the operation of the pump can be followed with the aid of Fig. 51.

The actual lay-out of the fuel-pump controls in the case of the Mercédès commercial vehicle is shown in Fig. 53, the key to the numbered items being given below the illustration.

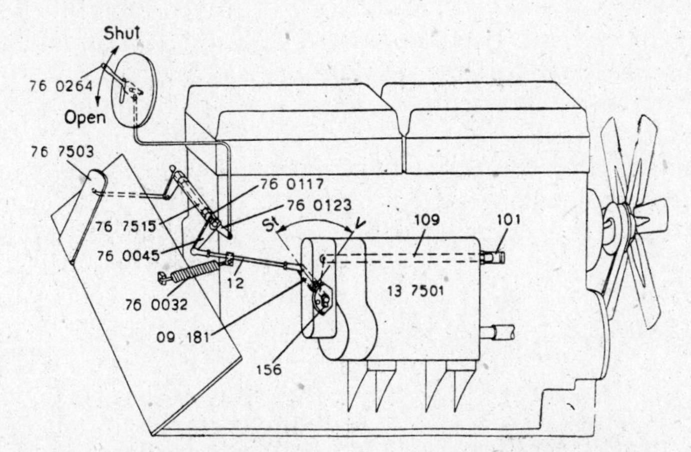

Fig. 53.—Arrangement of Fuel-pump Controls on Mercédès Vehicle.

12,	Rods for Metering the Fuel Supply.
101,	Stop for the Control Rod.
109,	Control Rod.
156,	Stop for the Lever 09 181.
09 181,	Lever for Metering the Fuel Supply.
13 7501,	Fuel-injection Pump.
76 0045,	Intermediate Lever for Adjusting the Fuel Quantity.
76 0117,	Stop Bush.
76 0123,	Intermediate Lever.
76 0264,	Hand Lever for Metering the Quantity of the Fuel Supply.
76 7503,	Pedal for the Metering of the Quantity of the Fuel Supply.
76 7515,	Transverse Shaft.

ADJUSTING THE FUEL-PUMP GOVERNOR

The engine's output is controlled by the travel of the fuel-pump's control rod, as previously explained. This travel is limited by two means, namely, by the control-lever set-screw stop (101*m*, Fig. 54), and by a pinned control-rod sleeve stop.

These stops are accurately set by the engine manufacturers and should not be altered except under unusual circumstances, and then, preferably, with the manufacturers' permission.

Should the adjustment be made the following is the procedure:

With the engine developing the desired power and speed and with a clear exhaust, the control-lever stop (110*ma*, Fig. 55), which on latest model governors comprises a set-screw and lock nut) is screwed into such a position as to limit the control-lever angular movement to keep the engine running with least exhaust. After doing this, and with the engine still running, the control-rod stop 101*n* in Fig. 54 (contained in the control-rod sleeve 101*m*) should be screwed in until it just touches the control-rod end. A small clearance may be allowed by unscrewing the " Stop " 101*n* one-

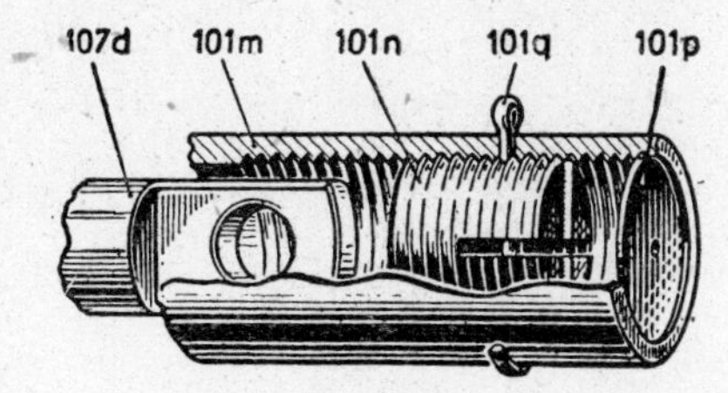

Fig. 54.

half to one turn back in the sleeve, which can only be done, of course, after removing the dust cap 101*p* and pin 101*q* provided in the sleeve.

Now, with the engine stationary and preferably cold, starting tests should be made to ascertain whether the permitted amount of fuel-control opening is sufficient for good starting. Should it not be so, then the "Stop" 101*n* must be further withdrawn, say at half a turn at a time, until good starting is obtained, when the pin will be replaced, securing the "Stop" 101*n* in position.

In practice a compromise is necessary between good starting and a good (smokeless) exhaust at starting. To do this, with the engine stopped and the control lever opened to the maximum permitted by the set-screw 110 *m*, the control-rod stop 101*n* may be screwed into the sleeve until it touches the end of the control rod 107*d*. Now, it may be turned inwards still more to the extent of about one-quarter of an inch against the pressure of the control rod until a considerable resistance is felt, or until the control-lever stop just leaves its limiting screw 110*ma* (Fig. 55). The control-rod stop screw 101*n* may now be unscrewed the required amount to facilitate starting. The adjusting screw must be secured with the cotter-pin 101*a*, and the dust cap 101*p*, afterwards inserted into sleeve. When the engine is started and the speed of revolution rises above that of idling the control-rod opening will be limited automatically to that originally determined by the control-lever stop 110*ma* adjustment.

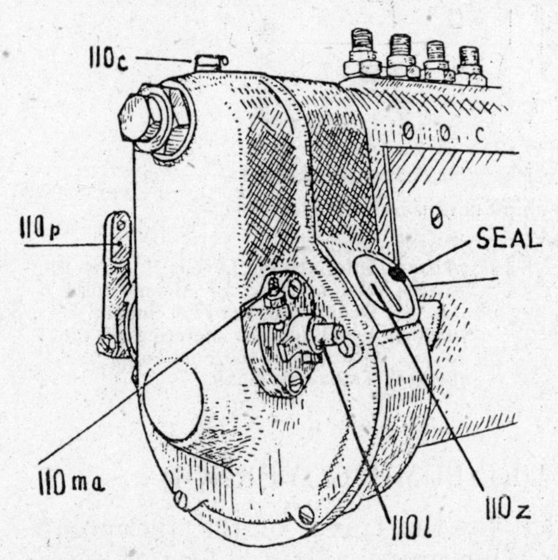

Fig. 55.—Adjusting the Governor Speed Range.

It is essential to note that of the two means of limiting the fuel control, the control-lever stop 110*ma* is the more important, as by it the maximum fuel delivery is limited at all speeds except those below idling, when the control-rod sleeve stop 101*n* functions if correctly adjusted. As an illustration, if with the control-lever stop 110*ma* a maximum travel of 12 mm. is allowed of the control rod when the engine is running normally, then when stationary about 18 mm. will be permitted, if the control-rod sleeve stop 101*n* has not been adjusted in any way to restrain further movement of the control rod.

THE PNEUMATIC TYPE OF GOVERNOR

Many modern oil engines, including some of the smaller models, are fitted with a type of speed governor which does not depend for its operation upon the centrifugal-force principle, but upon the degree of vacuum or suction existing in the air-inlet pipe of the engine.

All of the air for subsequent compression in the engine is taken through a "throat" or venturi—as in carburettor practice—and a butterfly valve is fitted in this throat, a lever being attached to operate this valve.

The variations in the suction effect in this throat (Fig. 56) are communicated by means of a pipe to a diaphragm unit mounted on the fuel pump. The diaphragm flexes under the suction effects and its movement is arranged to alter the position of the fuel-pump control rod. The driver's accelerator pedal is connected to the butterfly-valve lever in order to

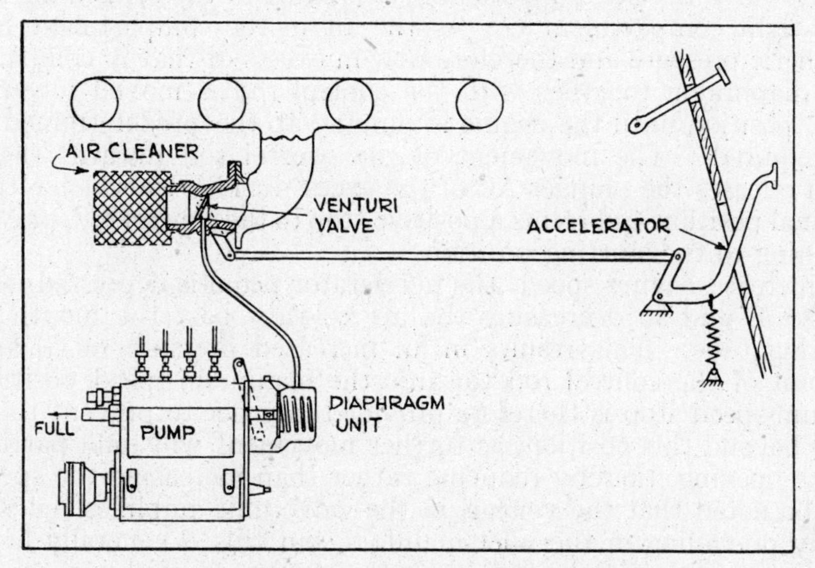

Fig. 56.—The Bosch Pneumatic Governor Scheme.

provide a means of varying the suction effect—and therefore the engine speed and output.

The various components and lay-out of the C.A.V.-Bosch pneumatic governor are shown in Figs. 57 to 58.

Referring to Fig. 59, the venturi consists of a body provided with a flange for mounting on the engine air-inlet pipe and it has a spigot opposite, for the air filter. At the smallest throat diameter of the venturi a butterfly valve C is fitted for the purpose of controlling the air flow; it is operated by the driver's pedal through the lever A; the amount of movement for maximum and idling speeds is governed by two adjustable stops AJ and AK. On the same centre line as the butterfly valve is a screwed connection D through which the air is exhausted from the diaphragm unit actuating the pump-control rod.

The diaphragm unit consists of a housing G mounted on a separate casting H with a special leather diaphragm clamped between the two, and providing an air-tight compartment within the housing G. A light spring K acting on the diaphragm is provided in order to damp out any oscillations which may occur in the vacuum ; it tends to keep the control rod in full-open position, an *additional level* L *being fitted for stopping the engine.*

The operation of the governor is as follows :

With the engine stationary and the lever L released, the spring K forces the control rod into the full-load position. Then by pressing the plunger AC on the excess-fuel device the control rod is allowed to open automatically to the extent of its travel and so provide an excess of fuel to be available for starting. When the engine has started it may be idled by releasing the accelerator pedal and thus closing partially the butterfly valve C when high vacuum is created in the connecting tube E and air-tight compartment G. As the air in the compartment H is at atmospheric pressure and therefore now in excess of that in compartment G, the diaphragm together with the control rod is moved towards the "stop" position until the engine is running at the predetermined idling speed required. The movement of the control rod towards the idling position releases the plunger AC of the excess-fuel device which returns to its original position and forms a positive stop to the control rod, preventing it returning to the starting position.

To increase engine speed, the accelerator pedal is depressed, opening the valve C and so decreasing the air velocity past the mouth of the connecting tube. This results in an increased pressure in G, and the movement of the control rod towards the maximum-speed position. A maximum-speed stop is therefore provided in order to prevent the valve moving beyond this position, as further movement will tend partially to close the opening, thereby reducing rather than increasing the speed. It should be noted that the venturi in the valve unit amplifies the vacuum normally prevailing in the inlet manifold, but this is generally less than the vacuum in the air-inlet valves, so that no loss of efficiency results.

ADJUSTMENT OF THE PNEUMATIC GOVERNOR

Should it be necessary to make adjustments, the following is the proper procedure :

(1) *To Alter Fuel Supply.*

(*a*) Remove sealing cover AE (Fig. 59).

(*b*) Release lock nut AA by means of a key spanner.

(*c*) To increase fuel supply the set-screw AB should be screwed inwards, whilst the reverse is necessary to decrease the supply.

A compromise between power, exhaust colour, and fuel consumption should be aimed at, and if, for example with the original setting, the power is ample but the exhaust colour and fuel consumption are not satisfactory, then by further slight alteration to the set-screw AB it may be found possible to diminish the smokiness of the exhaust and perhaps in consequence reduce the fuel consumption to some extent. Obviously this may be done until a loss of power and subsequently speed is sustained, when it will be necessary to reopen the set-screw control to give the desired conditions.

(*d*) Relock nut AA and replace sealing cover AE.

(2) *Maximum Speed.*

The absolute maximum speed is entirely governed by the diameter of the venturi in the valve unit and cannot, therefore, be altered. The speed may be decreased, however, by the adjustment of the control-valve movement by means of the screw AJ (Fig. 59).

(3) *Idling Speed.*

To reduce the idling speed, unscrew set-screw AK (Fig. 59) to the required amount in order to allow the venturi valve more movement towards closing point. Screw in slightly to increase the idling speed. Re-adjustment of auxiliary spring set-screw Q (Fig. 57) or cam movement V (Fig. 58) should only be made if the idling performance of the engine

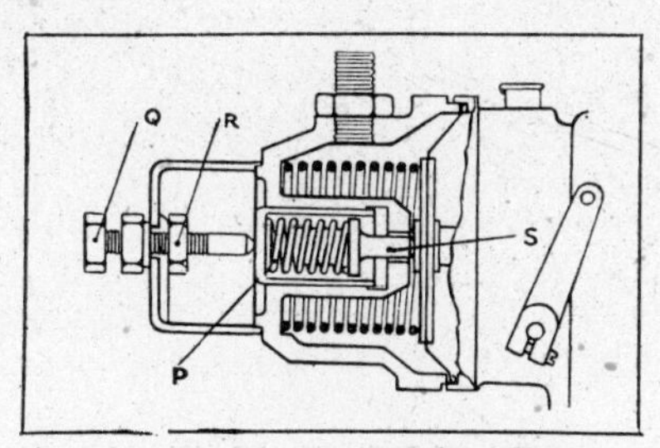

Fig. 57.—Diaphragm Unit with Idling Spring adjusted by Set-screw.

P, Auxiliary Idling Spring.
Q, Set-screw.
R, Lock nut.
S, Plunger.

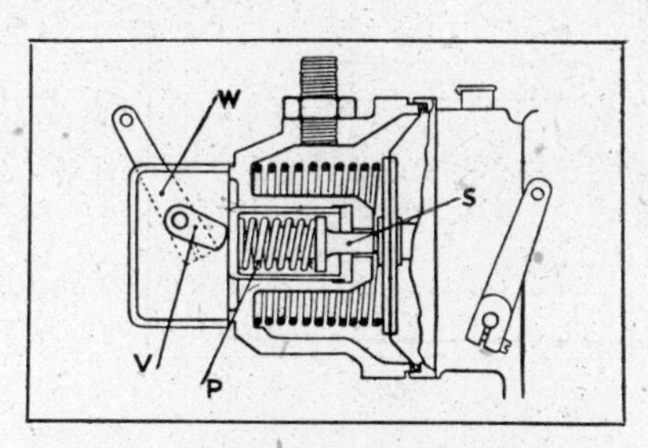

Fig. 58.—Diaphragm Unit with Idling Spring adjusted by Cam.

V, Cam.
W, Cam-operating Lever.

becomes unstable, and should not be touched in order to modify the idling position. In any case, make sure that the unstable performance is not due to other causes relative to the engine or nozzles before attempting any readjustment to the auxiliary springs.

MAINTENANCE OF PNEUMATIC GOVERNOR

Beyond the necessary lubrication of the moving parts, very little maintenance attention is required. The special leather diaphragm should last a considerable time, but *in the event of a leak* occurring the following procedure should be adopted :

(*a*) Remove vacuum pipe E (Fig. 59). (*b*) Move the stop lever L into " stop " position. (*c*) Place a finger over the diaphragm-housing union F in order to seal it. (*d*) Release the stop lever. (*e*) The control rod should then slowly return back to the maximum-speed position after a quick initial movement for a fraction of the distance.

If it returns quickly for the whole movement and the housings G and H are clamped firmly together, then the diaphragm is leaking and should be replaced, preferably by the manufacturers.

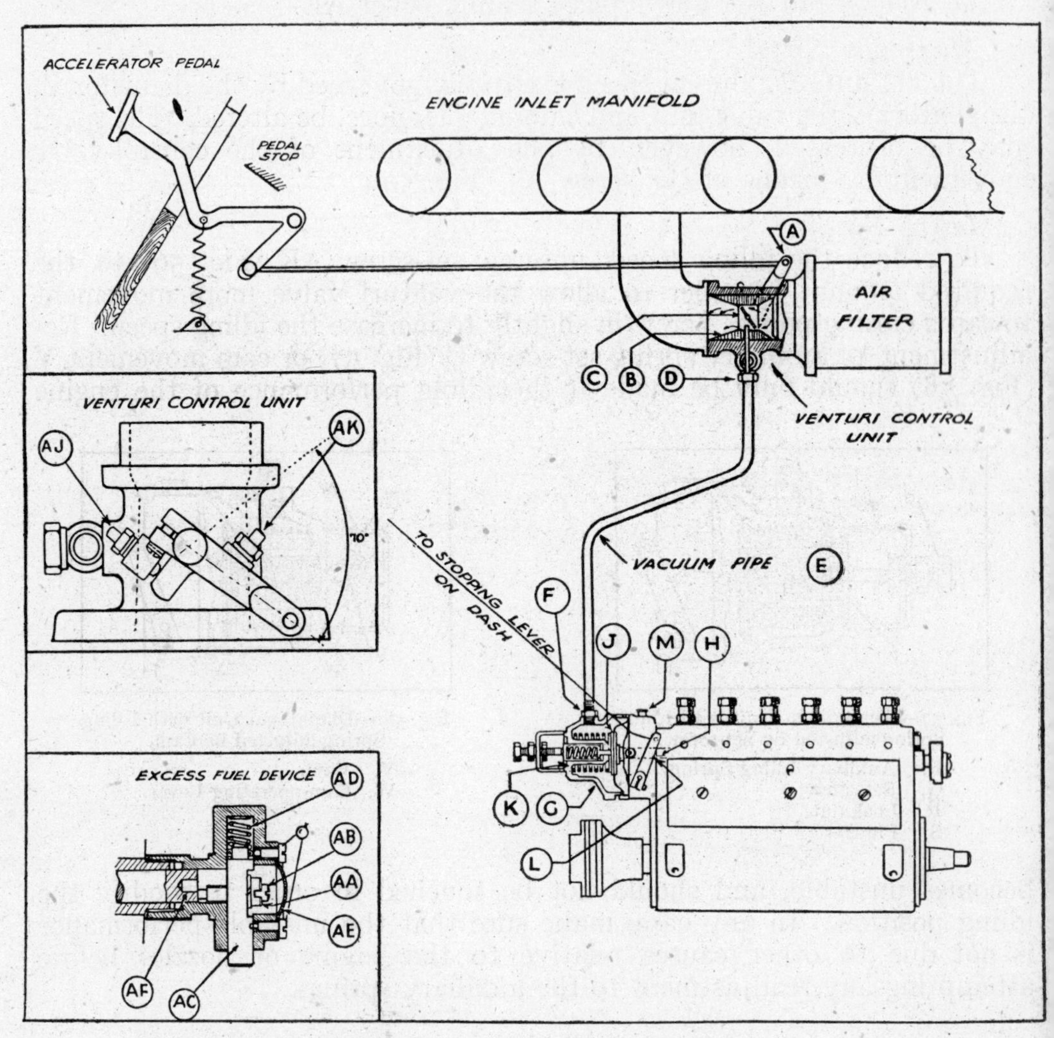

Fig. 59.—General Arrangement Diagram.

A,	Venturi Valve-control Lever.	L,	Stop Lever.
B,	Venturi Throat.	M,	Oil Cap.
C,	Venturi Valve.	AA,	Lock Nut.
D,	Vacuum-pipe Union.	AB,	Adjusting Screw.
E,	Vacuum Pipe.	AC,	Plunger.
F,	Diaphragm-housing Union.	AD,	Plunger Spring.
G,	Diaphragm Housing.	AE,	Sealing Cap.
H,	Main Housing.	AF,	Control Rod.
J,	Diaphragm.	AJ,	Adjustable Screw for Idling.
K,	Main Diaphragm Spring.	AK,	Adjustable Screw for Maximum Speed

The diaphragm should be kept pliant by the addition of one tablespoonful of lubricating oil through the oil cap M every 1,000 miles.

Vacuum pipe E can be tested for leaks in exactly the same way as the diaphragm, except that the diaphragm-housing end is connected to union F and a finger applied to the venturi end of the pipe.

HOW TO SET THE FUEL-PUMP TIMING

The correct timing of the fuel-injection system, so that the fuel commences to spray into the combustion chamber at the correct moment, is a very important factor in oil-engine operation.

In most cases the manufacturers set this timing correctly at their works and the setting selected is that giving the best all-round performance; it should not, therefore, be interfered with. On the other hand, should it be necessary to replace or dismantle the fuel pump, it will be necessary to retime the fuel injection. Usually, the injection of the fuel commences at an angle of 10° to 30°—as measured on the flywheel—before the piston arrives at its top dead centre, on the compression stroke; the actual angle of advance is invariably furnished by the engine manufacturers. Further, it is now the recognised practice to mark the engine flywheel with the top dead centre position of No. 1 piston and also with a line showing the fuel-injection commencement position of the flywheel (or piston) (Fig. 61).

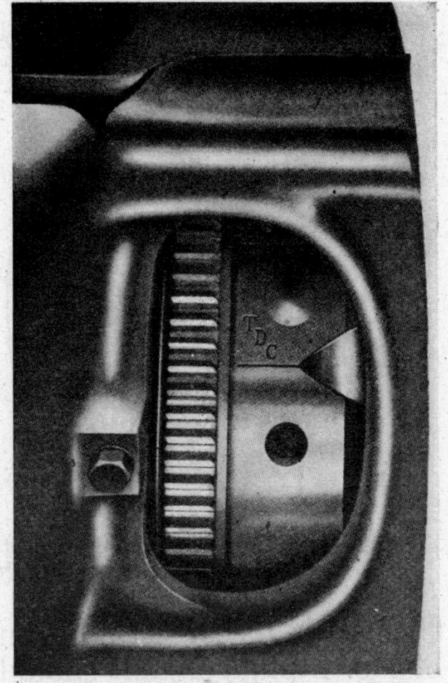

Fig. 60.—Method of Indicating Top Dead Centre (T.D.C.) of No. 1 Piston (A.E.C.).

The procedure recommended for timing the fuel injection is then as follows: First set the piston of No. 1 cylinder on its top dead centre, compression stroke. Do not make the mistake of setting it on the exhaust stroke; both inlet and exhaust valves should therefore be closed for the compression stroke.

The flywheel should then be rotated backwards slightly until the fuel-injection advance mark comes opposite the pointer or index mark on the crankcase. If no such mark exists the angle may be measured on the flywheel, by first measuring the circumference of the flywheel with a steel tape and then measuring off the backward distance equivalent to the angle of advance.

Thus, if the injection advance is 20° and the circumference of the flywheel is 36 in., the following formula enables the distance d corresponding to the injection advance to be estimated:

$$\frac{d}{36} = \frac{20}{360} \text{ whence } d = 2 \text{ in.}$$

It is now necessary to set the fuel pump so that the plunger of the No. 1 cylinder unit is just on the point of delivering its fuel. It will be assumed that the engine-shaft drive to the fuel-pump camshaft is disconnected, so that the latter shaft can be turned by hand.

In order to ascertain when No. 1 plunger is about to deliver its fuel, the pump plunger in question should be examined for any indication marks—since the fuel-pump manufacturers generally provide such marks. Thus, in the case of the Bosch fuel pump (Diagram 8, Fig. 49), timing marks are arranged on the sleeve, which must coincide when the plunger is about to commence delivery. In other cases, small windows are provided on the plunger sleeves or barrels through which marks on the plunger are observed. When these marks coincide with fixed marks on the sides of the windows the plungers are then about to commence delivery of the fuel.

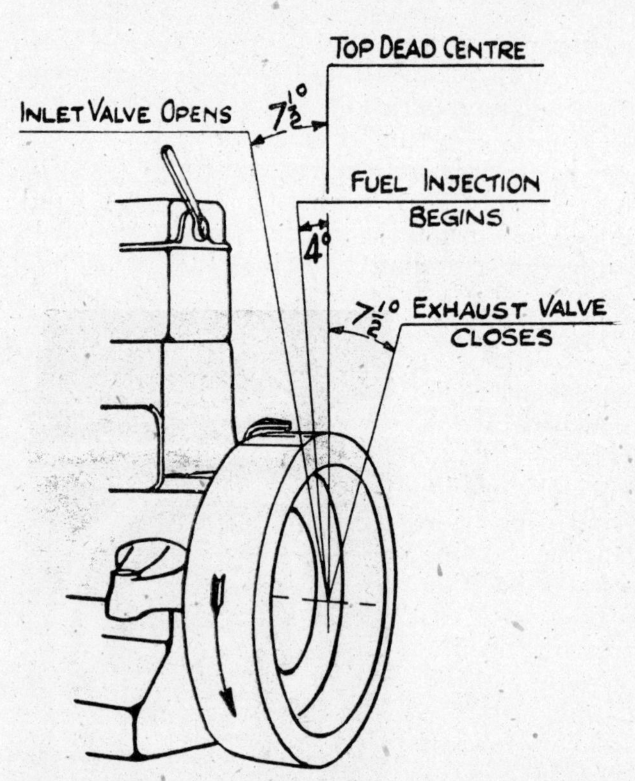

Fig. 61.—Method of Timing Fuel Injection by Flywheel Marking (Dorman-Ricardo).

In cases where *no marks can be found on the plungers* the fuel should be turned on to the fuel pump and the control lever then set in its correct position for delivering fuel. The delivery-pipe union of No. 1 plunger unit should be disconnected at the pump end and any surplus fuel wiped off with the aid of the finger so as to leave a concave surface on the fuel that is left. Now, *turn the camshaft of the pump in its correct direction of rotation*, slowly, until *the concave surface suddenly flattens.* This indicates that the fuel pump has just commenced to deliver fuel. Without disturbing either the engine or the fuel-pump camshaft, couple up the engine drive to the fuel pump, when the injection timing will be correct.

TIMING THE LEYLAND OIL ENGINE

As an example of the method of timing a commercial-vehicle oil engine let us consider the Leyland direct-injection model. In this case the correct injection timing is 27° before top dead centre. The timing may be checked as follows :

Turn on the fuel and set the control lever forward to deliver fuel.

Disconnect the delivery pipe to No. 1 plunger unit at the fuel-pump end and rotate the fuel-pump camshaft until the pump just commences to deliver fuel, as tested by the concave-surface method previously described.

Now check that the mark "INJ." on the flywheel coincides with the fixed mark on the clutch housing and that both valves of No. 1 cylinder are closed. If the marks do not coincide, set the engine correctly and reset the pump by slackening the drive-coupling set-screws and turning the pump-driven coupling by hand until injection commences. One notch (3°) on the pumpshaft corresponds to $\frac{3}{4}$ in. on the flywheel rim and the pumpshaft rotates in the opposite direction to the flywheel.

THE A.E.C. OIL-ENGINE TIMING

The A.E.C commercial-vehicle engines are fitted with C.A.V.-Bosch fuel-injection equipment, the fuel pump being driven from the engine half-speed shaft through a special coupling which permits the fuel-pump camshaft being rotated through a small angle, relatively to the half-speed shaft. Fig. 62 illustrates the coupling in question. It will be observed that it has a scale and index engraved upon the two members of the coupling, and also the letters "O" in four places. *If the pump has been removed* from the engine and is to be replaced, when the engine half-speed shaft has not been disconnected from its chain drive, then all that is necessary is to assemble the pump and its coupling so that the letters "O" are opposite one another; the fuel-pump timing will then be correct.

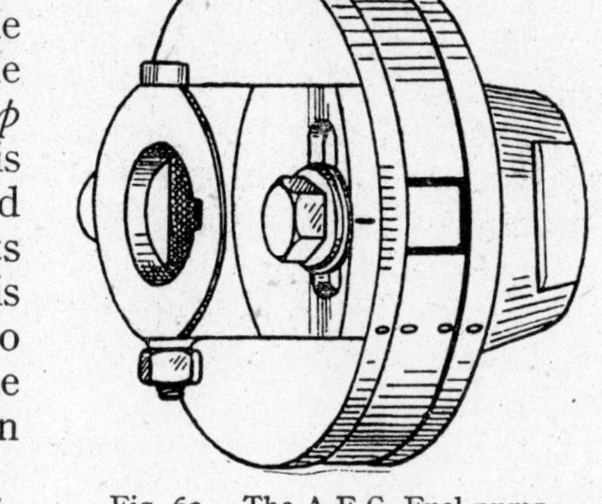

Fig. 62.—The A.E.C. Fuel-pump Coupling.

If the timing chain has been disconnected: Timing marks are provided on the flywheel (Fig. 61) to facilitate retiming the fuel pump in cases where the chain has been disconnected.

The fuel pump rotates in the opposite direction to the crankshaft. The pumps themselves are provided with two timing marks, one for each direction of rotation and marked R and L. *That marked with the correct direction of rotation, only, is the one which must be used.*

To time the pump, turn the crankshaft so that the pointer is opposite to the T.D.C. mark on the flywheel when No. 1 cylinder (the forward one) is on compression stroke and then couple up the fuel pump so that the *line marked L on the coupling* is opposite the centre line cut on the end of the fuel-pump casing.

TO DISCONNECT A.E.C. FUEL PUMP

After disconnecting the several pipes, remove the pin securing the governor rod to the regulating rod of the Bosch pump, disconnect the advance link, and, after undoing the strap bolts, lift the rear end of the pump and slide towards the rear to disengage the coupling. A dowel is fitted at the rear end so that, when replacing the pump, the timing may not be upset by swinging the pump slightly on its bored seating.

TIMING THE GARDNER L.W. OIL ENGINE

The L.W.-type Gardner engine is fitted to a large number of heavy motor vehicles on the roads, so that the following information concerning the valve and fuel-injection timing will be found useful by service engineers.

The valves must be correctly reassembled and the valve timing correct, when the valves are put back after an overhaul. Unless the correct valve timing is employed the valves will foul the pistons, for the clearances, even in the correct positions, are very small. The following is the valve timing of the L.W. engine :

Air-inlet valve opens at 12° before top dead centre.
Air-inlet valve closes at 42° past bottom dead centre.
Exhaust valve opens at 54° before bottom dead centre.
Exhaust valve closes at 19° past top dead centre.

The valve-tappet clearances should be ten-thousandths of an inch in all cases.

The fuel injection commences at 16° before top dead centre in the maximum advance position and 11° before top dead centre in the minimum advance position.

The rim of the Gardner flywheel has a number of timing marks on it, these comprising a group of three for each cylinder. A short line is also engraved on the top of the crankcase at the base of the cylinder to form the *zero line*.

In the case of No. 1 cylinder, when the longer line, marked "No. 1 T.D.C.," registers with the zero line, crank No. 1 is exactly on the T.D.C. and when the two shorter lines marked, respectively, "No. 1 cylinder injection 11 and 16," register with the zero line, fuel injection begins in No. 1 cylinder. The numbers 11 and 16 denote the number of degrees before T.D.C., corresponding, respectively, with minimum and maximum advance.

It is important, when timing the fuel injection, to set the pointer of the advance-and-retard device to the corresponding positions being timed.

Each pump is provided with a sight hole or window through which the plunger can be seen working. There is a horizontal line on the sides of the window and also one on the plunger. When these two lines coincide the pump is at the beginning of its injection period, and this occurs at the same time that the corresponding injection lines on the flywheel register with the zero line, as previously described.

The flywheel must be rotated in its correct working direction when setting or checking the fuel-injection timing.

The latest method of setting the injection timing utilises a lower line on the side of the fuel-pump window. This line is marked with a dot, at a lower position in the fuel-pump tappet stroke. The figures 11° and 16° become 25° and 30°, respectively, and the flywheel is marked similarly.

Should the tappet-adjusting screw become deranged, it should be adjusted so that when the tappet has lifted 0·140 in. from the base of the cam, the line on the plunger coincides with the lower or dotted line on the window.

ADJUSTING THE FUEL-PUMP CONTROL STOPS

The Bosch fuel pump, as used on the A.E.C. and similar oil engines, is provided with adjustments, as previously explained, for limiting the idling and maximum engine speeds. In the case of the A.E.C. engines, the idling speed is 340 to 400 r.p.m. and the maximum speed for the four- and six-cylinder "Comet"-type engines 2,000 r.p.m., or according to special requirements.

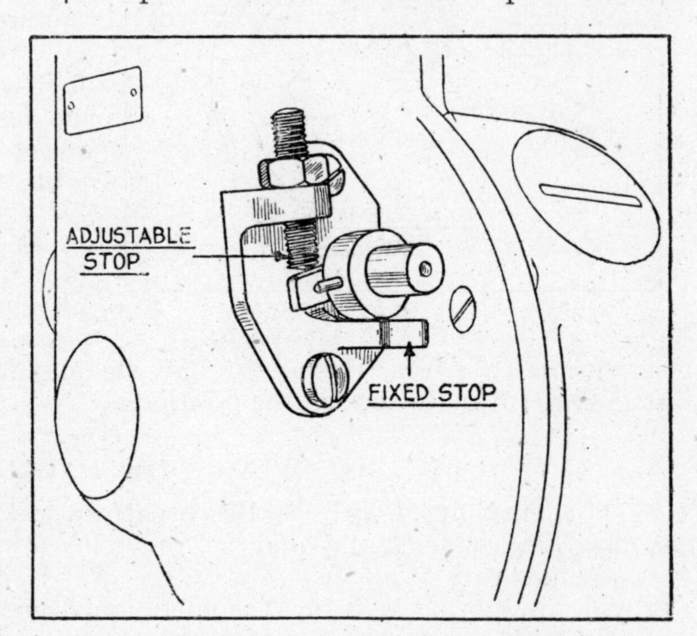

Fig. 63.—The A.E.C. Fuel-pump Speed-regulating Stops.

It should be mentioned that only a small change of speed can be made by altering the governor springs, so that to effect any appreciable change different springs must be fitted.

The fuel-pump control lever is provided with two stops, as shown in Fig. 63; one of these is fixed and the other adjustable. When the lever is brought against the fixed stop, *no fuel is delivered* to the cylinders, so that the engine stops. The *adjustable stop* limits the maximum quantity of fuel that can be delivered to the engine.

To adjust the idling speed so that the engine will run steadily at a low speed, the control lever must be held a short distance away from the fixed stop referred to above. Provision for this is made on the levers which are mounted on the off-side of the engine, as shown in Fig. 64, which shows the arrangement adopted for the six-cylinder engine; that for the four-cylinder engine is similar. The lever which is coupled to the accelerator pedal carries an adjusting screw, any manipulation of which changes the position to which the governor control levers return when the accelerator pedal is released. Screwing the screw inwards increases the speed of idling.

The engine, it should be observed, must be at its correct working temperature when making idling-speed adjustments, and the correct idling speed should, as previously stated, be about 340 to 400 r.p.m.; this is rather higher than for petrol engines. If the speed is brought lower, then "hunting" will occur.

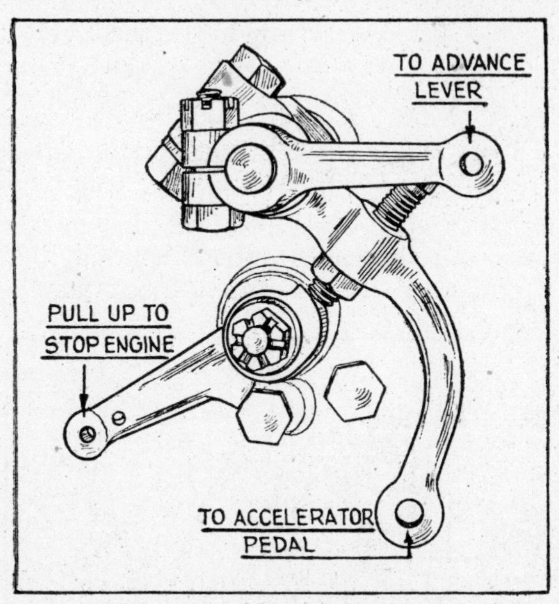

Fig. 64.—A.E.C. Fuel-pump Controls.

To adjust the maximum quantity of fuel, the adjustable stop on the governor control lever (Fig. 63) should be used. The position of this stop is fixed by the engine manufacturers on the test bed, to give the maximum amount of fuel which can be used in the engine *without any trace of smoke in the exhaust;* this adjustment is sealed at the A.E.C. works.

It is important to observe that in some instances *an improved fuel consumption can be obtained by reducing the maximum quantity of fuel;* this affects only the maximum power and not that at the intermediate accelerator positions.

STOPPING THE ENGINE

Oil engines fitted with the Bosch-pattern fuel pump are shut down, or stopped, by reducing the quantity of fuel below that which will enable the engines to idle at their lowest speeds. It is therefore necessary to provide means for bringing the fuel-pump control lever to a suitable position. Thus, in the case of the A.E.C. engines, the adjusting screw, previously mentioned, is provided with a movable stop against which it rests when the accelerator pedal is released; this movable stop and its operating lever is shown in Fig. 64. The stop consists of a cam-shaped projection on the boss of the lever. Rotating the latter allows the adjusting screw to drop off the nose of the cam and this brings the governor control lever below the position necessary for idling, so that the engine stops. On depressing the accelerator pedal the idling position is again restored.

It is important to remember that *on no account should an oil engine be stopped by shutting off the fuel supply to the fuel-injection pump.*

FUEL-PUMP TROUBLES

Of the possible troubles that can be experienced with fuel-injection systems, whilst some of these may be due to the fuel-injection nozzle and others to the effects of air in the fuel system and choked fuel filters, some may be traceable to the fuel pump. Although the latter seldom gives trouble, if this does occur, the first step is to uncouple the piping, between the pump and the nozzles. If the engine compression is then

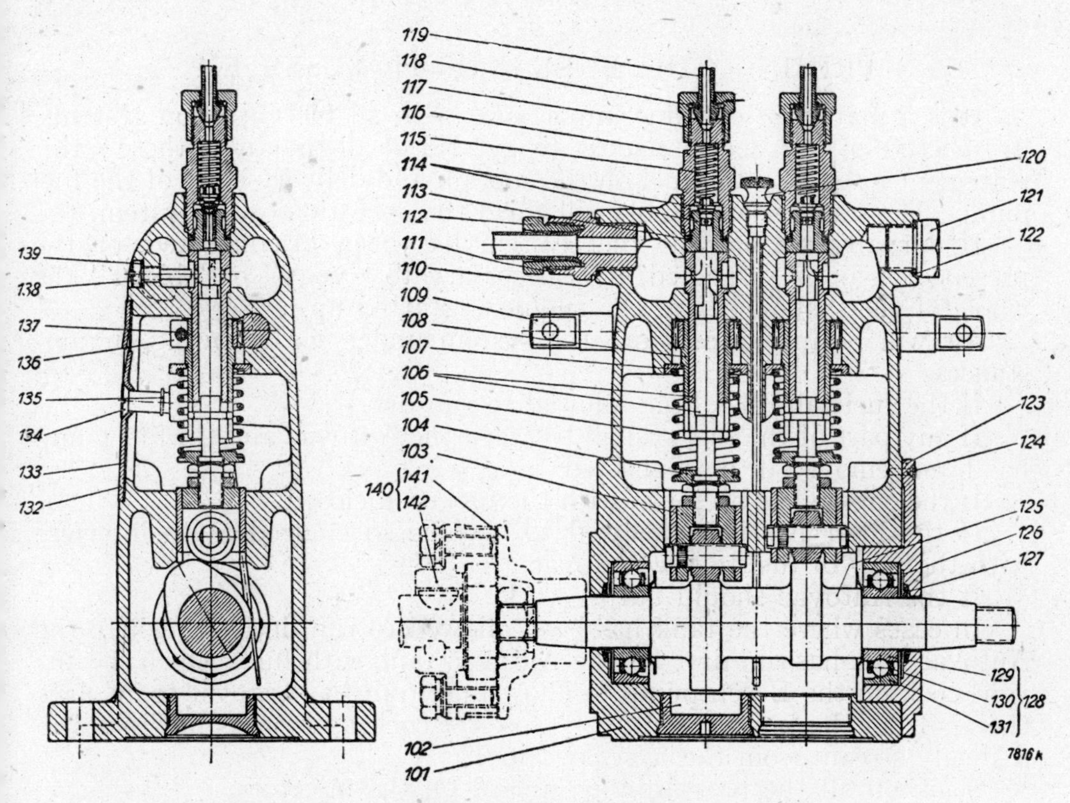

Fig. 65.—The Bosch Fuel-injection Pump, in sectional views.

101, Housing.
102, Closing Plug.
103, Plunger Guide.
104, Spring Plate, Lower.
105, Spiral Spring for Plunger.
106, Pump Element (Plunger and Barrel).
107, Spring Plate, Upper.
108, Control Sleeve.
109, Control Rod.
110, Joint for Inlet-connection Stud.
111, Inlet-connection Stud.
112, Inlet-connection Union Nut.
113, Joint for Delivery-valve Holder.
114, Delivery Valve and Seating.
115, Delivery-valve Spring.
116, Delivery-valve Holder.
117, Delivery-nipple Nut.
118, Washer for Delivery Nipple.
119, Delivery Piping.
120, Lubricating Oil Gauge Rod.
121, Inlet-closing Plug.
122, Joint for Closing Plug.
123, Bearing End Plate.
124, Screws for Fixing End Plate.
125, Camshaft.
126, Bearing End Disc.
127, Felt Packing.
128, Ball-bearing complete.
129, Internal Ball-race Bearing.
130, Ball Cage with Balls.
131, External Ball-race Bearing
132, Inspection Cover Plate.
133, Joint for Cover Plate.
134, Screws for Cover Plate.
135, Spring Ring.
136, Regulating Toothed Quadrant.
137, Clamp Screw for Regulating Toothed Quadrant.
138, Locking Pin.
139, Joint for Locking Pin.

released and the engine cranked around by hand with the fuel-pump control set at full-load position, it can at once be observed whether or not fuel is being delivered. Each discharge outlet should be examined to see whether it is giving its proper discharge.

The table on page 61 gives the possible troubles likely to occur with Bosch fuel pumps, the probable causes and their remedies. In this connection the word "pump" applies to the pump-unit block as a whole or to individual elements, and the component numbers to those shown in Fig. 46.

PRIMING THE FUEL-INJECTION SYSTEM

It is a matter of extreme importance with all fuel-injection systems, irrespective of the actual makes, to get rid of all the air in these; this statement applies to the fuel on the suction and delivery sides of the fuel pump. The smallest air bubble will affect the operation of the system.

If, for any reason, the fuel system has been disconnected, or the presence of air is suspected, it is necessary to "vent" or "bleed" the whole of the system before the engine is started up.

Air will be introduced into the system under the following circumstances:

If the fuel tank has been allowed to run dry.

If any part of the fuel system between the Autovac and the fuel pump has been removed or disconnected.

If the engine has been run with the fuel cock closed.

If the filter has been allowed to become so clogged as to interfere with the flow of fuel to the Autovac.

If the Autovac should fail to work.

In cases where the tank has been allowed to run dry, and where the Autovac tank has run dry, fill the Autovac tank with fuel. Open the air-vent cock on the Bosch pump to allow fuel from the Autovac to displace the air from the pump chamber. Close the cock as soon as fuel issues in a steady stream from the overflow pipe.

Slack off all the pressure-pipe unions on the injectors.

Fully depress the accelerator and crank the engine until fuel flows from all six fuel connections. Tighten up the fuel connections and start the engine in the usual manner.

It will sometimes happen that one or more of the pump elements, usually those at the forward end of the pump, will refuse to deliver fuel. This is on account of air not having been properly cleared out of the pump chamber. If this cannot be cured by use of the vent cock on the Bosch pump, disconnect the fuel pipe concerned from the pump and remove the delivery-valve holder, lift the valve from its seat, to enable the air to escape, and allow the fuel to flow until free from bubbles. Should the fuel not flow, turn the engine slightly by means of the cranking handle. To avoid the risk of losing either the valve or spring, it is advisable to keep the delivery-valve holder over its place, lifting it just far enough above the body of the pump to allow the valve to lift sufficiently for the air to escape.

Do not handle the valve with dirty fingers.

Replace the delivery-valve holder and reconnect the pipe. Crank

FUEL-PUMP TROUBLES, CAUSES AND REMEDIES

Trouble.	Probable Cause.	Suggested Remedy.
Pump does not deliver fuel.	1. Fuel tank empty.	Refill tank with fuel.
	2. Fuel-tank cock closed.	Open cock.
	3. Fuel-inlet pipe choked or filter element dirty.	Clear the pipe, cleanse filter element in clean paraffin.
	4. Air lock in pump.	Prime the fuel system.
	5. Pump plunger 105*a* remains suspended in its barrel.	Send the complete pump to the nearest C.A.V.-Bosch branch for examination.
	6. Plunger guide 104 remains suspended in its guide sleeve.	Dismantle pump and withdraw the plunger guide. If badly damaged, replace parts, as required, from spares.
	7. Delivery valve 106 remains suspended.	Remove and examine valve face and guide, as well as seating face. If either are damaged, the pair should be replaced from spares.
The pump does not deliver fuel uniformly.	8. Air lock in pump shown by air bubbles, issuing when the delivery-valve holder 106*d* has been unscrewed.	Proceed as at 4.
	9. Delivery valve spring 106 broken.	Replace from spares.
	10. Delivery valve 106 damaged either on face or guide.	Fit new pair from spares (i.e. new valve and seating complete).
	11. Plunger spring broken.	Replace from spares.
	12. Tappet roller in 104 worn.	Fit new plunger guide from spares.
	13. Pump plunger 105*a* occasionally remains suspended in barrel.	Dismantle, thoroughly clean, and refit. If trouble still continues, proceed as at 5.
	14. Supply of inlet fuel to pumps insufficient.	
	(*a*) Inlet pipe choked or filter element dirty.	Proceed as at 3.
	(*b*) The "head" between the tank and the pump is too small.	Increase the "head" or install fuel-feeding pump.
Quantity of fuel delivered per stroke insufficient.	15. Delivery valve 106 leaky.	Fit new pair (i.e. valve and seating) from spares.
	16. Leaky joints in the pressure system.	Clean joint faces and tighten down.
Quantity of fuel delivered per stroke excessive.	17. Clamp screw of regulating tooth quadrant is slack (only in case of multi-cylinder pumps).	Adjust quadrant 107*b* with mark on control sleeve 107*a* and tighten screw 107*c* hard (Fig. 43).
The movement of injection commencement has altered.	18. The adjusting tappet in the plunger guide 104 has worked loose.	Readjust and tighten nut hard.
	19. Cam profiles are damaged.	Send the complete pump to the nearest C.A.V.-Bosch branch to have a new camshaft 102 fitted.
Control rod 107*d* has jammed.	20. A pump plunger 105*a* has seized or the control-rod toothed rack is coated with dirt or other foreign matter.	Dismantle and cleanse.

the engine, and as soon as fuel issues from the injector end of the pipe, tighten up this union also.

Repeat the process for all pump elements which are not delivering fuel and start up the engine in the usual manner.

TESTING THE ENGINE

When the engine has warmed up, place the injection lever in the advance position and accelerate the engine to a good speed several times.

The engine should accelerate rapidly and without any hesitation or fluffiness if the system is properly clear.

If this does not happen, slack off each injector union in turn, just sufficiently to allow the fuel to seep out, and watch for air bubbles between the pipe and the union nut. Should bubbles be detected, leave the nut slack until all bubbles disappear.

Treat each union in turn in this manner. It is a wise precaution to do this, even though the acceleration test indicates that all air has been removed.

If the union nuts are slacked off more than just enough to allow the oil to seep out, the force with which the oil issues from the pipe will produce a froth even if no air is present in the pipe.

After running for a few minutes, open the vent cock on the Bosch pump for a few moments to make sure that the pump chamber is full.

The procedure has been described in detail, as it is of highest importance that all air should be removed from the system, otherwise the engine will not operate properly. *Knocking, sluggishness, and boiling will result from air in the fuel system.*

PUMP OR FUEL PIPE DISCONNECTED

If either the pump or the fuel pipe connecting the Autovac to the pump has been removed, the procedure detailed above should be employed, as air will certainly have entered the pump chamber.

If the engine is run with the fuel cock closed, any air which has been dissolved in the fuel will be released and will either collect in the pump chamber, where its presence may prevent one or more of the plungers from delivering fuel, or it may be passed into the fuel pipes and interfere with the uniformity of the injection. It may sometimes happen that no trouble will follow, but in all cases, after having opened the cock, restart the engine and open the pump vent cock until the fuel flows freely. When the engine is hot, apply the acceleration test already described above. The acceleration should be clean and with no signs of woolliness. Woolliness, lack of pull, or a sharp knock in one or more cylinders will indicate either that there is air in the fuel pump or in the fuel pipes, and this must be removed as already described.

As a rule, opening the pump vent cock for a few seconds is all that is required.

It is a good plan to vent the fuel pump periodically, while the engine is running, and thus make sure that the system is kept free of air at all times.

If an injector has been removed, the fuel pipe should be vented as described above, before finally coupling up again.

TESTING THE FUEL PUMP

Fuel pumps which have been removed from their engines are usually checked for satisfactory operation by mounting them on test beds and coupling up their camshaft drives to suitable electric motors ; the discharges from each of the delivery pipes are then measured, at different pump speeds.

It is usual to arrange for each outlet of the pump to discharge into a graduated glass vessel and to measure the quantity of fuel discharged into each vessel, corresponding to 100 revolutions of the fuel pump. If the discharges are not equal, this shows that one or other of the fuel-pump plungers requires an adjustment in order to increase or diminish the output. On the Bosch fuel pump a special clamp is provided for the toothed segment on each plunger ; by releasing the clamping screw the plunger can be rotated so as to alter the discharge in the desired manner.

The plunger of the fuel pump can be tested for leakage by applying hydraulic pressure, through the delivery-pipe union, to it, from an injection-nozzle testing pump. If the plunger will withstand a pressure of 250 atmospheres without leakage, it may be considered satisfactory.

THE FUEL FILTER

It is of more importance to filter the fuel thoroughly in the case of high-speed oil engines than with petrol engines, for whereas in the latter type any solid matter reaching the carburettor will, at the worst, tend to stop the jets, in the former type it will cause increased wear of the delicate fuel-pump plungers and their barrels, besides tending to block the fine orifices of the injection nozzles. In instances where plunger and barrel wear has been found to occur under about 60,000 to 70,000 miles of road service, the cause has invariably been a breakdown in the fuel-filtering system so that the solid inclusions have reached the fuel pump.

In view of the fact that the size of dust particles in ordinary air is of the order of ·0008 in. to ·00008 in., it is essential to employ a fuel filter which will effectively stop such particles from passing through.

Most fuel filters for oil engines use woven fabric filters supported in brass or Monel-metal casings, and the fuel flow is generally from the outside to the inside of the filter, the clean fuel being led from the centre to the fuel-pump suction pipe.

Fuel filters of the fabric type are generally fitted in duplicate ; in addition, the fuel introduced into the fuel tank of the vehicle is strained as it is poured in.

The fabric elements should be removed and cleaned in petrol every 2,000 to 3,000 miles, although these elements are so cheap that it is usually advisable to employ new ones at the intervals stated. In the case of new engines, the filters should be opened up and inspected at the end of the first 1,000 miles. When sediment plugs or cocks are fitted to the filter casings these should be opened after every long run, or once a day, and the sediment and water drained away.

After a filter has been cleaned or its element replaced, *it is important to open the air-venting plug* on the filter in order to get rid of any air in the system. A better plan is to soak the fabric filter element in fuel oil before replacing and to fill the filter with fuel before connecting up its pipe unions. The air vent should be used in order to get rid of any remaining air in the system.

Before replacing a filter element, it should be examined for any perforations, cuts, or tears; if any are found, a new element should be fitted.

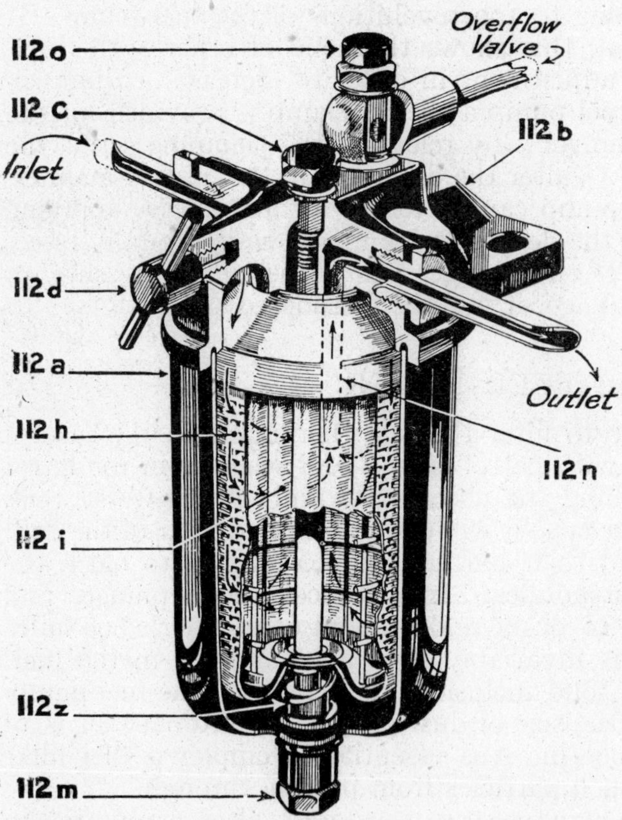

To test for a choked fuel filter, turn on the fuel supply from the main tank, after disconnecting the outlet pipe union on the filter. If the fuel does not flow freely, this is a sign of a choked filtering element.

TYPICAL FUEL FILTERS

Fig. 66 illustrates the Bosch fuel filter (Type BF 11B), the various parts being indicated by the figures and the key below the illustration. This filter is fitted with a cloth filter element and it has an outer casing of about one-litre capacity; the cover 112*b* carries the inlet and outlet connections.

Fig. 66.—The. C.A.V.-Bosch Fuel Filter (Type BF 11B).

112*a*, Housing. 112*d*, Air-vent Screw. 112*m*, Sludge Plug.
112*b*, Cover. 112*h*, Coarse Filter (Metal). 112*n*, Stand Pipe.
112*c*, Cap Nut. 112*i*, Fine Filter (Fabric).

The oil, on entering the container, passes through a preliminary metal filter 112*h*, which removes any coarse particles of dirt, and then through a specially prepared cloth 112*i*, which is stretched over a wire framework. This gives the oil its final filtration, whence it passes through the stand pipe 112*n* and out into the main pipe line.

The filter can be dismantled with ease by removing the cap nut 112*c*, which permits withdrawal of both filter elements for inspection and cleaning. A sludge plug 112*m* is provided at the base of the container, through which dirt can be withdrawn periodically.

Whilst the cloth filtering elements of these filters can be cleaned, it is considered safer and more economical to replace them, since spares can be obtained for a few pence, protectively wrapped in cellophane to facilitate storage. This course is recommended since, if the cleaning process is not correctly carried out, the cloth may become punctured or the dirt merely transferred from the outside to the inside of the element, whence it can pass to the main filter feed.

Fig. 67.—The Tecalemit Fuel Filter.

The Tecalemit fuel filter (Fig. 67) has a corrugated or fluted type of felt filter element, presenting a relatively large filtering surface. It comprises a thin layer of a special grade of felt stretched over a star-sectioned corrosion-proof former.

The fuel enters near the top through a union on one side and flows down around the outside of the filtering element, and then through the latter to the centre, whence the filtered fuel passes upwards and out from the other union connection at the top. An air release is provided on both sides of the filter element for priming purposes, and there is a sludge trap at the base provided with a draining plug.

The Simms fuel filter (Fig. 68) belongs to the edge-flow type in which a large number of accurately made flat discs are mounted parallel, but at very small distances apart, namely, about one-thousandth inch.

The interior of the body A is slightly tapered from top to bottom and the filter element C has an equivalent taper on its outer surface. The two are held in contact by the spring D. The unfiltered oil enters at E, whilst the filtered oil leaves by the tapped hole F. The tapered filter elements only fit accurately at the extreme ends, the remaining surface being cut away to give a clearance of ·002 to ·005 in.

Several grooves G are formed on the outer surface of C; these grooves end a short distance from the upper end of C. The lower ends are blocked by a serrated plate H and these grooves at their upper ends have ports J connecting with the upper end of the body. A second set of ports K communicates between the alternate grooves (open at their lower ends) and the interior of the filtering element.

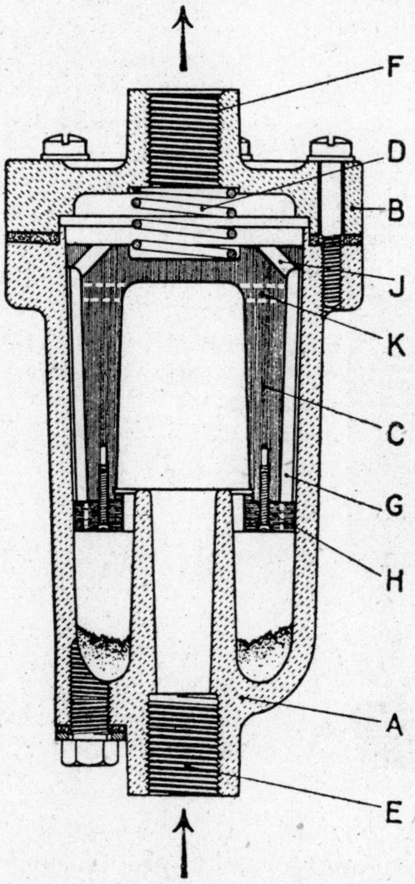

In action the oil from the central part flows via the ports K into the grooves communicating therewith. The only egress is through the clearance spaces between adjacent grooves, filtration taking place here; the filtered material gravitates downwards and is collected in the lower part of the filter, as shown. The filtered oil flows up through the ports J and thence into outlet port F.

It will be seen that filtering is accomplished by the direction of flow down the filter lines which produces a dislodging action. Vibration also tends to displace the filtered particles, which gravitate downwards.

Fig. 68.—The Simms Edge-flow Type Fuel Filter.

NOTES ON ELECTRIC HEATER PLUGS

There are two principal types of heater or glow plugs, namely, the single- and the double-pole ones (Fig. 69). These plugs are simply electric resistance elements which are heated by means of current from the starting battery, for about half a minute, before the engine is started up. The resistance elements become red-hot and heat the cold combustion chamber so that when the fuel is sprayed into this chamber the compressed-air charge is made hot enough to ignite the fuel; the resistance does not ignite the fuel directly, however.

The *single-pole plugs* have insulated central terminals and earthed outer shells, similar to sparking plugs. They are *connected in parallel* to a 2-volt accumulator (Fig. 70).

The *double-pole plugs* enable the resistance element to be insulated entirely from the metal of the engine, and they are *connected in series* to a 12-volt battery, as a rule (Fig. 71).

It is necessary to fit a switch and also a bulb type of indicator on the dashboard or instrument panel, in order to show when the glow plugs are being heated from the battery. This resistance indicator is shown in Fig. 72, together with the connections to the indicator lamp, for use in cases where the indicator itself cannot be placed in a convenient position.

Single-pole plugs are made in two patterns—one known as the 18-ampere type and taking from 15 to 18 amperes at 2 volts, according to

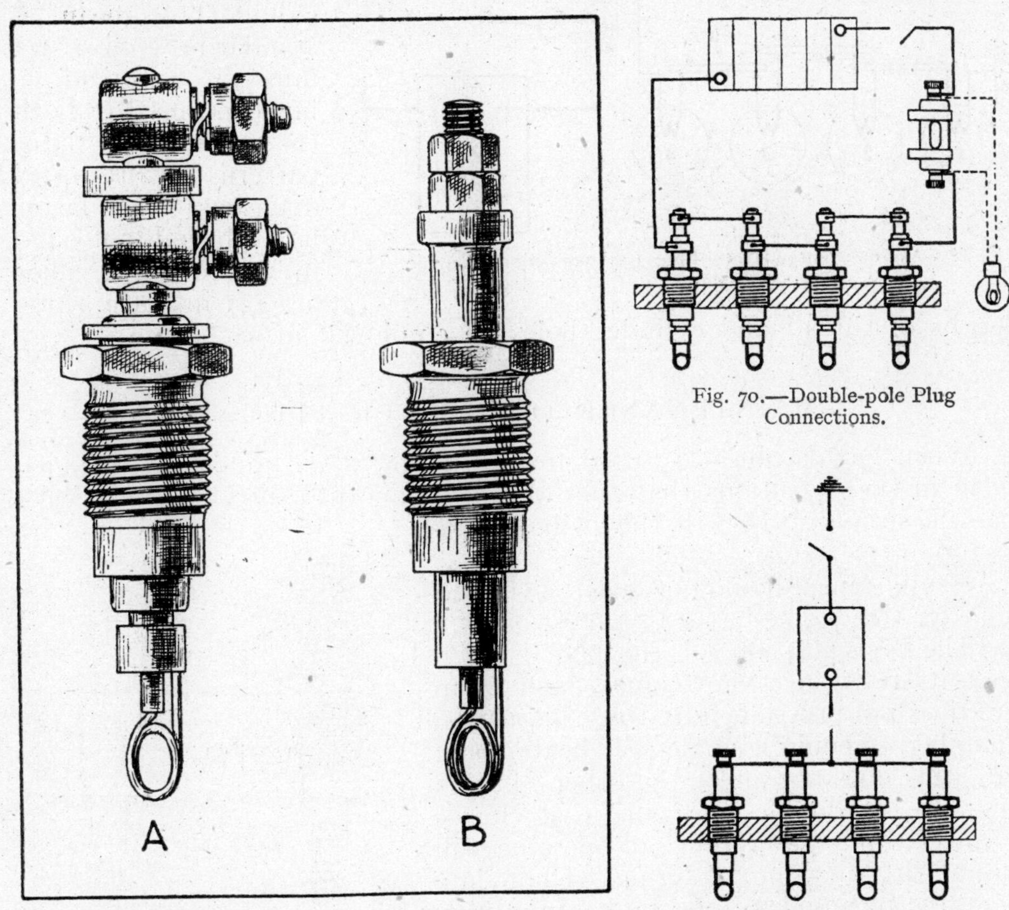

Fig. 70.—Double-pole Plug Connections.

Fig. 69.—Electric Heater Plugs (Lodge).
A—Double Pole. B—Single Pole.

Fig. 71.—Single-pole Heater-plug Connections.

the state of the battery; the other is classed as 30 amperes and takes from 25 to 30 amperes at 2 volts. If a battery of sufficient capacity is employed, the latter type is probably the best, as it gives nearly twice the heating effect. Incidentally, a 1-volt pattern glow plug is made by Messrs. Lodge, Ltd., for connecting to one cell of the nickel-iron type of battery, such as the Nife or Edison.

Double-pole plugs are usually made in one pattern, rated at 2 volts, 30 amperes, but can if necessary be supplied to take a smaller current. The advantage of the double-pole plug is that the whole set of four or six plugs is connected in series to a 12-volt battery from which they take only 30 amperes as compared with, say, four or six 30-ampere single-pole plugs requiring 120 or 180 amperes from a single cell.

The earlier plugs had the dimensions shown in the left-hand diagrams of Fig. 73, the diameter of the barrel being ·375 in., and of the cylinder hole ·390 in. A standard 18 mm. × 1·5 mm. pitch thread is, however, used in both the earlier and later patterns (right-hand diagrams). The latter have barrels of ·425 in. and cylinder holes of ·437 in.; the same depths of thread and cylinder hole are employed in each case.

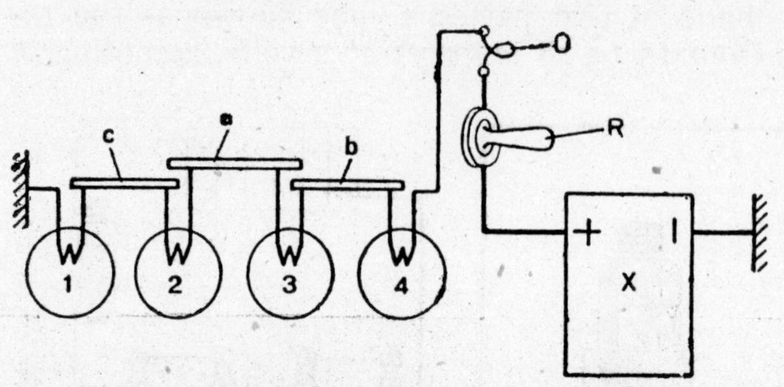

Fig. 72.—Arrangement of Heater Plugs for Four-cylinder Engine. The Cylinders are denoted by 1, 2, 3, and 4.

MAINTENANCE OF HEATER PLUGS

When heater plugs are used for oil engines it is important to place them in such positions that they do not come into direct contact with the fuel spray; otherwise they will quickly corrode.

Heater plugs should not be left switched on after the engine has started to work.

The best position for the plug is such that its resistance wire comes flush with, but does not protrude into, the combustion chamber. Should a single-pole heater plug fail, this does not affect the others, but in the case of double-pole plugs, which are connected in series, failure of one plug will put all the others out of action. To obviate this, the terminals of the faulty plug may be short-circuited as a temporary measure, to allow the other plugs to heat up.

The reason for this is illustrated in the example shown in Fig. 72, for the Mercédès-Benz oil engine (four-cylinder). The four heater plugs are numbered 1, 2, 3, and 4, and the conductor bars connecting their terminals at *a*, *b*, and *c*. The indicator lamp is shown at O, the switch at R, and the battery at X. It will be observed that one terminal of heater plug No. 1 is earthed, as is the negative pole of the battery. When the switch is "On" there is thus a continuous circuit

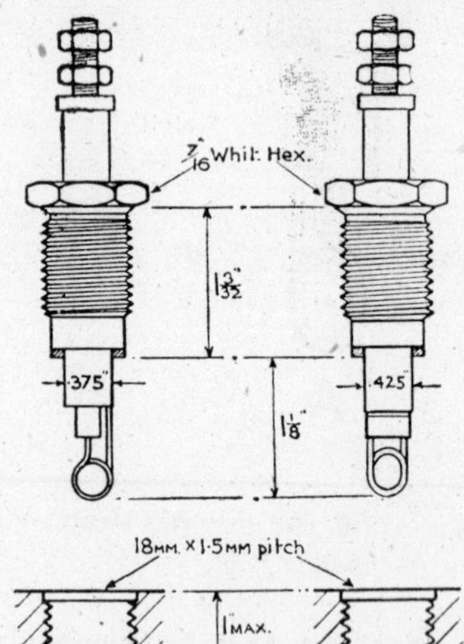

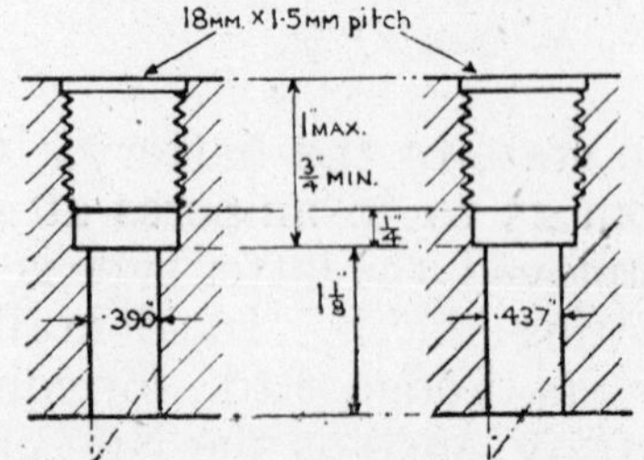

Fig. 73.—Dimensions of Heater Plugs.

from the positive of the battery through the heater-plug resistances to earth and back to the negative of the battery.

Now, should a heater element burn out or break, the whole circuit will be broken. Thus, if No. 2 element breaks there will be no path for the current, but by connecting the conductor bars *a* and *c* together, this will enable the current to flow through the heaters Nos. 4, 3, and 1, leaving No. 2 out of action.

STARTING HIGH-SPEED OIL ENGINES

On account of their much higher compressions than petrol engines, oil engines offer more resistance to cranking over, and unless special arrangements are made for relieving this greater starting torque they are more difficult to start. If, in addition, the engine is very cold, then some of the compression heat will be lost to the cold metal walls of the combustion chamber and the temperature of the air charge may not be sufficient to ignite the fuel injected ; the use of heater plugs overcomes the latter difficulty.

The former drawback, namely that of greater resistance to cranking over, is now overcome by fitting devices, known as *Decompressors,* which enable the compressions of some, or all, of the cylinders to be released, in order that the engine may be cranked, or motored, more easily. When a sufficient speed has been attained in this manner, the decompression gear is cut out of action, and the momentum acquired by the crankshaft, flywheel, etc., enables the compression of one or more cylinders to be overcome so that the engine will then commence to " fire." Many designs of direct-injection engine are so efficient that they do not require heater plugs, but will start readily from the cold.

In very cold weather, however, it is a good plan to heat the induction pipe with a piece of waste dipped in fuel oil and ignited with a match ; there is no danger of fire as with petrol engines. Provided no direct damage is done to any of the parts around, such as the heater cables, a blow-lamp can be used to heat the air-inlet pipe, prior to starting up, so that when the engine is cranked around heated air will be drawn into the cylinders.

The position of the fuel-pump control lever is important when starting engines. In some cases the makers stipulate that the fuel-pump lever shall be in the fully opened position for starting, whilst in others that it shall only be opened a little way. Similarly, some makers advocate *full injection advance* for starting, whilst others recommend an intermediate position. The actual method adopted in regard to the pump-control lever and the injection advance depends to a large extent upon the particular type of engine, and in this respect the makers' instructions should always be followed. The methods advocated by certain well-known manufacturers are given herewith.

STARTING THE LEYLAND (CAVITY-PISTON) ENGINE

Assuming that the fuel system has been properly primed beforehand to eliminate any air bubbles, press the foot throttle or accelerator (controlling the quantity of fuel supplied by the pump) right down once, to ensure that the governor is not sticking in its " stop " position ; then let it come back to the normal position and press the starter switch. If necessary, open the accelerator wider. Control the engine speed with the accelerator and set it to the best idling position by means of the adjustable screw-stop on the pump.

STARTING THE ARMSTRONG-SAURER (PRE-COMBUSTION CHAMBER) ENGINE

Before starting see that the gear lever is in neutral, the hand brake on, the fuel-supply tank has plenty of fuel, and that there is sufficient oil in the engine sump.

Switch on the Autopulse fuel-supply pump by means of switch on instrument board. Open test cock on top of Bosch main fuel filter and leave open until there is a continuous flow of fuel free from air bubbles ; then close the cock.

The injection system should also be checked for freedom from air bubbles in the fuel.

Next, place pump-control lever in fully open position and injection-advance lever (above steering wheel) to fully advanced position. Switch on the glow plugs for 30 seconds, and whilst keeping the heater-plug handle down, depress the starter foot switch, when the engine should at once " fire." As soon as it has gathered sufficient speed, release glow-plug switch and starter switch and push back the pump-control-lever to the " idling " position. Also slightly retard the injection-advance control lever.

In very cold weather it is advisable to ease the engine by turning it by hand after injection of a few drops of paraffin into the compression tap.

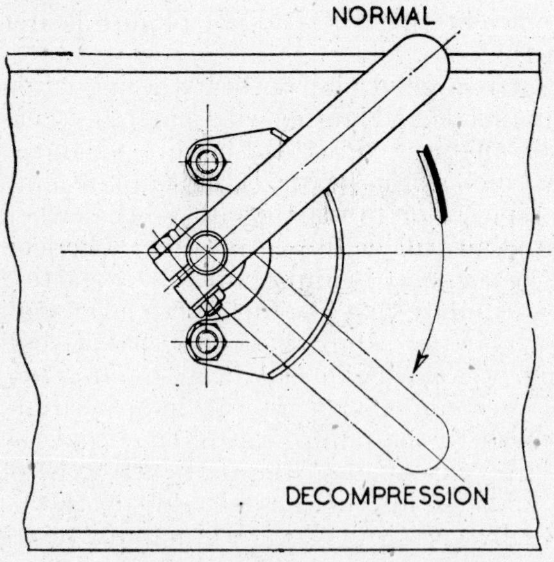

Fig. 74.—Decompressor Lever on Dorman-Ricardo Engine.

STARTING THE DORMAN (RICARDO-COMET HEAD) ENGINE

The six-cylinder engine employs electric heater plugs as with other makes of engine fitted with " Comet " heads. Decompressors are fitted for starting purposes, on each of the three-cylinder block heads. To start the engine, after the heater plugs have been switched on for 30 or 40 seconds, the decompressor lever should be moved over as far as possible, as shown by the arrow in Fig. 74. Next move the pump fuel-control lever towards the rear of the engine, as far as it will go. This allows the maximum amount of fuel for starting. As soon as the engine is motored to a sufficient speed, the decompressor lever is moved over to the " normal " position. When the engine " fires," move the control lever slowly back to the " idling " position.

STARTING THE CROSSLEY (COMET-HEAD) ENGINE

Assuming that the engine sump has been filled with oil, and that the fuel tank has also been filled, the following procedure is necessary to start from cold: It should be noted that the only controls in the driver's cab appertaining to the engine, other than the accelerator pedal, are the decompressor device, the electric-starter button, and the heater switch.

A tell-tale plug is also fitted to indicate the glow of the wire element at the heater plugs in the combustion chamber.

Assuming now that the operator is seated in the driver's cab:

Operation 1.—Pull the decompressor lever to its fullest extent towards the rear. This opens the exhaust valves and releases the compression.

Operation 2.—Connect the two-volt battery plug to its socket and leave this connected until the wire element on the tell-tale or resistance-indicator lamp is a cherry red.

Operation 3.—Press down the accelerator pedal to its fullest extent.

Operation 4.—Press electric starter button until engine is revolving at a reasonable rate.

Operation 5.—Now smartly push forward decompression lever to close the compression, leaving the foot on the accelerator, when the engine should at once start. Immediately the engine has started, release electric starter button. It will be found necessary to leave the foot on the accelerator pedal (not of necessity in the maximum opening position) for a minute or so until the engine runs evenly at the slow-running position, that is, when the foot is removed entirely from the accelerator pedal. The above method should also be adopted if the engine stops, after it has been warmed up.

Care should be taken to ensure that all the atomisers are functioning correctly; this can be detected by the evenness of the exhaust note.

STARTING A WARM ENGINE

When the engine is thoroughly warmed up it requires far less effort to motor it around, but nevertheless, it is a good plan always to use the decompressor gear, since this will definitely relieve the starting-motor battery and, incidentally, enable a somewhat higher starting speed to be attained. Generally, it will be unnecessary to employ the heater plugs for starting, since the combustion chambers will be kept warm by the water in the jackets for some time after the engine has stopped.

The usual procedure for starting a warm engine is to engage the decompressor, slightly depress the accelerator pedal whilst the engine is motored around and then quickly cut the decompressor out of action, whilst leaving the accelerator pedal depressed as before. As soon as the engine "fires" regularly, release the accelerator pedal, when the governor will automatically assume the "idling" position.

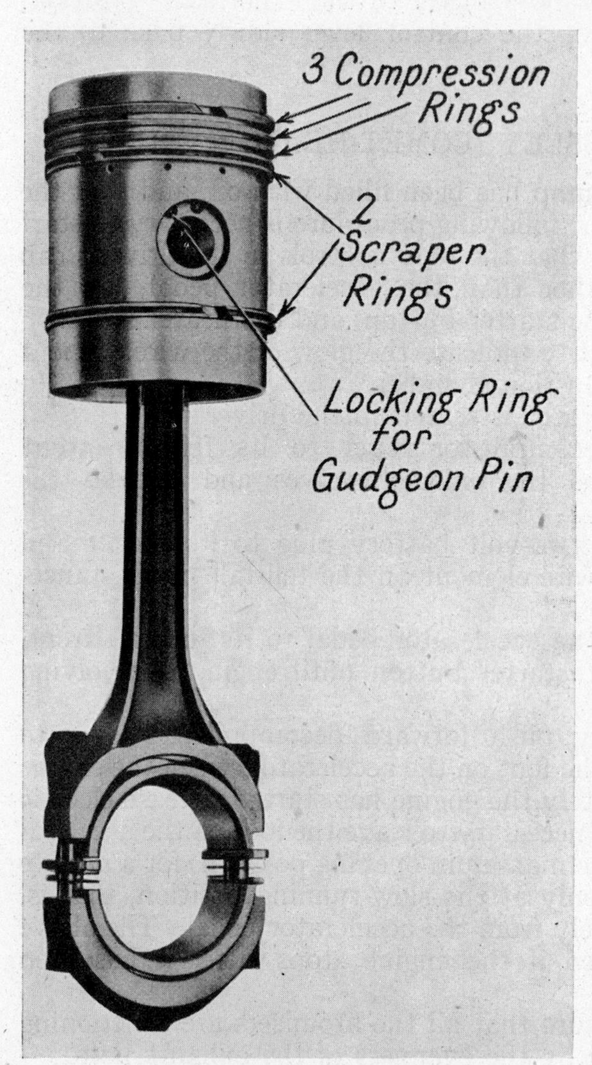

Fig. 75.—The A.E.C. Oil-engine Piston and Connecting Rod.

PISTONS FOR OIL ENGINES

As previously mentioned, most of the components of high-speed oil engines are similar in design—if not always in dimensions—to those of petrol engines, for the marked progress in weight reduction of oil engines has been due to the application of petrol-engine design principles and materials.

The pistons employed on oil engines are now invariably made from aluminium alloys, such as aluminium-copper, aluminium-silicon, Hiduminium and Y-alloys, in order to reduce the weight and at the same time to take full advantage of the better heat-conduction property of aluminium-base alloys. The pistons used in high-speed oil engines for motor-transport purposes are appreciably longer, in relation to their diameters, than petrol engines. Thus, it is usual to make these pistons with lengths varying from 130 to 140 per cent. of the diameters, so that the length of a 4-in. diameter piston would be 5·2 to 5·6 in. This increased length gives a greater piston-thrust surface and at the same time affords a longer leakage path for the gases.

Further, owing to the higher compression and combustion pressures, it has been found necessary to fit a greater number of piston rings than in petrol engines of similar dimensions. It is seldom that less than five piston rings are employed on modern oil-engine pistons, whilst many engines have six rings per piston.

Fig. 75 shows the aluminium-alloy piston and connecting-rod used on

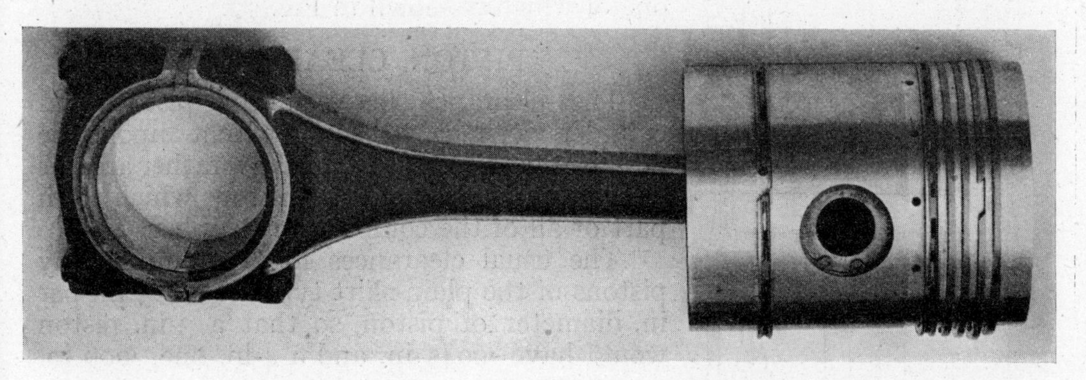

Fig. 76.—A.E.C. Six-ring Piston and Connecting-rod Assembly.

the A.E.C. 130-h.p. six-cylinder Comet-type oil engine, fitted to motor vehicles. This piston has five piston rings, including three compression and two oil-scraper rings. The latter are the two lowest rings, one being above and the other below the gudgeon pin.

The piston in question has a diameter of 115 mm. (about 4½ in.);

Fig. 77.—Some Oil-engine Components. From left to right, these are, the Connecting Rod, Piston, Gudgeon Pin, Circlip and Wet-type Cylinder Liner.

each piston is numbered from 1 to 6, to facilitate replacement in its proper cylinder.

The clearance of the skirt of the piston, when new, is ·008 in. The four-cylinder 85-h.p. A.E.C. engine, Fig. 76, employs six-ring pistons, there being four compression and one oil-scraper ring above and another scraper ring below the gudgeon pin. The cylinder bore, in this engine, is 108 mm. (about 4¼ in.).

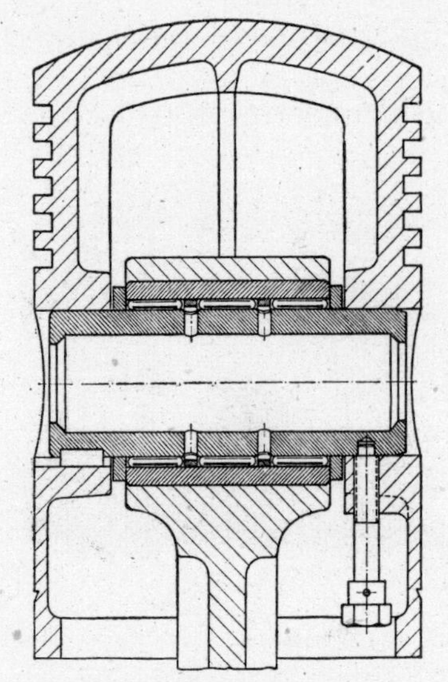

Fig. 78.—A Needle-bearing Gudgeon-pin Oil-engine Piston.

The hollow gudgeon pins, in each case, are of the floating pattern and are located endwise in the piston-boss holes by means of "circlips," one of which is shown in Fig. 77.

PISTON CLEARANCES

The clearance between the piston and cylinder depends to some extent upon the design, it being necessary to allow rather greater clearances for cavity-type pistons which form part or all of the combustion chamber.

The usual clearances for aluminium-alloy pistons of the plain-skirt type are ·0015 in. per in. diameter of piston, so that a 3-in. piston would have ·0045 in. and a 4-in. one, ·006 in. clearance.

The clearances are different along the length of the piston, the latter being tapered, as a rule, from the top to about the gudgeon-pin position, the skirt being left parallel. The clearance is greatest at the top piston land and it diminishes progressively for the other lands. The reason for this is that the piston is hottest at the top, the temperature falling along the length of the piston. It is necessary, therefore, to allow for the greater expansion near the top by giving the piston more clearance.

The usual piston-land clearances in the case of a 4-in. aluminium-alloy piston are as follows:

Top land	·020 in.
Second land	·016 in.
Third land	·014 in.
Fourth land and skirt	·006 in.

These clearances increase slightly as the diameter is increased, except in the case of the fourth land, the clearance of which is constant for pistons ranging in diameter from 3 in. to 5 in. The other land clearances increase at the rate of about ·005 in. per in. of diameter increase.

The Armstrong-Saurer pistons are of aluminium alloy and when new are 109·53 mm. on the second and third lands, and 109·78 mm. on the lower 50 mm. of the piston skirt.

The maximum clearances of the piston in its cylinder at the above two places are 0·54 mm. (about ·02 in.) and 0·39 mm. (about ·016 in.), respectively.

Fig. 79 shows the cylinder head of the Cummins high-speed oil engine with the piston, gudgeon pin, and small end of the connecting rod in cross-sectional view.

The engine in question operates on the constant fuel-pressure system, whereby the fuel is stored at an approximately constant pressure and, at the correct moment, is injected through a mechanically operated fuel-injection valve, from an overhead camshaft. The engine works on the direct-injection principle, fuel being sprayed over a wide angle into the combustion chamber which is formed between the flat cylinder head and the dished type of piston. A plug in the centre of the latter assists in deflecting the fuel spray into the piston cavity around it.

The piston has five compression rings and one oil-scraper ring. Another design of Cummins engine piston (Fig. 80) has four compression and one oil-scraper ring.

The large-diameter hollow gudgeon pin in each case is locked to the piston boss by means of the lock pin shown on the left. The piston has a baffle plate above the piston bosses in order to prevent oil splashed inside the piston from carbonising under the hot piston crown.

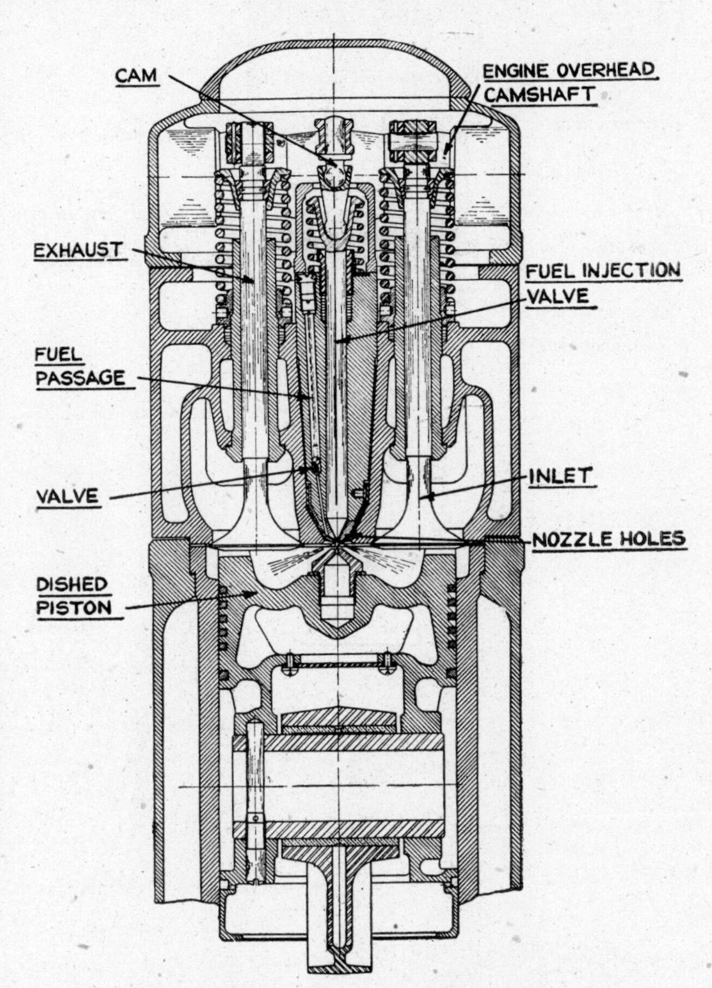

Fig. 79.—The Cummins High-speed Oil-engine Cylinder Head.

THE BIG-END BEARINGS

Although in many cases white-metal-lined big-end and main bearings have given satisfactory service over fairly long periods, cases have occurred—notably in some of the earlier makes of motor-vehicle engines—where the white-metal has cracked and finally become disintegrated, with the result that a final breakdown has occurred.

In order to overcome this trouble, which is believed to be due to the heavy impact loads on the bearings, it is now usual to employ a much stronger lining material than white-metal. The material most favoured in this country, as previously stated, is an alloy known as *lead-bronze*, a hard alloy composed of copper, tin, and lead, having a typical coppery appearance. With this alloy it is possible to obtain service periods exceeding 80,000 miles before reconditioning becomes necessary.

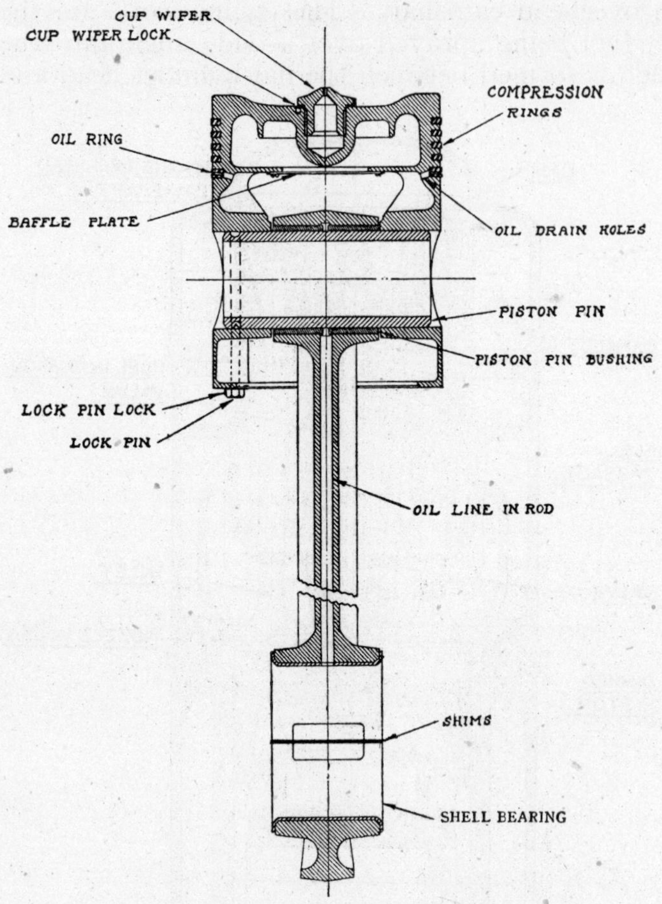

Fig. 80.—Piston for Cummins Oil Engine.

As this alloy is more expensive than white-metal, it is the practice of certain manufacturers to use it only for the halves of the bearings which are subjected to the greater bearing loads. Thus, the A.E.C. engines use lead-bronze for the upper halves of the big-end bearings and the lower halves of the main bearings; the other half-bearings are of a good quality white-metal. In regard to the *bearing clearances,* for the composite type of big-end and main crank-shaft bearings, previously mentioned, the following are the recommended clearances for A.E.C. engines :

	Minimum	*Maximum*
Connecting Rods		
Clearance on diameter	·0045 in.	·0055 in.
Side clearance	·006 in.	·008 in.
Main Bearings		
Clearance on diameter	·005 in.	·007 in.
Side clearance	·008 in.	·010 in.

THE LEYLAND ENGINE BEARINGS

The amount of clearance in the big-end bearings should not exceed ·006 in.; if there is any greater clearance the bearings should be taken up by filing the cap joints; great care is necessary in this operation to ensure that the faces are kept absolutely flat and true, in order that the bearings bed evenly on the crank-pins. A side clearance of ·0015 in. to ·0030 in. is given to both the big-end and the main bearings.

In regard to the crankshaft the end-play should lie between ·0035 in. and ·0070 in.; in no instance should it exceed ·012 in. The crank-pins and main journals should be inspected when the engine is given its thorough overhaul. If these are found to be oval by more than ·003 in. they should be reground.

ARMSTRONG-SAURER BIG-END BEARINGS

The big-end bearings of the Armstrong-Saurer engine are given an initial clearance (when new) of ·0015 in. on the crank-pin and a maximum side clearance of ·005 in.

MASKED VALVES IN OIL ENGINES

In the majority of oil engines the inlet and exhaust valves are of the overhead type, operated by push rods and rocker arms from the camshaft below. In order to reduce the lengths of the push rods it is the practice, in many designs, to employ a high camshaft position; the illustration of the A.E.C. engine given on Plate facing p. 14 shows a typical high-position camshaft. In other respects the valves and valve gear are practically identical with those employed on petrol engines.

In certain turbulent-combustion chamber designs, however, the inlet valves are provided with shields or deflectors arranged near to the seating areas, for the purpose of diverting the incoming air charge, so as to give it a spiral movement as it enters the cylinder; these valves are known as *masked* ones.

The Leyland and the Armstrong-Saurer cavity-piston type engines use such valves.

Fig. 8 shows the Leyland masked inlet valve, with the deflector arranged over part of the underside of the valve head.

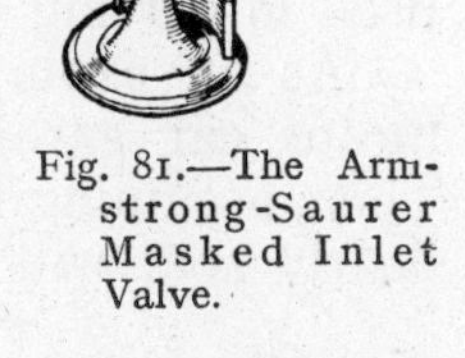

Fig. 81.—The Armstrong-Saurer Masked Inlet Valve.

When replacing or fitting new inlet guides care must be taken to locate these so that the valves have their deflectors in the correct positions. The correct positioning of these is effected by means of pegs in the cylinder head and slots in the valve-guide flanges. The inlet valves are keyed in their guides and cannot be removed until their circlips are removed. The valve keys, one of which is shown in Fig. 8, must, of course, be replaced after valve grinding.

The Armstrong-Saurer engine has two masked inlet and two ordinary exhaust valves per cylinder. The position of the mask is shown in Fig. 10, whilst the method of ensuring the correct location of the deflector is indicated in Fig. 81.

CHAPTER II

THE GARAGE AND ITS EQUIPMENT

THE term "garage" is now generally recognised as meaning any building in which an automobile is, or automobiles are, stored and overhauled. It applies equally well to the small wooden shed in which a motor cycle is housed, to the ordinary motor-car house, and to the large motor-engineering works where motor vehicles are stored and repaired. We shall confine our present remarks to the two latter meanings of the term, and, following a short account of the design, dimensions, and equipment of the private garage, shall devote the greater part of the present chapter to a description of the lay-out, equipment, and other items concerning the modern motor repair works.

THE PRIVATE GARAGE

The private owner of a motor car should certainly endeavour to house his car near his private residence, for by so doing he can relieve himself of a considerable amount of expense and inconvenience. Moreover, if he looks at the matter from the viewpoint of economy, he can in a year or two save the initial cost of erection of a private garage, when taking into consideration the amount of money he would otherwise spend in housing the car at a commercial garage, and in fuel, etc., used in driving to and from the latter.

As an example, we will suppose that the owner of a medium-size motor car garages it a mile away, at a weekly cost of ten shillings. Then, assuming he uses his car at least five times a week, the approximate yearly cost will be as follows:

One year's garage charges	£26
240 journeys to and from garage at 4*d*. per mile (overall cost)	8
Total	£34

Now, the cheapest garage which can be built for a medium touring car will cost about £12 to £18 if made of wood (weatherboards and tarred felt roof), whilst a good coke-breeze slab garage, with one window, double doors, and concrete floor, will cost from £40 to £60; a good brick-built garage, with slate tiles, stucco finish to match the adjoining residence, will run into from £70 to £120, according to its size, design, and the building locality. It will be evident, then, that even in the case of an owner living, temporarily, in a given residence, it will usually save him both time and money to erect a garage near-by.

Many large firms of builders supply portable garages, complete with windows, doors, and wooden flooring, for quite reasonable prices. These buildings are so designed that the sides all bolt together snugly, so that they can readily be erected or dismantled.

It is desirable that the garage should be built on a strong deal frame, of $2\frac{1}{2}$-in. or 3-in. square section. The boarding should not be less than $\frac{3}{4}$ in., and should be V-jointed, tongued, and grooved. The roof boards should be of $\frac{3}{4}$ in. thickness, covered with ruberoid or stout tarred felt. The floor boards should be of 1 in. thickness, well supported by the floor joists; the latter should be spaced not less than 18 in. apart for heavy cars, and 2 ft. for medium and light cars. It is necessary to provide ridge-pieces, guttering, and a lead-away for the water which falls from the roof, in order to prevent dampness.

The usual prices of portable motor houses, complete with wooden floors, range from about £14 for 12 ft. × 8 ft., £18 for 14 ft. × 9 ft., and £24 for 18 ft. × 10 ft., for wooden structures complete with double doors, two windows, and double sloping roof.

The enterprising mechanic can, of course, build a motor house much cheaper than he can purchase one, and we have personally seen several really good motor houses made in this manner at one-half to two-thirds the cost of the commercial type. Experience has shown that a private garage should possess certain desirable features, in order to obviate the necessity of having recourse to motor engineering repair shops for numerous small repairs and adjustments, and to enable the owner, or his chauffeur, to carry out conveniently and expeditiously any work on the car. Let us first consider the question of garage dimensions.

GARAGE DIMENSIONS

If economy is the keynote in erecting a garage, the latter must of necessity be as small as possible, consistent with housing the car, and one can lay down no definite rules regarding its dimensions, except that the minimum length should be about 2 ft. more than the overall length of the car, and width 1 ft. 6 in. to 2 ft. greater than the overall width of the car.

In the smallest size, the height of the door (or doors) should be a few inches more than the top of the windscreen, but unless there is more height inside, this will prevent the hood from being kept up, as it should certainly be, when wet. It is better, of course, to allow sufficient door height to enable the car to be driven into the garage with the hood up.

In the case of a small car (8 to 10 h.p., R.A.C. rating), the necessary door height for the car to pass through with its hood up is about 4 ft. to 5 ft.

For a 12-h.p. car this height would be 5 ft. to 5 ft. 6 in., and for a larger touring car 6 ft. 6 in. to 7 ft. The width of the doors, overall, should be at least 18 in. to 2 ft. more than the width overall of the car.

The length of the garage should be at least 2 ft. more than the overall length of the car.

The most convenient "minimum" dimensions which should be adopted by those who are building garages should be based upon the considerations that to get all round a car conveniently, and to have a bench for doing odd repairs and other jobs on, the length and width

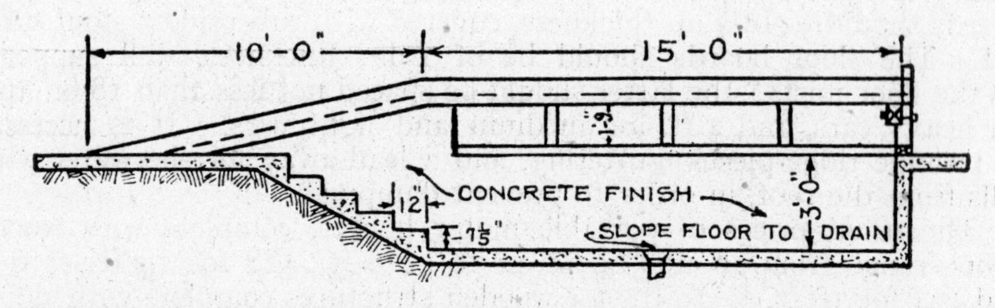

Fig. 82.—Design in Concrete for a Service Pit, and Raised Run-way for enabling Car to be raised above Floor Level. This Construction requires only a Shallow Pit.

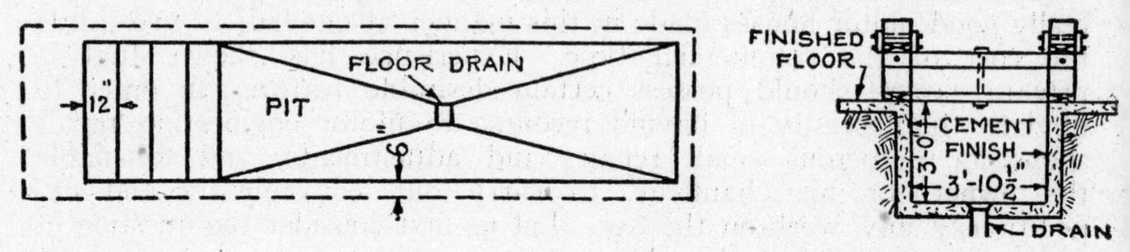

Fig. 83.—Details of Floor and Drain of Service Pit.

inside of the garage should not be less than 5 ft. and 4 ft., respectively, greater than the overall length and width of the car.

The following table shows the average dimensions of the four principal types of motor car in present use, and suggests the most convenient internal dimensions of the garages appropriate to these cars:

Type.	Overall Dimensions.			Internal Dimensions of Garage.		
	Length.	Width.	Height (hood up)	Length.	Width.	Height.
	ft. in.	ft. in.	ft. in.	ft. in.	ft. in.	ft. in.
Small Car	9 2	3 10	5 0	12 0	6 0	7 0
Light Car	12 0	5 2	5 9	15 0	8 0	7 0
Medium Car	14 0	6 0	6 0	17 0	9 0	7 6
Large Car	15 ft. to 17 ft.	6 ft. to 6 ft. 6 in.	6 3	20 0	10 0	8 0

The larger the garage available the better, from the point of view of accessibility, and for this reason one should not cut dimensions too fine. In many cases, also, the motorist who commences with a small car usually gets a larger one later on, so that if the garage is made large enough in the first place, no further considerations become necessary.

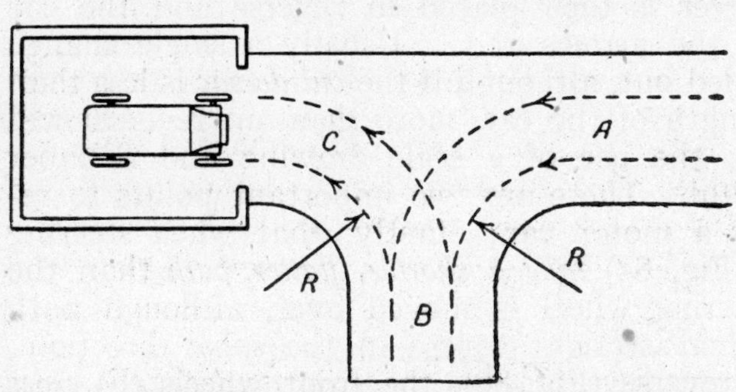

Fig. 84.—Illustrating Method of Reversing Car near Garage.

Regarding the door dimensions, the width overall should be at least 1 ft. more than the overall car width, if there is a straight run into the garage. If, however, the approach is a curved one, more room will have to be allowed, in order to clear the door posts.

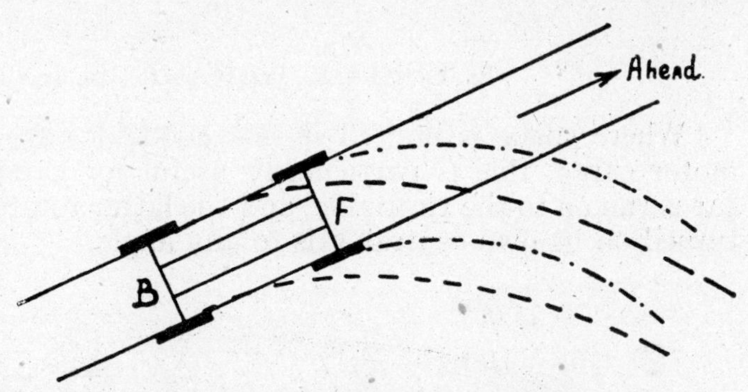

Fig. 85.—Track of Wheels, Steering Ahead.

A very good plan for those about to build garages is to make *a scale drawing of the proposed garage* in plan, together with an outline, to scale, of the approach. Then, if a paper or cardboard model of the car, in plan view, be cut out and laid on the drawing, a good idea of the suitability of the garage dimensions will be obtained. If the model can be manœuvred along the approach and into the garage, with a fair amount of clearance on each side, allowing for the limited lock of the front wheels in steering, one should not go far wrong.

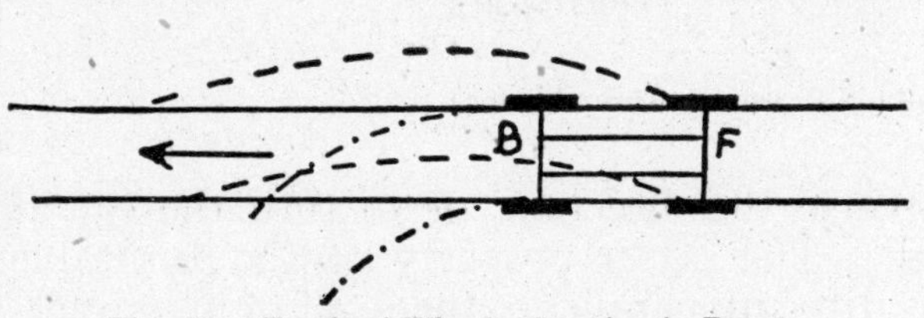

Fig. 86.—Track of Wheels, Steering in Reverse.

It is important to remember when planning garages and drives, that cars have to be driven into the garage at night, and also have to be driven in reverse gear in one direction, as a rule; both introduce more difficulties in manœuvring the car. Perhaps the best scheme, where space allows, is to have a turning space in front of the garage, so that the car can be backed into the latter, ready for driving straight out. Fig. 84 shows how this can be arranged. The car is driven straight in from the road in the direction indicated by the arrows at A. The steering is put hard over to the left, so that the car turns into the *cul-de-sac* B. The gear lever is then placed in reverse and the car backed in the direction of the arrows at C. Usually a single change of steering only need be carried out, although if the *cul-de-sac* is less than one and a half times the length of the car, more than one reversal will be necessary. Here, again, the use of a scale drawing and a paper model will prove most helpful. There are two important points to remember when manœuvring a motor car: firstly, that when steering ahead *the back wheels* (B, Fig. 85) *take a shorter, flatter path* than the front wheels when the steering wheel is moved over, although both wheels turn from the original straight course in the *same* direction; secondly, when steering in reverse (Fig. 86), the front wheels (F) *cross over* the original course, whereas the rear wheels (B) turn from the course without crossing it.

When considering the question of garage and drive design, these two points should be carefully regarded.

A USEFUL GARAGE TURNTABLE

Where space is limited it is a good idea to provide a turntable for motor cars; this is particularly useful for car parking purposes. The car is run on to the turntable, and the latter rotated so that the car can be turned on its own central axis to any angle.

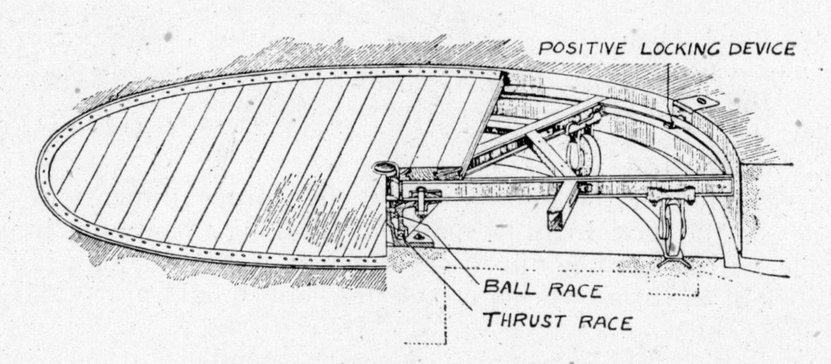

Fig. 87.—The L.S.D. Garage Turntable for Cars.

One is therefore able to reverse the direction, or to turn the car at right angles in its own length. The latter property of the turntable enables the car owner to run his drive up parallel to the front of his garage, thus saving a good deal of space. Fig. 87 shows the Laycock[1] L.S.D. garage turntable which is used for these purposes. It is a soundly constructed affair consisting of a 14-ft. diameter circular table of wood, mounted on eight radial arms of "H" section girder steel.

[1] The Laycock Engineering Co., Ltd., Sheffield.

The wheels are mounted on roller bearings, and run on a steel track. A ball-race and also a thrust-race on the pivot render this turntable particularly easy to manipulate. The turntable in question is provided with a locking device to hold it in a definite position when not in use.

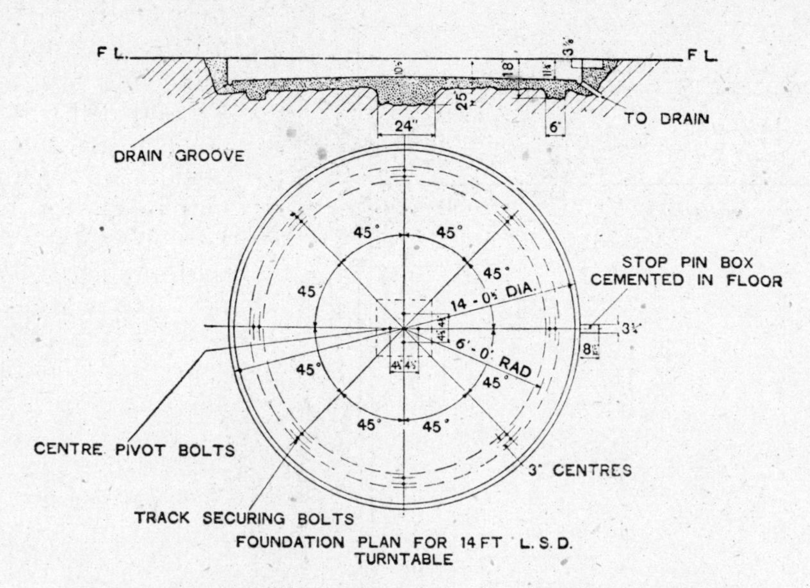

Fig. 88.—Showing Concrete Foundations and Draining Arrangement.

Fig. 88 shows the concrete arrangement and drain for the turntable illustrated in Fig. 87.

GARAGE LAY-OUT

It is not our purpose to discuss the subject of garage design or building construction—this is a matter for building journals—but rather to consider the planning of the building from the viewpoint of the motor owner or chauffeur who wishes not only to have a building to house his car, but also one in which he can undertake certain adjustments, repairs, and overhaul.

The first essential is plenty of room for working; in this connection the preceding remarks on garage dimensions should be studied, for in addition to being able to get all round the car for inspection purposes, space must be provided for a working bench.

Fig. 89 shows a typical example of a modern owner-driver's garage, intended for carrying out overhauls and repairs. It will be observed that there are two large windows, to give plenty of light, and that a work bench covers the width of the garage at one end and under one of the windows. A "drop" or hinged bench under the other window will also be found convenient when doing overhauls; it provides a place to put the component parts upon, for storage and adjustment purposes.

The main bench should be substantially built, preferably of $1\frac{1}{2}$-in. to

2-in. deal planks, well supported. The width of the bench should not be less than 2 ft.; three 9-in. planks will be found to provide a convenient width. The bench should be fixed about 3 ft. above floor level; this height is about right for working in the vice, as, for example, when filing and drilling (with a hand drill).

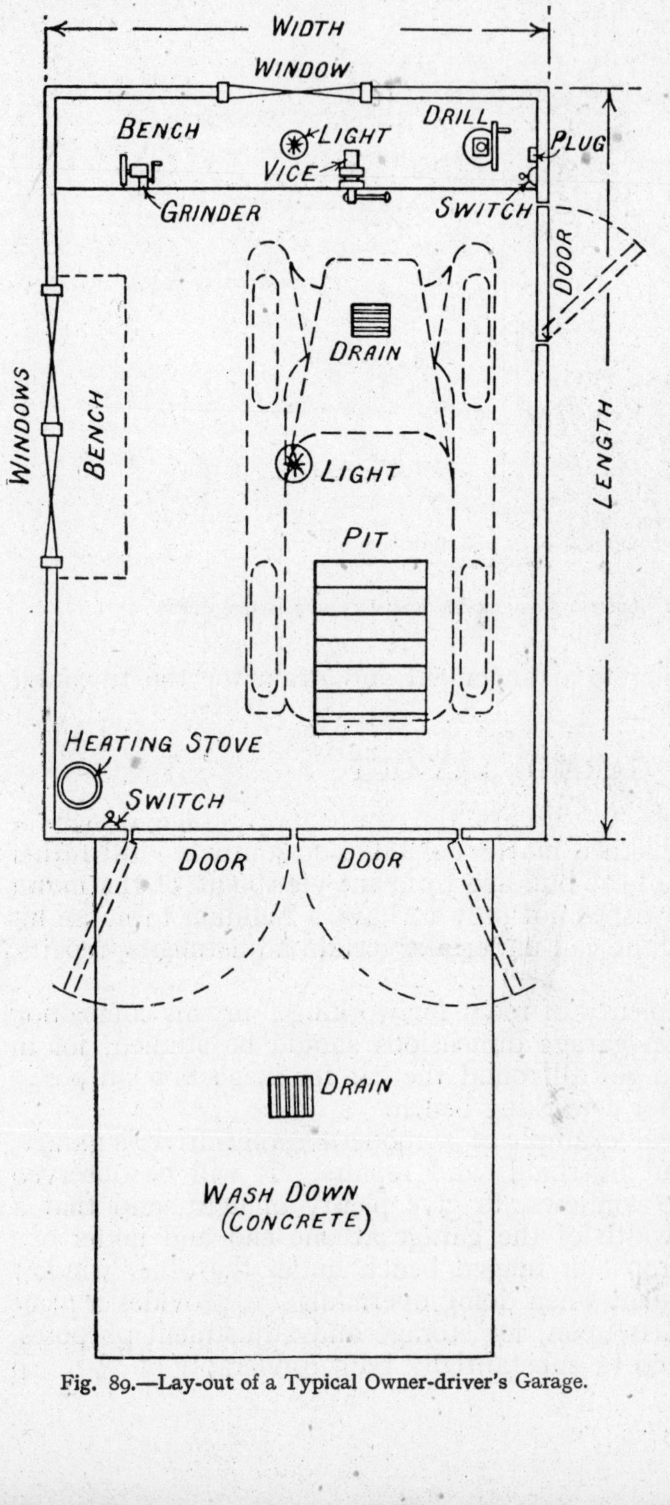

The space under the bench can usefully be employed for stowing tool boxes, storing motor oil, greases, cleaning materials, and in providing cupboard space for general storage purposes.

Proceeding with the smaller garage lay-out (Fig. 89), and having dealt with the question of benches and vices, we shall now consider the subject of the general equipment and arrangements of the smaller type of garage.

The garage dimensions are not shown in the illustration, but should be taken from the table previously given.

There should be a *concrete floor* to the garage, and also a concreted area in front of the garage (or behind if double sets of doors are fitted) for the purpose of washing down. Both inside and outside concreted sections should be sloped slightly towards *the drains* provided (Fig. 89). The inside

Fig. 89.—Lay-out of a Typical Owner-driver's Garage.

drain is for emptying the water from the radiator on cold nights; without this drain one has either to push the car from outside when the radiator has been emptied, or to make the garage floor damp.

A suitable disposition of *electric light* should be arranged, with

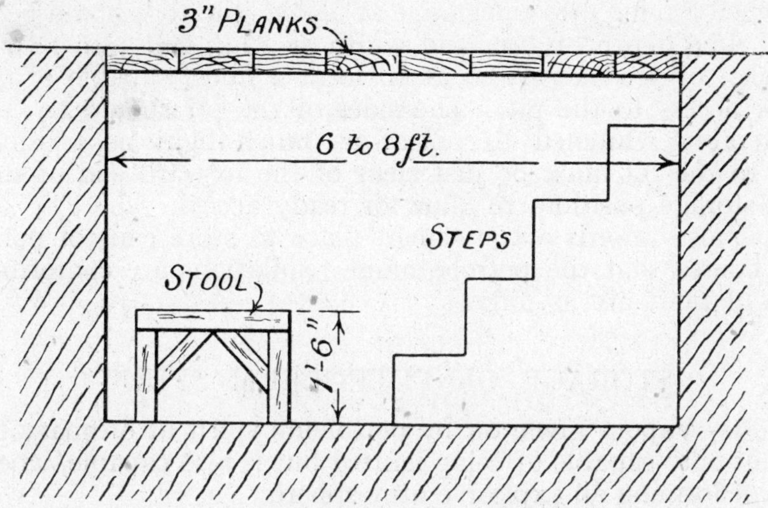

Fig. 90.—Garage Pit in Side Sectional View.

switches convenient to the main and (if fitted) side doors. A good arrangement is to have a 60-watt lamp in the centre or, better still, nearer the window end of the garage, so that it throws a good light down into the front part of the car. There should be another light above the work-bench, and a power plug and switch on the wall near the bench. From the latter a *wandering lead* can be taken for a portable electric lamp, so that any part of the car can be reached and repairs or adjustments executed at all times. The same plug will also supply power for a fan, electric drill, electric soldering iron, radiator heater (for frosty weather), and similar electrical items. It is an advantage to have a pit in the garage, for working underneath the car. Those who have used motor pits will agree that they are a great convenience, and save a good deal of time and trouble in " underneath " repairs and adjustments.

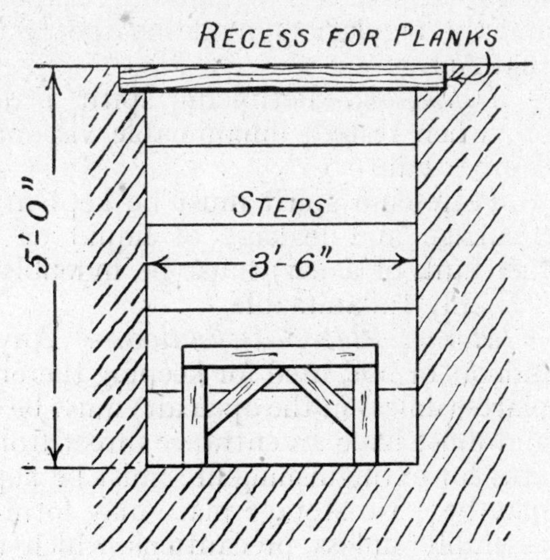

Fig. 91.—Garage Pit in End Sectional View.

The *pit* for a medium-size car should be about 3 ft. wide by 6 ft. to 10 ft. long, by 4 ft. 6 in. to 5 ft. deep. In order to reach different parts of the chassis from below, which are of course some 12 in. to 18 in. above ground level, a small box or stool should be kept handy. The pit itself should be bricked, with a concrete floor and drain. It should have an iron wall ladder or steps at one end, for getting down. Further, in order to safeguard against accidents with individuals, or with the car—as when driving into the garage at night—the top should be recessed all round, to a depth of 3 in. and width of 3 in., and 3 in. × 9 in. wide deal planks, bridged across so as to form a floor, capable of quick removal for access to the pit. The sides of the pit should be cemented, and preferably whitened to reflect as much light as possible. The entrance to the pit must be just clear of the forward end of the car in its usual storage position, to allow of ready access.

The pit also affords a convenient place to store cans of petrol, provided of course that the petrol-storage regulations are conformed with. These regulations are as follows:

STORAGE OF PETROLEUM SPIRIT[1]

Caution.—Vapour given off by petroleum spirit at ordinary temperatures is not only capable of being ignited but is also capable, when mixed with air, of forming an explosive atmosphere.

The exhaust fumes given off from a car with the engine running are highly poisonous, and the engine should never be allowed to run in any confined place.

Storage.—The storage and use of petroleum spirit for use in connection with motor cars is regulated by the provisions of the Petroleum Act 1928 and the regulations made by the Secretary of State under Section 10 of that Act.

Definition.—Petroleum spirit is defined as " petroleum which gives off, when tested, inflammable vapour at a temperature of less than 73 degrees Fah."

Petroleum spirit must be kept in metal vessels made secure against breakage and leakage of liquid or vapour. Each vessel (except the fuel tank of a car) must be indelibly labelled " Petroleum Spirit " and " Highly Inflammable."

Storage Place.—Definition.—" Any room, building, or place, whether indoors or not, used for keeping therein spirit for a motor vehicle." Such places (unless in the open air) must be effectively ventilated to the open air and must have an entrance direct from the open air. An efficient apparatus for extinguishing fire must be kept in the place or as near thereto as may be. No storage place may form part of a dwelling-place or place of assembly unless precautions which are strictly prescribed against fire exist. A substantial partition or floor, not readily inflammable, must separate the storage place from the dwelling-house; and if more than two 2-gallon vessels of petroleum and a full tankful are in the storage place there must be no opening in the partition or floor. The total amount

[1] R.A.C. Summary.

permitted to be kept in *one* storage place is sixty gallons, inclusive of any spirit which is in the fuel tank of a motor car while the car is in the place. *Two* storage places if in the same occupation within twenty feet of one another count as one.

Containers of petroleum spirit must not be of more than two gallons capacity except fuel tanks of motor vehicles. This capacity may be exceeded if the storage place be twenty feet away from a building or road and precautions against it flowing out in case of fire are taken, and when such large containers are required *Notice* must be given of such intention to the licensing authorities annually in January. Where a storage place is within twenty feet of any building or inflammable substance, the total amount of petroleum spirit to be kept in a storage place must not exceed the contents of the fuel tank of the motor vehicle and two 2-gallon vessels *carried thereon* unless such notice as before referred to is given. Wilful or careless discharge of petroleum spirit into any drain communicating with a sewer is forbidden.

Penalty.—On summary conviction for offences under the Act and the regulations—Fine up to £20 for every day on which the offence occurs or continues and *forfeiture* of the spirit and containers.

Fire Extinguishers in Private Garages.—Under the above Regulations it appears obligatory on a private motorist when he keeps his car in his own garage and has petrol in the fuel tank of his car, to have a fire-extinguishing apparatus fitted to his car, or a supply of sand in the garage, and if he keeps any petroleum spirit in the garage as well he should have a fire-extinguishing apparatus fitted to the garage (or a supply of sand), or other effective means of extinguishing burning petrol, as the garage, by reason of the presence of the petrol, remains a "storage place" within the meaning of the Regulations when the car is out of the garage.

CALCIUM-CARBIDE REGULATIONS

Whilst on the subject of storage of inflammable materials, it should be mentioned that calcium carbide, from which acetylene gas is generated by the addition of water, was brought into the Act in 1922 and modified subsequently in 1929. This Act allows the storage of carbide up to 5 lb., in 1-lb. tins, without licence. From 5 lb. to 28 lb. may be kept subject to certain conditions, e.g. notification to the local authorities, storage in a dry place in hermetically closed containers, and labelled as required by the Order. For quantities over 28 lb. a licence is required.

BENCH EQUIPMENT

The motorist or small garage engineer who does most of his own repairs will find it advisable to provide himself with a good bench and tool equipment.

Apart from the fitting of one or more vices as permanent fixtures, there are other useful small tools which should form part of the bench equipment.

The first of these is a small bench drilling machine, hand- or electrically-operated. It should preferably be placed at one end of the bench—as it is not used to the same extent as the vice and other tools.

Fig. 92 shows a useful bench arrangement for taking an ordinary hand drilling machine, supplied by Brown Bros., Ltd. It will clamp on to the edge of any bench, has a hand feed and a traversing drill table.

Fig. 93 illustrates a convenient pattern of power-bench drilling machine,

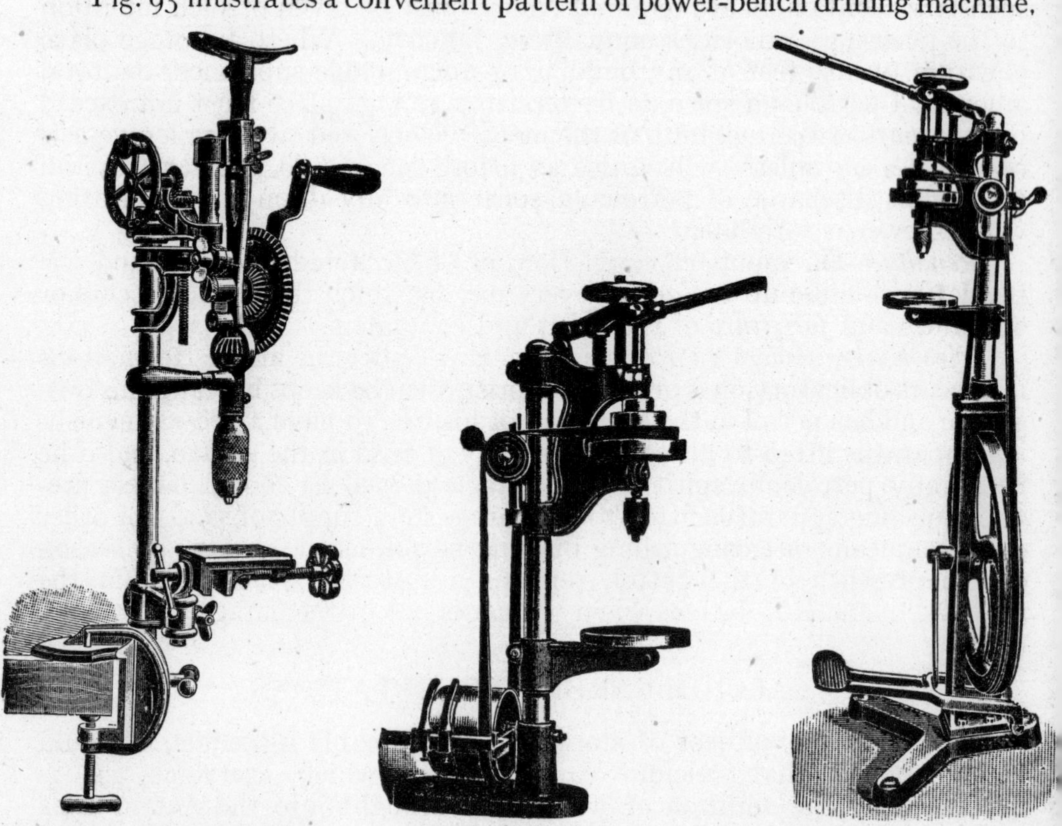

Fig. 92.—A Hand Drill Adapter for Bench Use.

Fig. 93.—A Useful Power-operated Sensitive Drill.

Fig. 94.—A Treadle-operate[d] Drilling Machine.

quite inexpensive but reliable. The machine shown will drill holes up to $\frac{1}{2}$-in. diameter, and has a self-acting feed, the pressure of the latter being adjustable to the size of drill in use. The end thrust is taken by ball-bearings. A three-jaw Goodall-pattern chuck, for taking drills up to $\frac{1}{2}$-in. diameter, is fitted.

Another convenient type of small garage or workshop manual-operated drilling machine is that shown in Fig. 94 (and supplied by Brown Bros., Ltd.), in which a foot treadle operates the drill spindle, thus leaving the hands free to feed the drill and to manipulate or to hold the work being drilled.

This machine has a lever-operated sensitive feed, and also a wheel feed. It will be observed that there are four pulley steps (above the drill chuck), giving four drilling speeds, by shifting the belt, and—to keep the latter taut—sliding the drill bracket up the post.

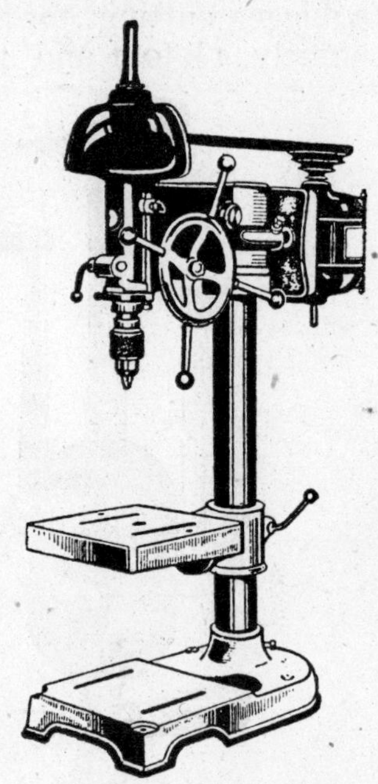

Fig. 95.—The "Driver" Drilling Machine.

The machine will drill holes up to $\frac{1}{2}$-in. diameter. It is 5 ft. 4 in. in height, and admits work, for drilling, up to 11 in. under the drill spindle. The drill table is 11 in. in diameter.

Other types of bench and power drilling machines will be described later, in connection with the larger machines.

The "Driver" drilling machine illustrated in Fig. 95 has an electric motor mounted at the top of the column, with belt drive to the spindle. It is made in several models, the largest one being that illustrated. Hand feed is provided by means of the star wheel shown, and an adjustable table is provided for the smaller drilling jobs. For large work, this table can be swung aside. The largest machine will take drills up to $\frac{1}{2}$ in., the drills being held in a Jacobs type of chuck. Ball-bearings are provided for the six-spline spindle. The maximum distance from the chuck to the table is $17\frac{1}{2}$ in. and spindle travel 4 in. The machines in question are marketed by E. P. Barrus, Ltd., Upper Thames Street, London, E.C.4.

HAND DRILLING MACHINES

The hand drill shown in Fig. 96 is very handy for small hole drilling, up to $\frac{3}{16}$-in. diameter. It has only a single speed, however, and is

Fig. 96.—A Single-speed Hand Drill.

therefore somewhat limited in range of work. The handle is hollow, and detachable for packing the whole outfit into a small space. The length is 11 in.

A two-speed gear hand drill is a big advantage over a single-speed one, for it enables heavier work to be tackled, as the lower gear provides a bigger cutting torque. The drill shown in Fig. 98 has two speeds, namely, $1\frac{1}{2}$ to 1 and 4 to 1 ratio; it is only necessary to turn a milled portion to change the speed. A ball thrust ring is fitted; this lessens the hand effort required. The type illustrated in Fig. 98 is known as the "M.F." and will take drills up to $\frac{3}{8}$ in. It has an overall length of $15\frac{3}{4}$ in.

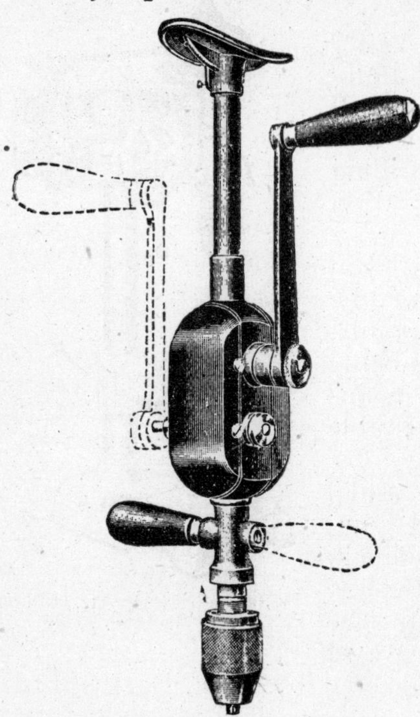

Fig. 97.—The "Duco" Two-speed Breast Drill, for drills up to $\frac{1}{2}$-in. diameter.

Some hand drills are provided with spirit levels attached to the drill-bearing bracket, to enable the drill to be held horizontally. Others have detachable breast plates, interchangeable with handles or knobs.

An advantage to be sought after in the case of breast and hand drills is a turning *handle lever of variable length*, or leverage, to suit different kinds of work; many makes provide slotted levers for this purpose.

The ordinary carpenter's type brace is sometimes used for motor work, and the engineer's ratchet also; the hand, breast, and electric type drills, however, are more frequently used.

In connection with the hand and breast type drills, it should be added that it is now possible to obtain a special bench standard whereby these drilling machines can be used as bench machines—hand-operated, of course. Fig. 92 shows a typical bench drill press of this type, known as the "M.F."

DRILL SIZES

Fig. 98.—The "M.F." Two-speed Drill.

Whilst on the subject of drilling machines, it may be as well to say a few words regarding types of drills and drill sizes. For thin metal work, and for certain other kinds of work where twist drills may break when just coming through, we prefer to use the straight-fluted drill—that is, a drill having two straight V-type flutes on opposite sides, and throughout its drilling length.

For ordinary purposes the straight-shank twist drill is most used. The ordinary amateur and private owner will find the following sizes more convenient: $\frac{1}{16}$, $\frac{1}{8}$, $\frac{3}{16}$, $\frac{1}{4}$, $\frac{5}{16}$, and $\frac{3}{8}$ in. These sizes are suitable for the ordinary hand drilling machines.

As a refinement, and where more important repairs are undertaken, the intermediate $\frac{1}{32}$ in. sizes, viz. $\frac{3}{32}$, $\frac{5}{32}$, $\frac{7}{32}$, $\frac{9}{32}$, and $\frac{11}{32}$ in., will be found most useful—more especially as they provide the correct thread-tapping holes for several sizes.

The small engineer will also find a rose-bit, or countersink drill, of about $\frac{5}{8}$-in. maximum diameter, and to the correct countersunk screw angle, namely, 45 degrees, very useful.

Another useful drill is the combination centre drill. This is used for starting larger drills and for drilling centres in the lathe.

For bench drilling machines the tapered shank type of twist drill is usually employed.

These drills can be obtained in sizes from $\frac{1}{16}$ in. to $\frac{1}{4}$ in. in $\frac{1}{16}$-in. steps; and from $\frac{1}{4}$ in. to 1 in. in $\frac{1}{32}$-in. steps.

Twist drills are also marketed in millimetre sizes from about $1\frac{1}{2}$ mm. in $\frac{1}{2}$ mm. steps up to 25 mm. Larger sizes of twist drills, in both English and metric measures, are available, but the motor engineer is only concerned with the smaller sizes.

It is a good thing to have a block of wood drilled with each of the drills kept, and to insert each drill, point upwards, in its own hole; this is a convenient method of keeping drills in the garage.

The flat type of drill is often used in garages, for special sizes of holes, and in emergency; it is usually supplied with $\frac{1}{4}$- and $\frac{1}{2}$-in. shanks.

HAND GRINDERS

Next in importance to a hand or bench drilling machine is the small hand-operated grinding machine. This will be found most useful in connection with the sharpening of chisels, centre-punches, cutting shears, drills, and similar tools of hardened and tempered steel. Burrs may be removed from hard steel parts, such as pins and bolt ends, and much useful work of a grinding nature carried out on steel parts which are too hard for a file to touch.

Fig. 99.—Bench Grinder used for Buffing Purposes.

The smallest size of hand grinder costs but a few shillings and has a 3-in. abrasive wheel, usually of carborundum. Wheels of different grades or cutting textures are obtainable. These hand grinders have usually a pair of enclosed gears, for obtaining the high wheel speed required, and an adjustable metal guard for guiding the part to be ground. The grinder is provided with a screw clamp for attachment to the bench. The sizes of machine obtainable range from one with 3-in. diameter grinding wheel to 7-in. diameter.

In using this machine a little practice is necessary, for the one hand must turn the handle whilst the other holds and manipulates the job; the help of an assistant will prove useful in these circumstances.

The hand-operated device shown in Fig. 100 enables the operator to grind twist drills and at the same time has a flexible shaft extension to the grinder shaft, provided with a drill chuck at the other end, to enable holes to be drilled in awkward places, or on the chassis itself, for the base of the machine can be clamped down to any convenient surface.

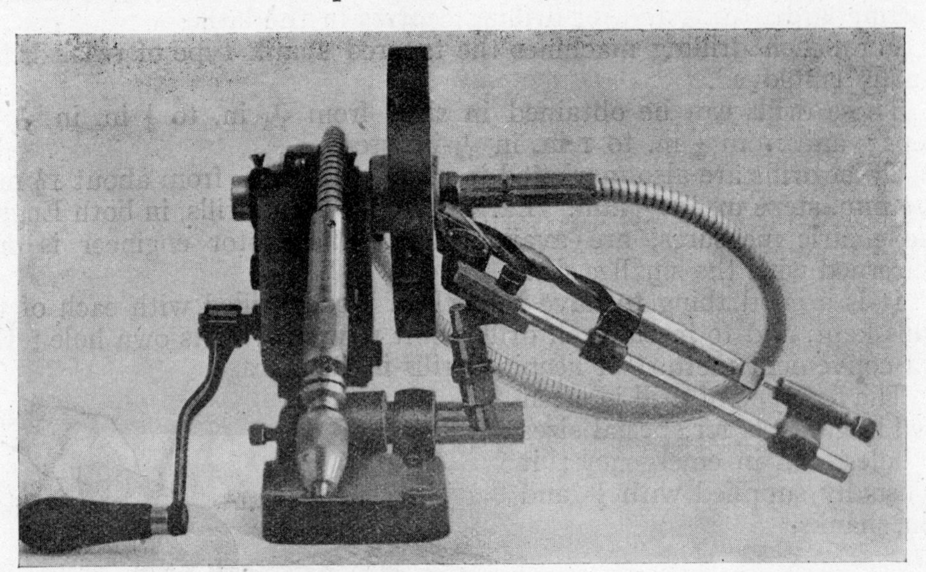

Fig. 100.—Combination Twist-drill Grinder and Flexible Shaft Drive for Drills, etc.

To those who desire to have both hands free whilst grinding the work, the foot-treadle machine, shown in Fig. 101,[1] will be found very suitable. The treadle gives a free-wheel motion, and by removing the grinding wheel, the machine may be used for polishing or buffing purposes. The grinding wheel supplied is 6 in. diameter by 1 in. thick.

SMALL LATHES FOR THE GARAGE

The addition of a small lathe to the garage equipment will be found very convenient, for it will enable the amateur mechanic to carry out a large number of constructional and repair jobs, which otherwise would be quite outside his domain. A good lathe enables its owner to save much of time and expense in carrying out his own jobs, and with it he can obtain much interesting employment, both as a hobby and for more serious purposes.

[1] The Billing Tool Co., London.

With a "three-inch" lathe, for example, the amateur mechanic can turn up bushes for bearings on his car, replacement pins for worn ones, special sizes and lengths of screws, gudgeon pins, small-end bushes, washers, and numerous other items used on the car.

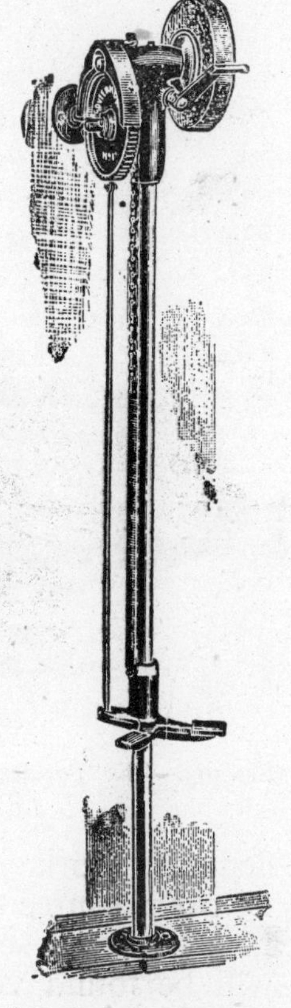

Fig. 101.—A Convenient Treadle-operated Grinding Wheel.

In addition he can actually *turn up* from the blank *a new piston* in cast-iron or aluminium, and can *bore out* a *rewhite-metalled connecting rod* or main bearing.

The *refacing of inlet and exhaust valves* which have become pitted is another simple lathe operation; *new valves* can also be turned from the blanks sold for this purpose or from larger valves.

There are many working parts on a car which can be rebushed, or reamered out and new pins fitted, in the garage workshop with the aid of a small lathe.

Apart from the jobs mentioned as examples of the motor work which can be carried out on a lathe, the replacement of lost or broken parts can usually be made with its aid, and a good deal of time and expense saved.

There are several excellent designs of small lathes now on the English market in various sizes up to about 3-in. centre. Among those which are particularly suited to the motor engineer's requirements are the models known as the "Economic" (Messrs. Caldwell & Co., Ltd., 130 Elliott Street, Glasgow), the "Portass" (Messrs. Heeley Manufacturing Co., Ltd., Abbeydale, Sheffield), the "Zyto" (Messrs. S. Tyzack & Son, Ltd., 341 Old Street, London, E.C.1). The "Economic" lathe is a small hand-driven model suitable for small metal parts and for wood-turning.

The "Zyto" lathe, known as the "T.R. Model," is a 3-in. centre lathe suitable for milling, surfacing, and screw-cutting. It has an improved back-gear, with tumbler reverse and ball-bearing thrust. The height between the centres is 3 in., the distance between the centres 12½ in., and the gap radius 4½ in. The tail-stock barrel will admit ⅜ in. and the mandrel the same diameter.

Fig. 102.—The "Portass" 3-in. Screw-cutting Lathe.

The "Portass" lathes are made in the $2\frac{1}{8}$-in. and 3-in. models. The latter is a back-geared screw-cutting lathe of excellent design. All cast portions of the machine are in best quality close-grained grey iron and the bed and slides are accurately machined and fitted with adjusting gibs. The saddle travels the length of the bed and is operated by a square-thread lead screw. A fully compound slide rest having accurately machined V-slides with adjusting gibs is included, the upper slide being capable of swivelling. The headstock bearings are parallel with split gun-metal bushes. The tail-stock is of the set-over type and is capable of fine adjustment for accurate work. A special 3-speed foot-motor is supplied for use where no other source of drive is available.

Fig. 103.—The "Portass" Sensitive Drilling Attachment for the Lathe shown in Fig. 102.

The small sensitive drilling machine attachment shown in Fig. 103 will be found very useful in the motor garage and workshop.

The small lathe is of good design, and is not only of use for turning operations, but with the aid of a few fitments and accessories can be used for drilling holes, boring operations, facing flat surfaces of irregular contour, screw-cutting, milling operations, and for gear-teeth cutting. It can also be fitted with a grinding wheel for small grinding operations, such as pins, journals, and hardened parts, and for sharpening tools, etc.

A useful model 3-in. lathe, marketed by Messrs. E. Gray & Sons, Ltd., London, is shown in Fig. 104. It will be seen that it has many valuable features. With regard to the capacity, the distance between centres is $12\frac{1}{2}$ in., and both tailstock and mandrel nose are bored No. 1 Morse taper, the latter being screwed

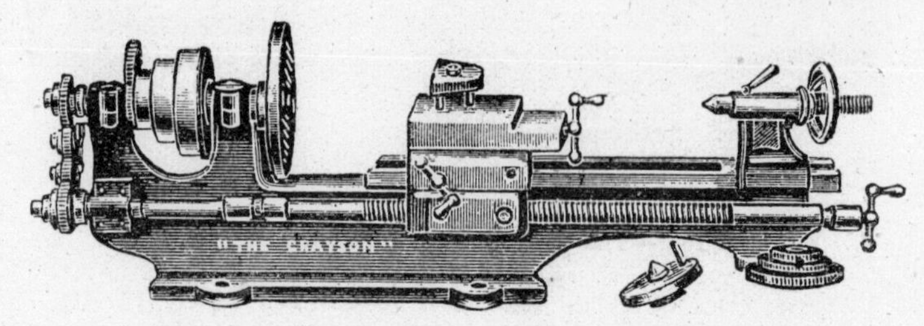

Fig. 104.—The Grayson 3-in. Screw-cutting Lathe.

$\frac{3}{4}$-in. Whitworth and bored for rod work $\frac{3}{8}$ in. in diameter. The set-over tail-stock is provided with a square-thread hand wheel, and the barrel is also bored for $\frac{3}{8}$-in. rods. The back gear is engaged by eccentric, and a set of change wheels for all English threads is provided. All bearings are sliding surface and capable of adjustment, and the leading screw is $\frac{5}{8}$-in. diameter thread, being square with 8 T.P.I. A $6\frac{1}{2}$-in. face plate is fitted and a catch plate is also included in the equipment. The lathe is marketed either as a screw-cutting lathe with plain slide rest or with a fully compound slide rest, and it may also be obtained as a screw-cutting lathe with a plain slide rest and back gear. In addition to this, the lathe is also made at a very reasonable price as a plain turning lathe, and it is interesting to note that longer beds may be obtained to any of the above types of lathe at a very slight additional cost.

To the amateur and ordinary motor engineer requiring a good small lathe for undertaking practically all the various kinds of work mentioned

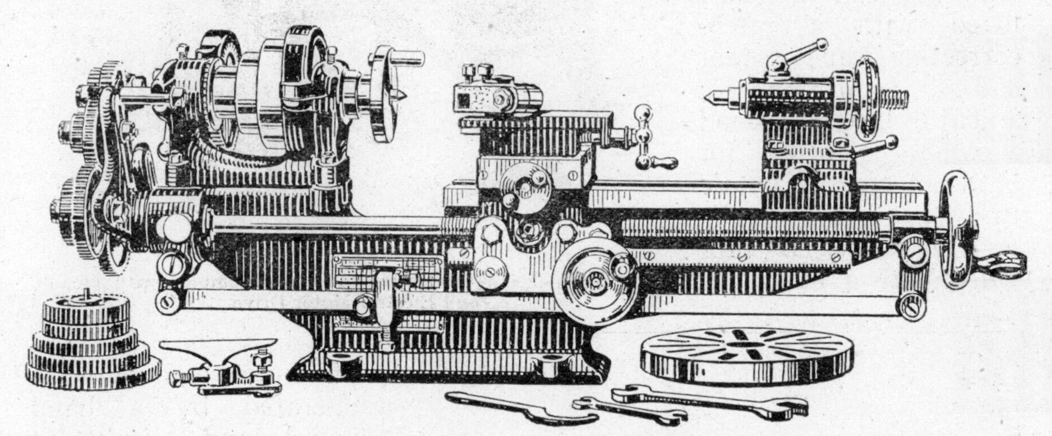

Fig. 105.—The $3\frac{1}{2}$-in. Drummond Lathe.

earlier in this section, one can recommend with confidence the Drummond[1] $3\frac{1}{2}$-in. lathe, known as the "M" type, and illustrated in Figs. 105 and 106.

Originally introduced in 1902, this lathe has been constantly improved, until to-day it represents a very high standard in small-lathe design and in completeness of equipment and accessories.

The height of the centres is $3\frac{1}{2}$ in., the maximum length between the centres on the standard model is 16 in.—longer beds are obtainable, however—the maximum swing over the saddle is $4\frac{1}{4}$ in., and the face-plate diameter 9 in. The lead-screw has a pitch of $\frac{1}{8}$ in.

The length of the bed is 2 ft. $8\frac{1}{4}$ in., and length overall, 3 ft. 3 in.

The overall breadth is 1 ft. $10\frac{1}{4}$ in.

The mandrel has a $\frac{3}{8}$-in. centre hole and a nose-thread of 1 in.

The lathe without stand and treadle weighs 1 cwt. 2 qr., and with the latter 4 cwt. 1 qr. 14 lb.

[1] Drummond Bros., Guildford.

Fig. 107 illustrates the manner in which the lathe is arranged *for boring operations*, and shows another advantage of the tool-holder, namely, in the manner in which the boring bar or tool may be used with as great facility as with a turning tool. The square hole in the tool-holder takes shanks up to $\frac{9}{16}$ in. square.

The *lead-screw* is cut on a special machine fitted with a pitch-correcting gear ; its rear end is bronze-bushed, and at its head-stock end a *clutch* is fitted for both hand and automatic throw-out.

The *saddle* is provided with a rack-and-pinion traversing motion operated by a hand wheel, and a split-nut device is used for disengaging the lead-screw.

Fig. 106.—The $3\frac{1}{2}$-in. Drummond Lathe, complete with Treadle and Electric Motor Drive.

Fig. 107.—The Lathe Set Up for Boring a Big-end Bearing.

The *cross-slide* is fitted with micrometer index for fine regulation of the depth of cut.

The *top-slide* is fitted with a graduated base ; its lead-screw is brought to the side of the vees, thus enabling the use of a much longer nut than usual, and giving better protection against chips and dirt.

In connection with the *cutting of screw-*

threads, the standard set of change wheels supplied is as follows: two 20, two 30, one each 35, 38, 40, 45, 46, 50, 55, 60, 65, and 73. These gears enable Whitworth threads from 8 to 40 threads per inch to be cut, and metric threads from ·5 to 5 mm. pitch, together with a wide range of other threads and feeds. The screw-cutting change-gear studs are fitted with a patent spring plug retainer.

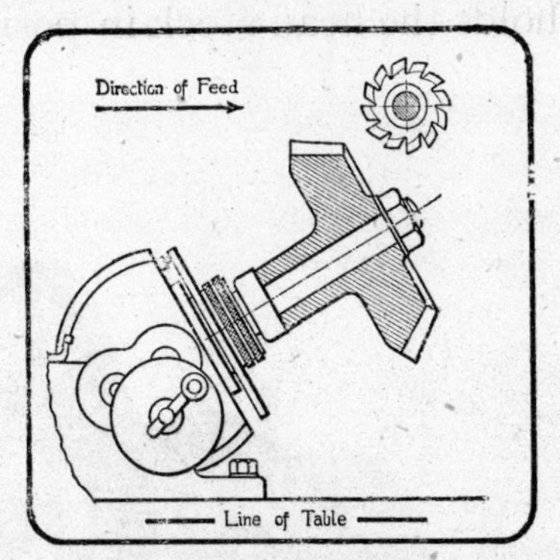

Fig. 108.—Cutting a Bevel Gear on an ordinary Milling Machine. Dividing head tilted. Work held on special mandrel, unsupported at outer end.

The *treadle-lathe flywheel* and the head of the pitman link run on large ball-bearings; the flywheel is balanced and heavy, so as to give a steady turning moment.

The usual accessories supplied with the lathe include a large face plate, driver plate, hand-rest, hardened-steel centres, and spanners. Additional accessories which can be obtained for use with this lathe include indexing, milling and gear-cutting attachment, tool grinder, turret attachment, internal and external grinding attachment, saw table attachment, fixed and travelling steadies, connecting-rod boring fixture for garage purposes, electric motor drive (shown in Fig. 106), and countershafts.

SOUTH BEND LATHE

A well-designed and comparatively inexpensive lathe for garage purposes is the 4½-in. centre South Bend lathe illustrated in Fig. 110. It is satisfactory for ordinary lathe work, as well as for turning car-engine pistons, valves, gudgeon pins, brake drums, etc., and reboring connecting rods which have been white-metalled.

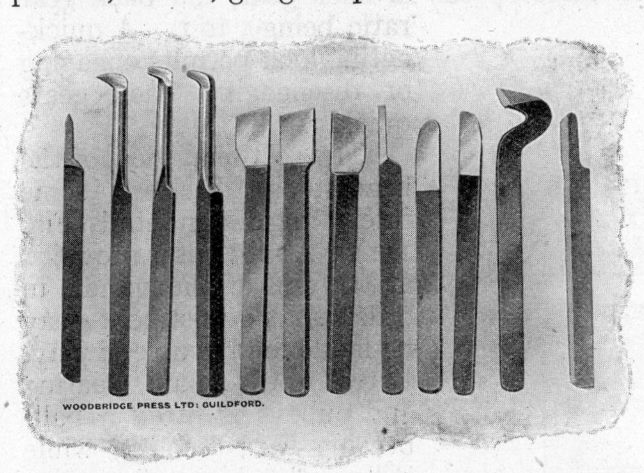

Fig. 109.—A Useful Set of Lathe Tools for Garage Purposes.

A great deal of attention has been paid to the design of the bed the manufacturers apparently having decided that production difficulties should not prevent the bed of most suitable design being adopted. There are three V-ways and one flat-way on the bed, all of which are machined and finished to very fine limits. On the underside of the flat-way is the rack for moving the saddle along bodily.

The head-stock casting is reinforced and webbed, giving it strength and rigidity, while the base is accurately machined, hand scraped to fit the lathe bed, and aligned by the inside V-way and inside flat-way on the bed. A strong, substantial clamp between head-stock and bed holds the head-stock in position. Six spindle speeds are provided on the

Fig. 110.—The South Bend 4½-in. Centre Screw-cutting Lathe.

standard head-stock, ranging from 39 to 630 r.p.m. Three speeds are obtainable on open belt and three speeds in back gear, the back gear ratio being 5 to 1. A quick-acting lock permits engaging or disengaging back gears quickly.

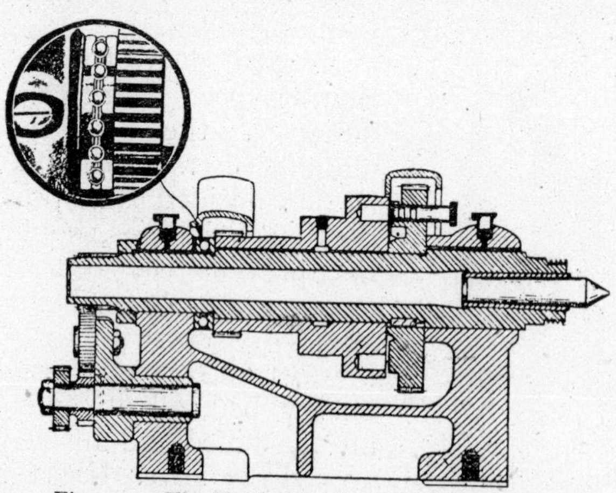

Fig. 111.—The Head-stock (South Bend Lathe).

The sectional view of the head-stock discloses some interesting design details (Fig. 111). A split nut is provided at the end of the spindle in order that adjustment may be made to take up end play. Between the main bearing and pulleys is fitted a ball-bearing thrust collar, while still another interesting point is the plunger on the larger head-stock gear wheel, which is engaged with a hole in the cone pulley when back-gear is thrown in thus affording a positive drive.

A three-position lever conveniently placed on the head-stock allows for the cutting of right-hand threads (it "up" position; left-hand threads in "down"), while the lathe spindle is running free with the lever in centre.

A wide, deep bridge provides rigid support for the compound tool rest. A clamping device is provided to lock the carriage on the lathe bed for facing and cutting-off operations. Gibs are provided at both front and rear of the saddle for taking up wear and for accurate adjustment. The dovetail cross slide is hand scraped and has gibs for delicate adjustment and for taking up wear. The cross-feed travel is $5\frac{1}{2}$ in., and the compound rest is graduated 180 degrees and can be swivelled and locked at any desired angle for machining or for turning and boring short tapers. It has an angular travel of $2\frac{1}{8}$ in. Feed screws for the compound rest and the cross slide have coarse-pitch "Acme" threads and are fitted with micrometer graduated collars reading in thousandths of an inch.

The tail-stock has $\frac{5}{8}$-in. set-over for taper turning, and is fitted with a No. 2 Morse Taper self-ejecting centre. The spindle travel is 2 in., while the cut-away design of tail-stock top permits the compound rest to swivel parallel with lathe bed over tail-stock base. A graduated index is provided for aligning the tail-stock.

A $\frac{1}{4}$-h.p. motor provides ample power for driving the lathe, and the manufacturers also supply a bench-mounting countershaft of compact design for use with the machine.

The machine, which is of American make, is marketed by Messrs. E. P. Barrus, Ltd., Upper Thames Street, London, E.C.4.

ADDITIONAL GARAGE EQUIPMENT

Apart from the small machines for garage use described in the preceding pages, we have dealt with the electric-lighting and power-plug arrangements and the inspection pit.

Further refinements which assist in simplifying garage work include suitable shelving for storage of spare parts, cleaning materials, nuts, bolts, washers, and numerous other items which invariably collect in most garages and workshops—many owner-drivers will use the garage work bench for doing other work of a mechanical nature, including repairs to domestic and gardening tools, wood-working, and even wireless work; the provision of shelves in plenty is then a necessity.

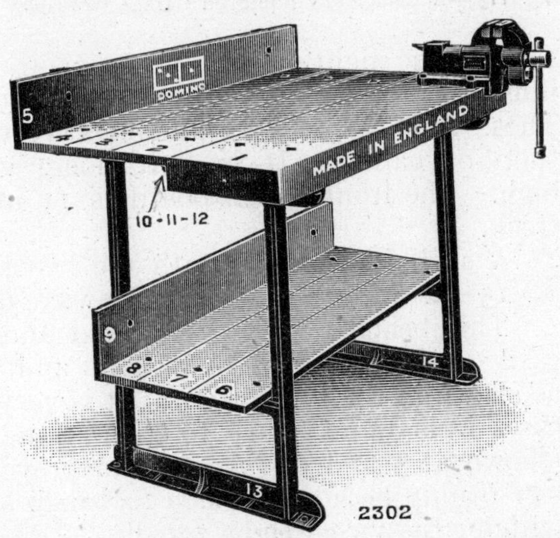

Fig. 112.—A Handy Portable or Fixed Type of Garage Bench.

The garage should also have some means of heating, in the

shape of a gas, electric, or slow-combustion stove. In the cold nights of winter if a stove is kept going no freezing troubles will occur, and the engine will start up readily.

Motor accessory firms supply a portable stove suitable for motor houses and garages, which burns a solid slow-combustion fuel known as "Carbotron." No smoke, smell, or dust is produced when the stove is in action.

The fuel mentioned is a chemical compound, which is supplied in blocks and gives off a good heat. The fuel consumption varies from 4*d*. to 6*d*. a day, according to the size of stove; the fuel is "started" by lighting it over an ordinary gas flame or a methylated-spirit lamp.

Fig. 113.—A Completely Equipped Garage Workshop Bench.

If it is not desired to build a work-bench in the garage, a portable one can be made or obtained, which will enable good work to be executed; moreover, the bench can be moved about to suit the lighting conditions or the position of the job. Fig. 112 illustrates a convenient and well-made portable bench, supplied by Thos. Ellin, Sheffield, which is very suitable for the small workshop or garage. It is 4 ft. long, 2 ft. 4 in. deep, and 2 ft. 9 in. high. The front bench board is 11 in. × 3 in., and the rear ones 1 in. thick.

A shelf is fitted beneath the bench, 44 in. × 12 in. (from ground) × 15 in. wide. A well-made vice is also supplied.

This bench can be dismantled and packed for transport, and it is easily erected by means of bolts and nuts, the parts being numbered, as shown in the illustration. It is very rigid when erected, and in most cases it is unnecessary to screw it to the floor. There is a back board (shown at 5 and 9, Fig. 112) to prevent articles falling off; the former can readily be adapted as a tool-rack attachment. The complete bench without the vice weighs 179 lb.

A more elaborate workshop bench, of the portable type, is shown in

Fig. 113. This is well fitted, and contains practically all the ordinary tools required in the garage.

The bench measures 3 ft. 6 in. × 1 ft. 9 in., and the front board to which the vice is fitted is 2 in. thick. The height from the ground is 2 ft. 8 in. Among the tools included are the following: 4-in. hand vice, geared emery grinder, hand drill, 3-in. rotary vice, set of 10 files, hammer, soldering iron, screw-drivers, punches, oil can, hacksaw, pliers, callipers, and dividers, set of 6 double-end box spanners, ratchet brace, and chisels.

Fig. 114.—The G.E. Bench Legs.

The "Steelpact" work benches, shown in Figs. 115 and 116, are well-designed benches, compact in form, extremely strong, and practically indestructible. They are made of heavy-gauge sheet-steel pressings, bolted or welded together, and have ample space above and below for lockers, shelves, and drawers.

They are designed on the extensible unit principle, using jig-drilled

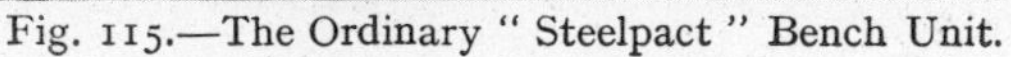

Fig. 115.—The Ordinary "Steelpact" Bench Unit.

Fig. 116.—Improved Model "Steelpact" Bench Unit.

work-bench units and vice stands; file racks are also arranged in these benches.

The type shown in Fig. 116 has a vice mounted on the left. It is of the portable type, having rollers or castors which are brought into or out of operation, according to whether the bench is portable or stationary, by means of the two handles shown near the base. These benches are made by Brookhirst Switchgear, Ltd., Chester.

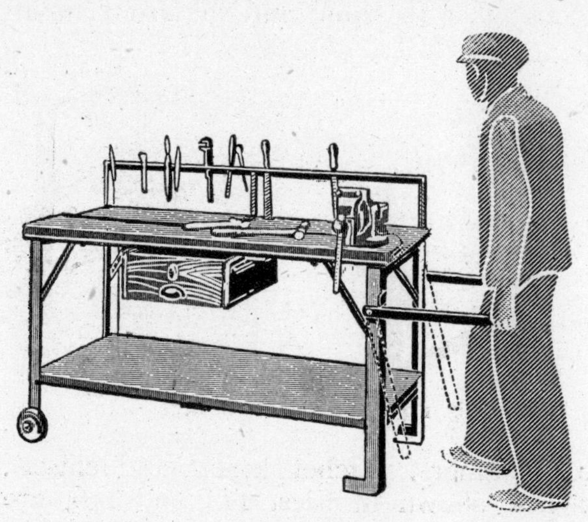

Fig. 117.—A Portable Bench for Garages and Engineering Shops.

Another type of bench leg, known as the G.E., is shown in Fig. 114. In this case the leg forms a complete end or centre support with faces for the bench timber and holes for bolting down to the floor.

It can quickly be erected or taken down, and is easily moved. The back support to the shelf shown serves to brace the bench so as to make it quite rigid. The bench leg is suitable for 9 in. × 2 in. and 9 in. × 3 in. timber ; it weighs 65 lb.

A particularly useful type of portable bench for garage purposes is illustrated in Fig. 117. This has a heavy timber top bolted to one-piece steel legs forming a light but rigid bench. There is a drawer, rack for tools, wheels at one end, and a pair of handles for moving the bench ; these fold downwards when not required.

CHAPTER III

THE EQUIPMENT OF LARGER GARAGES

HITHERTO we have confined our remarks concerning the lay-out and equipment of garages to the smaller types, including motor houses and small garage workshops, but it should be pointed out that a certain amount of the information given in the preceding chapter is applicable also to larger garages, more particularly in connection with tools. It is now proposed to preface the present account of the machine and other equipment of the larger commercial garages and motor works with a few remarks on the subject of garage lay-out.

THE LAY-OUT OF THE GARAGE

A survey of the various types of commercial garage—by which term is here meant motor garages and repair works of the commercial type—in this country shows that the majority of these are in the nature of buildings built for some other specific purpose, which were rented or purchased by enterprising persons who foresaw the great development of the automobile. Only a small proportion of existing garages have been designed and built to fulfil the requirements of modern car storage, maintenance, and overhaul. The majority are simply ordinary buildings of various designs—usually shops, sheds, stables, and small factories—which have been converted to the requirements of motor work to the best advantage. In many cases the garage met with in provincial towns consists of one large room, as it were, in which perhaps an office, storeroom, and shop-window have been partitioned off, and the rest of the space used as one big storage and repair shop.

Indeed, it is a common experience to find cars being garaged in one part of the floor space, others being dismantled or overhauled in another, and another part of the floor space occupied by benches, machine tools, and perhaps a battery-charging plant.

Where there is any first choice, preference should be given to any arrangement of rooms which enables the storage of customers' cars to be made in a separate garage, the overhaul and repairs in another shop, the machine tools in another, and so on. Not only is it an economy in both time and expense to do each type of work in its own department, but it is a matter of the best condition of working for the garage hands. No man can efficiently perform his work in a large, draughty shop in which all sorts of minor operations and interruptions are apt to occur; in a properly arranged machine shop, for example, he can work in comfort, more rapidly—as he has everything for use at hand—and without distraction.

The *smaller type of commercial garage* suitable for a provincial town will usually consist of a converted large single-room building, such as that depicted in plan view in Fig. 322. In the example shown, one large building has been divided into two main portions: one for storage and overhaul of the cars, and the other into a section, sub-divided by means of suitable partitions into a workshop containing a few essential tools and machines, a store-room for motor requisites, two offices, and a show-room with shop frontage on the road.

The main garage has large double or sliding doors opening on to the road; two petrol pumps (PP) are arranged near the road frontage of the main garage. Two inspection pits and a work-bench with a few vices and other smaller tools are provided, and there would, perhaps, be a compressed-air supply in this main garage, taken from a fixed or portable electrically driven compressor, one or two convenient power plugs arranged on the walls, and other useful incidentals.

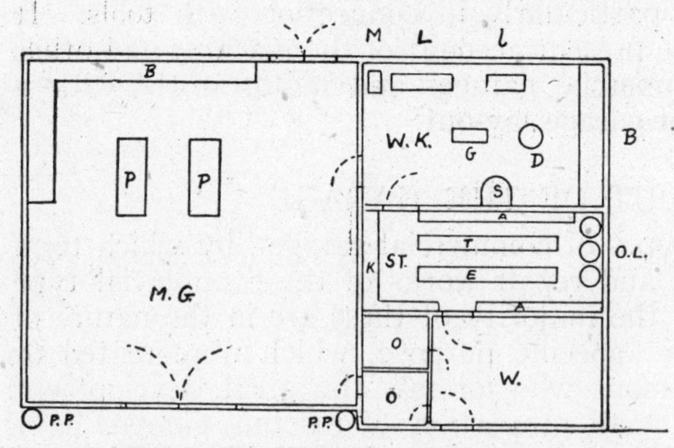

Fig. 118.—Showing Plan View of Typical Small Town Garage. A—Accessories. B—Benches. D—Drilling Machine. E—Electrical Stores. G—Grindstone. K—Tool Store. L,l—Lathes. M—Milling Machine. P—Pit. O—Office. S—Forge. W—Show-room and Window. PP—Petrol Pump. MG—Main Garage. WK—Workshop.

The workshop shown contains a large (6-in.) lathe and a small $3\frac{1}{2}$-in. or 4-in. lathe, small milling machine, sensitive drilling machine, emery wheel grinder, and a portable forge for brazing and small smith work. Other items which might usefully be included in the equipment of this small workshop would be an engine-stand, anvil, hacksaw (power), portable garage hoist, and small vulcanising plant; the usual special tools for jobs such as valve-seat facing, bush extracting, wheel drawing, bearing remetalling, tyre removal and refitting, brake relining, and other motor work would form part of the equipment.

Nature of Work Undertaken.—The type of provincial garage in question does not, as a rule, undertake the more serious repairs and overhauls, but can carry out emergency jobs, such as the making of new pins, bolts, screws, bushes, rewhite-metalling of bearings, repairing and straightening parts bent in accidents, small smith, lathe and milling machine jobs, decarbonising, tyre repairs, magneto and carburettor repairs or adjustments, battery repairs, the fitting of new parts and accessories, etc.

In many cases the spare parts needed would not be made on the premises, but would be procured from the car makers or large motor factors; this is usually the more economical procedure. Jobs such as cylinder regrinding, the repair of cracked or broken crankcases, cylinder blocks, and other motor castings, the more important radiator, lamp, wing, and body panel repairs, regrinding or remaking of crankshafts and camshafts, gear wheels, worms, and worm wheels would be dispatched to specialist firms who have highly skilled men fully competent to do this work. It is usually a mistake for a small garage to attempt to do the latter classes of work, for seldom is the experienced staff or the proper equipment available, and in many cases the job is not satisfactory when finished; moreover, it is invariably more expensive, on account of the makeshift methods which are usually employed.

Take a specific example, namely, that of repairing a cylinder block which has been cracked owing to an accident on the road or to the freezing of the water in the jackets. The smaller garage, even with an

Fig. 119.—Work which must be done by the Expert. (A) A Cylinder Block after an accident. (B) The same Block after complete Welding Repair.

oxy-acetylene welding plant and the proper composition welding rods, can seldom make a satisfactory job of this class of repair; there are so many special precautions necessary, and a special procedure for each particular job, that the garage man who only gets an occasional welding repair of this nature has no opportunity of obtaining the necessary experience. On the other hand, such work can be undertaken with every satisfaction by specialist firms, such as Messrs. Barimar, Ltd., London, for they have exceptionally skilled men and methods, and the results of fifteen to twenty years' continuous experience on this class of work behind them. We have seen a large cylinder block, which had a large piece broken away and lost from its jacket and one of the cylinder heads, completely repaired by welding, in just over fifteen minutes, by one of Messrs. Barimar's men; this work would have taken an unskilled man about a day, and then would probably not have been satisfactory.

Similarly, it is not advisable for the smaller garage to attempt special gear cutting and hardening, cylinder boring and grinding, dynamo and starting-motor repairs, etc., the specialist firms will do this work better, quicker, and usually cheaper. We shall not, in these considerations, waste time in attempting to outline the *recommended store equipment* of a small commercial garage, beyond stating that the type of store stocked is dictated by the demand. In passing, it might be added that in laying out a new store, a good plan is to keep the mechanical items (bolts, nuts, washers, pins, etc.), the electrical goods (cables, sparking plugs, terminals, batteries, etc.), the tyres and their sundries (repair outfits, valve parts, tyre levers, etc.), motor tools, oils, greases, and consumable stores (patent cleaners, dopes, waxes, polishes, mist preventers, etc.), in distinct and separate sections; a section list, with store contents, will simplify the rapid finding of any particular item required.

Fig. 120 illustrates a typical arrangement for a larger type of town garage, comprising a commodious garage for the storage of vehicles, including a number of private lock-ups, the usual clerical offices, shop, stores, machine shop, forge, repair shop, vulcanising, paint and wood-working shops.

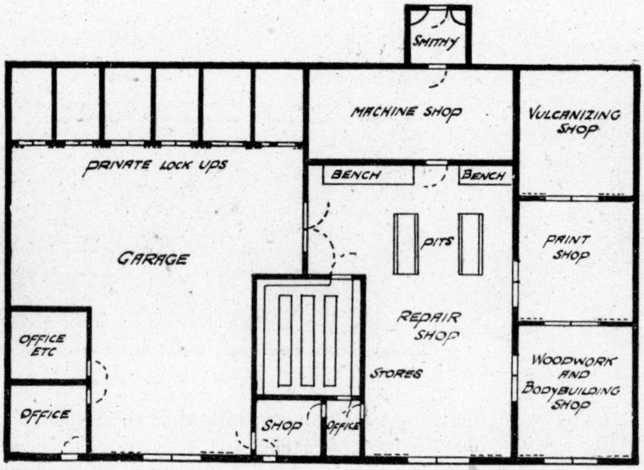

Fig. 120.—Arrangement of Larger Town Garage and Repair Shops.

The type of garage shown would accommodate from fifteen to twenty-five cars, and could repair or overhaul from five to eight cars at a time. It could completely overhaul cars, do any type of tyre repair, undertake the alterations to or repair of motor bodies (and could actually make new bodies), repaint cars, and make special mechanical parts when spares were not obtainable.

In connection with the main garage, although only one large double door is shown, it would no doubt be possible to arrange another double door on the left side wall to facilitate the quick movement of customers' cars, and also separate outside doors to each of the private lock-ups.

MACHINE EQUIPMENT OF LARGER GARAGES

We have already described a number of machines, tools, lifting devices, and special apparatus suitable for garage equipment, but hitherto have confined our remarks chiefly to the equipment of the smaller garage or motor workshop; where the subject has merited it, we have extended the accounts given for the sake of completeness. A number of the items described is applicable, therefore, to the larger type of garage, and beyond enumerating them in the following account, we shall not enter into any further descriptions.

The actual equipment recommended for any particular garage is largely dependent upon existing conditions and circumstances, and no hard-and-fast rule can be laid down to cover all garages. In the first place, the equipment will be governed largely by the *size* and situation of the garage. Thus a small, unpretentious concern, catering only for minor repairs, overhauls, and the sales of motor goods, will not require much in the way of machines, tools, and fittings.

On the other hand, the large city garage, having a big clientele, will need to be sufficiently well equipped to tackle practically any job from simple chassis and engine repairs and overhauls to complicated breakdowns and renewal of parts.

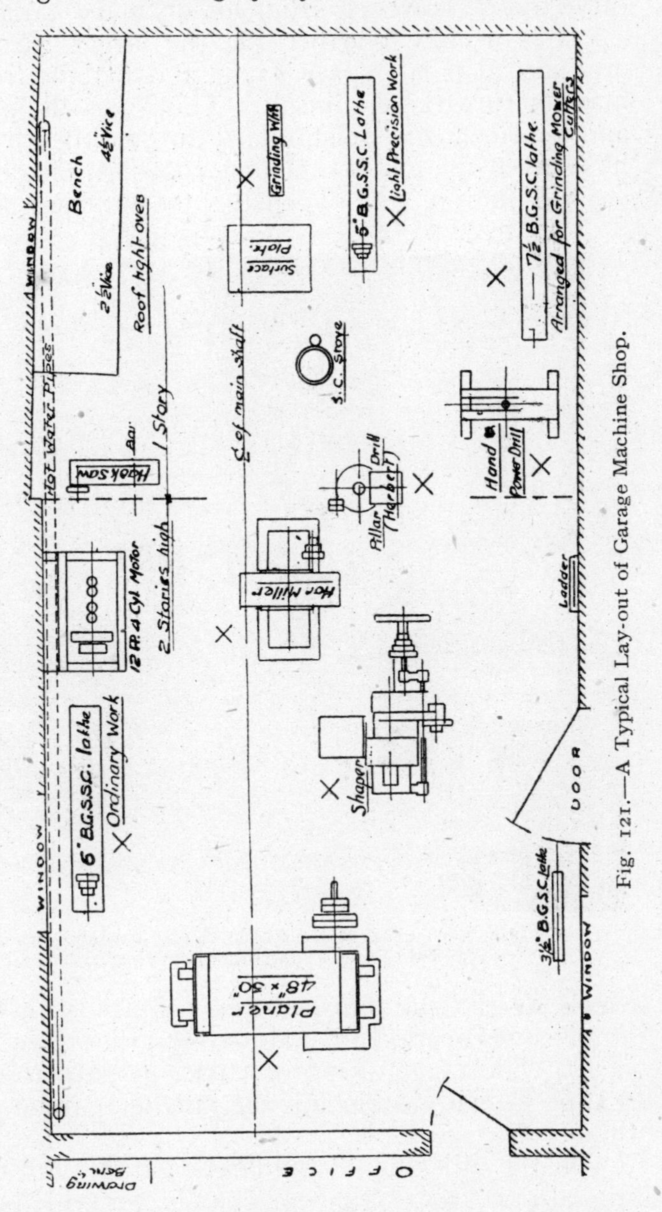

Fig. 121.—A Typical Lay-out of Garage Machine Shop.

Actually one does not find the machine-tool equipment of the ordinary engineering works in many garages, but only a selection of the more useful ones. The principal reason for this is that most large garages act as *Service Depots*, and are concerned more with maintenance and light overhauls than with constructional jobs, such as the making of a new chassis, the refitting of special engines, manufacture of gears, pistons, and similar parts.

There are so many specialist firms nowadays in the motor engineering industry, that it hardly pays the ordinary large garage to equip itself for all kinds of special motor constructional work; where firms have taken up as a sideline the manufacture of some special item, motor tool part, or gadget, they have invariably started a separate works apart from their garage workshop. Many a garage engineer, in the course of his experience in the repair of cars, has evolved an idea or improvement in connection with some useful tool, accessory, instrument, or similar automobile item, and has found it profitable to manufacture this, quite apart, however, from his ordinary garage work.

It is usually cheaper for the larger garage proprietor to purchase any special parts, spare parts, and fittings from specialist firms than to manufacture these himself. Thus he will invariably order spare parts and replacements of standard automobiles from the manufacturers. If he is given the job of replacing cast-iron pistons by aluminium-alloy ones, he will find it less expensive to purchase these direct—either in the

Fig. 122.—A Typical Motor Repair Shop, showing overhead runway for block and tackle used for lifting engines and other heavy parts from cars (Messrs. Laystall, Ltd.).

rough, oversize, or finished dimensions—than to cast and machine them in his own workshop. Moreover, the large motor factors now stock such a wide range of motor parts, in both the rough and finished state, that it is inadvisable for the smaller garage man to attempt to make these.

On the other hand, the larger garages are often called upon to make special parts for engines or chassis, for which no spares can be obtained—usually out-of-date designs—or for alterations to the special whims or requirements of the owner. Occasionally also, in the case of a standard or new make of car, some faulty design will manifest itself, and the owner will prefer to have a stronger part made at the garage than risk a replacement by a spare part. Some garages also undertake to build up special cars—such as sports models—or to modernise, by conversions, existing makes of car. These are but a few of the varied classes of work which the larger garage may have to undertake; in this respect, one must not overlook the fact that breakdowns and accidents to motor vehicles have to be attended to, and usually rectified, in the garage workshop. In considering the essential equipment for this type of garage, the prospective proprietor must make up his mind as to the range of work he is prepared to undertake, and it is here largely a question of previous experience.

As we have stated, it is not possible to lay down any definite rules but rather to indicate, as a result of personal experience, the average equipment of a well-appointed motor garage able to tackle practically any job, be it a serious breakdown—the result of a road accident—a conversion, body alteration, or the rebuilding of a complete chassis.

The following is the recommended bare equipment of such a garage with its workshop:

(A) MACHINES AND TOOLS

Lathes, 4 and 6 in. (or larger), with screw-cutting, milling, drilling, grinding, and similar attachments and accessories.

Small milling machine with horizontal and vertical table movements. The verticle spindle type is preferable.

Radial drilling machine. Capacity up to 1-in. drills.

Sensitive drilling machine. Power-driven. Capacity up to ½-in. drill.

Bench or hand drilling machine.

Bench or power shaping machine for keyways, gears, etc.

Power hacksaw.

Grinding machine. For cylinder regrinds, pistons, pins, crankshafts, etc.

Grindstone and/or emery wheel.

Sheet metal working tools. Shears, punch, beader, bending rolls.

Small riveting machine for brake and clutch repairs, etc.

Electric drilling machine (portable), with wire brush attachment for decarbonising, valve regrinding attachment, buff, etc.

Presses, for bush removals, force fits.

Special tools and fixtures made for repetition work, e.g. valve lifters, wheel drawers, remetalling jigs, crank-pin truers, gauges, etc.

(B) MISCELLANEOUS EQUIPMENT

Garage breakdown equipment, such as hoists, ambulances, towing tackle, steering locks.

Garage jacks.

Air compressor, preferably of the trolley or portable type.

Forge or brazing hearth.

Work bench with vices and other bench fittings.

Engine stands.
Car elevators or ramps.
Cleaning equipment for dirty motor parts.
Battery charging and repair plant.
Electrical repair equipment and instruments.
Portable garage crane.
Hardening furnace, electric or gas.
Tyre-vulcanising plant and accessories.
Tyre removal and replacement tools and machines.
Welding plant ; oxy-acetylene or electric for welding and decarbonising.
Electric motors for machine driving and similar purposes.

(C) COACHWORK AND PAINTING EQUIPMENT

Woodworking tools.
Saw-bench. Circular saw or bandsaw.
Planer.
Sandpapering machine.
Car paint-spraying plant.

LATHES

We have described the smaller lathes suitable for the ordinary small garage workshop, and with which the greater number of motor repair jobs can be undertaken. It is now proposed to describe a typical example of a larger lathe intended for heavier work, and also for use with special accessories to enable the smaller motor engineering works to tackle many milling, boring, grinding, wheel-cutting, and similar jobs, which otherwise would require special machines. Although these lathe attachments certainly perform the functions claimed for them by their manufacturers, their use necessitates a certain amount of delay in rigging up the lathe, and in some cases of compromise. Moreover, the lathe is temporarily out of use for its normal functions of turning and screw-cutting, so that where there is a pressure of work, it is better not to attempt to do everything on the lathe, but to provide other machines designed for the special purposes.

Perhaps the best all-round lathe for garage use is the 6- or 8-in. centre type, with full equipment. A typical stand type of lathe, showing the principal components with the names by which they are commonly known, is indicated in Fig. 123. In selecting such a lathe, attention should be given to the following requirements, namely :

(1) It should be of very rigid construction in all its parts and movements.

(2) There should be accuracy of construction in all important parts, e.g. bearings, centres, slide-rests, table, and screws. The alignment should be accurate in the case of the centres and table, and permanent.

(3) Good substantial bearings for the head-stock, with long life and provision for adjustment, when wear occurs.

(4) Large wearing surfaces in the case of the table, slide-rests, tail-stock, lead, and slide-screw nuts.

(5) Provision for taking up the wear in the sliding parts, such as the saddle, slide-rests, and tail-stock.

(6) Protection of wearing surfaces, by suitable covers, from the abrasive or wearing action of dirt, dust, and metal chippings.

(7) A good gap, permitting the swinging of the largest work. In the

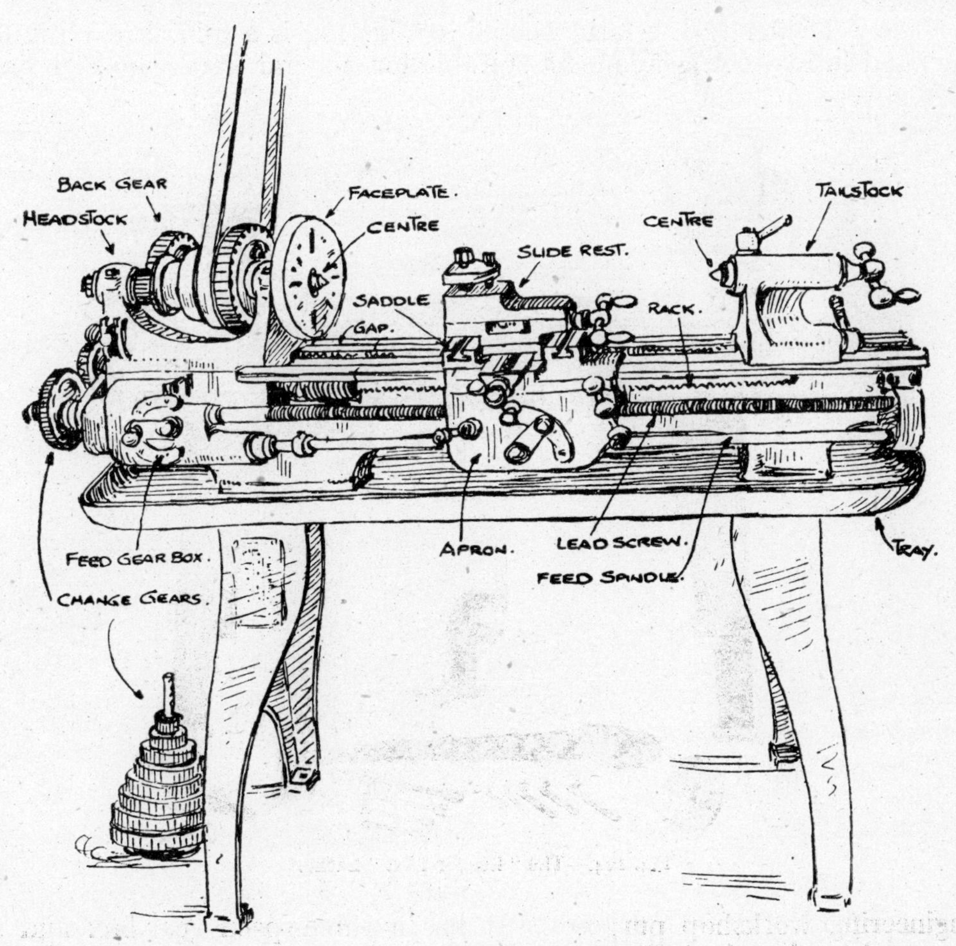

Fig. 123.—A Typical Stand-type Lathe.

case of a 6-in. lathe work of a radius of not less than 18 in. and depth of 9 in. should be provided for.

(8) The lathe bed should be sufficiently long to permit most automobile shafts and parts to be dealt with. Thus in the case of a 6-in. lathe the maximum possible distance between the centres should not be less than about 3 ft. 6 in.

(9) The lead-screw and gear wheels provided should enable any standard pitch of right- or left-handed thread to be cut.

(10) The cone pulleys should enable a fairly wide range of mandrel speeds to be obtained, namely, from about 12 to 320 r.p.m.

(11) The saddle should be so designed that when turning large-diameter jobs between the centres, it does not foul the work.

(12) The standard accessories should certainly include the following, namely, set of gear wheels, large face plate (slotted), self-centring chuck, steady-rest, set of centres, countershaft, driving plate, and set of lathe spanners.

The "Leader IXL" lathe shown in Fig. 124 is a 6-in. centre totally enclosed head-stock gear model suitable for general garage and motor-

Fig. 124.—The "Leader IXL" Lathe.

engineering workshop purposes. It has a three-speed gear box and is arranged to give eight different spindle speeds. Screw cutting and heavy and light machining are readily possible with this machine. With the belt pulley running at 500 r.p.m., the spindle speeds can be altered in eight steps from 22 to 548 r.p.m.

The lathe has a 40-in. centre turning length and will swing articles up to $16\frac{3}{4}$ in. diameter by 3 in. in width; the gap shown is provided for this purpose. The hollow spindle has a central hole of $1\frac{9}{32}$ in. diameter. The lathe bed is 60 in. long by 8 in. wide.

The lathe requires about $\frac{3}{4}$ h.p. to operate it under full-capacity conditions.

Fig. 125 illustrates the 7-in. Drummond lathe,[1] which was specially designed during the Great War for military and naval workshop requirements, necessitating a moderate-sized lathe capable of standing up to the very heavy work and severe strain of war conditions. This lathe is very well made, rigid and accurate; in the latter respect it may be added that the limit of accuracy throughout is less than ·001 in.

To obtain rigidity in the tool, stiff sections are used in preference to mere mass, and closed box sections are employed in every possible in-

Fig. 125.—The Drummond 7-in. Lathe.

stance. Owing to its rigidity in operation, good, heavy cuts can be taken on all classes of work.

The bed is of heavy box section, of the front square and V-section type, giving a long, narrow guide for the saddle. The design gives a 90° V-saddle guide at the front of the bed, the centre line of which coincides approximately with the average line of cutting thrust. The vertical downward component of this thrust is taken on the top surface of the front way; the horizontal forward component of the cutting thrust is met squarely by the back face of this way. The rear way is separated from the saddle by clearance, and the saddle is held firmly to the top face of this way by the stiff gib shown. The strip has thus no part in the linear guidance of the saddle, which has not only

[1] This pattern is also supplied in the 5- and 6-in. sizes.

a long, narrow guide as in the raised V-type of bed, but a much better provision for resisting side thrusts, and very much larger weight-taking and wear-resisting surfaces. The lead-screw is brought close in under the ways of the bed.

The bed is of heavy box section, the apron being also of hollow box form; the apron gears run between two bearings, and are bronze bushed in parts.

The following are the principal dimensions of the lathe described: Length of bed, 6 ft.; length between centres, 3 ft. 9 in.; centre height, $7\frac{1}{8}$ in.; swing over saddle, $9\frac{1}{2}$ in.; swing in gap, 21 in.; length admitted in gap, $8\frac{1}{2}$ in.; face-plate diameter, 18 in.; traverse of saddle top slide, 4 in.; traverse of saddle cross-slide, $9\frac{3}{4}$ in.; spindle-hole diameter, $1\frac{1}{8}$ in.; pitch of lead-screw, $\frac{1}{4}$ in.; range of speeds: 8·5 to 320 r.p.m., for countershaft speed, 160 r.p.m.; back-gear ratio, 9·45 to 1; power required to drive lathe, $1\frac{1}{2}$ h.p.; overall dimensions: length 7 ft. 5 in., width 2 ft. 6 in.; weight, 13 cwt.

The standard equipment includes a driver plate, face plate, travelling and fixed steadies, one hard and one soft centre, spanners for all nuts, table of change-speed wheels for both English and metric threads, set of machine-cut change wheels for cutting all standard threads from 2 to 60 per inch, including gas, B.S.F., and metric threads from 0·5 mm. to 10 mm. A suds tray and pump can be supplied if required. Provision is made for either treadle, countershaft, or electric motor drive as required.

Special attachments include the following: Indexing, milling, and gear-cutting attachment for spur, bevel, and worm-gear cutting, cutting splines, flutes and squares, covering a large range of plain milling. Comprises dividing arrangements, with the necessary plates, to index the lathe spindle; universal milling head fitted to topslide; and complete overhead countershaft gear, carried on standards, with jockey pulleys for driving milling spindle.

Heavy slotted boring table to fit on lathe saddle; used in conjunction with a boring bar; this attachment converts the lathe into a boring machine for cylinder boring and similar work.

Fig. 126.—Slotted Boring-table Attachment for Lathe.

Grinding attachment for all external and internal grinding work.

Saw table for use by coachbuilders, etc. This converts the lathe temporarily into a circular-saw bench.

Connecting-rod boring fixture for use in garages, etc. This fits on the lathe topslide, and aligns the connecting rods for boring the big-ends. This enables much larger rods to be machined than could be swung on the face plate.

The slotted boring table shown in Fig. 126 is a useful accessory. It is heavy, well machined, and provided with six slots for holding-down bolts. It can be used for heavy boring jobs.

CONNECTING-ROD BORING

The Drummond lathe described has a special fixture for boring connecting rods.

This attachment is very useful in the garage where the rebushing and boring of connecting-rod big-ends are carried out. The gudgeon pin is used to align the rod in the fixture; it rests in the V-blocks at the rear, and is held down by clamp plates. The big-end rests on a screw jack, provided with a locking screw, and this enables the rod to be brought to correct centre height. A clamp plate straps the rod down in such a manner as to prevent springing. The V-block for the gudgeon pin is adjustable along the body of the fixture to accommodate rods of varying length, and is held by two bolts, a spigot in the centre slot preserving the alignment.

The fixture shown above on the boring table of the Drummond 3½-in. lathe (Fig. 107) is on exactly similar lines as the 5-in., 6-in., or 7-in. lathes; it has a register turned on its underneath face to suit the cross slide of these lathes.

The ordinary method of bolting the rod down on the boring table of the lathe, while effective, is very inconvenient, for it means that every rod has to be lined up before machining. The fixture gives a correct setting every time, and a whole set of rods up to 14-in. centres may be rebored in the time previously taken to do two.

The Herbert capstan lathe shown in Fig. 127 should be a valuable addition to the machine shop of a modern motor garage or small works. It is electric-motor driven and has a number of useful features for the rapid production of turned parts. The height of the centres is 5½ in. and the swing over across the slide is 5¼ in. It is driven by a 3-h.p. motor of 1,400 r.p.m. speed. Provision is made for five alternative ranges of fast speeds; the actual speeds vary with the spindle speeds.

The driving mechanism is carried by the head-stock cabinet. The high-speed flanged motor is bolted to the right-hand side where it is protected under the tray.

The driving box is bolted to the left-hand side of the cabinet. It is driven by a shaft which forms an extension of the rotor shaft of the motor, and contains gearing enabling changes in spindle speeds to be made. The last shaft of the driving box extends into the cabinet and carries a three-step cone pulley which drives a similar pulley on the main spindle by a belt.

The cone pulleys are made of steel and are very light, so that there is a minimum of inertia in the spindle and its driving mechanism.

The arrangement of the driving box, which is patented, enables a very wide range of spindle speeds to be obtained.

The operator can instantly obtain either of two speeds by moving the ball-ended lever at the head-stock end of the bed. The two speeds thus obtainable are determined by:

1. Position of driving belt on three-step cone.
2. The pick-off gears used. Two pairs of pick-off gears are always in use, one pair determining the fast speed and the other pair the slow speed.

Fig. 127.—The Herbert No. 2S Capstan Lathe.

Three different pairs of pick-off gears are supplied with the machine, and any pair can be used for determining either the fast or the slow speed. A table of fast and slow speed ranges is supplied.

Among the other interesting features of this capstan lathe are the roller-bearings head-stock; the starting switch for the motor, with "Forward," "Off," and "Reverse" positions; the automatic bar feed; the belt-tensioning device; the capstan slide's automatic feed and six selecting stops; the pump feed for the coolant and the automatic lubrication of the bearings.

The lathe in question is known as the Herbert No. 2S type.

DRILLING MACHINES

Every garage should have a drilling machine, either hand, bench, or power type. We have already described examples of hand and bench type, so that our present remarks will be confined to power drills suitable for garage purposes.

Of the various power drills available the following can be recommended for motor workshop use, namely, (1) The sensitive drilling machine taking drills up to about $\frac{3}{8}$ in. (2) The portable electric drill. (3) The ordinary engineer's drilling machine taking drills up to about $\frac{7}{8}$ in. or 1 in., with table, change-speed pulleys, automatic and hand feeds. (4) The radial drill. An example of a typical sensitive drilling machine is shown in Fig. 93; this particular type is suitable for fixing on a bench or shelf. Some of the larger sensitive drilling machines stand on pillars, or columns of round section provided with a large base. The table slides up and down this column and can be clamped in any position to suit the job. Most machines of this type will drill holes up to $\frac{3}{8}$ in. or $\frac{1}{2}$ in., and are very suitable for small-diameter holes. The drill is fed downwards by means of a hand lever working a pinion engaging with a rack cut in the spindle. Ball-bearings are usually fitted. The belt (Fig. 93) passes over a pair of idle pulleys from the lower horizontal shaft to the spindle. Fast and loose pulleys are supplied.

Fig. 128.—The Herbert High-speed Drilling Machine.

A particularly useful type of high-speed drilling machine is illustrated in Fig. 128. This machine is operated from an electric motor and is suitable for drills up to $\frac{1}{4}$-in. diameter for steel and to $\frac{3}{8}$ in. for softer metals such as aluminium and brass.

The maximum speed is 12,000 r.p.m., the three standard speeds being 6,000, 9,000, and 12,000 r.p.m.

The feed is by hand or foot operation, the stroke of the drill spindle being $2\frac{1}{2}$ in.

The drive to the spindle is from a high-speed electric motor carried on an adjustable bracket projecting from the spindle head into the column. The motor is started and stopped by a neat switch.

The rotor shaft of the motor has a large three-step cone pulley keyed to it, which drives a small three-step cone concentric with the spindle. This cone is mounted on ball-bearings in the spindle head in such a way that the belt pull is taken entirely on the bearings and does not affect the spindle, which slides through the cone and is driven by a multiple spline fitting. The belt can be moved on to the different steps of the cones after taking off covers on the column and spindle head. If preferred, a smaller cone pulley for the motor shaft can be supplied alternatively, giving a lower speed range.

For the fine work which this machine is intended to do it is necessary that the illumination should be particularly good. This is ensured by the use of an electric lamp, which is carried in a holder in the spindle head behind the spindle. The lamp is fixed at such an angle that it throws its light directly on to the drill and the work.

Fig 129.—The Herbert Type CB Drilling Machine.

The motor fitted is $\frac{1}{3}$ h.p. and the total weight of the machine is 260 lb. It is made by Alfred Herbert, Ltd., of Coventry.

Fig. 129 shows another design of drilling machine suitable for the motor engineering workshop, and known as the Herbert ball-bearing drilling machine, Type CB. It is driven from a line shaft, and has self-contained countershaft with fast and loose pulley and a constant belt speed from the countershaft to the spindle-driving pulley.

The pulley is mounted on the top of the first gear shaft, and is driven from a pulley on the countershaft, the belt passing over two idlers carried on a bracket bolted to the back of the driving box. The idlers can be adjusted by a screw and small hand wheel and clamped, for giving proper tension to the belt. This is the only adjustment that has to be made in connection with the drive. As there are no cone pulleys the belt is never touched by hand.

An endless belt is furnished with each spindle.

The machine can be finished in the multiple-spindle pattern if desired.

The drilling capacity of the machine with plain spindle is $\frac{3}{4}$-in. diameter holes in mild steel and in the geared-spindle model 1-in. diameter. The machine with geared spindle taps up to $\frac{5}{8}$ in. Whitworth thread in mild steel and $\frac{7}{8}$ in. in cast-iron. The spindle speeds available in the plain-spindle model are 448, 800, 1,362, and 2,415 r.p.m.; in the geared-spindle model they are 104, 185, 318, and 562 r.p.m.

Three ranges of feeds from 90 to 200 cuts per inch are possible in the plain-spindle model. The speed of the pulleys is 800 r.p.m.

THE PORTABLE ELECTRIC DRILL

The portable electric drill is a very handy machine, since, not only can it be taken to the job, but it can be used for a number of other purposes where a portable power unit is required. For example, it can be used equally well for valve refacing and reseating, carbon removal (by means of rotating wire brushes), brake relining, motor tyre and electric battery repairs. It can also be employed for driving a saw, cleaning tyre rims, cleaning rust off brake bands, sharpening tools, driving polishing buffs and mops, and burnishers.

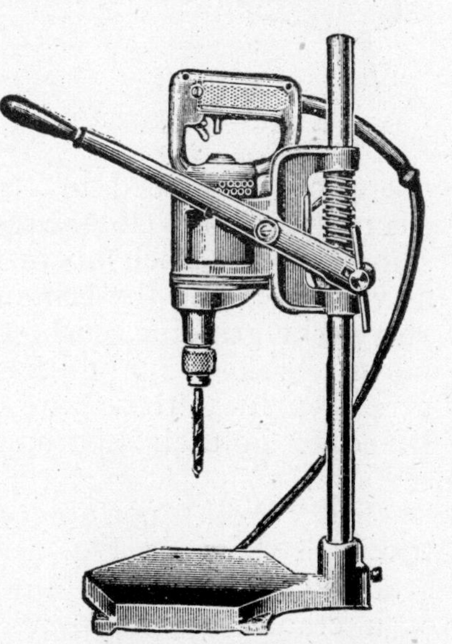

Fig. 130.—Showing Electric Drill mounted on Bench Stand.

Fig. 130 illustrates the U.L.A. electric tool,[1] which is supplied with attachments for drilling, grinding, sawing, scratching, and buffing.

There is an electric motor, supplied with current from the ordinary mains through the medium of a plug and leads. The motor spindle has the drill chuck attached in the ordinary way, and a trigger control switch for starting and stopping purposes.

Our illustration shows the electric tool driving a polishing or scratch brush the saw-bench attachment being shown above. With this tool the following operations can be carried out: (1) Drilling holes up to $\frac{1}{4}$-in. diameter in steel. (2) Grinding and sharpening tools, knives, and cutters. (3) Removing dirt and rust with rotary wire brush. (4) Polishing and buffing with polishing mop. (5) Decarbonising motor cylinders, pistons, and valves. (6) Sawing wood, ebonite panels, fibre, parquet floorings, and similar materials.

[1] Messrs. Benn Patents, Ltd., 96 Victoria Street, London, S.W.1.

Figs. 130 and 131 illustrate the Black & Decker electric drill, which is much used in the motor workshop for a variety of purposes. It is well designed and balanced, being fitted with a convenient handle of pistol-grip form and a trigger-type switch; it is relatively light in weight. A pair of flexible leads in a single casing and plug are supplied. As shown, it is fitted with a drill chuck of the self-centring type, to take drills up to $\frac{1}{4}$ in. The drill runs at 2,000 r.p.m. without load.

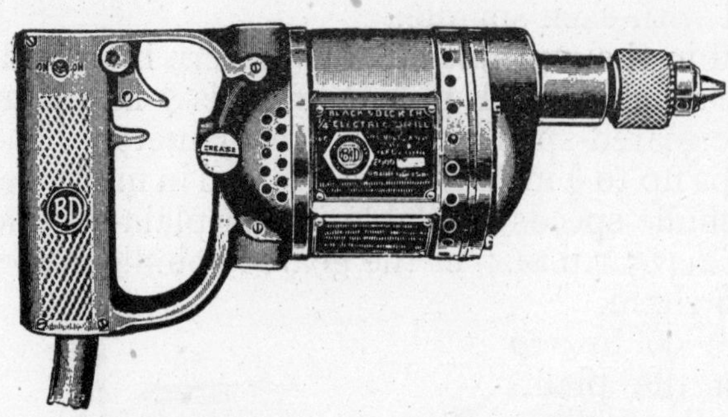

Fig. 131.—The Black & Decker Electric Drill.

It can be fitted with special holders or spindles to enable it to do most of the operations described in the earlier part of this chapter, but special electric machines closely resembling the drill are now marketed by the same firm for such operations as valve refacing (by grinding), valve-seat grinding, carbon removal, brake-lining jobs, and tyre repairs; these are referred to in their appropriate sections.

The "Wolf" portable electric drill, shown in Fig. 132, is attached to its stand by means of a cradle or recess, and a chain which can be tensioned quickly. The drill and its cradle can be moved up and down in a vertical direction by means of the lever shown. The base of the machine enables a vice angle plate or jig to be attached for holding or locating the parts that are to be drilled. The drill can also be adjusted in a radial direction, about the axis of the column.

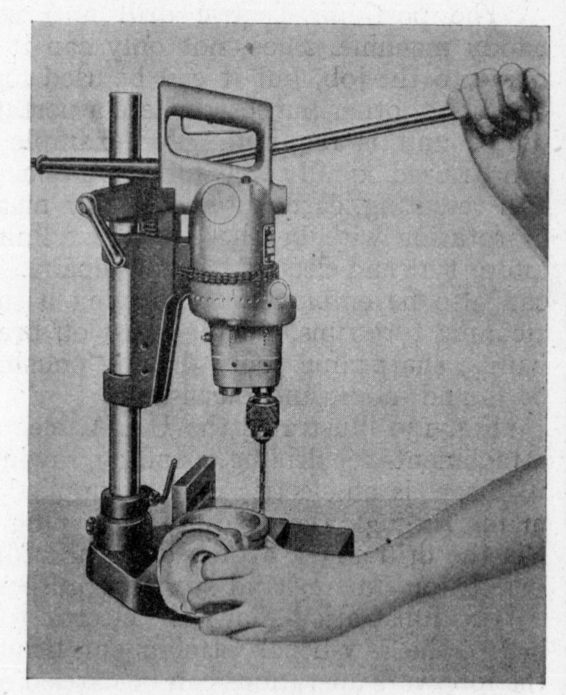
Fig. 132.—The "Wolf" Electric Drill, attached to its Drilling Stand.

A particularly useful small drilling machine, known as the Desoutter drill gun, is shown in Figs. 133 and 134. This operates from an electric supply; has alloy-steel helical gears running on ball-bearings; spare brushes accommodated in the machine; former-wound armature; taped coils; vacuum impregnated insulation, and ball-bearings throughout. It is fitted with a $\frac{1}{4}$-in. chuck and is designed for one-hand operation. The machine is made in several models, the smallest (Type A), for non-ferrous metals, takes drills up

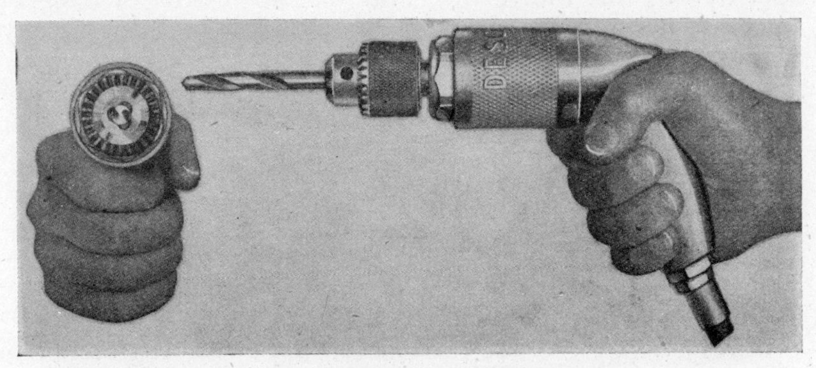

Fig. 133.—The Desoutter $\frac{3}{16}$-in. Drill Gun.

to $\frac{3}{16}$ in., runs at 5,000 r.p.m., consumes 60 watts when running light and 180 watts when under load, and weighs only $2\frac{1}{2}$ lb. A readily accessible thumb-operated switch is provided on the drill casing, whilst the cable is led to the base of the handle-grip portion. The machine

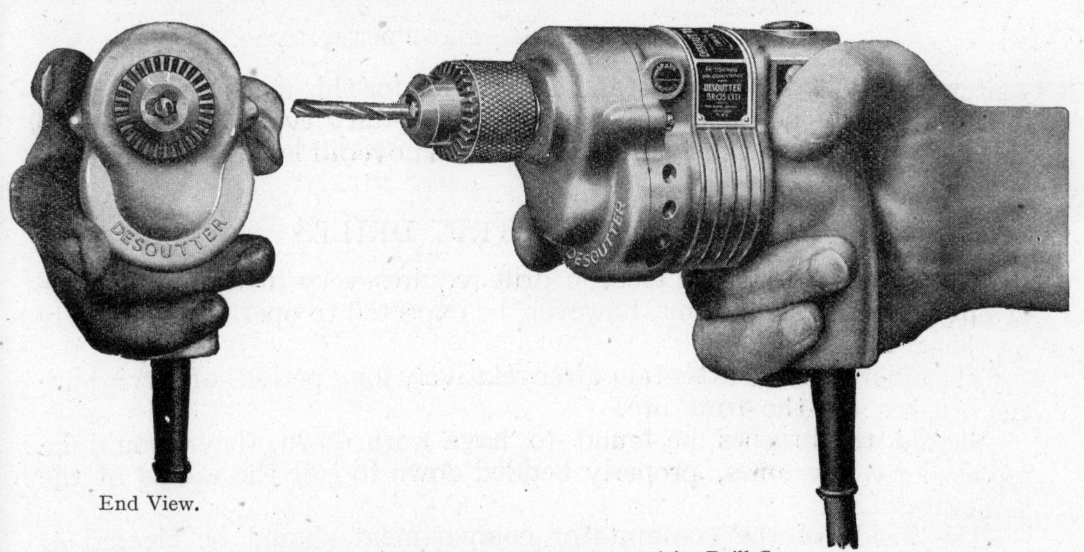

End View.

Fig. 134.—The Desoutter Geared-type $\frac{1}{4}$-in. Drill Gun.

is well constructed, and as the ball-bearings are grease-packed, very little maintenance attention is necessary.

As a contrast to the Desoutter drill previously described, we have at the other end of the portable electric drilling-machine range the Rotax $1\frac{1}{4}$-in. machine shown in Fig. 135. This machine is fitted with a universal electric motor operating equally well on either A.C. or D.C. It has a capacity for drilling holes up to $1\frac{1}{4}$ in. in steel, and a reaming capacity in steel up to $\frac{7}{8}$ in. It runs at 290 r.p.m. (no load speed) and lower speeds under load. The machine has a self-contained feed screw with a 4-in. travel, operated by the four-armed star wheel shown. A trigger-pattern

Fig. 135.—The Rotax $1\frac{1}{4}$-in. Heavy Electric Drilling Machine.

switch is provided. A drill stand is available for this machine to convert it into a handy bench machine of the heavy-duty type. The machine shown in Fig. 135 weighs 35 lb. and it has an overall length of 13 in.

CARE OF ELECTRIC DRILLS

The modern design of electric drill requires very little maintenance attention, but it should not, however, be expected to operate indefinitely on this account.

The chief items of attention after relatively long periods of service are the brushes and the armature.

Should the brushes be found to have worn down, they should be replaced by new ones, properly bedded down to suit the radius of the commutator.

The inside of the commutator compartment should be cleared of carbon dust from the brushes by blowing out with a compressed-air jet, after which the commutator segments should be cleaned. If they are not scored, any dull surface deposits may be removed with emery paper; sometimes a piece of rag moistened with petrol will be found effective.

The bearings should be repacked with ball-bearing grease after long periods of running.

The switch contacts and cable attachments should also be examined for faults after these periods.

ELECTRIC DRILL POLISHING DEVICE

The ordinary electric drill having its spindle attached to the armature shaft or a parallel shaft is not very convenient for driving a polishing brush or mop. For this reason a right-angle drive is essential, for it enables the garage man to undertake the sanding, paint removing, polishing, and buffing of motor body and coachwork. Fig. 136 shows a particularly convenient right-angle drive which is made by the firm of Van Norman.[1] By means of this compact drive it is possible to get into very

Fig. 136.—Electric Drill Right-angle Drive for Polishing Mop (Van Norman).

small spaces, not only for sanding and polishing, but for drilling, buffing, and many other operations. The milled handle above the drive affords a convenient means of holding and guiding the device in question with the one hand, the other hand being used for holding the drilling-machine handle.

HIGH-CYCLE ELECTRIC TOOLS

A new development in electric tools is to be found in the Van Dorn Black & Decker "high-cycle" tools. The particular advantages of these new tools may be summarised as follows:

(1) Power and speed maintained under load. (2) Lighter in weight and more compact than the ordinary electric tool. (3) Negligible maintenance costs due to simple construction. (4) Danger of shock to operator practically eliminated owing to low voltage required.

These high-cycle tools are so named because the motor is built to work on an electric supply of a frequency of 180 or 200 cycles.

The normal supply on which ordinary electric tools work is 50 cycles. This necessitates a universal motor containing a commutator and bushes and a rotor wound with very fine wire.

[1] Marketed by Messrs. Brown Bros., Ltd., London.

In comparison, the high-cycle motor is of squirrel-cage type without commutator or brushes and the rotor consists of copper bars welded in position—a simple construction which renders the motor practically free from breakdown. In operation the motor maintains a practically constant speed at all loads, thus giving a much greater output than that of an ordinary tool of the same capacity. In addition, the compactness and lightness of the tools enable them to be handled much more easily.

Although the motors have been standardised for an electrical supply of 110 volts, 3 phase, 180 cycles, they can also be used on a supply of 3 phase,

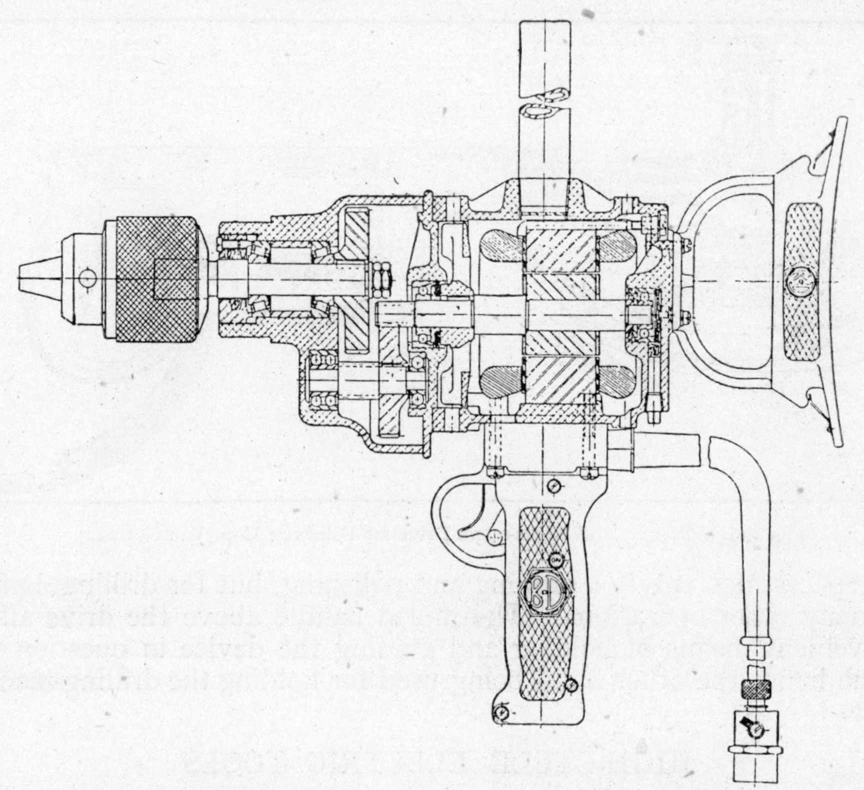

Fig. 137.—A Sectional View of High-cycle Portable Electric Machine.

200 cycles, when it is necessary to increase the voltage to 120 to maintain output.

A special plant is required to provide this high-frequency current.

Where direct current is available a high-frequency motor alternator is required. This consists of a motor to suit the electric supply, direct coupled to an alternator giving power at 110 volts, 3 phase, 180 cycles.

For alternating current similar equipment may be used, but it is cheaper to use a frequency changer unit, comprising a suitable motor direct coupled to a frequency changer.

Assuming a supply of 2 or 3 phase, 50 cycles, the output should be 120 volts, 3 phase, 200 cycles.

Fig. 138.—Illustrating the use of High-cycle Electric Tools (Alfred Herbert, Ltd., Coventry).

For general work the output of the alternator or frequency changer should be 60 per cent. of the total power required for the tools installed.

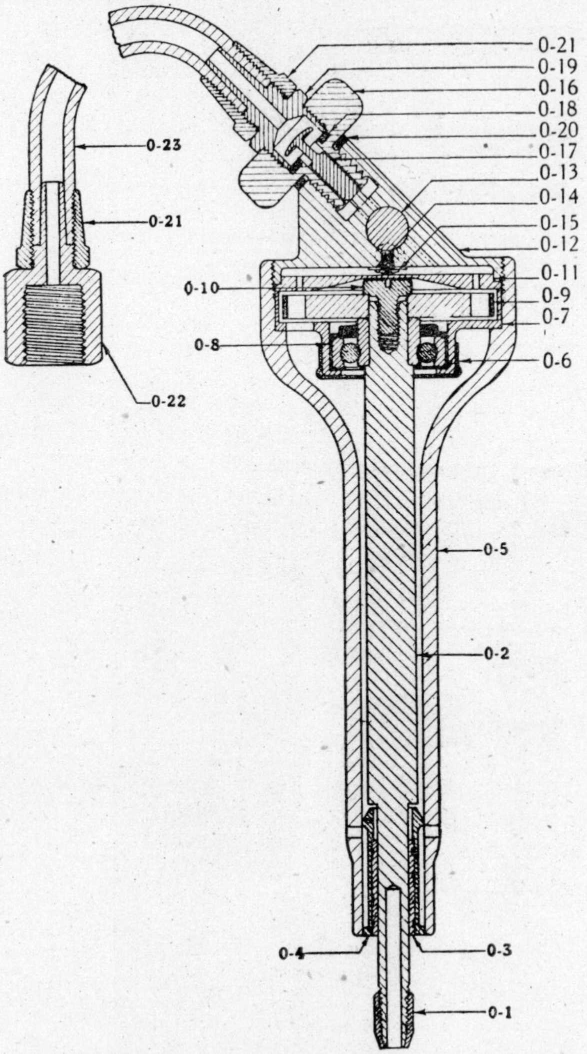

Three-core wiring is required throughout, where the tools are installed.

Anti-friction bearings are fitted throughout.

The gears are of high-grade steel, heat treated, and the motor housing, gear casing, and switch handle are of high-grade aluminium alloy.

The full range of tools includes drills, reamers, screw-drivers, tappers, nut runners, stud drivers, grinders, buffers, and sanders.

These electric tools are marketed by Messrs. Alfred Herbert, Coventry.

SMALL PNEUMATIC MACHINES

Compressed-air-driven tools for drilling, grinding, and similar purposes are employed as an alternative to portable electric tools, and also in cases where much higher rotor or spindle speeds are required. These small machines can be operated from any convenient source of compressed air, through flexible pressure tubing so that they are just as portable as the electric machines. Typical pneumatic tools of this class are those made by the firms of Desoutter (Hendon, London, N.W.9) and Broome & Wade, Ltd. (High Wycombe).

Fig. 139.—Sectional View of Desoutter Pneumatic Tool.

Key:

0-1—Spindle Nut. 0-2—Spindle. 0-3—Front Bearing Bush. 0-4—Cooling Adapter. 0-5—Case. 0-6—Grease Cap. 0-7—Ball-race Housing. 0-8—Ball-race. 0-9—Rotor. 0-10—Rotor Screw. 0-11—Jet Plate. 0-12—Control-top Housing. 0-13—Control-top Plunger. 0-14—Control-top Spring. 0-15—Control-top Screw. 0-16—Breech-thread Connector Body. 0-17—Body Valve. 0-18—Body-seating Washer. 0-19—Body Screwed Nipple. 0-20—Connector Fibre Washer. 0-21—Connector-hose Nut. 0-22—$\frac{1}{4}$ in. Gas-connector Body. 0-23—10 ft. Hose, $\frac{3}{8}$ in. O/D. 0-24—Chuck Spanners. 0-25—Head Spanner. 0-26—Dressing Stone. 0-27—Control-plunger Location Ball.

The Desoutter machine, illustrated in sectional view in Fig. 139, and in outside view in Fig. 140, is suitable for air pressures of 30 to 100 lb. per sq. in. and will run at speeds up to 70,000 r.p.m.; the air consumption is only 4 to 5 cu. ft. of free air per minute. A range of machines for drilling, grinding, driving screws and nuts, and with right-angle drives for corner drilling is available. The air grinder tool (Fig. 139) is used for grinding intricate shapes, tools, and engineering parts; by fitting different

Fig. 139A.—Examples of Grinding Heads.

shapes of grinding heads, some typical examples of which are shown in Fig. 139A, it is possible to deal with practically any shape of object or surface to be ground. The machine consists of an impulse turbine-driven spindle contained in a light aluminium-alloy casing, fitted with a push-button control head. The turbine rotor runs on ball-bearings which are effectively sealed against loss of lubricant at the rotor end, whilst at the spindle end a specially designed bush is provided, which is lubricated from an oil bath and is kept cool by radial vanes between which the exhaust air passes.

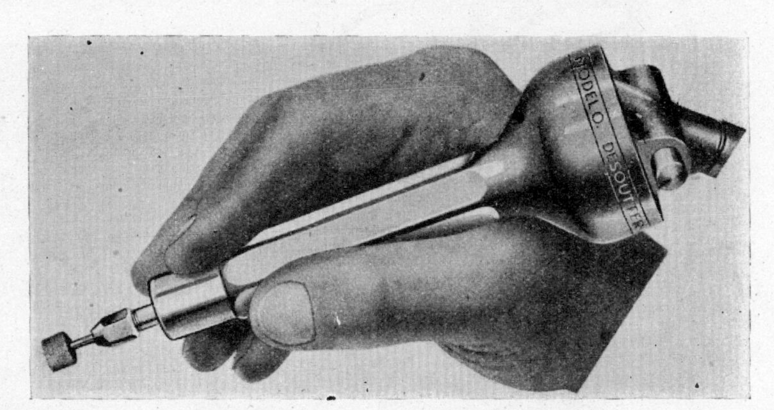

Fig. 140.—The Desoutter Pneumatic Grinder.

The hose is connected to the machine by a breech-thread connector; with this form of coupling the hose can be detached in a quarter of a turn, whilst a valve in the connector automatically seals the hose against loss of air.

The complete machine weighs $12\frac{1}{4}$ oz.

The pneumatic rotor drill shown in Fig. 140 is available in different models for taking drills of $\frac{3}{16}$ in., $\frac{1}{4}$ in., $\frac{5}{16}$ in., and $\frac{3}{8}$ in., respectively. The $\frac{3}{16}$-in. model operates at a free speed of 13,000 r.p.m., and lower speeds when actually drilling. It weighs $2\frac{1}{4}$ lb. and takes 11 cu. ft. of free air per minute. The chuck is driven at a lower speed than the air turbine rotor, through epicyclic gears. Air pressure of 80 to 100 lb. per sq. in. is required with these drills.

FLEXIBLE-SHAFT MACHINES

In cases where the work cannot conveniently be taken to the par-

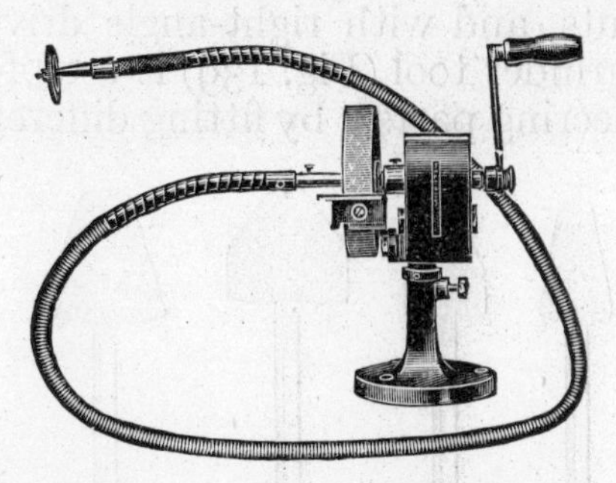

Fig. 141.—"Terry" Hand-driven Flexible-shaft Machine.

ticular machine, e.g. grinding or milling machine, owing to its size, a

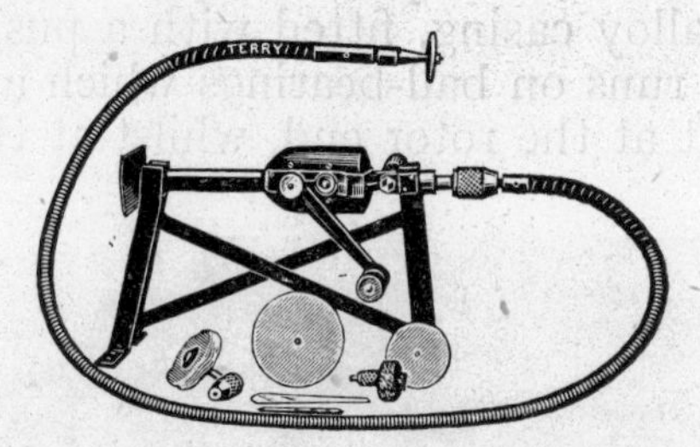

Fig. 142.—The "Terry" Hand-driven Machine on Special Stand.

portable type of machine—of which the electric and pneumatic tools

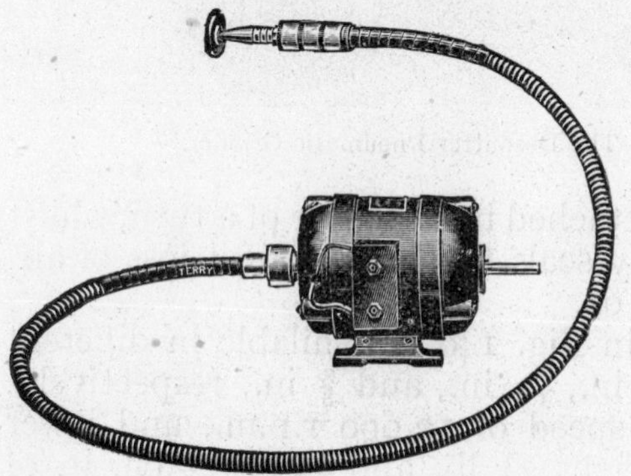

Fig. 143.—"Terry" Electric Motor-driven Machine.

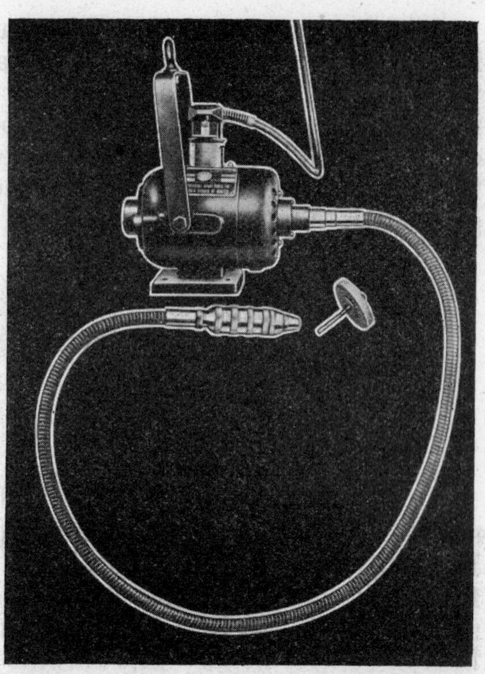

Fig. 144.—The "Wolf" Electric Flexible-shaft Machine (Single-speed Model).

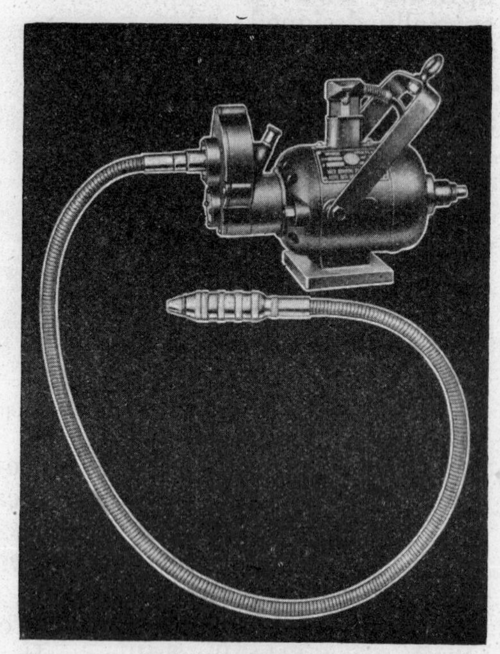

Fig. 145.—"Wolf" Two-speed Electric, Flexible-shaft Machine.

previously described are examples—is usually employed. In this connection, the weight of a portable electric or pneumatic machine, when used in the hands, is often a drawback where accurate results are essential.

In such instances, the flexible-shaft machines illustrated in Figs. 141 to 146 are an advantage, for the source of power supply can be fixed to a bench, wall, or overhead girder and the flexible shaft only held in the hand.

The simplest type of machine is that having hand-power drive; a typical machine of this class is the "Terry" model shown in Fig. 141. This has a 6-ft. flexible shaft, with drill chuck capable of taking drills up to $\frac{1}{4}$ in., filing attachments, or a grinding wheel. The power-driven machines, such as the "Terry" and "Wolf" models, employ $\frac{1}{4}$-h.p. electric motors for bench, roof, or wall mounting. Both single, and two-speed gear drives are available, and these machines can be used for filing, recessing, or shaping intricate parts, by using various shapes of rotary file cutters (Fig. 147). They are also available

Fig. 146.—Showing "Wolf" Machine in Operation.

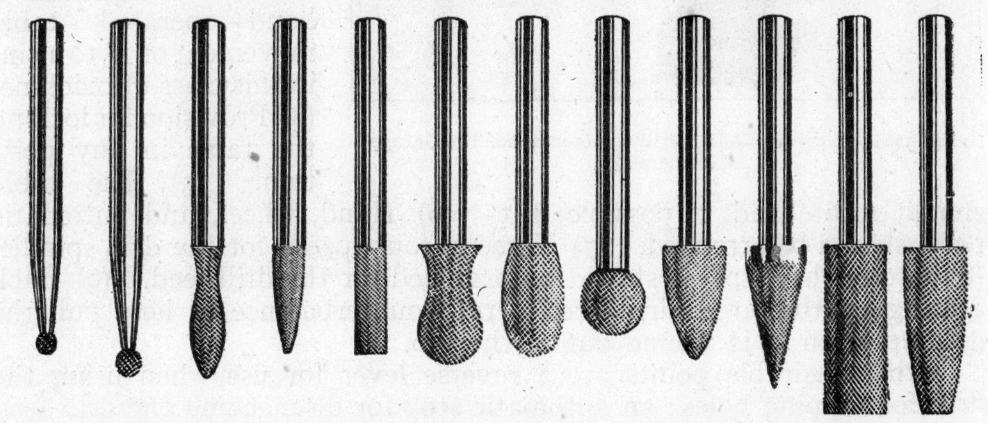

Fig. 147.—Some Typical Shapes of Rotary Files, used with Flexible-shaft Machines.

for similar shapes of grinders, for ordinary grinding wheels, and for polishing purposes. The "Wolf" two-speed model (Fig. 145) has a shaft running at 1,000 r.p.m. for filing and another for giving a speed of about 9,000 r.p.m.

LARGER DRILLING MACHINES

It is not proposed to describe the third type of drilling machine mentioned previously, since this is more appropriate for the manufacturing motor works; full particulars of a range of these machines can be obtained from such firms as Messrs. Alfred Herbert, Ltd., Coventry, and Messrs. Buck & Hickman, London.

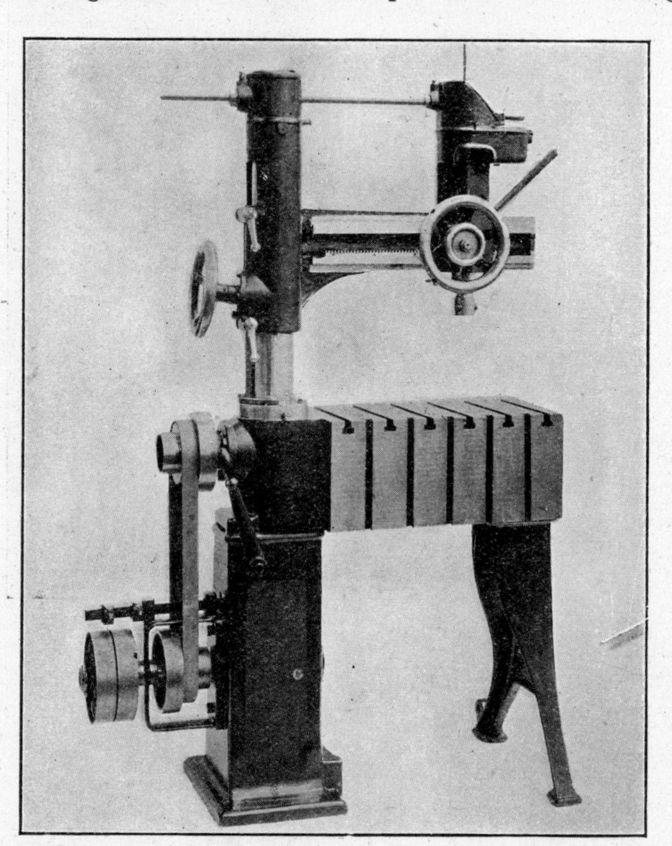

Fig. 148.—A Useful Radial Drilling Machine for the Garage Machine Shop.

In passing, it should be mentioned that in selecting a machine of this type attention should be given to the following points: (1) Rigidity and freedom from vibration when running. (2) Maximum drill size taken—this should be 1 in. to $1\frac{1}{4}$ in. (3) There should be ample clearance available between the drill spindle in its uppermost position and the table when fully lowered. It is usual to provide a hand-operated table movement of 18 to 24 in. in this class of machine. (4) Provision for locking the table in any position. (5) The table should rotate and, if possible, tilt. (6) Hand, wheel, and automatic feeds should be arranged. (7) Three or four speeds for the drill spindle. (8) Two or three speeds should be provided for the drill feed. (9) Back gearing for the larger drill sizes. (10) Counterbalance to help pull the drill up when it is wound out of the job.

Other desirable points are a reverse lever for use when using the drill for tapping holes: an automatic stop for disengaging the drill feed when a specified depth or distance has been drilled; enclosed self-oiling bearings and provision for taking up end and journal wear.

Fig. 148 illustrates the Drummond sensitive radial drill, which has a drilling capacity for holes up to 1-in. diameter in steel; if pilot holes are first drilled, much larger sizes can be undertaken. A fairly large table is provided; the top measures 23 in. × 12 in. T-slots are arranged on both horizontal and vertical surfaces. The drill spindle has a sensitive movement of $4\frac{1}{2}$ in.; the vertical adjustment of the radial arm is 5 in. The drill spindle has a total radial movement along the arm of 17 in., and the radial arm an angular range of movement of 130°.

The machine is driven by belt, a fast-and-loose pulley being fitted near the base of the stand. There is a three-speed belt drive to the upper cone pulley shaft, whence the drive is transmitted through bevel gears to a vertical shaft inside the pillar, from which it proceeds through a second set of bevels to a sliding horizontal shaft, which in turn drives the spindle through a final set of bevel gears. A large hand wheel controls the vertical feed through a rack and pinion. The approximate spindle speeds are 35, 60, 104, 180, 311, and 536 r.p.m., for a main pulley speed of 310 r.p.m. This machine is also supplied with an electric motor drive.

MILLING MACHINES

The possession of a milling machine enables a good variety of jobs involving the removal of metal to be accurately undertaken, thus dis-

Fig. 149.—The M.E. Bench Milling Machine.

pensing with filing and chipping. Milling machines are of two principal patterns, namely, the vertical and horizontal types, according to the position of the axis of the milling spindle. The latter is the more popular machine for motor garage work, since many of the vertical-machine jobs can be done in the lathe or in a good drilling machine.

Fig. 149 shows a useful small miller for motor repair purposes ; this machine can be mounted on the bench or on a suitable table.

One of the operations frequently required in a repair shop is the milling of small shafts, spindles, gears, and keyways. Owing to its initial expense, the ordinary type of manufacturing milling machine is not within the reach of a small workshop, and the M.E. hand-operated bench milling machine provides a cheap and efficient tool for the purpose. All classes of small plain milling work can be handled, and many hours saved on a job which would otherwise be taken up by hand fitting. The cutter arbor of the M.E. machine is detachable to allow for the insertion in the head of end mills, woodruff key seaters, etc. The range of the machine is 12 in. × 6 in. × 6 in. Specially designed V-blocks can be supplied for holding such parts as axle shafts, etc. A countershaft can also be supplied for use in conjunction with the machine if required.

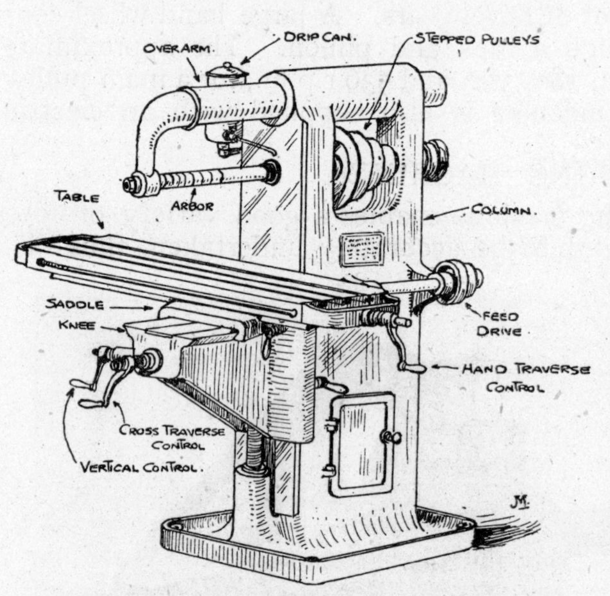

Fig. 150.—Showing Principal Components of Plain Milling Machine.

Fig. 150 shows the principal parts, and their names, in the case of a plain milling machine.

A more elaborate but inexpensive milling machine of the horizontal type is that shown in Fig. 151, and supplied by Messrs. Drummond Bros., Guildford. It has a massive vertical column and base, and is provided with a very robust overhead steady arm, so that heavy milling cuts or feeds can be used safely. The table has an up-and-down movement of 20 in., and can be fed either automatically or by hand, over 15 in. ; the table measures 30 in. × 18 in. It has a cross-adjustment of 4 in. A most useful feature is that the table can be tilted (Fig. 151), so that it can be used for inclined cuts, as when making bevel wheels from the solid.

The machine is supplied with self-acting horizontal and vertical feeds, but it is also made in a simpler design without these feeds. The longitudinal, vertical, and cross-slide screws are fitted with indexes and large dials graduated to thousandths of an inch.

Provision is made for three-cone pulley speeds, and for spindle speeds of 16 to 450 r.p.m. (in geometric progression).

The cutter spindle has a diameter of 1 in.; the greatest distance from the end of the spindle to the outboard bearing is 15 in., and the swing under the arm is 5 in.

The machine can be supplied with a simple strong dividing head and a tail-stock. Special attachments include self-centring, independent, and combination chucks, drill chucks, special centres, and face plates similar to those used on the Drummond 7-in. lathe. *A vertical milling attachment* can be supplied, consisting of a bracket fitting to the steady arm with an attachment to the body of the machine also. The drive is taken from the main spindle, through gearing, to the vertical spindle, which is carried on two adjustable bearings with thrusts. The standard equipment includes the following: One cutter arbor, complete with collars, nut, and draw bar; steel centres and Morse socket; driver plate to fit spindle nose; spanners to fit all nuts.

Fig 151.—Horizontal Milling Machine for Garage Purposes.

The design and equipment of this machine, it will be seen, enable practically any milling operation likely to occur in automobile work to be undertaken satisfactorily.

The electric-drive plain hand-milling machine illustrated in Fig. 152 has a horizontal spindle which is driven from an electric motor mounted at the back of the column, near the lower part. It has a hand-operated feed, the knee and table being moved by adjustable hand levers, pinions, and racks. The saddle is moved by a fluted hand wheel, screw, and nut. Adjustable stops are provided for table and knee movements in each direction. Automatic feed or cam feed can be supplied for the longitudinal movement of the table.

The longitudinal movement is 7 in., transverse movement, $3\frac{1}{8}$ in., and the vertical adjustment, 7 in.

The $\frac{3}{4}$-h.p. motor runs at 1,420 r.p.m. and operates a gear system with pick-off gears, giving six spindle speeds, viz. 257, 460, 610, 820, 1,080, and 1,940 r.p.m. The final drive to the spindle is by belt. The machine illustrated is the Herbert No. 1 plain hand-milling machine, made by Alfred Herbert, Ltd., Coventry.

Fig. 152.—Herbert Electric-drive Hand-operated Milling Machine.

HAND SHAPING MACHINE

The hand-worked bench shaper will be found a useful part of the garage equipment, for it saves a good deal of the manual labour and time expended in filing and chipping metal, and, moreover, gives much more accurate final results.

A particularly useful design of hand-operated shaping machine for the bench is the 6-in. stroke model shown in Fig. 153.

The stroke of the machine is 6 in., traverse $4\frac{1}{2}$ in., depth under tool $3\frac{3}{4}$ in. (maximum). The work table is in two pieces, and the vertical face of the main table is "T" slotted, so that long pieces of work, such as vertical engine columns, can be easily machined on the ends. This table is guided on the cross-feed slide by means of an accurate circular bar of large dimensions, and is actually under three-point pressure.

Adjustment for wear is rendered simple by means of the adjusting screws at either end of the slide frame. In order to ensure minimum friction and ease in working, the ram is fitted with a steel slide which gives maximum stiffness with the minimum of friction.

The small vice included has jaws $\frac{7}{8}$ in. deep by $1\frac{3}{4}$ in. and admits work up to $2\frac{1}{4}$ in., size of tools either $\frac{1}{4}$ in. or $\frac{3}{8}$ in. square.

This machine is made by the Liverpool Castings and Tool Supply Co., Ltd., Liverpool.

The model shown in Fig. 154 consists of a horizontal sliding member carrying the shaping or cutting tool, and worked by means of the hori-

Fig. 153.—A Hand Shaping Bench Machine with Angle Plate (left) and Vice (right).

zontal lever shown on the right. Provision is made for fixing the position and length of stroke to suit the job in hand. The table can be raised or lowered by means of the hand wheel and vertical screw shown below it. It has also a cross-traversing motion, operated by the hand wheel on the right, or by a self-acting feed motion. The direction of the feed is reversed in the usual manner by reversing the direction of the pawl. The table is fitted with a well-designed vice for holding the work to be placed, and the vice can be rotated about a

Fig. 154.—Another Hand Shaping Bench Machine (Drummond).

vertical axis and clamped in any position. A useful feature is the provision for swivelling the movable jaw out of its parallel position, so as to hold taper work. The vice can be removed from the table, leaving the latter clear for clamping work ; strong T-slots are provided for this purpose.

The friction block is fitted to the lead-screw in such a manner as to provide just sufficient hold on the latter to hold it from rotating back when the feed pawl is lifting.

The ram is operated by the powerful hand lever shown, this having a slot to allow the driving pin to slide in it. The ram carries the tool slide on a circular graduated base, with locking bolts for angular settings. On this is mounted the strong clapper-box, which can be swung over for side-cutting in the usual manner. The tool is held by means of two set-screws, $\frac{3}{8}$-in. square-section tool steel being used.

The type of miller described is particularly useful for *cutting keyways in long shafts*, cutting *slots*—either square or dovetailed—for planing the "split" faces of bearing brasses, and, in general, for all kinds of garage and model-engineering work.

BENCH GRINDING MACHINES

Owing to the fact that many small parts of a motor car are subjected to excessive friction, it is usual, to obviate wear, for a special steel to be used and the parts made glass-hard by some hardening process. To deal with hardened work of this description, such as gear shafts, gudgeon pins, spindles, etc., the only method possible is by grinding with abrasive wheels.

A simple belt-driven double-wheel grinder, having a twist-drill grinding attachment, is shown in Fig. 155.

For the convenient grinding of small automobile parts, tools, etc., the type of machine illustrated in Fig. 156 is particularly suitable. It is of the bench-mounting pattern and has a central electric-motor drive for the grinding wheels, which are mounted on the armature-shaft extensions. Adjustable tool rests are provided so that the operator can work close up to the rims or sides of the grinding wheels.

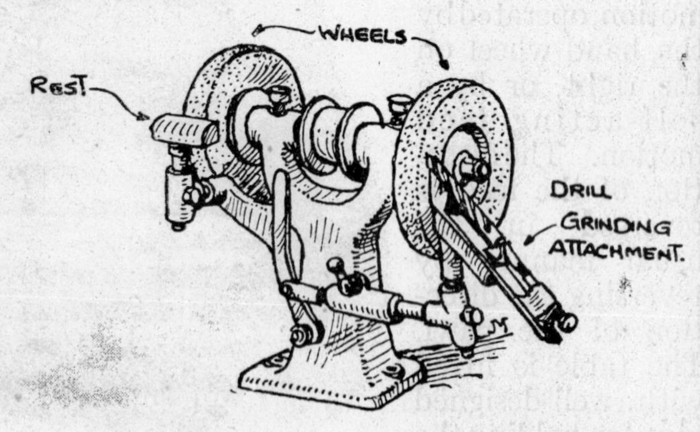

Fig. 155.—Plain Belt-driven Double-wheel Grinder.

For buffing or polishing purposes, the wheels can be removed and replaced by the extension pieces shown on the right. These screw on to the wheel-spindle threads and have the usual stepped conical ends for mounting the felt or calico buffs on.

Fig. 156.—Electric Motor-driven Double-wheel Grinder with Polishing-wheel Spindle Attachments.

The M.E. bench grinding machine (Fig. 157) fulfils a need of small repair shops in handling parallel and taper cylindrical work, such as that met with in motor-car repairing, and obviates the laying aside of considerable capital in the installation of a production grinding machine, its cost being only one-tenth of the standard type. No overhead gearing is required, as all countershafts are contained in the machine.

The working surface of the table is 24 in. $\times 5\frac{1}{2}$ in.; it has a travel of about 12 in. The maximum diameter of work which can be ground

Fig. 157.—The M.E. Bench Grinding Machine.

is 5 in. The head has a cross-travel up to $4\frac{1}{2}$ in. The machine can be arranged to grind either parallel or taper. The swivelling-top table is adjustable by a knurled screw and can be locked at any angle. The table has a hand feed. The poppet is friction geared and driven by a leather belt on a jockey slide. A small V-steady and diamond tool-holder (for truing purposes), small water drip tank, and splash guards are included in the equipment. The countershaft is combined in the machine, so that the latter is self-contained and no overhead gearing is required. The standard grinding wheel supplied is 8 in. $\times$ $1\frac{1}{4}$ in. $\times$ 24 in. outside diameter.

LARGER GRINDING MACHINES

For precision grinding of parts such as crankshafts, camshafts, axles, and similar components which can be mounted between centres, special

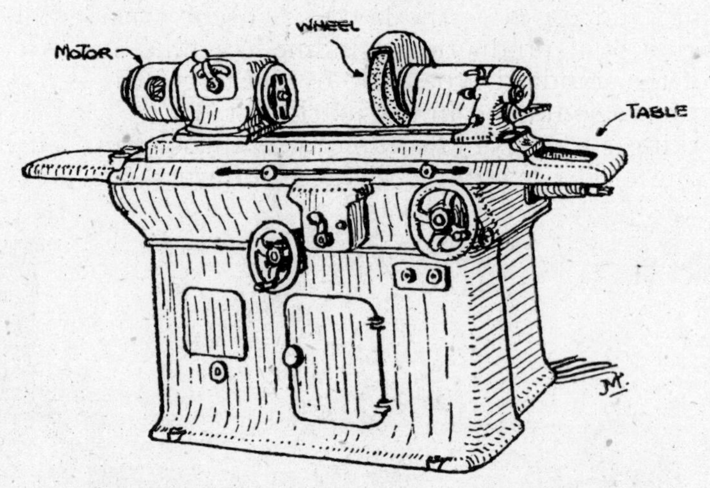

Fig. 158.—Hydraulic Pattern Plain Grinding Machine.

grinding machines are now available. They are intended for large motor-repair shops, reconditioning and motor-manufacturing works, where routine grinding of these parts has to be undertaken.

A typical machine is the hydraulic one, shown in Fig. 158; this is employed for the grinding of plain circular or tapered work.

In this machine the table grinding wheel and work-head are provided with independent motors. The table may be traversed either by hand or hydraulically at an infinitely variable speed between 8 ft. and 20 ft. per minute. The feed of wheel to work is either by hand or automatic, optionally, and the work-head may be swivelled.

In hydraulic drives, motion is obtained from a cylinder and piston. The cylinder may be fed with oil under pressure from each end, the supply being obtained from a motor-driven pump via a two-way valve which is interconnected with stopping apparatus arranged to give the necessary travel. The motion obtained is perfectly smooth and positive, and adjustment of speed is controlled by by-passing the motive fluid. In older types of grinders where gearing and belts were employed, variation in speeds was limited, the method of driving was complicated, and the finish obtainable was comparatively imperfect.

An all-hydraulic universal machine is illustrated at Fig. 159 in which the table traverse, cross-feed, and work-head are operated hydraulically, the wheel is driven by a motor, and hydraulic drives are separately powered. This type of machine is applied to the grinding of all kinds of work, plain, tapered, and formed, and also may be used for face-grinding discs and internal bores or recesses. For the surfacing of thin discs which cannot be conveniently held in the work-head chuck, a magnetic chuck is employed on the face of which the work is held perfectly flat and secure

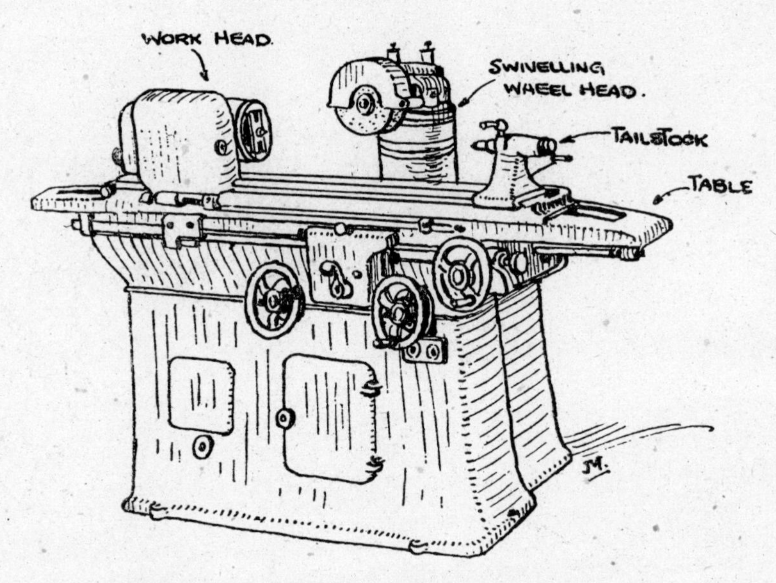

Fig. 159.—Hydraulic Universal-type Grinding Machine.

during the grinding process. Automatic feed stops are fitted to both longitudinal and cross-feed motions and hand control is incorporated capable of instant operation. In this, as well as most plain grinders, the grinding wheel may be trued and dressed while running and without removal of work from the centres, by the application of a diamond truing device fitted to the table or tail-stock of the machine.

For internal grinding, an attachment is fitted to the wheel head. This consists of an extended spindle and bearings. The spindle is of small diameter in order to take miniature wheels when used for grinding very small holes. All precision-grinding machines employ adjustable-type bearings in order that any wear may be taken up. In some designs the shaft is tapered at the journals, and end adjustment of the bushes controls the clearance between the spindle and bush. In other types the spindle is parallel at the journals and the bushes are split and tapered on the out-

Fig. 160.—Crankshaft Grinding Machines. (Above) Main-bearing Type; (Below) Crank-pin Type. [Churchill].

side diameter, and end movement takes up any slackness in the running-fit of the spindle.

The design of the table ways is very important, and machine tables are made in such a manner that the ways are always covered to eliminate dust and water, which would have harmful effects.

The Churchill crankshaft grinding machines shown in Figs. 160 and 161 and also in Plate facing p. 142 are of the hydraulic pattern. The upper illustration in Fig. 160 depicts the machine used for grinding the main

Fig. 161.—Showing Churchill Grinding Machine in Operation, on the Main Bearing Journals of Automobile Six-cylinder Crankshaft.

bearing journals, whilst the lower one shows the somewhat different model employed for grinding the crank journals.

These machines are intended for the rapid grinding of batches of crankshafts, without having to adjust them in between these operations. Special features of these machines include hydraulic automatic positioning interlocked with hydraulic withdrawal and return of wheel-head ; automatic grinding-spindle bearing adjustment ; positive control of the space between the crank webs; slow hydraulic traverse for wheel truing, and full hydraulic control of the grinding wheel-head with diminishing grinding feed.

The crank-journal grinding machine has a synchronised double-end drive for the crankshaft—to eliminate distortion in long crankshafts; variable-speed motor drive to the work; electrical indicator for balancing the crankshaft; fixed-type throw blocks and work-steady which withdraws simultaneously when the grinding wheel-head is run back. The machines are made by the Churchill Machine Tool Co., Ltd., Broadheath, Manchester.

A CRANKSHAFT LAPPING MACHINE

The Norton machine illustrated in Fig. 162 has been designed for the purpose of lapping, simultaneously, the crank-pins and the main bearings of crankshafts up to 42 in. in length and $2\frac{1}{2}$ in. diameter.

Each crank-pin, or main journal bearing, is provided with a separate

Fig. 162.—The Norton Crankshaft Lapping Machine.

lapping arm mounted on a shaft above and to the rear of the centre line of the shaft. These arms are counterbalanced and they swing on antifriction bearings. The arms are locked in position when removing or replacing the crankshafts.

The crankshaft is motor-driven, the lapping arms working in a similar

GRINDING THE CRANK-PINS OF A PETROL-ENGINE CRANKSHAFT ON A CHURCHILL GRINDING MACHINE.

manner to the connecting rods of the engine so that a rotary lapping action is obtained. In order to obviate grooving or local lapping action the crankshaft is given a small-end movement, or reciprocation.

When used for lapping the main bearings the lapping arms are suspended from a shaft directly above the work centres and are stationary. Both sets of arms are arranged to use either abrasive paper or lapping sticks as a lapping medium. A 5-h.p. electric motor is used to drive the machine; it is mounted in the base below the head-stock and drives the latter's shaft by a chain.

A tank for the lubricant is provided in the base of the machine, a centrifugal pump distributing the liquid to the lapping arms. The lapping time can be set to vary from ½ to 1½ minutes; at the end of this period the machine stops automatically.

The machine is marketed by Messrs. Alfred Herbert, Ltd., Coventry.

SHEET-METAL WORKING MACHINES

A good deal of information in connection with sheet-metal working equipment is given elsewhere in this work, but it may be of interest, when considering the machine equipment of large garages, to give a brief account of a few of the more useful sheet-metal working tools. These include: (1) Bending rolls. (2) Shears. (3) Beading and swaging machines. (4) Wheeling and raising machines.

Fig. 163.—Bending Rolls.

Fig. 163 shows a typical bending rolls[1] in which a pair of hard-steel rollers is rotated, by means of geared wheels at one end, in opposite directions. Any flat sheet metal fed between the rollers is curved in passing through. In the design shown both ends of the curving roll are instantly adjusted by means of a lever at the handle side of the machine, and the roller is mounted so as to produce true bends with either plain or folded edges.

The top roller moves sideways for the quick removal of tubes when

[1] Messrs. W. Frost, Rochdale.

bent to small diameters; provision is made for taking conical tubes. The rolls illustrated can be provided with an attachment for bending material at *right angles*, and to produce square-shaped and round-edged boxes and tanks. The three illustrations seen at the foot of the machine (Fig. 163) show samples of the work done.

Fig. 164.—The "Miracle" Hand Bending Machine.

A HAND BENDING MACHINE

A useful hand bending machine for metal, known as the "Miracle" machine, is illustrated in Fig. 164. This machine is designed for the accurate and rapid bending of metal of various sections whilst in a cold state. The principle adopted is simplicity itself, yet is remarkably efficient.

A common wall bracket of, say, 4 in. by ¼ in. metal, containing four bends would, under the ordinary method, require to be heated at the points where the bends are to be made, and considerable skill would be required in the operation. By the use of this bender, the same bracket can be made of cold metal, and the machine makes it unnecessary to rely upon the intelligence or skill of the operator to turn out an accurate piece of work. Production, therefore, is considerably increased and labour costs reduced accordingly.

METAL SHEARS

This machine is for cutting sheet metal, not only in plain lengths but into fancy shapes. The type shown in Fig. 165 is known as a "snip shear," and it has a pair of circular cutting plates, the upper one of which is rotated by means of the hand wheel shown through bevel gearing; in this way the work is fed through during the cutting

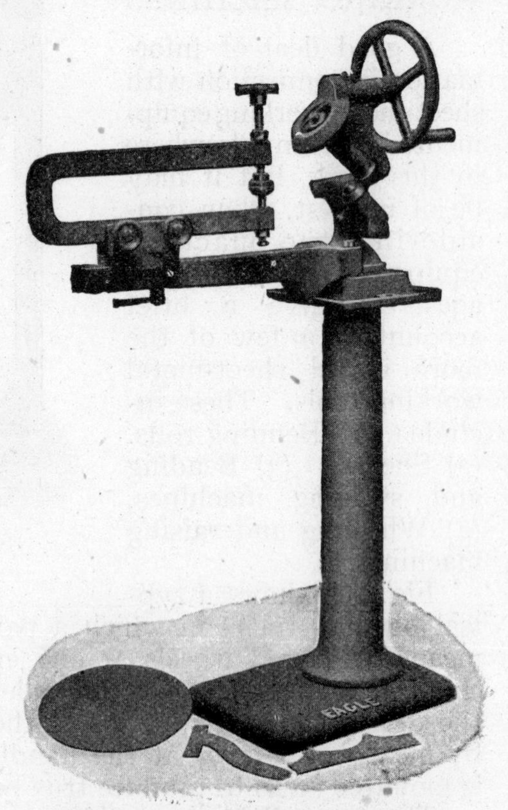

Fig. 165.—Snip Shear with Circle-cutting Attachment.

process. The clamping attachment shown on the left is for the purpose of cutting circular disks from sheet metal; circles up to 3-ft. diameter in material up to 16 S.W.G. thick can be cut in this manner. The steel bow shown is instantly removable to allow room for cutting sheets of any size, the fixture bracket arm acting as a support. This machine will cut practically any shape, either straight, irregular, or curved, for automobile purposes.

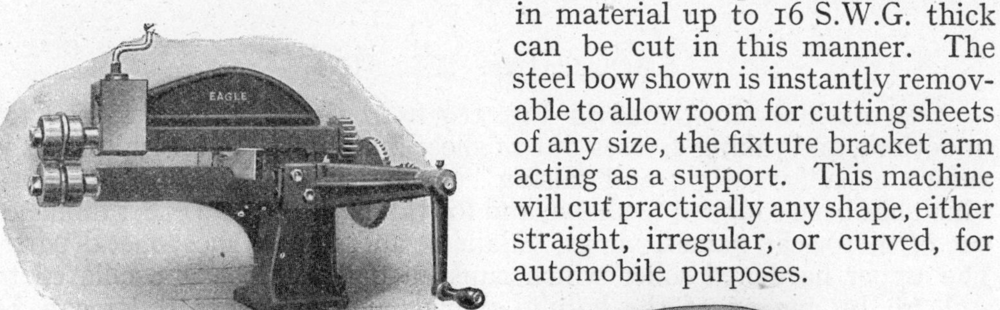

Fig. 166.—Beading and Swaging Machine.

BEADING AND SWAGING MACHINE

A frequent operation in sheet-metal work is that of turning over the sharp edges of the metal, so as to form a smooth end of double thickness; this is known as "beading." Fig. 166 shows a suitable machine for performing this operation. Here the metal to be beaded is fed between the two hardened rollers shown; the latter rotate in opposite directions, and have sufficient (adjustable) clearance for the thickness of metal being beaded. The operating handle is very conveniently placed in front, so that the operator can both control and see the work going through. The machine shown is fitted with a parallel gauge, and can also be used as a rotary shear for cutting strips. It can

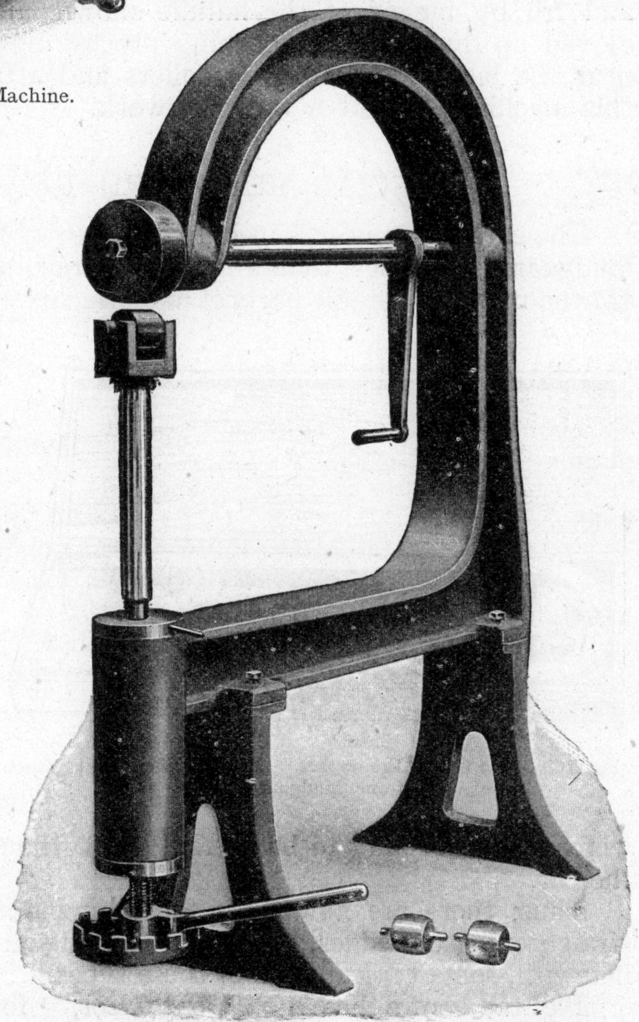

Fig. 167.—Smoothing and Raising Machine.

be fitted with special heads for swaging and other operations; the gap is 36 in. in the case of the largest machine.

SMOOTHING MACHINE

The machine illustrated in Fig. 167 has been specially designed for smoothing and taking creases out of sheet metal-work of all types. It is known as a "wheeling and raising" machine, and is useful for work which has been roughed to shape, and for taking dents and other damages out of motor-car panels, wings, valances, and similar sheet-metal parts. The upper hardened roller which runs on ball-bearings is oscillated to and fro by means of the handle shown, and the lower roller can be moved up during the smoothing process by means of the lever shown near the base. A variety of rollers and attachments is supplied with this machine, to suit a range of work.

SPECIAL MUDGUARD REPAIR TOOLS

The garage engineer is usually confronted with more cases of damaged mudguards, or wings, than any other minor repairs to cars, for the wings are the most vulnerable parts of modern cars, despite the almost universal adoption of bumpers.

It was hitherto the practice either to return the damaged wings to the manufacturer or to replace them with new ones, as most garages could not make a satisfactory job of this type of repairs with the ordinary tools available.

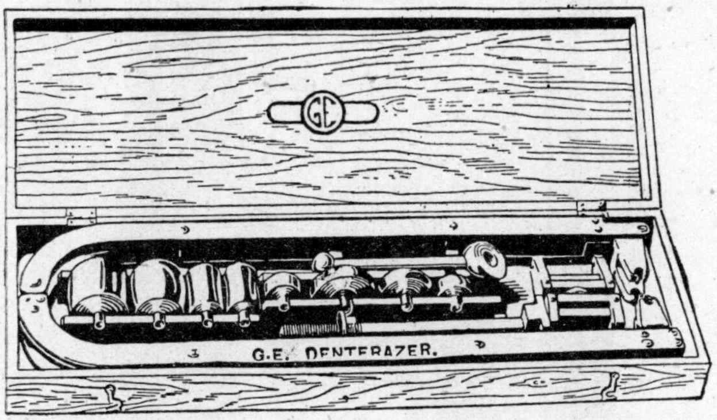

Fig. 168.—The G.E. "Denterazer" Outfit for Removing Dents from Mudguards.

A number of special tools have more recently been devised, and marketed by firms of garage equipment supplies, which enable repairs to be carried out without removing the wings from the car.

Thus, there are now tools for taking out dents in mudguards, for straightening the edges, resetting the mudguard stays, etc. We illustrate, herewith, some typical tools of these types.

Fig. 168 shows the G.E. "Denterazer,"[1] for taking dents out of mudguards. It is adjustable to suit various sizes and shapes of mudguard.

It consists of a hinged frame carrying rollers at the two ends. These rollers are of different shapes and sizes to suit the particular job in hand.

[1] Made by Messrs. Joseph Bradbury & Sons, Ltd., Braintree, Essex.

The rollers are arranged above and below the mudguard, the pressure between them being adjustable by means of the handle shown on the top.

The method of using this tool (Fig. 169) is as follows: Remove all dirt and tar from the upper and lower surfaces, select suitable rollers, adjust the heads to the most convenient position, pass the tool over the damaged part, and with moderate pressure work around the dent until it is removed. Gradually increase the pressure on the rollers and work over the area until all of the smallest imperfections are removed.

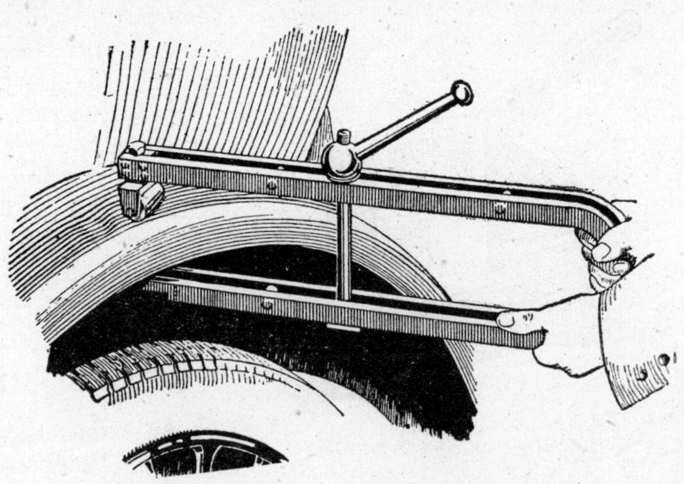

Fig. 169.—Showing how the "Denterazer" is used.

Fig. 170 shows a particularly useful tool made by the same firm for setting of the turned-down edges of damaged wings. The ordinary wringing iron, owing to its lack of adjustability, is unsuited for this purpose. With the tool in question wings of any depth can be straightened; the tool is most efficiently used in pairs.

To set the edge outwards engage the hook end of the tool under the strengthened edge and adjust the leather-covered block to come in con-

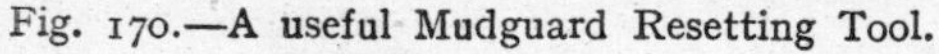

Fig. 170.—A useful Mudguard Resetting Tool.

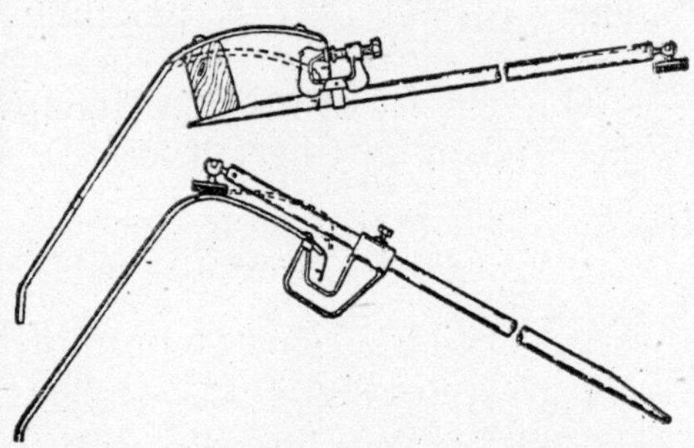

Fig. 171.—(Above) Bending Mudguard downwards. (Below) Bending it upwards.

tact with the top edge of the wing. Being able to localise the pressure by adjusting the block, it will be found a simple matter to set the wing exactly as required.

The U-shaped end of the tool serves the double purpose of bending the edge *inwards*, or of holding the wing in position while the other end is used to pull the straightened edge *outwards*.

A useful tool for resetting wing stays which have been bent in accidents is the G.E. pattern shown in Fig. 171. It is adjustable over a wide range, and is rubber faced to prevent scraping or chipping of the enamel.

To *bend the stay downwards,* fix the clamp firmly on the turned-down edge of the mudguard. Insert the flattened end of the lever between the stirrup and the mudguard and lever the mudguard down as shown in Fig. 171 (upper diagram). If the edge of the guard is too deep insert a block of wood between the lever end and the underside of the stay.

Fig. 172.—Hand Bench Shears.

The method of *bending the stay upwards* is illustrated in Fig. 171 (lower diagram).

BENCH SHEARING MACHINE

A particularly useful machine for cutting sheet metal in connection with motor-vehicle body work, etc., is shown in Fig. 172. It is hand-operated, the leverage being sufficient to shear most thicknesses of metal met with in ordinary motor repair work; it can be used also for brake-lining materials.

In cases where curved shapes have to be cut out of sheet metal the "Bocarno" bench shearing machine, shown in Fig. 173, will be found to save a good deal of time. The pedestal of this machine is designed to give clearance at the "throat" to enable the sheet-metal plate to be manipulated when cutting curves.

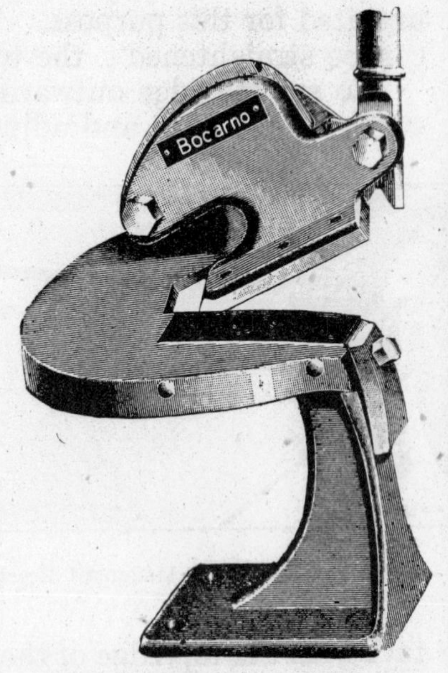

Fig. 173.—The "Bocarno" Shearing Machine, for Curved Shapes.

HACKSAW MACHINE

Every large garage or motor workshop doing constructional engineering work should have a machine for sawing metal rod, bar, angle, tube, etc. It is a laborious job cutting through a large steel bar with an ordinary hacksaw. With a hacksaw machine, on the other hand, the bar can be inserted in a quick-grip type of vice, the machine set for its length of cut, started, and left; it will stop itself automatically when the bar is cut through.

There are many types of hacksaw machine on the market, one of the best being the Millers Falls pattern shown in Fig. 174; a short account of this machine will indicate the essential points of such devices.

The machine illustrated is provided with the usual vice for holding the job—in this case a 4-in. steel bar is shown—and there is a gauge piece for cutting off a number of pieces all the same length. The stroke of the saw is adjustable in some machines, but not in the one illustrated.

Fig. 174.—Power Hacksaw, fitted with Special Devices.

An ingenious device is fitted for enabling the return or idle stroke of the saw to be made at twice the speed of the cutting stroke; moreover, the blade is slightly lifted on the return stroke to prolong its life. When the bar is sawn through the frame drops a certain distance, and in doing so operates a mechanism to stop the machine; in most cases this mechanism moves the belt striker from the fast to the loose pulley. Another useful fitting is that of the lifting lever A, which enables the saw to be held clear of the job whilst the latter is being adjusted. There is a support on the lathe bed to prevent the blade from breaking when the cut is nearly through. A removable vice nut in the bed can be replaced in case of wear.

The normal working speed of this and most other machines is 60 strokes per minute. The power required to work it is about $\frac{1}{3}$ h.p.

BRAZING HEARTHS OR FORGES

The equipment of every modern garage should include a forge or brazing hearth, for there is a variety of jobs which require the use of such a heating apparatus.

In most towns coal-gas is available, and a coal-gas and air blow-pipe flame can readily be arranged. If in addition the garage equipment includes a source of compressed air—a tyre-inflating plant is suitable for this purpose—then no difficulty will be experienced in providing an automatic supply of air and coal-gas for heating purposes. Most firms of engineering suppliers (e.g. Messrs. Buck & Hickman, Brown Bros., East London Rubber Co.) provide blow-pipes for coal-gas, and also foot-operated bellows to give the necessary air-pressure, when a compressed-air supply is not available.

The use of coal-gas is preferable to that of a coal forge, as it is more convenient to use, cleaner, and is always ready at a moment's notice.

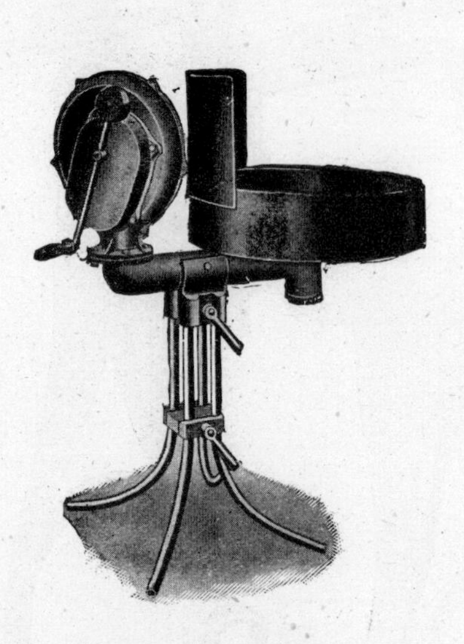

Fig. 175.—A Portable Fan Forge for Coal.

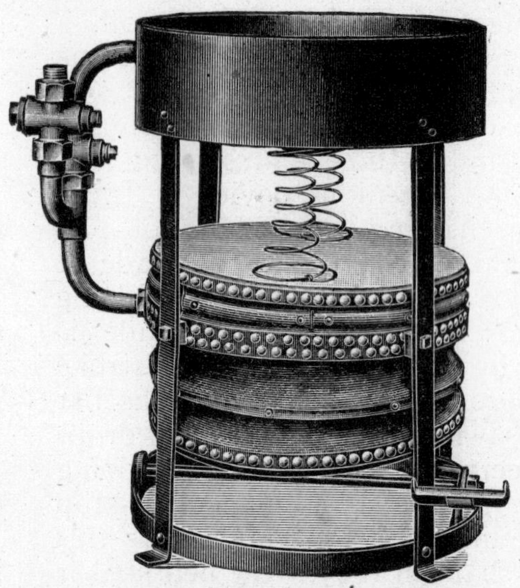

Fig. 176.—A Combined Forge and Brazing Hearth suitable for Garage Work.

It is not advisable to have a coal forge in a motor-engineering works or repair shop.

A coal-gas plant will be found useful for small forging work on steel, and for brazing purposes.

The oxy-acetylene blow-lamp flame is often used for these purposes, but care is essential or the metal parts may easily be burnt.

AIR COMPRESSORS

An air-compressing plant of the portable type should form part of the equipment of every garage, large or small. With it a good deal of time and trouble can be saved in connection with the inflation of motor tyres.

It can also be used (in the larger sizes) for *paint spraying*, using the Aerograph spray-pistol method; for *light brazing work*, *welding*, and *blowing out dust* from cylinders and other automobile parts, as well as for cleaning the dirt out of corners of the bodywork and upholstery.

The most commonly used air compressor is the small portable pattern mounted on a trolley, complete with its electric motor for driving purposes.

An example of a portable garage compressor is shown in Fig. 177. It is necessary to provide a fairly long piece of inflator tubing, namely, from 15 to 20 ft., and sufficient electric cable to allow the compressor to be used all around a car.

The essentials of a good portable garage compressor are as follows: namely, (1) It should have a sufficient capacity to inflate any tyre

Fig. 177.—A Portable Air Compressor.

quickly; a pressure of 150 to 200 lb. per sq. in. is usually obtained. (2) It should be able to inflate a normal size of car tyre, say, 880 × 120 mm., in 1 to 1½ minutes. (3) An oil trap or collector should be provided to extract the oil which finds its way from inside the compressor with the air. (4) It should have a minimum pumping capacity of about 4 cu. ft. of air per minute at 100 lb. per sq. in. (5) A suitable pressure-relief valve should be fitted to the reservoir. (6) It should not be noisy in action.

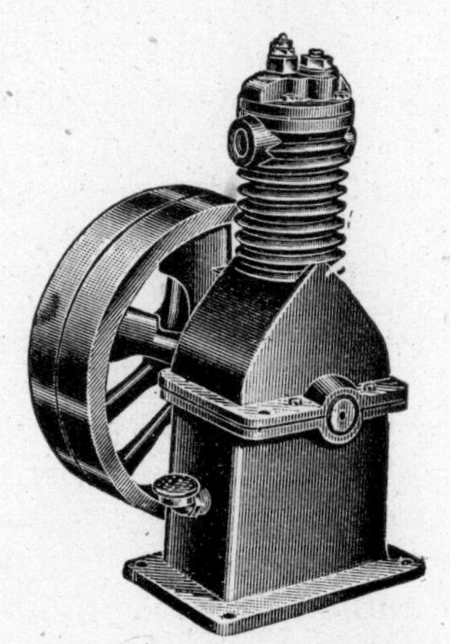

Fig. 178. — Stationary Air Compressor for Garage Use.

Fig. 178 illustrates a suitable single-cylinder, single-stage compressor intended for belt-driving from the existing line shafting. The compressor, which gets fairly warm in the ordinary way, is provided with air-cooling pins. The compressor is lubricated on the usual splash system; it has white-metal bearings. When run at 450 r.p.m. it gives about 190 lb. per sq. in. pressure, with a

Fig. 179.—The Dunlop Belt-driven Rotary-type Air Compressor.

maximum for intermittent work of 200 lb. per sq. in. The compressor shown requires about $\frac{1}{4}$ h.p. to work it.

There is a wide selection of portable and stationary air compressors available for garage and motor-repair shop purposes, typical examples being the B.E.N., Harvey Frost, Tangye, Kismet, Tecalemit, Laycock, and Dunlop ones.

These vary in size and capacity, from the smaller portable units fitted with $\frac{1}{4}$- or $\frac{1}{2}$-h.p. electric motors, giving from 2 to 4 cu. ft. of free air per minute, up to the larger stationary models fitted with large reservoirs, operated by electric motors of $1\frac{1}{2}$ to 2 h.p. and providing from 6 to 10 cu. ft. of free air per minute.

These compressors are of the single- or twin-cylinder types in the smaller portable models which are used for tyre-inflation purposes, whilst four- and six-cylinder compressors are often used in the larger models.

The Harvey Frost stationary model (Type X) employs a large single-cylinder air-cooled compressor, belt-driven from a 2-h.p. electric motor. It has a bore of 3 in. and stroke of 4 in. and delivers its air into a vertical cylindrical

Fig. 180.—Compressed-air Storage Tanks of Different Capacities.

reservoir of 14-in. diameter by 36-in. height, at a pressure of 100 lb. per sq. in. (maximum); the compressor gives 8 cu. ft. of free air per minute.

The larger Dunlop model, N.S.E.6 (Fig. 182), has an output of 9 cu. ft. of air per minute and is provided with a six-cylinder compressor of 1·99-in. bore and 1·22-in. stroke, the cylinders being water-cooled by pump circulation from a 5-gal. tank. The normal speed is 500/600 r.p.m. The compressor is driven from a $1\frac{1}{2}$-h.p. motor, which has an automatic cut-out for regulating the maximum pressure (150 lb. per sq. in.). The complete unit measures 56 in. long, 34 in. high, and 19 in. wide. It weighs 508 lb.

Fig. 181.—Portable-type Garage Inflator (Dunlop).

A small portable Dunlop compressor for tyre-inflation purposes is shown in Fig. 181. This has a single-cylinder compressor of 2-in. bore and 1-in. stroke, and it is driven by a $\frac{1}{2}$-h.p. repulsion induction motor. The compressor has an output of $2\frac{1}{2}$ cu. ft. of free air at 1,425 r.p.m. and

Fig. 182.—The Dunlop N.S.E.6 Air-compressor Plant.

the dimensions of the machine are 16 in. × 16 in. × 16 in., with handle 30 in. long; it weighs 88 lb.

A good example of a hand-operated garage tyre inflator is the H.F. model shown in Fig. 183. It has at least twice the capacity of the ordinary foot pump, thus shortening the time of inflation. The pump shown is of the two-stage type, and it is a good substitute in the garage for a small mechanically-operated air compressor. Trolley wheels, double foot-rests, and a long operating handle are other special features of this inflator.

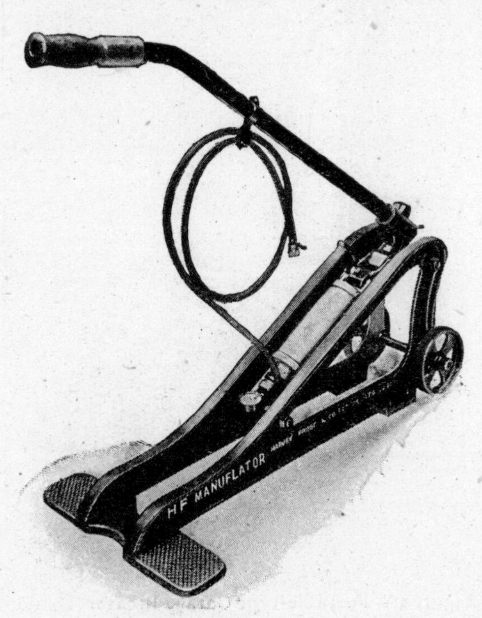

Fig. 183.—The H.F. "Manuflator" Garage Tyre Pump.

ENGINE STANDS

Apart from engine assembly work in motor manufacture, it is often necessary to carry out complete overhauls of engines in motor garages. This cannot always conveniently be done with the engine in the chassis, more especially when the engine repair shop is separate from the shop or garage in which the car is housed; in any case, it is important from the point of view of convenience, accessibility, and saving of time in working between the bench and the engine to have the engine close to the bench.

A number of special stands for holding engines is now on the market; most of these possess important improvements over the earlier rigid steel structures.

The essentials of a good engine stand are as follows:

(1) It should hold the engine in a similar manner to the chassis, and rigidly.

(2) It should be readily adjustable so as to take a wide range of engine sizes, from light car to lorry types.

(3) It should be portable, i.e. be provided with rollers or wheels which, however, can if necessary be lifted clear of the ground when the stand is to be made rigid.

(4) It should allow the engine to be tilted to any angle and turned upside down; the engine should be firmly clamped in any desired position.

(5) It should be capable of being operated by one man; this implies that the engine's centre of gravity should be on the axis about which the engine stand's bearings pivot.

(6) The engine stand should be of the correct height for the average mechanic to work comfortably.

There are other minor points of importance, but these need not be dwelt upon here—most of them will be apparent from the descriptions of particular models which are given in the following pages.

Fig. 184.—The M.E. Engine Stand.

The engine stand shown in Fig. 184 is made by Messrs. Mann & Egerton, Ltd., of Norwich. It has been designed for general garage and repair work, and will accommodate a wide range of engine sizes. Thus, it can be expanded from 18 in. to 36 in. in the width between the engine bearers, telescopic slides being provided for this purpose. The engine is bolted to bearers made of mild-steel angle of $2 \times \frac{3}{8}$ in. section, 36 in. in length. These angles are slotted to take various bolt centres, and are mounted on $1\frac{1}{2}$-in. diameter trunnions working in cast-iron bearings. The engine can therefore be turned completely over, or may be locked at different angles by means of the drilled strips shown on the left-hand side of the trunnion. The side frames are made of mild-steel angle, welded and bolted rigidly together, and mounted on four heavy wheels to facilitate moving about. By means of plunger pins the wheels can be locked if desired.

A tray is fitted beneath the engine.

Fig. 185 shows a well-designed but more expensive engine stand having several novel points. The stand shown can be quickly adjusted to take any width of engine bearer. It is only necessary to unslack four clamping screws at the ends of the engine-stand longitudinal bearers and to slide the latter along the transverse rods to adjust the width. The engine can be bodily adjusted and fixed 5 in. above or 5 in. below the trunnion centres, so as to obtain a good balance for enabling the engine to be turned to any angle ; this is an important adjustment. Further, it will be noted that the engine is tilted about a longitudinal axis ; this is preferable for most engine-repair purposes.

The trunnion flanges are provided with eight fixed stop positions.

Lifting screws are provided on the base plates of the stand, so as to lift the wheels clear of the ground. It is interesting to note that the stand in this position is sufficiently rigid to enable *the engine to be run in from a main-line shaft,* using the flywheel of the engine as a pulley;

after the bearings have been taken up, or new ones fitted, they can be bedded in conveniently in the manner described. The tie rods shown are necessary when the engine is being run in as described.

The brackets to which the engine is attached may be moved and fixed in a large number of positions, and the side frames can either be

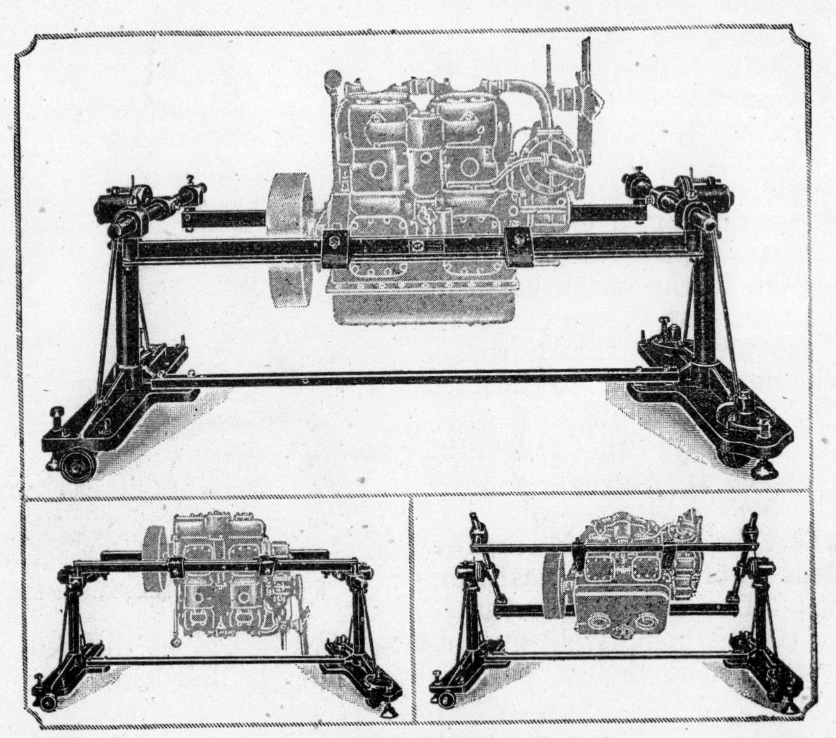

Fig. 185.—A Well-designed Engine Stand.

fixed parallel or inclining to each other. This enables the stand to be used for other purposes, such as for holding gear boxes and back axles.

The engine stand in question will accommodate equally well any engine from a light car model to a heavy commercial vehicle, and is applicable to three- and four-point suspension engines. It is made in four principal sizes, the smallest being 6 ft. 6 in. long by 3 ft. 2 in. wide by 3 ft. high, and the largest 8 ft. long by 3 ft. 5 in. wide by 3 ft. high.

THE H.F. ENGINE STAND

An improved design of engine stand is shown in Fig. 186; this contains a number of improvements which have been embodied as the result of the makers' experience with their earlier stand models.

Particular attention has been paid to securing as close coincidence as possible between the centre of gravity of the mounted engine and the pivots of the stand, this being of special importance when ungeared models are used.

A number of useful operating positions are available simply by turning the engine over to the required angle, either by hand or in the geared model, by worm and worm-wheel mechanism. In regard to the latter, it should be noted that the gearing is at both ends of the frame, and that the operating handle acts simultaneously through both sets of gearing.

This stand is strongly made, the use of cast-iron having been avoided. It is mounted on heavy ball-bearing castors so that it can readily be moved, bodily. Steadying screws are also supplied in order to lock the stand in position for working. The height from the ground is such that

Fig. 186.—The H.F. Universal Engine Stand, showing Engine being turned over in swinging part of Frame.

the foot of a floor crane can pass underneath, bringing the jib into the correct position for lifting.

The stand is made in two models, viz. Models A and B. The former is 8 ft. 9 in. long, 2 ft. 8 in. wide, and 3 ft. $9\frac{1}{2}$ in. high ; it has worm gearing. Model B is of the ungeared type. It is 6 ft. 1 in. long, 3 ft. wide, and 3 ft. 2 in. high.

THE G.E. ENGINE STAND

A simple, but robust, engine stand suitable for garage repair work is shown in Fig. 187. The engine crankcase, or cylinder block, is clamped to a pair of steel channels, by means of long screwed bars and a top bar member. The engine can then be rotated into any convenient position for working upon. In the left-hand diagram (Fig. 187) the engine is shown in the vertical position, and in the right-hand diagram in the horizontal one. The hand wheel, shown, is used for rotating the (previously balanced) engine unit ; it can be clamped rigidly in any position.

An improved engine stand, made by Messrs. Bradbury, Ltd., Braintree, is shown in Fig. 188. This has larger wheels than the model shown in Fig. 187 and it is adjustable for different widths of engine from 18 in.

Fig. 187.—The G.E. Engine Stand, with a Cylinder Block in the vertical (left) and horizontal (right) positions.

Fig. 188.—The G.E. Engine Stand (Improved Model).

to 26 in. Slots are provided to accommodate varying belt sizes. The frame can be reversed entirely or locked at any intermediate position.

The wheels can also be locked, so as not to rotate by means of spring plungers. The length of the supporting arms is 36 in. and the height from the ground to the arms is 30 in.

GARAGE PRESSES

The mechanical type of press for exerting heavy pressures is a very useful garage machine, for it can be employed for a wide range of opera-

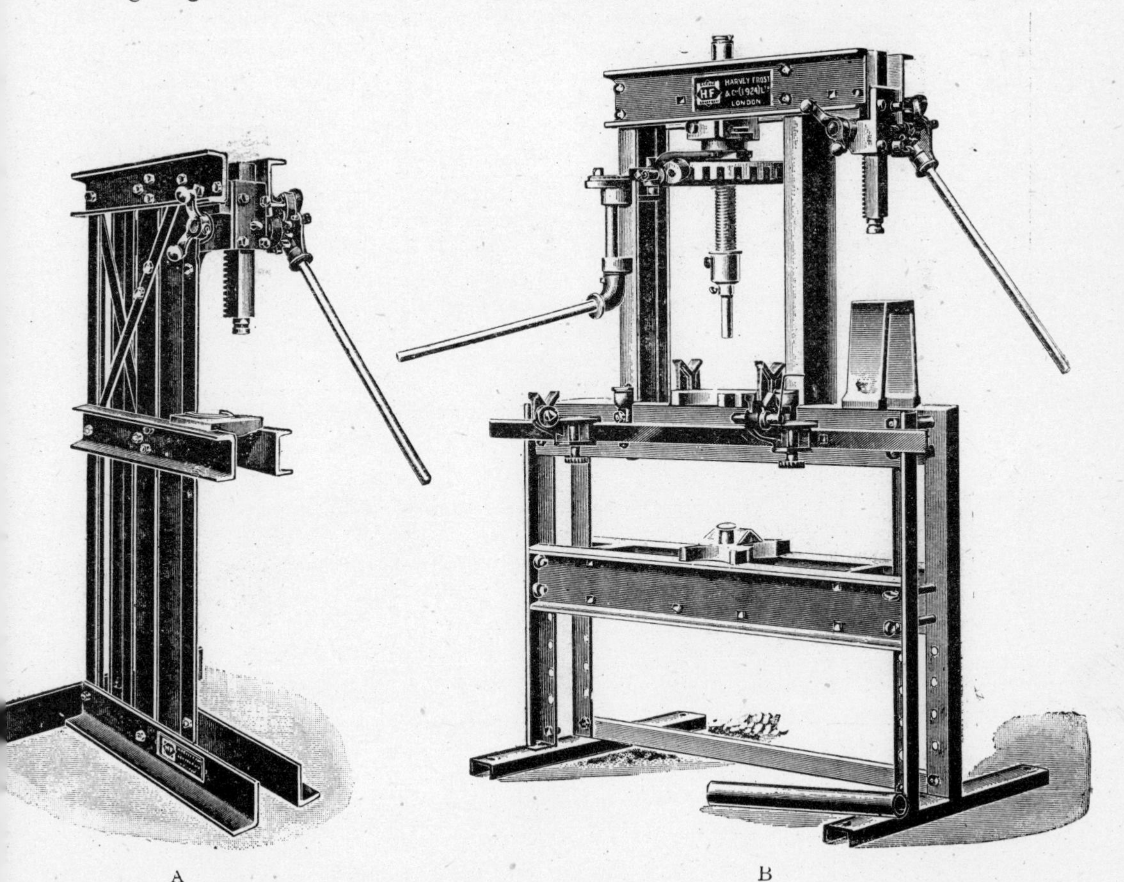

Fig. 189.—Examples of useful Garage Presses. A, The H.F. 3-ton Rack and Press. B, The H.F. 30-ton Steel Press for Large Bushes, Bearings, Bent Shafts, etc.

tions, including the removal and insertion of bearing bushes, the forcing out of tight pins, pressing gear wheels on to, or off, shafts, straightening bent shafts, etc.

Various types of presses are now available, ranging from the small lever-operated ones exerting relatively low pressures up to the 20- to 30-ton models for heavy duty.

Fig. 189, A, shows a 3-ton press, operated by a ratchet and rack-and-pinion mechanism ; it belongs to the cantilever or overhung table class and is used chiefly for direct-pressure action.

Another pattern of garage press is illustrated in Fig. 190. This has a central ram unit operated, manually, by square-threaded nut and shaft, by means of a worm and worm-wheel drive; adjustable V-blocks are provided for shaft-straightening purposes. On the right-hand side of the structure is a smaller rack-and-pinion type of press, with its table, for direct-pressing operations, such as the insertion or removal of pins or bushes.

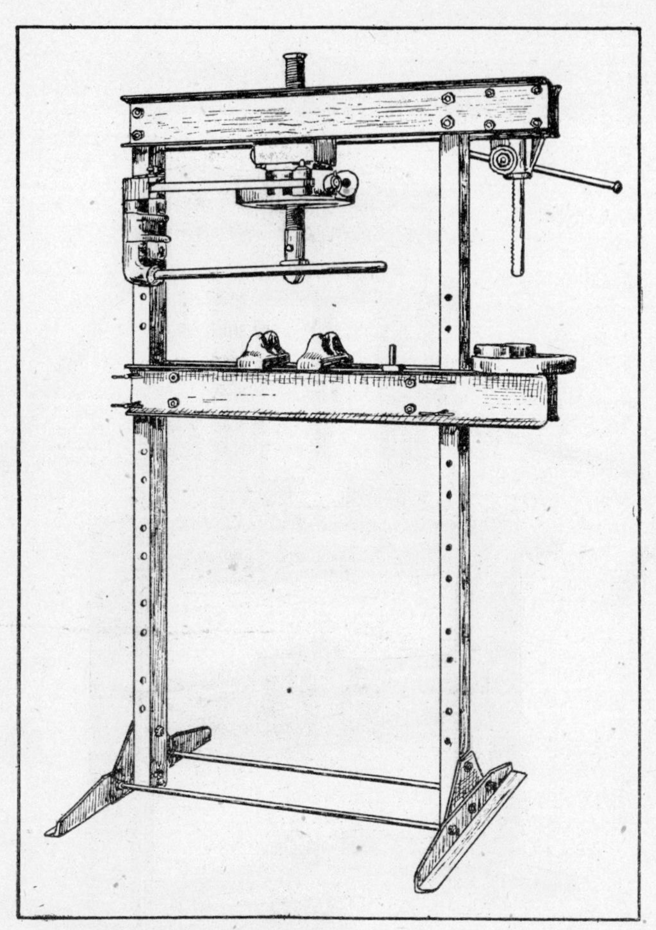

Fig. 190.—A Double-purpose Press.

The heavier pattern screw press shown in Fig. 189, B, is used for larger bushes, bearings, bent shafts, frames, etc. It is manually operated by worm and worm-wheel driven square-threaded nut and screw, and is capable of exerting a force of 30 tons; on the right is a direct-operating rack-and-pinion type of press.

A later development of this press is the H.F. 30-ton geared model, which is operated by similar mechanism, and embodies a device for giving a hammer blow by means of a vertical drop hammer working by means of a chain passing over a pulley at the top of the press; this blow will give the necessary jar to start stubborn pieces of work.

Hydraulic presses are also used in certain modern shops, where high pressures are required. A typical example of the use of such hydraulic presses is the one used for forcing cylinder liners into cylinder blocks.

CHAPTER IV

BREAKDOWN EQUIPMENT

HAVING dealt with the subject of road breakdowns, it may not be inopportune at this stage to consider breakdown equipment—that is to say, equipment and appliances for use on the spot for damaged motor vehicles unable to proceed under their own power.

The garage engineer will frequently be called in to deal with a badly damaged car or motor cycle which has been left just after an accident, and which must be cleared off the road and taken to the nearest garage for repairs or disposal. It is, therefore, a very important matter to have the correct equipment for handling any case of this kind which may occur, and the garage engineer will find it well worth while to provide himself with the most up-to-date lifting and towing appliances, so as to quickly cope with emergency cases of this kind.

It is regrettable that many garages employ only makeshift methods for dealing with road-accident cases, thereby wasting a good deal of valuable time, entailing more labour costs to their clients, and risking further damage to the vehicle they have to remove or repair.

In many cases, also, speed is the most important factor, for the occupant, or occupants, of a car which has been involved in a road accident may be pinned beneath the car, and it frequently becomes a matter of life or death to release them as quickly as possible. Apart from this, there is the question of the obstruction likely to be caused to other road users by the presence of a damaged vehicle. It is, therefore, in the public interest that the modern garage should be equipped with the best breakdown appliances. Apart from this, the possession of a breakdown car is an excellent means of publicity for the garage engineer, for it cannot fail to be observed and commented upon on such occasions.

The modern breakdown equipment consists of four principal items, as follows:

(1) The breakdown-equipment transport car or lorry.
(2) The lifting appliances or cranes.
(3) The towing undercarriage or "ambulance."
(4) The towing pole or connection.

Little need be said concerning the first item, beyond the fact that the flat platform type of commercial lorry is usually the best adapted to this purpose, for it must carry the other three items (sometimes the third is towed behind). Very often, also, the lorry itself will prove most useful for a built-up type of hoist or crane, the latter being secured to the chassis frame.

LIFTING APPLIANCES

For dealing with the commonest types of car salvage work the lifting appliance should be capable of dealing with a maximum load of not less than 2 tons. For this reason the majority of salvage cranes or breakdown jibs are designed to lift loads up to 2, $2\frac{1}{2}$, 3, $3\frac{1}{2}$, and 5 tons, according to size; the latter type will deal with salvages of commercial cars or lorries.

Fig. 191 illustrates a neat form of breakdown lifting tackle, of the collapsible jib type—a convenient form for stowage on the service car,

Fig. 191.—A Convenient Design of Breakdown Jib.

and for portability. It resembles in principle the well-known shear-legs used in shipbuilding and dock practice, and has two stout jibs or struts hinged together at their upper ends, and to the lorry frame or platform at their lower ends; the legs are inclined outwards for stability. The two inclined chains take the pull, or tension, due to the load lifted. In this case there are side channels permanently fixed on the lorry to take the anchoring attachments of the chains and jibs; when not in use, these struts fold downwards.

The jib is constructed for use with a standard block and tackle-lifting device; the latter merely hooks on to a convenient steel eye at the junction of the two jibs. The breakdown jib illustrated is made by Messrs. Mann & Egerton, Ltd., Norwich, and is designed to lift up to two tons. The standard size has 3-in. floor runners of T-section, 8 ft.

(*Courtesy Harvey Frost, Ltd.*)

A COMPLETELY EQUIPPED BREAKDOWN SERVICE CAR, SHOWING AMBULANCE PACKED FOR TRANSPORT BY THE AID OF THE CRANE.

long, and the jibs are of 3-in. steel tubing, 7 ft. in length.

Fig. 192 illustrates the Harvey Frost 2-ton Type A salvage crane, which has been specially designed for the purpose in question. It is of all-steel construction, and has been built for rough and gruelling work. As will be apparent from the illustration, the foot members of the crane distribute the weight over the chassis frame, and the crane itself can be bodily detached from the service car without difficulty. This crane embodies its own lifting tackle, consisting of a hand-operated winch and 30 ft. of steel cable. The two operating handles are arranged at right angles, and they are adjustable in length to vary the leverage. A special feature of the crane illustrated is the swivelling nose, which ensures a safe tow on the straight, whilst at the same time enabling the cable to accommodate itself when towing a car around corners.

Fig. 192.—A 2-ton Salvage Crane.

The 2-ton crane illustrated is made in three types, A, B, and C, for general-duty purposes. The width of base for all three models is 36 in., the base depth $26\frac{1}{2}$ in., and the total weight 4 cwt. 3 qrs. The type A salvage crane has a balanced jib, which renders screw adjustment unnecessary under usual operating conditions, as the angle of the jib can be adjusted by hand without undue effort. This model is therefore supplied without any adjusting screw, and the winch is controlled by handles located close to the sides. Model B crane is similar to A but has a tilting screw. Model C crane is provided with a tilting screw for adjusting the jib and with outside wind from both sides of the breakdown lorry ; the winch is arranged at a lower level than in the other two types.

In the H.F. 3-ton salvage crane there is provision for operating it from the ground from either side of the salvage car. There are two hoists each of 30-cwt. capacity and each is worked independently of the other. Both the models mentioned have a tilting beam and weight-equalising construction.

The 8-ton crane, shown in Fig. 193, is a development of the heavy model, described in a previous edition of this work.

It is provided with two independent hoists, each terminating in a swivel head, giving any degree of angularity and ensuring command over the load in awkward situations. The crane is mounted on a turn-table base ; this enables it to be swung over to the side of the vehicle on which it is mounted, or to be used at any intermediate angular position. When lifting the full 8-ton load from the side of the vehicle it is usually necessary to counterbalance the load ; the rear drum of the crane provides

Fig. 193.—The H.F. 8-ton Crane.

an anchorage cable to meet this requirement The lifting mechanism is of the geared-winch pattern, a sufficient ratio of reduction being provided for manual operation.

The diameter of the base ring is 5 ft. 6 in. ; overhang of the jib, 2 ft. 6 in. ; run-out of jib cables, 12 ft. ; run-out of rear winder, 32 ft. ; capacity of front winder, 17 cwt. ; capacity of rear winder, 10 cwt., and total weight, 17 cwt. 2 qrs.

Breakdown cranes of 2 and 8 tons capacity are also made by the firms of Mann & Egerton and Weaver.

DESIRABLE FEATURES OF SALVAGE CRANES

It is important for the garage engineer, when obtaining salvage lifting gear, to make sure not only that the gearing supplied will lift the load without too great a physical effort on the part of one or two men—as the case may be—but also that it will extend sufficiently far beyond the rear of the car to get well over any job. Further, it should be capable of ready attachment (and detachment) to the service car, and should preferably have a swivelling head to allow for change of direction when towing the wrecked vehicle. Another desirable feature is the provision of a gear locking pin, or similar device, so that when a wreck is lifted it can be held for towing purposes in the lifted position.

Fig. 194.—Car Ambulance for Towing Damaged Car.

TOWING AMBULANCES

So far our remarks have been confined to the necessary means for lifting vehicles damaged in accidents, and it now remains to consider what shall be done after the vehicle is lifted. It will generally be found—at least in the large majority of cases—that the vehicle is damaged at one end only; either the front or the back pair of wheels have been put out of action. In such cases it is only necessary to lift the damaged end of the vehicle well clear of the ground, and then, if it is a light type of car, it can be towed on its undamaged wheels, the lifting chain or cable of the salvage crane acting as a towing "bar," as shown in Fig. 191.

On the other hand, it is frequently impossible or very inconvenient to tow a heavier car in this manner, so that some sort of trolley or truck must be run under the lifted car, and the latter then lowered on to this truck; in this way the wheels of the truck, thus used, replace the damaged ones, and the truck itself forms the towing means. Such trucks are termed "Towing Ambulances"; their use makes it easy to tow a disabled car any distance in perfect safety if the necessary simple precautions are taken.

Figs. 194 and 195 illustrate two of the H.F. towing ambulances, suitable for towing all types of private cars. They consist essentially of a pair of strong, solid, rubber-tyred wheels running on ball-thrust and roller bearings and axle, with a turntable type of double clutch above for

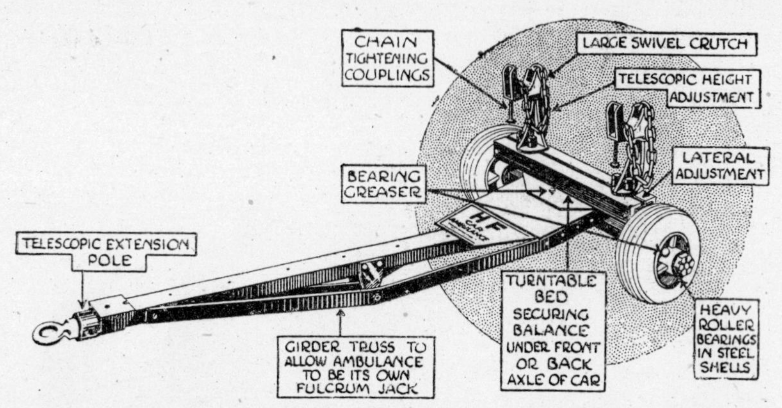

Fig. 195.—Another Car Ambulance in Detail, showing its Components.

accommodating the front or rear axle of the damaged car. Chains are provided to ensure the attachment of the axle of the damaged car to the ambulance cradles. The towing tube is telescopic, and can be altered in length over a distance of from 7 to 12 ft. The wheel tracks of the ambulances illustrated are 32 in.

Fig. 196.—The Bradbury Ambulance.

Fig. 196 shows the Bradbury general-duty ambulance, for vehicles up to 2 tons. It has crutches adjustable from 12 to 24 in.; each crutch has three slotted height positions. It is fitted with 16 by 3 in. solid tyres, and has a tubular bar adjustable from 8 ft. 3 in. to 12 ft. A pneumatic-tyred model is also made.

Another type of ambulance (Fig. 197), for heavy lorries, is made by Harvey Frost. This has twin solid rubber tyres 16 in. in diameter and 9 in. wide (overall). The inner wheel-track distance is 26 in., and outer 44 in. The saddle clearance for the differential casing in this case is $5\frac{1}{2}$ in. The towing bar is variable in length from 7 to 12 ft. Provision is also made for handling vehicles with offset differentials.

A neat design of ambulance is that made by Mann & Egerton, Ltd. It is very light, yet strong in construction, measuring overall 42 in. by 17 in. by 9 ft. 3 in. A 2-in. steel axle is employed, and the 12-in. cast disc wheels are fitted with Dunlop solid rubber tyres. A telescopic draw-bar of 2-in. heavy-gauge steel tubing has an adjustable inner bar $1\frac{3}{4}$ in. diameter extending from 7 to 12 ft.

Mention should be also made of a very useful heavy ambulance designed for large commercial vehicles, including double-decker 'buses. The H.F. ambulance (Fig. 198) has a load capacity of 5 tons and is of the low-lift pattern which allows the necessary clearance for double-

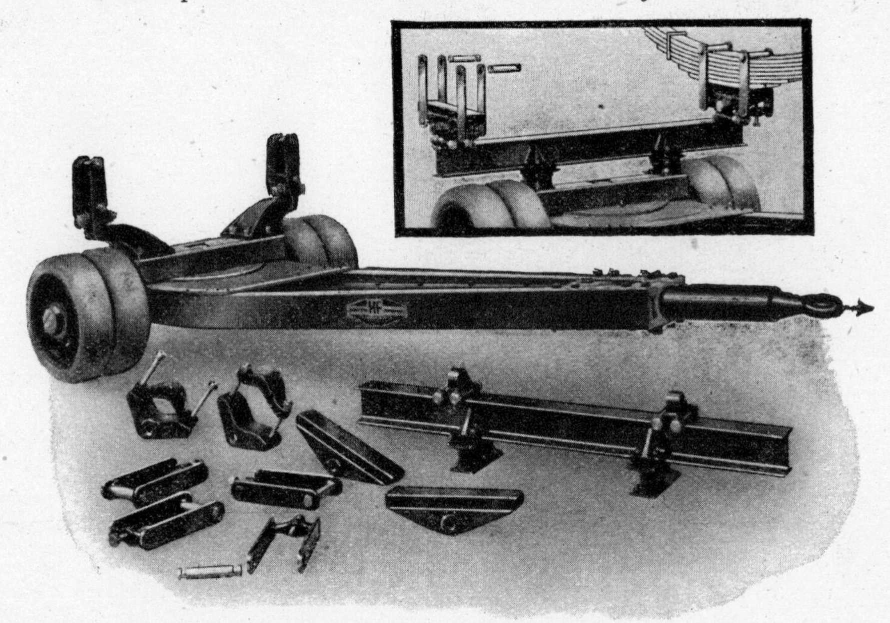

Fig. 197.—Ambulance for Large Commercial Vehicles.

decker 'buses under bridges. Vehicles up to 10 tons can be handled by the bogie type of towing ambulance shown in Fig. 199, which will steer up to an angle of 30 degrees and in any position, the weight being evenly distributed on all four of its wheels. It is only necessary to raise the damaged vehicle's wheels to 2 or 3 in. above the ground.

The frame of the ambulance enables the crutches to be kept very low for this purpose. The steel wheels are mounted on Timken combined thrust and radial roller-bearings.

The method of use when the rear wheels of a damaged vehicle are to be raised and the vehicle carried on the ambulance is to place the latter under the rear axle (usually under the spring pads), the pole being lashed to the cross-bracing of the chassis. When the front wheels are damaged, the ambulance is placed under the front axle in the usual manner.

When all of the four wheels are out of action the ambulance is positioned under the back axle and the fore part of the vehicle is raised by a

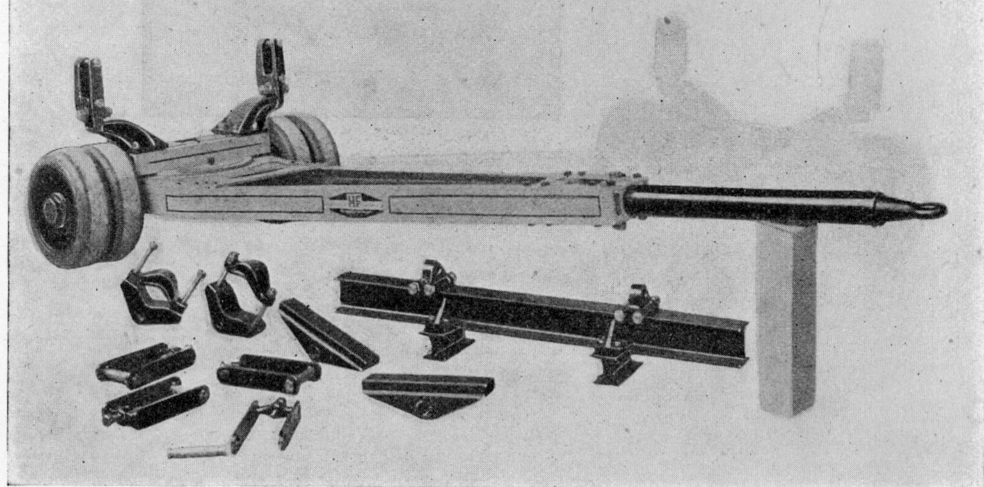

Fig. 198.—The H.F. 5-ton Ambulance, with its various fitments for Front and Rear Axles with Central and Offset Differentials.

Fig. 199.—A 10-ton Ambulance for Heavy Vehicles.
A—Crutches for Front Axles. B—Crutches for Back Axles. C—Spring-pad Brackets. D—Spring-pad Yokes. E—Spring Pads.

crane mounted on the breakdown lorry, for towing ; alternatively, two ambulances can be used, one at the front and the other at the back. The towing speed should not exceed 10 m.p.h.

The ambulance in question has 13-in. wheels, 6 in. wide, with wheel track of 48 in. The total weight is 10 cwt. 3 qrs.

TOWING POLES

Although the common method of towing by means of an ordinary chain or rope is applicable in many cases, without any risk of serious damage if there is a second driver in the towed vehicle, it is quite inexpedient for modern repair and accident service purposes, for the flexible towing member is liable to become entangled in the steering gear of the vehicle being towed. In addition, unless there is another person in the latter vehicle whenever the service or towing car is braked, the one behind is apt to bump into its rear. For these reasons the towing pole, illustrated in Fig. 201, is particularly convenient. This device embodies certain improvements upon the earlier model towing poles. One of these is the anchoring device, which has been altered in a way which greatly facilitates the application of the pole to the damaged vehicle. The attachment to the salvage vehicle consists of a pin and shackle which engages with a fixed bracket on the vehicle. The shackle is connected to the pole through a shock-absorbing spring. The anchoring device, which can readily be attached to the axles of all sizes of vehicles, comprises a pair of jaws

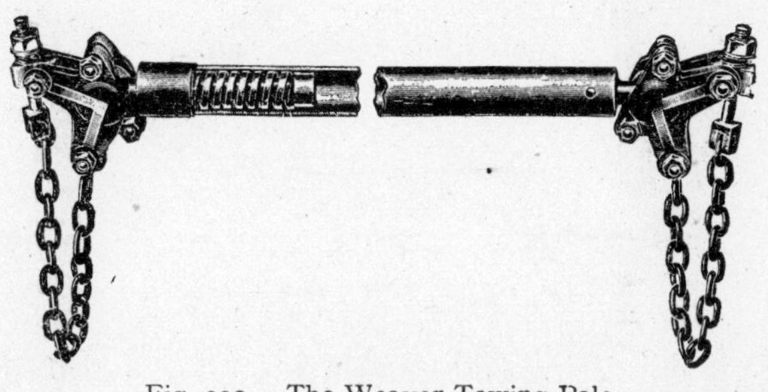

Fig. 200.—The Weaver Towing Pole.

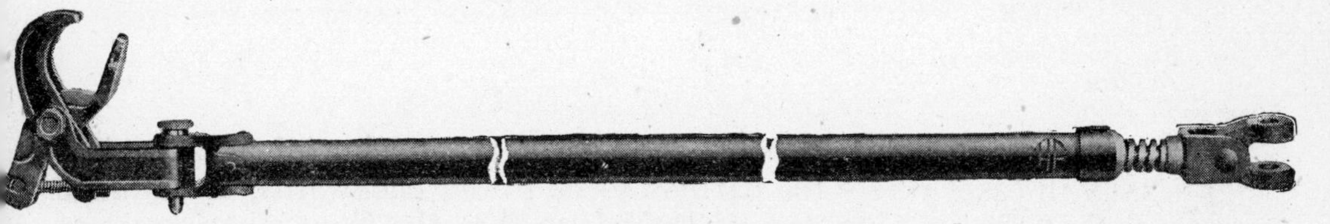

Fig. 201.—The H.F. Improved Towing Pole.

which are anchored to the axle in the manner shown in Fig. 201. It will be seen that the jaws are separated from the pole so that they can be handled in a simple way for fixing. The draw-bar end of the anchoring device is then raised to the horizontal position and is instantly attached to the towing pole by passing a pin through a shackle.

The Weaver towing pole, shown in Fig. 200, has universal jaw clamps at each end for attachment to convenient members of the salvage and damaged vehicles ; in addition it has hook-on connectors to the towing bar. The length is adjustable and a shock-absorber spring is fitted inside

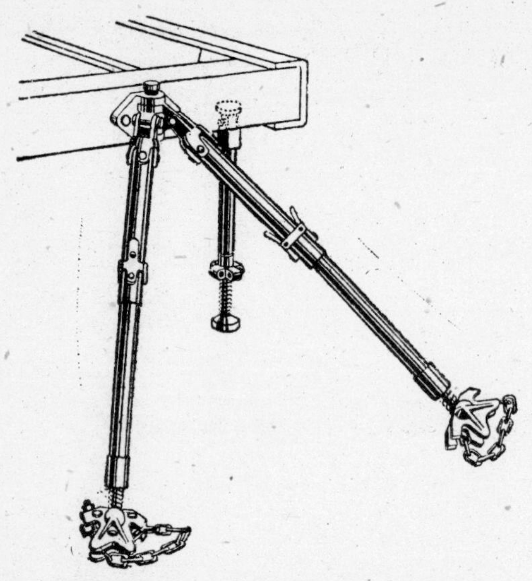
Fig. 202.—The H.F. Distance-bar Unit.

the bar. The towing pole is made so as to withstand compression as well as the normal tension due to towing.

In connection with the use of touring poles, these should always have universal joints at one end or both ends, and should be adjustable in length.

When towing a damaged vehicle which is partly suspended from the jib of the breakdown-lorry crane, it is an advantage to keep the correct distance between the two vehicles; more particularly is this desirable when towing damaged vehicles at good speeds. The H.F. distance bar, illustrated in Fig. 202, enables this condition to be maintained. It consists of two towing bars, attached to the breakdown vehicle by universal joints and to the damaged vehicle by double-grip clamps. The bars incorporate spring shock absorbers.

SUPPORTING JACKS

It is often necessary to support the rear end of the salvage vehicle when using the lifting crane, in order to prevent undue strain or actual tipping of the vehicle. This can be effected by the use of supporting jacks having square-thread adjustment members for altering their lengths to suit the road contour or the height of the chassis frame above the road. These devices—one of which is shown in Fig. 202, behind the right-hand distance bar—are usually arranged as permanent fixtures on the salvage vehicle. When not in use they can be swung up and clipped under the frame.

STEERING-LOCK DEVICES

An important point in connection with the towing of a car, more especially in cases where the car has to be towed backwards, is to make certain that the steering gear is locked, so that the front wheels cannot move relatively to the front axle. As a makeshift expedient, the steering tie bar can be lashed to the front axle, but this tends to bend the usually frail tie bar.

A better method is to employ a pair of steel strips each having suitably drilled holes, and to clamp the front axle and steering tie bar together, or, rather, in their respective normal positions, as shown in Fig. 203. This ensures rigidity of the front wheels and their stub axles.

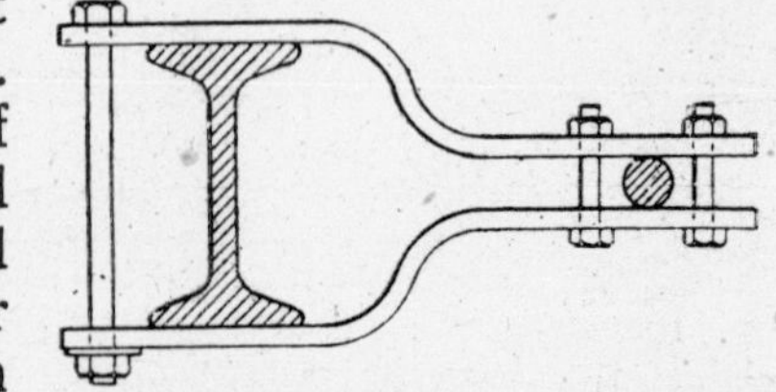
Fig. 203.—Showing Method of Clamping Steering Tie Bar for Towing Purposes.

Special steering-lock devices now available provide for practically any size or design of steering gear. Fig. 204 illustrates the M.E. steering lock, which is an anchorage device for securely locking the steering tie bar to the front axle. The adjustable clamping unit on the left-hand side is intended for attaching rigidly to the front axle, whilst the serrated fork member on the right, with its two clamping bolts and plates, enables a rigid attachment to be made to the steering tie bar in two places. A useful feature of this steering lock is the inclusion of a swivel joint between the front-axle clamp and the steering tie-bar clamps, to allow a vertical movement between the latter, so as to provide for different designs of car having different vertical dispositions of the front axle and steering tie bar.

Fig. 204.—The M.E. Universal Steering-lock Device.

Whenever a car has to be towed with the breakdown ambulance under the rear wheels, the front ones being on the ground, the steering mechanism should be locked by one or other of the methods outlined above.

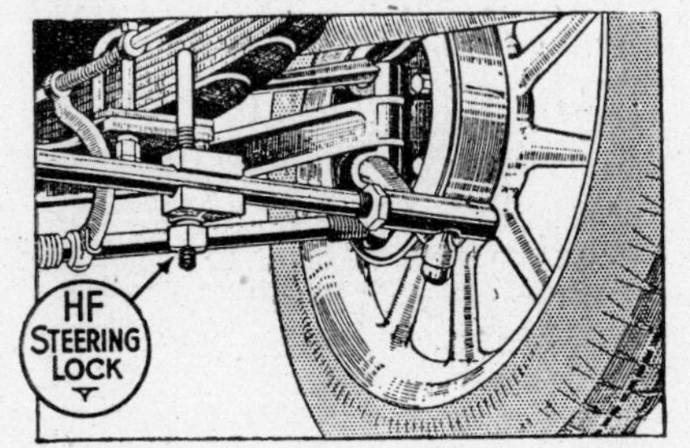

Fig. 205.—The H.F. Steering Lock in position.

The H.F. steering locks consist of two adjustable steel drop forgings mounted on a screw-threaded steel spindle which is attached to the rod, as shown in Fig. 205. One lock is used at each end of the wheels, and it holds with absolute security, so that the front wheels are locked in position for towing the vehicle backwards.

CHAPTER V

CAR ELEVATING FOR INSPECTION AND REPAIR

ALTHOUGH the usual motor pit is desirable for the purpose of working in comfort underneath the car, many owners do not possess such refinements in their garages, and must adopt some other means for achieving the same object.

The other alternative is to elevate the car above the ground in some manner, so that one can work on it from ground level. In most cases, owing to the small amount of clearance between the chassis members and the ground, it is only possible at considerable discomfort to get underneath the car, and certainly it is not possible to work conveniently when in such a cramped position.

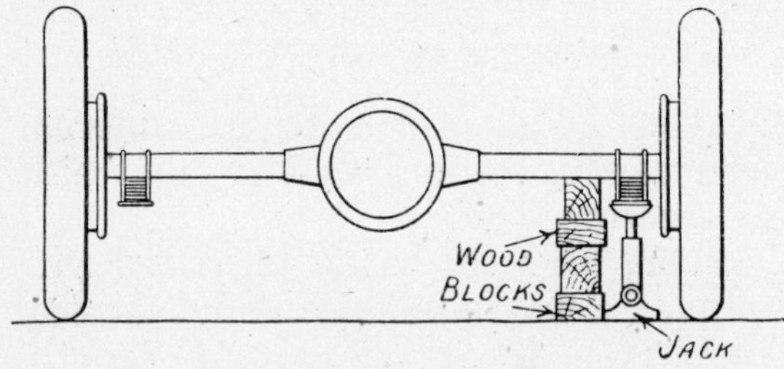

Fig. 206.—Lifting the Car progressively.

The light-car owner has one or two alternatives available, and with a little ingenuity and patience it is a fairly easy matter to elevate his car for inspection, overhaul, or repair. The simplest method is one of direct lifting and blocking; this necessitates the use of an ordinary motor-car jack and a few blocks of wood of different thicknesses. As the usual axle clearances are about 8 to 10 in., the worker should provide himself with a few blocks or short pieces of board of the following thicknesses, namely, 1, 2, and 3 in. The jack is usually placed under the spring attachment to the axle, and the car jacked up to the full extent of the jack (Fig. 206).

See that the hand brake is applied, or that blocks of wood are placed in front of and behind one of the wheels on the ground, to prevent the car moving off the jack whilst it is being lifted.

Next insert a number of the blocks first mentioned between the axle and ground, as close to the upraised jack as possible and under a suitable part of the axle or spring to bear the weight. The jack is then lowered so that the weight is transferred to the blocks, the jack being taken away. This process is repeated in the case of the other end of the (front or rear) axle.

It is then found that the one end of the car has been lifted about 6 to 8 in. The other end may now be lifted in the same way.

By placing blocks under the jack, the car can again be lifted another 6 or 8 in.

When the end of an axle is lifted sufficiently high, a proper retaining stand may be inserted and the temporary blocks removed. Fig. 207 shows a suitable type of stand which can be made from a 3- or 4-in. square-section piece of wood. A base-plate of timber, and a metal strap to prevent splitting, complete the stand in question.

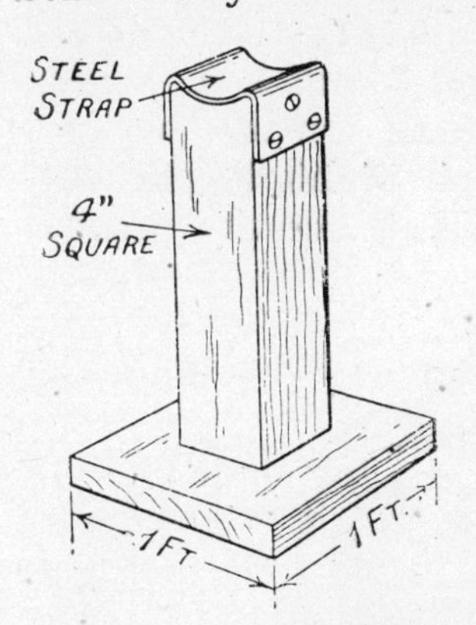

Fig. 207.—Car Axle Stand.

Figs. 208 and 209 show the G.E. car props for motor cars and commercial vehicles respectively. It has two independent height ranges.

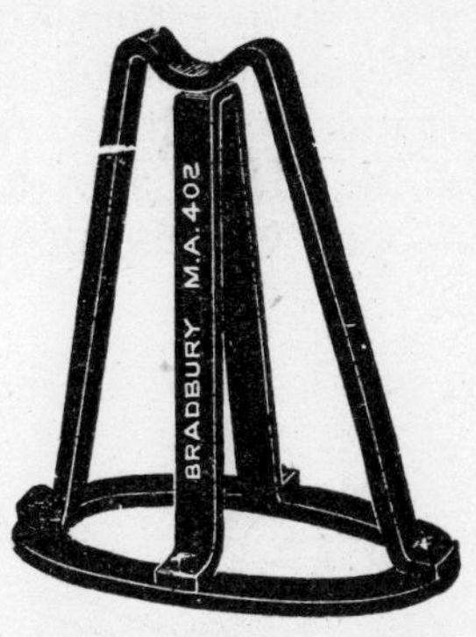

Fig. 208.—The G.E. Axle Support (Fixed Type).

These stands are useful for holding a car off the ground when it is being stored, for it is unwise to leave the tyres in contact with the ground for long periods when not in use.

An improved design of axle stand is shown in Fig. 210. This type will

Fig. 209.—The G.E. Car Prop.

Fig. 210.—The G.E. Adjustable Axle Stand.

accommodate practically any car axle, even if fitted with radius rods, the swinging arm giving a vertical position which is useful when assembling split axles. The jaws of the clamp are of forged steel. The clamp for the swinging arm will grip firmly at any angle with positive stops for the vertical and horizontal positions. An adjustable stand for supporting the propeller shaft, etc., and a detachable grease tray are other features of the stand illustrated.

Another method which enables a light or medium car to be quickly elevated at either end is that depicted in outline in Fig. 211. It consists of a pair of stout planks about 2 to 3 in. thick and 9 to 11 in. wide, provided with trunnions at their centres and a strong central fulcrum stand. It is advisable to have a side plate on each plank to prevent the car wheels moving over the edges, and a solid stop for preventing

Fig. 211.—Illustrating a Simple Method of Raising Car.

the front wheels from moving past a certain point at the farther end of the plank. Also it is necessary to have a movable stop which can quickly be inserted behind the rear wheels once the car is on the planks.

The car is slowly driven up the inclined planks until the front wheels are up against the stop blocks; the front or higher end of the "see-saw" arrangement must, of course, be supported by means of suitable props so as to make a rigid, inclined-plane system.

Once the car is on the inclined planks, it can be moved a little one way or the other until its centre of gravity is over the trunnion axis; the car can then be tilted right up at either end. The height of the trunnion from the ground should be about 15 to 20 in.; this will give a ground clearance, at the uplifted end, of about 2 ft. 6 in. to 3 ft. 4 in. Once the car is balanced, it is quite easy to tilt it one way or the other.

An original design of motor-car lifter, marketed by a German firm, is shown in Fig. 212. This device works on the "see-saw" principle, the two long channel-section ramps being first brought to the inclined position so that one end of each touches the ground. The car is then slowly driven up the steel

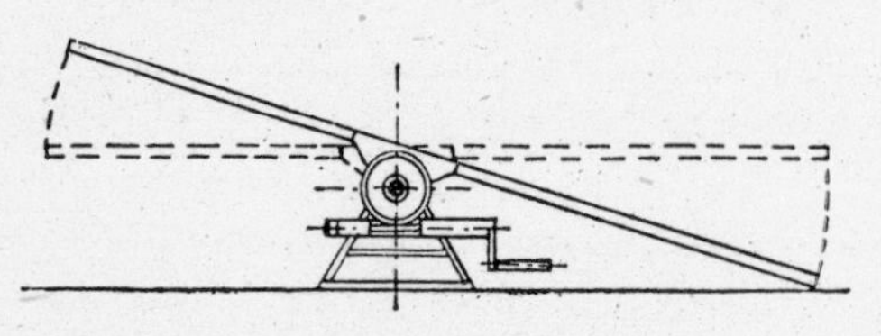

Fig. 212.—A Simple Car-lifting Device.

channels until it is over the centre in a balanced position; stops are provided at the front to ensure that it does not overrun the central positions.

By means of the worm and worm-wheel gearing shown the ramps are then brought into the horizontal position, the car then being about 3 ft. 6 in. to 4 ft. above the ground. It is advisable to fit "chocks" to both front and back wheels before the car is brought to the horizontal position.

Fig. 213 illustrates an American type of car elevator, somewhat on the same principle. It consists of a pair of longitudinal channels up which the car is run. By means of a worm and worm wheel—the former

Fig. 213.—A One-man Balancing-type Car Elevator.

being actuated by means of the long shaft and handle shown on the left, a wheeled support is moved along so as to rock the complete frame about its central runners. The wheels of the support are operated by means of cables from the worm-wheel shaft.

The elevator illustrated enables the car to be tilted either forwards or backwards, or kept level; the car is raised approximately 2 ft. 6 in. from the ground. The frame shown is capable of elevating a load of 3 tons, and it can be operated by one man. Special cleats are provided to prevent the car from slipping once it is in position on the channel runway.

It is useful to note that it is often more convenient to tilt a car sideways than longitudinally, from the point of view of accessibility of the lower parts.

MAKESHIFT CAR-LIFTING DEVICES

Another temporary or makeshift expedient in connection with the elevation of the car consists in making a wooden runway out of 9-in.

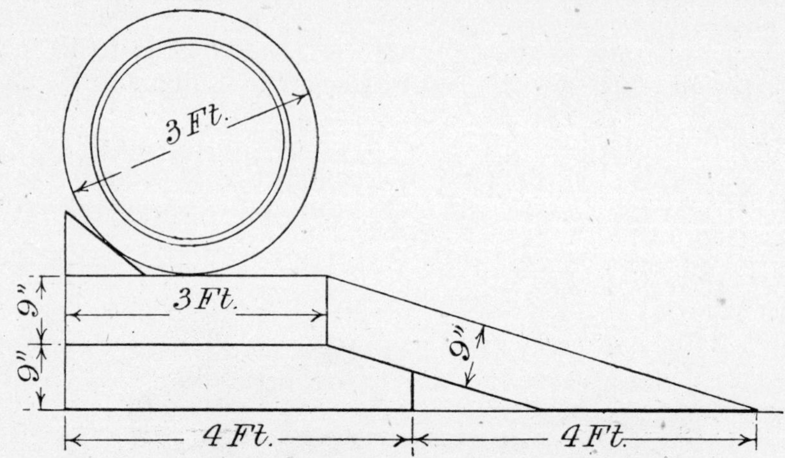

Fig. 214.—Illustrating Easily Constructed Light Car Elevator.

planks of timber. In this connection old railway sleepers will be found very useful, for these are about the right width and thickness for the purpose; moreover, they are very strong.

Fig. 214 shows a suitable runway built up of planks. The dimensions shown are appropriate for a light car, and allow the front (or rear) wheels to be lifted about 18 in. from the ground. It is necessary to have a slope of not more than about 1 in 4 for the runway. A suitable stop should be provided to prevent the wheels dropping over the front edges of the runways after being slowly driven up the slopes.

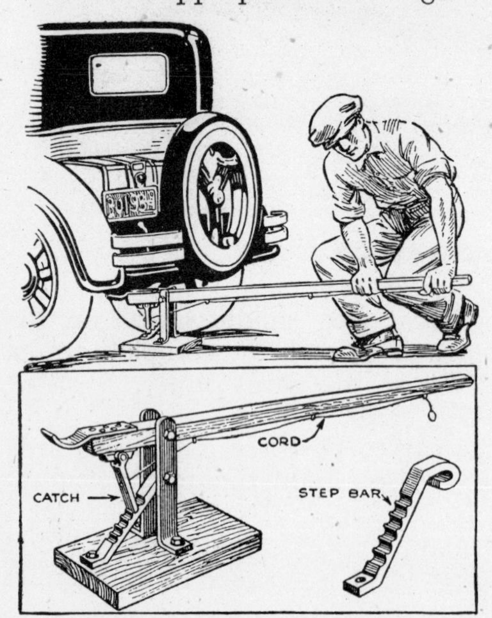

Fig. 215.—A Simple Car-lifting Device.

A SIMPLE CAR-LIFTING DEVICE

The usual car-lifting devices are often too expensive for use in the smaller workshops and garages, so that the mechanic uses either the ordinary type of car jack or devises his own lifting gear.

It is not a difficult matter to make a simple lifting jack, using timber for the main parts and metal for the essential stress-bearing members.

Fig. 215 shows a home-made jack (described in *Mechanics*) made from a wooden base-board and a wooden lever with metal fittings for the bearing brackets, lifting lip, and stop device. The catch and step bar are fitted for the purpose of holding the car in the lifted position. To release the catch the lever is pressed downwards so as to lift the car a little and the cord under the lifting lever is pulled so as to disengage the catch; the car can then be lowered on to the ground.

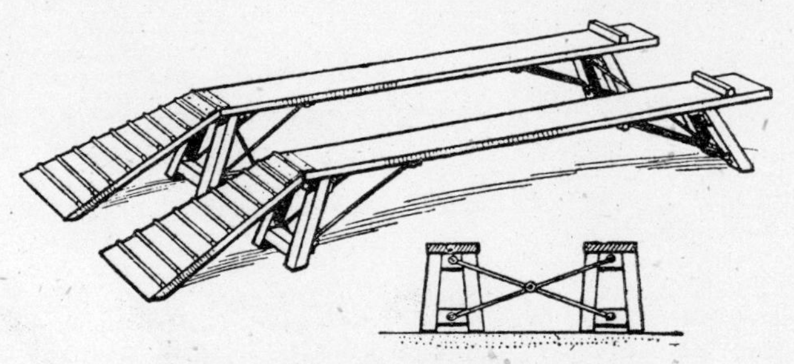

Fig. 216.—The Dove Folding Car Ramp.

CAR RAMPS

The Dove folding car ramp shown in Fig. 216 consists of a pair of trestle tables and a "run-up"; the tables are inter-connected by means of diagonal rods to maintain them at the correct distance apart. When not required these rods can be disconnected and the trestles folded flat for storage purposes.

The H.F. car elevator, illustrated in Fig. 217, consists of a pair of horizontal channels, raised 2 ft. above the ground, and a corresponding pair of sloping channels. The troughs thus provided are arranged to take the wheels of the car; the flanges of the channels prevent the wheels from moving sideways off the troughs.

The elevator has a kind of winch for pulling the car up the inclined channels and along the horizontal ones. Provision is also made for raising either the front or rear wheels clear of the tracks. The overall length is 25 ft. and width of tracks 1 ft. 5 in. each. The distance between the tracks is 3 ft. 1 in., so that all sizes of car wheel tracks are provided for. The elevator will raise cars up to 3 tons weight on to the horizontal channels. When not in use, one track can be closed on to the other for space-saving purposes.

Fig. 217.—The H.F. Car Elevator.

A convenient pattern of garage elevator for motor cars of all types is that made by Messrs. Mann & Egerton (Figs. 218 and 219). This consists of a pair of channel-section longitudinal members forming the runways for the wheels, mounted on strong inclined supports attached to channelled base-members.

The ramp is so designed that when it is desired to lift the car, the runways are inclined, with the left-hand sides on the ground. A winch

Fig. 218.—The M.E. Car Ramp, showing Car Partly Elevated.

Fig. 219.—The M.E. Car Ramp, showing Car in Elevated Position.

is provided on the right-hand side; and a hook and cable for attaching to the car and pulling it up the runways. As the car is hauled up, the car and frame tend to balance on the base-plate, in "see-saw" fashion, so that the car gradually assumes a horizontal attitude above the ground and automatically balances itself. When in this position, adjustable safety legs, which are provided at the left-hand corners, are

Fig. 220. Fig. 221.

hinged downwards and secured by strut members, so that there is no likelihood of the stand moving.

The stand itself when in position offers practically no obstruction to the mechanic working under the car; a more convenient car elevator and working arrangement could hardly be imagined.

The members of the frame are made of mild steel. The longitudinal channels forming the wheel runways can be adjusted laterally by

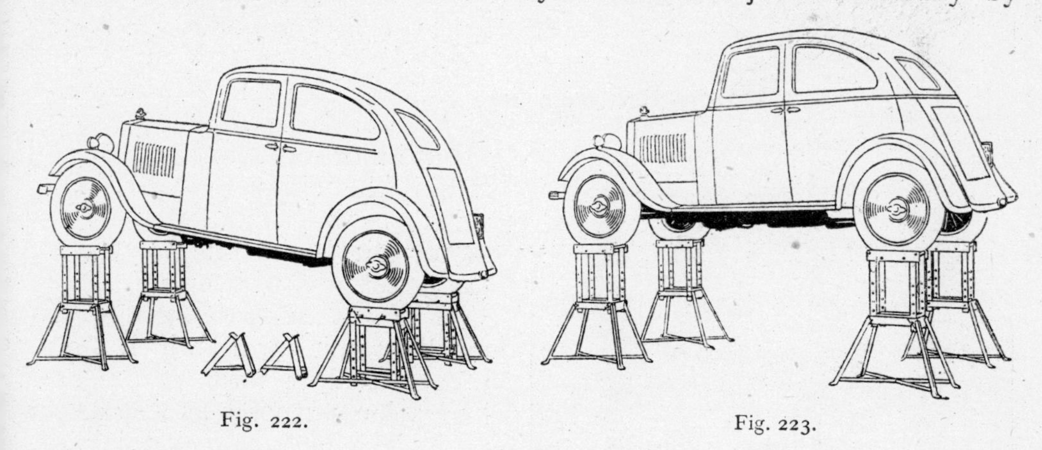

Fig. 222. Fig. 223.

means of slotted cross-bars, so that a car of any track width within its limits can be accommodated.

An easy and inexpensive method of raising a car for servicing and inspection purposes in establishments not possessing hydraulic or electric lifts is the G.E. Jack Hoist one, illustrated in Figs. 220 to 223. The rear end of the car is first jacked up with a high-lift jack, such as the G.E. "Hi-draulic" Jack, or "Herculift" Jack shown in Fig. 234. When raised to a sufficient height, the wheels are lowered slightly on to the wheel stands shown in Fig. 220. Next, the front end of the car is jacked up and the front-wheel stands placed in position; the wheels are then lowered on to these stands (Fig. 221), when the car is raised about 2 ft. above ground. By repeating the jacking and lowering procedure and inserting the extended wheel stands shown in Figs. 222 and 223, the car can be raised about 3 ft. in all above the ground. Special axle supports can, however, be used instead of the wheel stands; the total lift can be extended to about 4 ft. above the ground.

The method in question is a quick one, for with a hydraulic lifting jack the car can be raised 3 ft. and supported on its four stands in six minutes.

HYDRAULIC CAR LIFTS

In order to examine the underneath parts of motor vehicles in the most convenient manner the motor pit is rapidly being replaced with the hydraulic car-lifting platform.

The motor pit is by no means an ideal method of examining a vehicle, for it is usually badly illuminated and invariably damp and dirty; moreover, the presence of a pit below the floor of the garage or workshop is always a potential source of danger.

Fig. 224.—The Tecalemit Hydraulic Car Lift.

The hydraulic car lift has the advantage of working above the level of the ground, so that the mechanic stands on dry ground and has a good illumination for his work. It is thus possible to work in comfort and to get all round the sides of the car or vehicle as well as underneath; the motor pit limits one to part of the underneath side only.

Fig. 224 illustrates the Tecalemit hydraulic car lift which is now widely used in large garages for inspection purposes as well as for rapid greasing and general lubrication of the car. In this lift the load is carried by a column of oil, but the actual operation is by compressed air, at a working pressure up to 150 lb. per sq. in.

The lift itself is a well-designed steel structure having runways for the wheels of the car. The car is run on to these channelled members, the brakes applied, or suitable wheel chocks used, and the complete structure and car are raised above the ground by means of a $10\frac{3}{8}$-in.-diameter hydraulic ram.

The latter is powerful enough to lift cars up to 3 tons weight. The runways have an overall length of 16 ft. 10 in. and an overall width of 6 ft. $0\frac{1}{2}$ in., with an individual runway of 21 inches. The ramps are well splayed so as to avoid damage to the tyres when running on the machine.

The lift can be raised to a maximum height of 5 feet *in about half a minute* and can be held at any convenient height with perfect safety.

The installation of the lift is simple and inexpensive. It requires only one supply pipe to the compressed-air line, this being fitted with two cocks, one for lifting and the other for lowering. Incidentally the lift can readily be *used as a turntable* for swinging the car around to any angle.

The lift in question is particularly convenient for *high-pressure greasing* of the car, the lubricant being forced by air pressure into the bearings of the chassis members, as shown in Fig. 223. In this connection the Tecale-

Fig. 225.—Showing Car Lift used for Rapid High-pressure Greasing of Chassis.

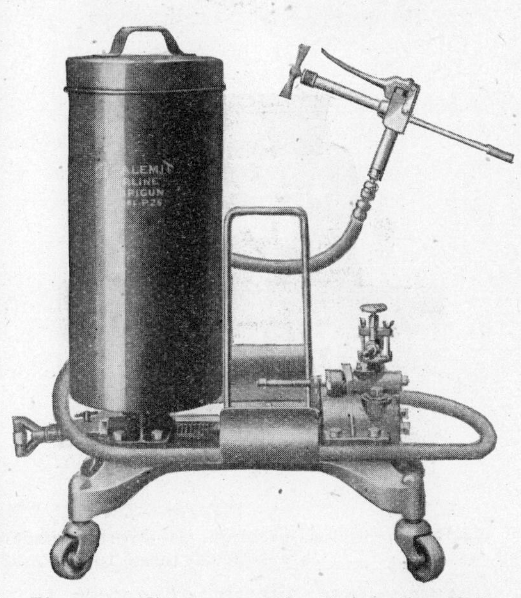

Fig. 226.—High-pressure Car Lubrication Unit (Tecalemit).

mit " Lubrigun " (Fig. 226) or " Lubriflator " device is now widely used. It is operated by compressed air and, by means of its differential piston, gives a pressure on the lubricant about twenty times that of the air pressure ; it has a capacity of one pound of lubricant.

Another type of British elevator, namely, the H.F. " Manulift," is illustrated in Fig. 227. This is an original type of car elevator designed to provide the utmost accessibility to the underneath parts of the chassis of cars. The car may either be driven up the tracks, or hauled up, for the latter are permanently elevated at one end. The car can be worked upon in this inclined position or it can be raised above the ground to the horizontal position by means of the crane supplied. The height when elevated is 3 ft.

A special feature of the " Manulift " elevator is that all cross-members and other obstructions have been avoided ; this provides a clear and

Fig. 227.—The H.F. " Manulift " Car Elevator.
A—Hauling the car up ramp. B—Working under front part of car. C—Lifting the rear part of body. D—The car raised to the horizontal position above the ground.

uninterrupted means of access to axles, gear boxes, crankcases, brake mechanisms, etc. A jacking system is available to lift the whole chassis clear of the runways so that the four wheels are completely free for removal, adjustment, etc. In conjunction with the lift special chassis supports are available, by means of which the back axle can be removed in a very short period—an operation which is otherwise difficult. One of the tracks is adjustable to suit the varying widths of different cars. Further, it is another advantage that this track may be pushed up close to the fixed track, so that it occupies far less storage space.

MOVING THE CAR IN GARAGE

It is frequently necessary to move a car from one part of the garage to another, and if there is little available room, fore and aft, for the car to be moved ahead or in the reverse direction, it is often a matter of difficulty to transfer it laterally. A good deal of useful time may be lost in the endeavour to shift the car to the desired spot. In order to facilitate this operation, more particularly in crowded garages, special ambulances, trolley jacks, and "car skates" have been devised, and are usually most effective for the purpose.

Any garage trolley-jack with pivoting wheels can be used for moving a car sideways. The jack is inserted under, say, the front axle and the car lifted. The jack, with the front of the car on it, is then wheeled sideways a certain distance and the weight lowered. If now the jack is placed under the rear axle and the latter lifted, the rear end may be moved sideways until the whole car is again parallel to its original position. The operation may then be repeated as often as desired and the car moved through any distance sideways.

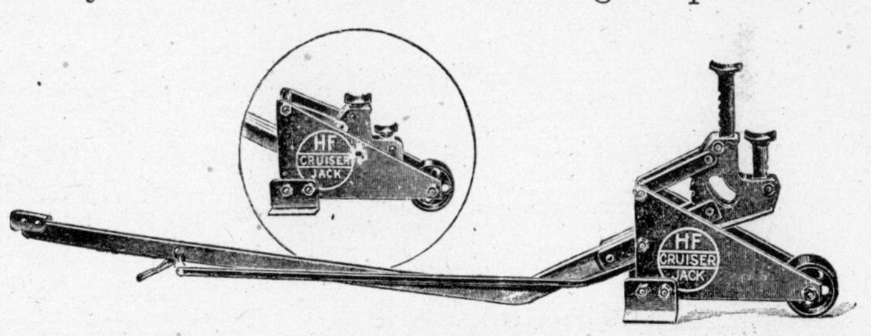

Fig. 228.—A useful Garage Car-lifting and Moving Jack.

Fig. 228 illustrates the H.F. "Cruiser" jack, which is particularly suited to the operations described. The axle rests on the two saddle members shown on the right, and the operation of elevating the car is a rapid one. The axle rests are placed under one of the car's axles, the handle being raised for this purpose, and the handle then pushed downwards, thereby lifting the car. As the rests are inclined backwards when the car is lifted, and the lifting lever rests on the triangular frame of the jack, it will be seen that there is no possibility of the axle dropping on to the ground again. There is a releasing lever fitted for lowering purposes.

CAR WHEEL SKATES

The car can also conveniently be moved about the garage in any direction by means of the appliances known as "*car skates.*" These consist of pressed-steel troughs, or forgings, provided with three or four castor wheels. The troughs are arranged to be as close to the ground as possible, and the car wheels are jacked up in turn and lowered into the troughs of the skates; they cannot accidentally run off. When all four wheels of the car are thus mounted, it is an easy matter to push the car in any direction.

Fig. 229 shows the H.F. car skates, which are strongly made and are provided with castors mounted on ball-bearings.

GARAGE LIFTING APPLIANCES

We have already described certain lifting devices in connection with breakdown work and car moving in the garage. There are several very useful lifting appliances which have not been described, and to which reference will now be made.

Coming within the category of garage jacks is a variety of makes of lifting devices, the general purpose of which is to quickly run under the car or vehicle and to lift one of the axles by means of a few strokes of a long handle. A ratchet device holds the car in the lifted position; a suitable release trip device is also essential. Garage jacks of this type should have a lift of at least 8 in., with a minimum height of about 6 in.; for low-pressure tyres this is essential. It is not proposed to describe the ordinary types of mechanical and hydraulic jack in this work (an account of these has been given in *Modern Motor Cars* [1]), but rather to confine our attention to lifting devices of special interest.

Fig. 229.—Car Skate, Single-wheel Type.

Fig. 230 shows the Bradbury garage jack which has been designed for lifting cars fitted with either balloon or high-pressure tyres. By means of an ingenious device an actual lift of 6 in. is obtained with one downward stroke of the handle. An auxiliary crutch is provided for very low axles and both crutches are fitted with adjustable extension pieces, making the jack suitable for the varying axle heights of different makes of cars. The working parts are constructed from malleable iron and of steel.

Fig. 230.—The Bradbury Garage Jack.

The jack shown has a bottom crutch height range of $5\frac{1}{2}$ in. to $13\frac{1}{4}$ in., and lift of 4 in. The top crutch height range is $8\frac{7}{8}$ in. to 19 in., and lift 6 in. It weighs 33 lb. and is suitable for cars up to 30 cwt.

Fig. 231 illustrates the "Robot" trolley jack which was designed

[1] The Caxton Publishing Co., Ltd.

for the quick and convenient handling of cars. It has a special tilting mechanism to expedite handling and positioning of the jack.

The front wheels can be tilted for easy manipulation. It has a vertical lift from the lowest position of 6 in. up to 17½ in., and will handle car weights up to 5,000 lb. Owing to its low construction, it can be used at right angles to a car. The crutch can be raised at once, to engage the axle by slight pressure on a pedal.

Fig. 231.—The H.F. "Robot" Jack.

The G.E. lorry jack shown in Fig. 232 is particularly useful for dealing with heavy commercial vehicles. It has a lifting capacity of nearly 5 tons, and a lifting range of 6½ in. (minimum) to 19½ in. (maximum). It is sufficiently long to accommodate vehicles with a lengthy overhang, and it has a quick-adjustment handle to enable the crutch to be raised rapidly to the axle height ready for lifting; it weighs 2 cwt. 3 qrs.

A well-designed general-purpose jack for garage use is that known as the G.E. "Hyer-lift." It lifts a dead load of 45 cwt. to a height of 40 in., so that the front or back of a car can be raised sufficiently far above the ground to enable inspection of its

Fig. 232.—The G.E. Lorry Jack which has a Lifting Capacity of about 5 tons and Lift of 13 in. from a Minimum Height of 6½ in.

underneath parts to be carried out. Fig. 233 shows the jack in position after lifting the front of a car.

A special design of jack, for heavy passenger-vehicle use, is shown in Figs. 234 and 235. Known as the G.E. "Herculift," it has a lifting capacity of 10,000 lb. and a vertical lifting range of $5\frac{1}{8}$ in. (minimum) to $39\frac{1}{2}$ in. (maximum). The width of the front wheels is 26 in. and of the castor wheels, 24 in. The jack is easily moved from place to place by swivelling on the rear ball castors; for this purpose a rigid socket is provided for the handle, and the jack can be swung round in its own length. It weighs 4 cwt. 1 qr.

Fig. 233.—The G.E. "Hyer-lift" Jack in Operation.

PORTABLE GARAGE CRANES

It is practically essential, in modern garages, to have one or more portable-type cranes for lifting engines and similar heavy parts from

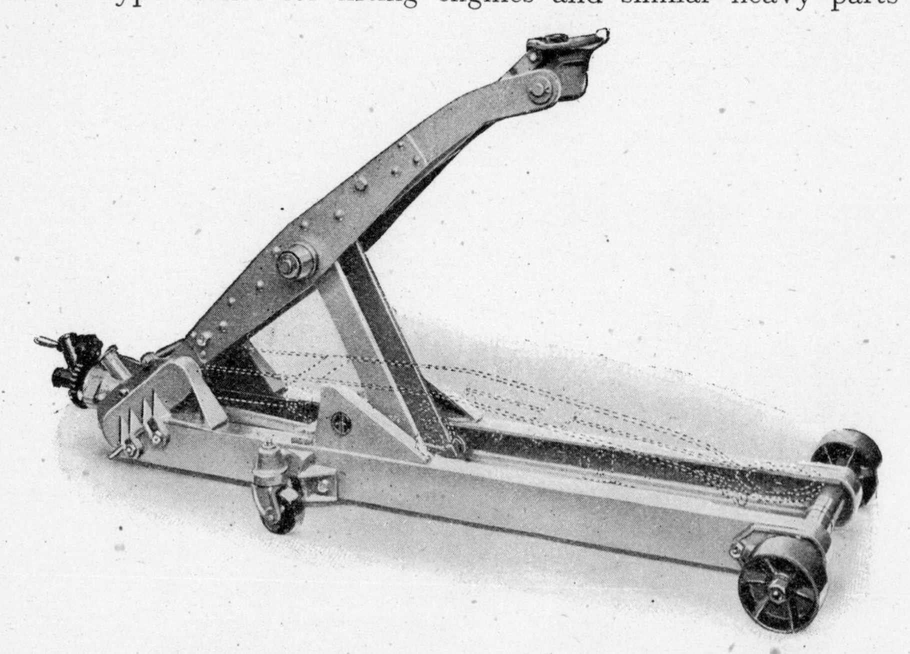

Fig. 234.—The G.E. "Herculift" Jack.

chassis and transporting them to other parts of the garage workshop or on to machines.

Whilst block and tackle can be employed for lifting the heavier motor-vehicle parts, it is seldom convenient for transport purposes. Various types of portable crane are now available for garage use. These possess the common features of two relatively long girder feet, provided with wheels at each end and an overhanging beam or jib, such that the vertical line through the centre of gravity of the weights of the lifted parts always falls well within the wheel base.

Fig. 235.—The "Herculift" Jack lifting the Front Axle of an A.E.C. Double-deck Motor 'Bus.

These portable cranes are made in various models, from 15 cwt., rising in 5-cwt. steps to 2 tons.

The lifting device is a winch of the geared type, with locking pawls for holding the lifted weight in any position for transport. The winch is generally arranged at one end of the crane in a convenient position for the operator to use; pulleys are provided between the winch and crane hook for the cable.

A useful garage floor crane is that illustrated in Fig. 236. This can be used for lifting heavy automobile components, such as engines, gear boxes, bodies, and even the fore or aft portions of cars themselves.

Fig. 236.—A useful Garage Crane.

It has a capacity of about 15 cwt., is very rigid and stable, i.e. it will not overturn when lifting, due to the two long feet. A worm and worm wheel operated by a shaft and long handle supply the lifting means. The winch handle is sufficiently near to the crane-hook for a single operator to manipulate or guide the job being lifted or lowered. Ball thrust bearings are fitted to the winch. Two screw jacks are provided, to enable the weight to be taken off the rear roller, when it is desired to keep the crane stationary.

An improved garage crane of the portable pattern, known as the "Jackrane," is shown in Fig. 237; it is designed for lifting heavy engines, etc., and moving them about the garage or workshop.

Of rigid construction, it is provided with a long base consisting of two channel members provided with fixed bearing-pin wheels at the front and castor wheels at the back, or winch end.

The hook to which the lifting tackle is secured is mounted on the end of a cantilever arm, the other end of which forms a frame having rollers for sliding freely up and down the vertical column. This frame is raised by means of a cable from the hand-operated winch below. Ratchet wheel and pawl gear is provided for holding the lifted weight in any position.

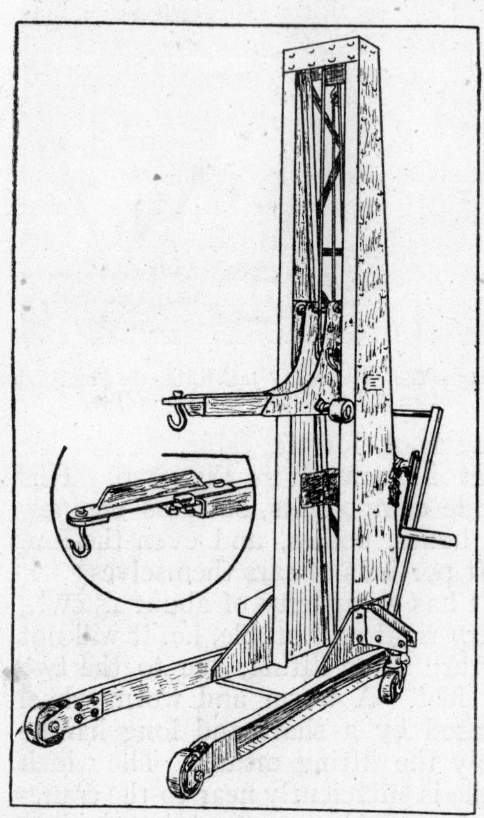

Fig. 237.—The "Jackrane" for lifting heavy engines.

Fig. 238.—The H.F. Lifting Gantry shown in Position for Engine Lifting.

When used as a high-lifting jack, this machine has a range of lift of 7 ft. It can be used to elevate either end of a heavy vehicle to a suitable height for under-chassis work; at its lowest point the crutch will easily pass under the lowest axles. The "Jackrane" is particularly suited to the lifting of engines from heavy commercial vehicles, such as 'buses, where the canopy overhangs the engine.

The overall height is 9 ft. 3 in.; maximum height of hook, 7 ft.; width of frame, 3 ft. 3 in. overall; width of base channels, 2 ft. 7 in.; length of frame, 6 ft., and weight capacity, 1 ton. It is made by Messrs. Harvey Frost, Ltd.

Fig. 239.—The Leyland Method of Removing the Engine.

Fig. 240.—Another View of the Leyland Engine-hoisting Portable Crane.

Fig. 238 shows a particularly neat car-engine gantry, or lifting device, that can be used for lifting the engines of cars and commercial vehicles. It can also be employed for lifting the front or back ends of

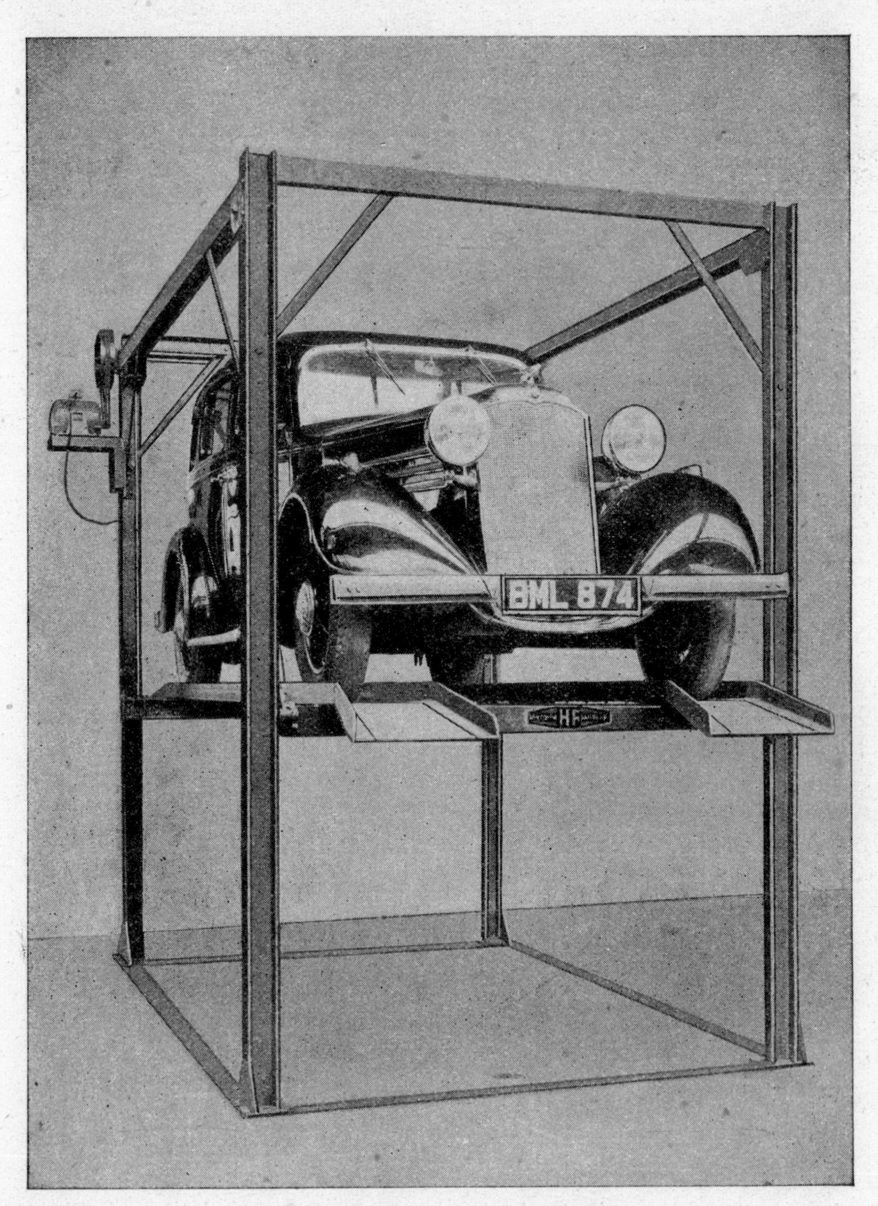

Fig. 241.—The H.F. Electric Car Lift.

vehicles above the ground, so that access is possible to the underneath portions.

This gantry is made in the 2- and 3-ton models. It has a height of 10 ft. in the car, and 9 ft. in the commercial model, and a lift of about 8 ft. 6 in. It is simply wheeled into position over the car or chassis, and lifting can at once be commenced.

Figs. 239 and 240 show the method employed by Messrs. Leyland Motors, Ltd., to lift the engine unit from (and to replace it in) the chassis. A three-wheeled lifting crane is run partly under the chassis so that the jib of the crane is directly over the engine. After the lifting tackle has been placed in position around the engine, the lifting handle is operated, when the engine is hoisted vertically upwards.

Fig. 242.—Inspection Pits for Motor 'Buses.

ELECTRIC CAR LIFT

As an alternative to the hydraulic ram type of lift, previously described, the electric lift has certain advantages. It does not require the provision of a ram cylinder pit and hydraulic pump for its operation.

Fig. 243.—End view of Pit, showing Electric Lamps for Illumination Purposes.

It is built entirely above the ground-level and can be installed at practically negligible cost. There is no oily ram or cross-bars to hamper the mechanic, although the presence of the four vertical channel supports does not afford the full accessibility of the ram-type elevator.

The car lift (Fig. 241) has been designed to deal with cars of all types, from the 7-h.p. baby car to the heavy car of 2 tons weight.

The ramp is lifted by means of cables from an electric motor drive using belt drive to the operating shaft, gear wheels, screw and nut device; the thrust of the screw is taken on ball-bearings. The 2-ton lift model requires a 2-h.p. electric motor and will lift its full load through a vertical distance of $4\frac{1}{2}$ ft. in $1\frac{1}{2}$ minutes. The minimum lift is $4\frac{1}{2}$ ft.; overall height, 10 ft. 7 in.; overall length, 15 ft.; overall width, 7 ft. 2 in., and clearance between tracks, 3 ft.

The platform when raised cannot run down, accidentally, as the screw lifting mechanism is self-sustaining, whilst the ropes have a factor of safety of six. In addition, a safety device is incorporated which will prevent the ramp from falling should a rope break, thus meeting the Board of Trade's regulations for hoists.

INSPECTION PIT FOR LARGE VEHICLES

In the case of large fleets of passenger or commercial vehicles it is much quicker and more convenient, as a rule, to inspect the underneath parts of the chassis by running each vehicle, in turn, over a specially designed "pit," similar to those shown in Figs. 242 and 243. The pits are provided with G.E.C. flood-lighting units on either side so that the underneath members are well illuminated. As the "pits" are deep enough for an operator to stand vertical they enable inspections and adjustments, lubrication, dismantling and similar operations to be carried out. Massive masonry stops are provided at the front ends to limit the forward travel of the front wheels.

CHAPTER VI

THE FUEL SYSTEM AND CARBURETTOR

SINCE the majority of modern cars employ either the vacuum or petrol pump methods of feeding the fuel to the carburettor, the present practical considerations will be confined to these two systems, more particularly to the latter one, but some notes will be given on the gravity-feed system also.

GRAVITY FEED

In this method the fuel tank is fitted at a higher horizontal level than the carburettor, so that the fuel flows by gravity to the carburettor.

In the fitting of this system of fuel feed, the only precautions which must be observed are as follows, viz.:

(1) To see that when the fuel is low in the tank, and the car is on the steepest incline it may be called upon to climb, the level of the fuel in the tank is at least 4 in. above that in the float chamber. Fig. 244 illustrates this point in the case of a car climbing a 20 per cent. gradient.

(2) To ensure that the fuel will

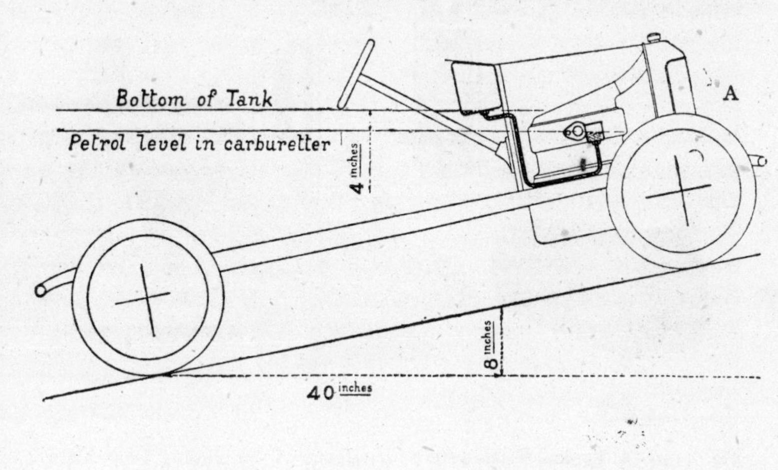

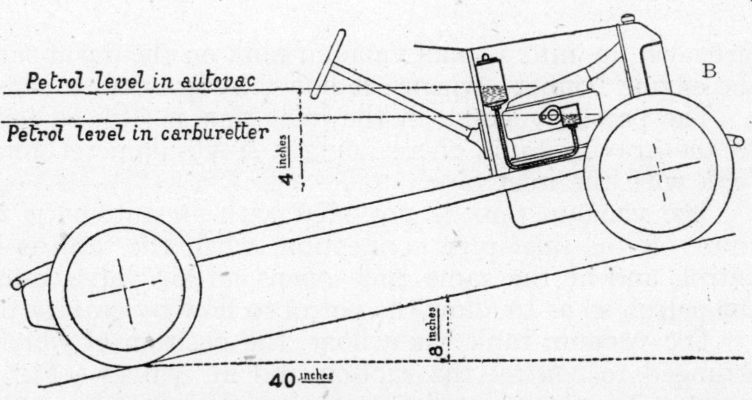

Fig. 244.—(A) Showing Lowest Permissible Position of Petrol Tank for Gravity Feed. (B) Showing Lowest Permissible Position of Vacuum-feed Tank.

be properly filtered before it reaches the jet. Most carburettors are fitted with filters in their fuel inlet connections, but we prefer to fit a filter at the fuel-tank end, if the latter is accessible for cleaning.

(3) Avoid soft-soldered joints in the petrol-pipe connections; these should be brazed or hard-soldered to prevent cracking under the constant road vibration.

(4) To introduce a spiral or loop in the petrol pipe leading from the fuel tank to carburettor. Never make a direct or straight connection, or the pipe will fracture sooner or later.

VACUUM FEED

In this system (Fig. 245) the fuel tank is situated below the carburettor level, either at the rear of car or below the seats, and the fuel is sucked,

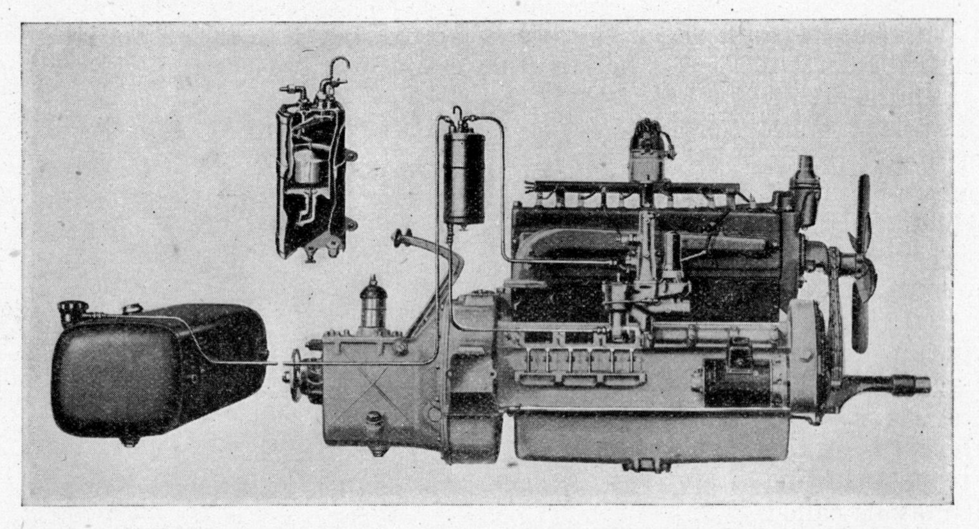

Fig. 245.—A Typical Fuel-system Arrangement, employing Rear Main Tank and Vacuum Feed.

or drawn up, into a small vacuum tank on the dashboard—usually under the engine bonnet—whence it flows, by gravity, to the carburettor.

The partial vacuum in the inlet pipe is utilised for sucking the fuel to the gravity tank, there being a small-diameter pipe connecting the tank with the inlet pipe.

The vacuum tank is provided with an automatic mechanism which shuts off the inlet-pipe connection, when the tank is nearly filled with petrol, and at the same time opens an air valve, admitting air above the petrol, so as to allow the petrol to flow by gravity to the carburettor.

The vacuum tank has a float, the position of which on the petrol is arranged to control the suction and air valves. Fig. 246 illustrates a popular American vacuum tank, and Fig. 247 the well-known Autovac system.

Fig. 246.—The Stewart Vacuum Tank.

1, Fuel-pipe Connection	10, Flapper Valve.
2, Filler Plug.	11, Drain Plug.
3, Fuel-filter Screen.	12, Vacuum-pipe Connection.
4, Cover.	13, Air-vent Connection.
5, Valve-toggle Lever.	14, Air Valve.
6, Valve-toggle Lever Spring.	15, Air Passage.
7, Float Lever.	16, Vacuum Valve.
8, Float.	17, Inner Chamber.
9, Float-guide Rod.	18, Outer Chamber.

19, Carburettor Fuel-pipe Connection.

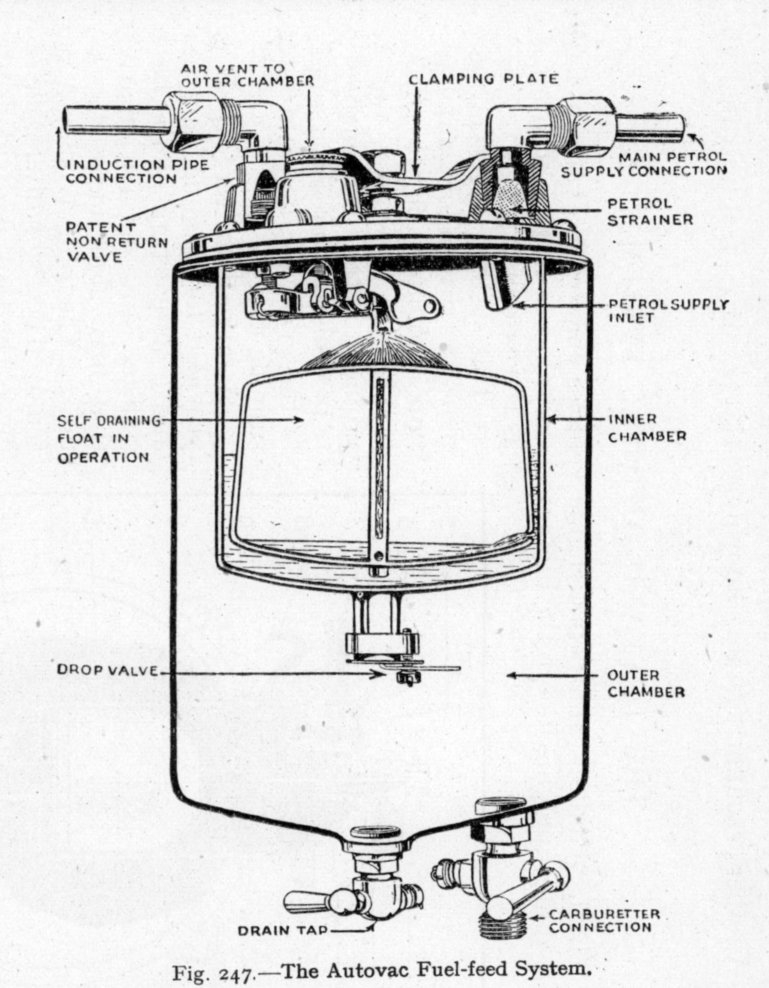

Fig. 247.—The Autovac Fuel-feed System.

Another vacuum system, known as the "G.G.," is illustrated in Fig. 248.

THE LEYLAND AUTOVAC SYSTEM

The Leyland oil- and petrol-engine vehicles employ the vacuum feed system for supplying fuel to the fuel-injection pump, or to the carburettor, as the case may be.

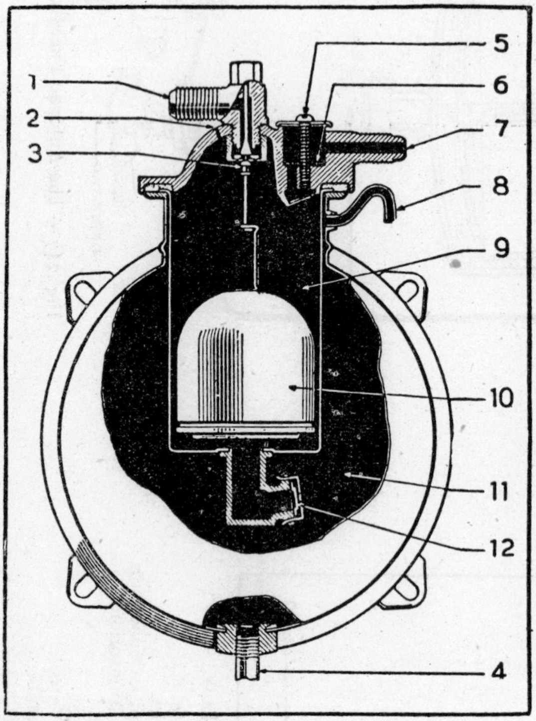

Fig. 248.—"G.G." Vacuum Tank.

1, Vacuum-pipe Connection.
2, Air Vent to Inner Chamber.
3, Vacuum Valve.
4, Carburettor Fuel-pipe Connection.
5, Fuel-filter Screw.
6, Fuel-filter Screen.
7, Fuel-pipe Connection.
8, Air Vent to Outer Chamber.
9, Inner Chamber.
10, Float.
11, Outer Chamber.
12, Flapper Valve.

This system (Fig. 249) employs a two-gallon auxiliary tank mounted on the front bulkhead. A two-way tap A, provided in the tank, enables it to be utilised as a reserve supply in the event of the main tank running dry.

A large-diameter cap B is provided for priming purposes and a sludge trap in the base collects any foreign matter that may gain access to the tank. The plug C should be removed occasionally for cleaning. The tank is divided into two compartments, the inner or vacuum chamber D being connected to the induction pipe and main tank, the lower or reserve chamber E to the carburettor. Communication between the two is effected by a drop valve F at the base of the inner chamber.

The engine suction causes a vacuum in the upper chamber, thus closing the drop valve and drawing fuel from the main tank. As the fuel flows in, the float G rises, and when it has reached a predetermined height two valves are operated. One, H, cuts off the suction and the other, K, admits air; this admission of air destroys the vacuum, releases the drop valve F and allows fuel to flow into the outer chamber E. As the outer chamber is always open to the atmosphere through the air vent L, the fuel flows to the carburettor by gravity. When the float falls with the outflow of fuel from the inner chamber, the valve mechanism is again operated and the process repeated.

MAINTENANCE OF VACUUM FEED SYSTEMS

Before proceeding to a consideration of faults and their detection in vacuum feed systems, a few remarks will be given on the subject of their maintenance. There are three principal items requiring occasional attention, namely:

(1) *The Filter.*—There is usually a filter, to be found at the top of the tank where the fuel enters from the main supply pipe from main fuel tank. This should be inspected periodically, and cleaned if necessary.

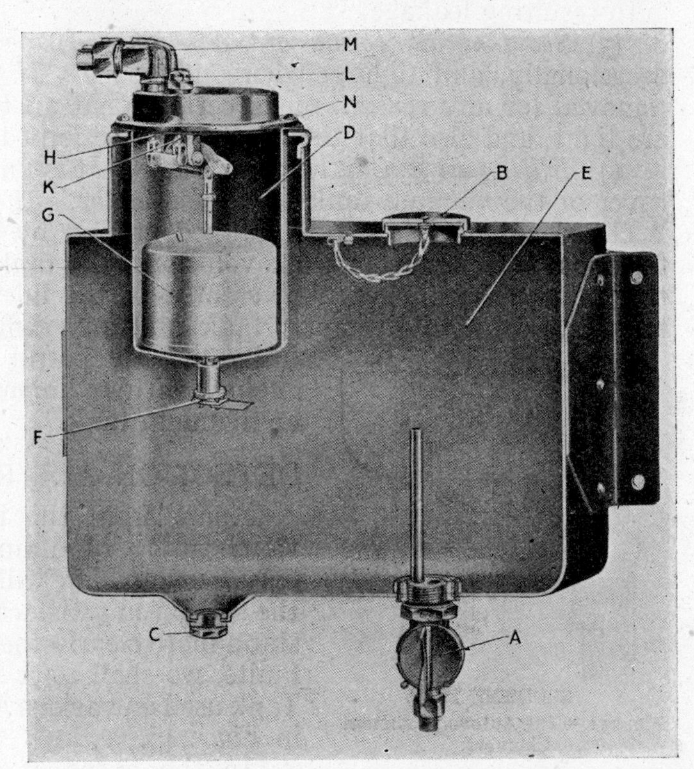

Fig. 249.—The Leyland Vacuum Feed Tank.

Most of the troubles experienced with vacuum systems can be traced to obstructions caused by foreign matter in the fuel. Fig. 250 illustrates the Autovac filter and petrol connection. To gain access to this filter, disconnect pipe at elbow marked PETROL, slack off clamp nut, and remove elbow; the filter cone lies underneath. Replace filter as shown in illustration (Fig. 247).

If elbow is tight, grip between jaws of a spanner and turn.

The filter should be cleaned about once every month.

(2) *The Sediment Chamber.*—The lower part of the vacuum tank is usually made conical in form, and provided with a plug or tap at its lowest part. After the car has been in use for some time, water and sediment from the petrol collect in this part of the tank, and should be drained off. The concave or conical base acts as a trap for fine sediment and water, the carburettor supply being taken at a slightly higher level. The petrol should be drained off, about once a fortnight, until it runs quite clear. If the petrol does not run when tap is opened or plug is removed, pass a piece of wire through the hole to clear the deposit.

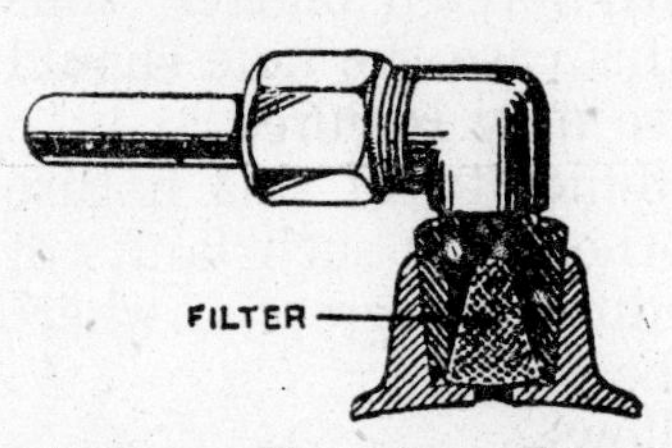

Fig. 250.—The Autovac Filter.

It is important to drain off this sediment from time to time, otherwise the lower part of the tank will rust. We have experienced cases in which water in the sediment chamber—and possibly other impurities in the fuels used—has actually caused rusting right through the tinned steel, with resulting leakage.

(3) *See that all Joints are Air-tight.*—Inspect the pipe connections occasionally, and tighten where necessary. If the top cover has been removed for any reason, make certain that all the holding-down screws are tight, and also that the washer for the joint is not damaged.

(4) *Filling an Empty Vacuum Tank.*—It is unnecessary to remove the cover of the vacuum tank to fill the latter. If the carburettor throttle is closed and the engine is cranked around by hand, or motor starter, for about one to two dozen revolutions, the tank will begin to fill under the influence of the vacuum created in the inlet pipe. If the vacuum tank has emptied the main tank and any difficulty is experienced in filling it, the petrol pipe or filter may be choked with sediment drawn from the base of the main tank.

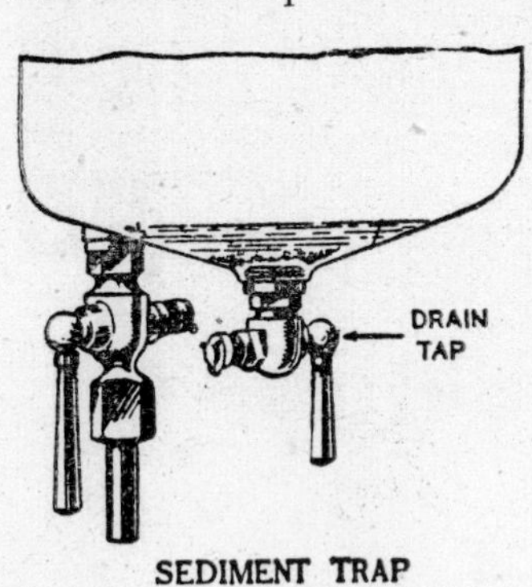

Fig. 251.—The Autovac Sediment Chamber.

DETECTION AND REMEDY OF FAULTS

Apart from the items mentioned under the heading of Maintenance, certain faults may occur which will render the working of the system unsatisfactory. In order to understand more clearly the nature of these possible faults, we shall refer to the Stewart Vacuum Tank used on various American cars illustrated in Fig. 246.

In the event of repairs or adjustments appearing necessary, it is as well to *make sure that the trouble is not due to some other cause.*

Vent Tube Overflows.—The air vent, 13, permits of an atmospheric condition being maintained in the outer chamber and also serves to prevent fuel overflowing in descending very steep grades. If it should happen at long intervals that a very small quantity of fuel leaks from the vent, no concern need be felt and no adjustment is needed. If, however, the vent tube overflows regularly, it is quite likely the air vent *in the fuel tank cap* is too small or clogged with foreign matter, thus preventing the entrance of air through it. In this case the hole should be enlarged somewhat or cleaned out, as the case may require.

Failure of Fuel Feed to Carburettor.—In a difficulty of this nature one should remember it may be due to causes other than such faults of the vacuum tank as are enumerated in succeeding paragraphs, where directions for correcting the difficulty will also be found.

In event of defective fuel feed, proceed as follows:

1. *See that the fuel shut-off cock is fully open.*
2. Alternately raise and lower the carburettor "tickler" to determine if

fuel is in the carburettor. If fuel is present it will flow from the bottom of the carburettor or the top of float chamber.

3. See that there is sufficient fuel in the fuel tank, at the same time noting whether the air vent—the small hole—in the fuel tank cap is free from obstructions. Remove the cap and look into the tank—*don't rely on the fuel gauge, as it, possibly, may not be working properly*.

4. Remove the drain plug from the bottom of the vacuum tank. Failure of fuel to flow from the vacuum tank drain indicates obstructions

Fig. 252.—A Modern Fuel System, showing Vacuum Feed, Glass Filter Carburettor, and Air Cleaner (on left of Carburettor).

or air leaks in the fuel pipe, vacuum-pipe fuel-tank outlet or suction pipe, a jammed vacuum valve, sediment in fuel filter, or a clogged air vent.

5. Remove and clean the carburettor fuel filters.

6. There may be dirt in the carburettor jets ; these should be cleaned.

7. There may be water in the carburettor ; the carburettor float chamber should be drained to remove this water.

If the above measures fail, remove the top of the vacuum tank and take out the float and other mechanism, leaving only the outer shell in place. If, after filling this shell with fuel, the engine still fails to run properly, the fault is clearly not that of the VACUUM system.

Should the fault be that of the vacuum tank, as indicated by the engine running properly when the outer shell is filled with fuel, and if repairs cannot be made at the time, plug the vacuum pipe to prevent the entrance of air into the inlet manifold and fill the vacuum tank with fuel drained from the fuel tank, replenishing the supply from time to time by hand.

Removing Vacuum-tank Top.—After removing the screws in the cover of the vacuum tank, insert a knife blade between the latter and the cover to separate them without damaging the gasket, which is shellaced in place to ensure an air-tight joint; if the gasket is damaged in removal, it must be replaced with a new one to prevent leakage.

Leaky Vacuum Tank Float.—The vacuum-tank float must be air-tight, for if a leak should develop the float would fill with fuel, thus making it too heavy to function properly. Such a condition would prevent the flow of fuel into the upper chamber being shut off when it should be. In this event, the fuel, after filling the upper chamber, would flow into the inlet manifold and thence into the cylinders, probably stopping the engine.

To repair the float, remove it and immerse it in hot water to locate the leak; bubbles will be noticed at the leak and this spot should be marked. Two very small holes should then be punched in the float, one at the top and the other at the bottom, to permit the fuel to flow out of the float. When the float is emptied of fuel and thoroughly dry, carefully solder the two holes and the leak and test the float by again immersing it in hot water.

In soldering the float, be careful to use no more solder than is actually required to make a substantial repair, because the addition of superfluous solder will make the float too heavy to act properly.

In removing and replacing the float, *be careful not to bend the float guide rod*, for if this rod is bent the float will not function properly; largely the same effect as a leaky float will result. If the rod is not perfectly smooth, improper action will follow; smooth it with fine emery cloth if necessary.

Flapper Valve.—Should foreign matter lodge on the flapper valve seat, the valve will not close tightly and will be rendered inoperative. To determine if the flapper valve is out of order, plug the air vent and disconnect the carburettor feed pipe. Crank the engine by means of the starter motor and apply a finger to the carburettor feed-pipe connection (in the bottom of the vacuum tank). If a continuous suction is felt, the flapper valve is not properly seated.

In this case, pour a half-pint (0·25 litre) or so of fuel into the tank to wash away the obstruction on the flapper valve seat. Should this treatment fail, remove the inner chamber and wipe the valve seat clean.

Air Leaks.—Should the connections at either end of the vacuum pipe loosen, or should this pipe be cracked, air will be drawn into the inlet manifold, which will not only cause the engine to run badly, but also will prevent proper action of the vacuum tank; very likely a hissing or whistling sound will be heard. Tighten the connections; if the pipe is cracked, repair or replace it.

This is also true of the fuel and fuel-tank suction pipes, which should be treated in the same manner.

FITTING VACUUM TANKS

As in the case of gravity fuel tanks, vacuum tanks should be mounted so that when the car is on a 20 per cent. incline there is at least 4 in. of fuel in the vacuum tank above the carburettor level (Fig. 244).

In the case of the Autovac, the following recommendations are made :

To Mount Autovac.—The best position for the Autovac is on the engine side of the dashboard ; if this is not convenient it can be fitted on the driver's side, or on suitable brackets fixed to the induction pipe or cylinder block.

The petrol flows under atmospheric pressure from the outer chamber to the carburettor ; therefore the bottom of the Autovac must be above the float chamber.

The top of the Autovac must always be above the level of fuel in the main tank, even when the car is descending hills ; if it were lower, petrol would leak through the air vent.

Connection to Main Tank.—A $\frac{1}{8}$-in.-diameter hole must be drilled in the main tank filler cap, or other convenient place, to allow free access of air.

Disconnect existing petrol pipe at carburettor and connect to elbow marked PETROL.

If the pipe is too large use a reduction coupling and short length of $\frac{5}{16}$-in. pipe, or sweat the latter to the bore of the larger diameter.

It is immaterial whether the outlet from the main tank is at the top or bottom, but it should be borne in mind that if at the bottom sediment is liable to enter and choke the pipe.

Connection to Induction Pipe.—Drill and tap a $\frac{1}{8}$-in. gas hole as nearly opposite to one of the cylinders as possible, and screw in the union provided.

Connect induction union to elbow marked SUCTION.

PETROL PUMPS

During recent years the vacuum feed system of supplying petrol to the float chamber of the carburettor has been challenged, seriously, by the positive pump method, whereby petrol is drawn from the main supply tank and forced under pressure to the float chamber of the carburettor by means of a reciprocating type of pump, having a positive action. The advantages of this system over the vacuum feed one are as follows : (1) Positive petrol supply under all conditions of running. (2) Amount supplied increases with engine speed. (3) No shortage on long hills as with vacuum feed system. (4) Independence of throttle position or vacuum in inlet pipe.

Petrol pumps used on motor vehicle engines belong to the mechanical or electrical classes. In the former case, the pump plunger or diaphragm is reciprocated by means of a mechanism deriving its movement from a cam on the timing-gear shaft ; usually the plunger movement is positive in one direction and spring-returned in the other.

In the electrically operated systems a solenoid is employed to move the pump plunger, or diaphragm, automatic contacts cutting off the electric current to the electro-magnet at the end of the stroke. The "Autopulse" and S.U. "Petrolift" pumps belong to this class.

Perhaps the best-known mechanical type of fuel pump is the A.C. This is fitted on a large number of different makes of motor vehicle; the individual designs vary somewhat, in detail, but the principle remains the same.

The A.C. petrol pump is of the diaphragm type operated by a lever that is given a reciprocating motion of $\frac{3}{16}$ in. to $\frac{1}{4}$ in. from camshaft or other rotating part of the engine. The pump draws fuel from the rear tank through a sediment chamber and strainer which is a part of the pump unit and feeds it under pressure to the carburettor in strict proportion to the requirements of the engine.

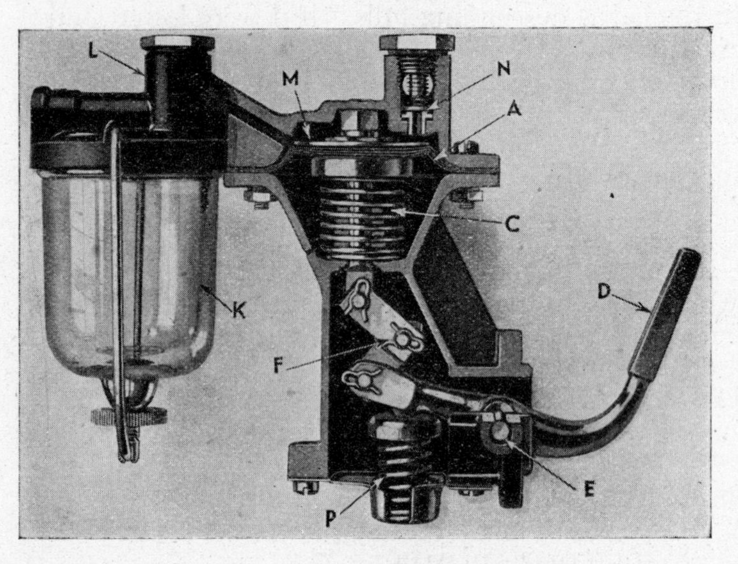

Fig. 253.—The A.C. Mechanical-type Petrol Pump.

The operation of the pump (Fig. 253) is as follows:

The turning of the camshaft lifts rocker arm D which is pivoted at E and pulls the linkage downward.

Diaphragm A is drawn downward against spring C, thus creating a vacuum in pump chamber M which causes fuel from the tank to flow through the strainer K and suction valve L into the pump chamber M. On the return stroke spring C pushes diaphragm A upward, forcing fuel through pressure valve N into the carburettor. When the carburettor bowl is filled its float shuts off the needle valve, thus creating a back pressure in pump chamber M. This pressure will hold the diaphragm A against the pressure of spring C, preventing further pumping until the carburettor requires more fuel and its needle valve opens. Spring P is merely to keep the operating lever D in contact with the eccentric on the camshaft.

As lever D follows the eccentric at all times, and as the diaphragm piston stroke is in proportion to fuel requirements, it will be evident that the linkage F will compensate for the difference in travel of these two moving parts. Under normal operating conditions the diaphragm stroke is only a few thousandths of an inch, which means that the life of the pump and its capacity will be far in excess of any engine requirements.

THE STANDARD CAR PETROL PUMP

Standard cars employ the A.C. cam-operated diaphragm type of pump shown in Fig. 254. The pump is mounted on the side of the crank-case and operated by an eccentric cam.

Petrol flows to a strainer before passing through the non-return inlet valve. The pump chamber contains a non-return outlet valve and at the lower end a diaphragm operated by a pull rod from the rocker arm which is in connection with the lever. The rocker arm constantly oscillates, and if the pump chamber is full of petrol, causing the diaphragm to be depressed, the rocker arm works freely and does not operate the diaphragm. The spring behind the diaphragm provides a constant pressure of fuel to the carburettor float chamber and thus the stroke of the diaphragm is automatically governed to meet the requirements of the carburettor. The rocker arm itself is spring loaded for the purpose of keeping the lever in contact with the cam and preventing noise. There is a drain plug fitted to the sediment chamber.

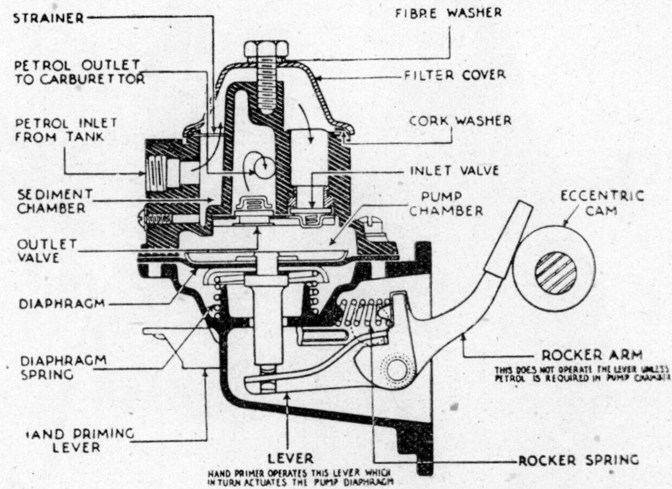

Fig. 254.—The Standard Car Petrol Pump (Models " Twelve " to " Twenty ").

The " Nine " and " Ten " Pump varies in detail, but is the same in principle as that shown above.

Filters are provided in the petrol tanks of models " Twelve " and upwards. There are filters incorporated in the petrol pump and carburettor union on all models.

Running Adjustments.—A hand primer is fitted to the pump so that it is unnecessary to turn the engine either by hand or by the starter if the tank has run dry and the pump become empty. A few strokes on the hand primer will soon fill the carburettor float chamber.

If the pump fails to supply petrol to the carburettor, attend to the following points :

Remove the filter cover and clean the gauze.

Make certain that the cork washer lies flat on its seat and makes an air-tight joint, and that the fibre washer is under the head of the cover screw.

Examine the pipes and connections for possible leakage. If petrol leaks at the diaphragm, tighten the screws alternately to ensure a good joint. If petrol does not flow from the pump to the carburettor, examine the small filter fitted inside the petrol-pipe union to the float chamber.

THE DAIMLER PETROL PUMP

The fuel pump used on the Daimler " 15 " car is illustrated in Fig. 255 ; it belongs to the lever-operated diaphragm class. This petrol pump is fixed on the near side of the engine and is driven from the camshaft. Its method of working is as follows :

By revolving the shaft A the eccentric will lift the rocker arm B which is pivoted at C and pulls the linkage D, together with the diaphragm E. The latter is held between metal discs and is pulled downwards

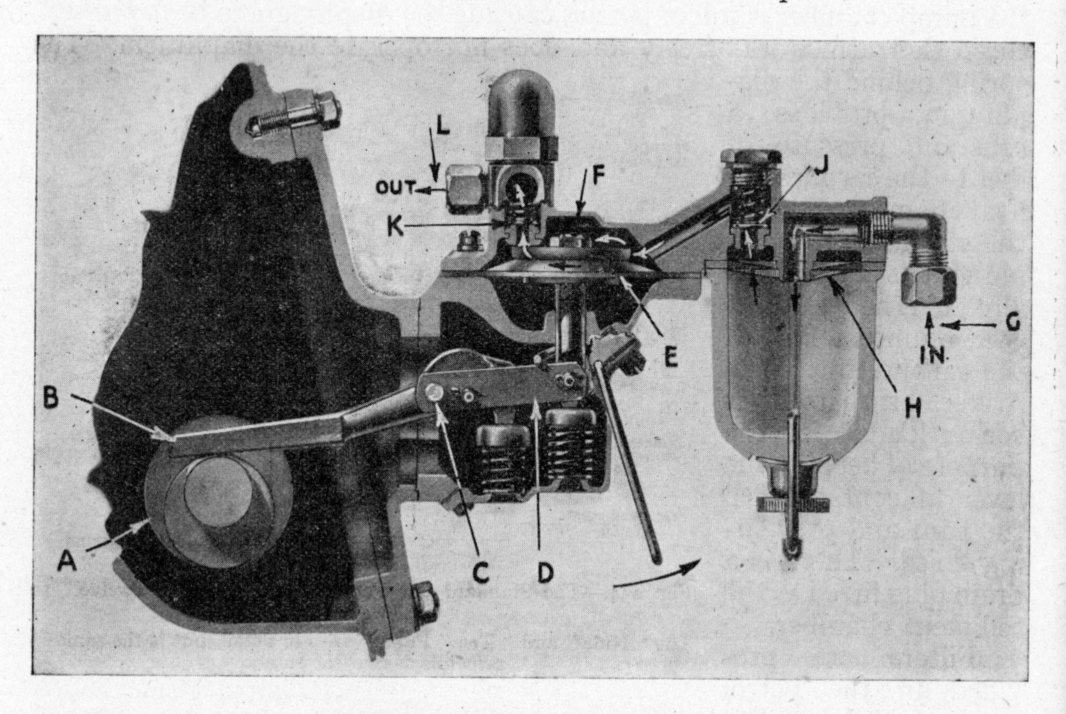

Fig. 255.—The Daimler Petrol Pump.

against the spring pressure, thus creating a vacuum in the pump chamber F.

Fuel from the rear tank will enter at G, through the strainer H and the suction valve J into the pump chamber F. On the return stroke the spring pressure pushes the diaphragm upward, forcing fuel from the pump chamber through the pressure valve K and opening L into the carburettor pipes. When the float chamber is full the float will shut off the inlet needle valve, thus creating a pressure in the pump chamber F. This pressure will force the diaphragm downwards against the spring pressure, where it will remain open in the downward position until the carburettor requires further fuel and the needle valve opens. In order to fill the float chamber *after the car has been left standing for a considerable period*, a hand auxiliary pump (shown to the right of D, near the arrow in Fig. 255) is fitted. A few strokes of this pump will draw petrol from the tank to the carburettor without having to use the self-starter or cranking handle for this purpose.

CARE OF THE PETROL SYSTEM

The following notes refer to the most likely troubles to be met with in petrol systems of the fuel-pump class, such as the Daimler system previously described.

1. *Leaky Tube or Connections.*—Renew tubing and tighten all pipe connections at the fuel pump and petrol tank.

2. *Glass Bowl Loose.*—Tighten thumb nut, making certain that the cork gasket lies flat in its seating and is not broken.

3. *Dirty Screen.*—Remove glass bowl and clean screen. Make certain that the cork gasket is properly seated when reassembling.

4. *Loose Valve Plug.*—Tighten valve plug securely. Renew valve-plug gasket if necessary.

5. *Dirty or Warped Valves.*—Remove valve plugs and valves. Wash valve in petrol. If damaged or warped, renew them. Examine valve seating, making certain there are no irregularities which prevent proper seating of valves. Place valve in valve chamber with the polished side downwards, making certain that the valve lies flat on its seat and is not left standing on edge. Dismantle valve plug and spring and make certain that the spring is around the lower stem of the valve plug. Use new gasket under valve plug if necessary.

6. *Choked Petrol Supply.*—Remove screen from pump and clean thoroughly in petrol. If necessary dismantle pipe line and blow through with an air pump to remove any obstruction. A second filter will be found in the carburettor and this also should be thoroughly cleaned by washing in petrol.

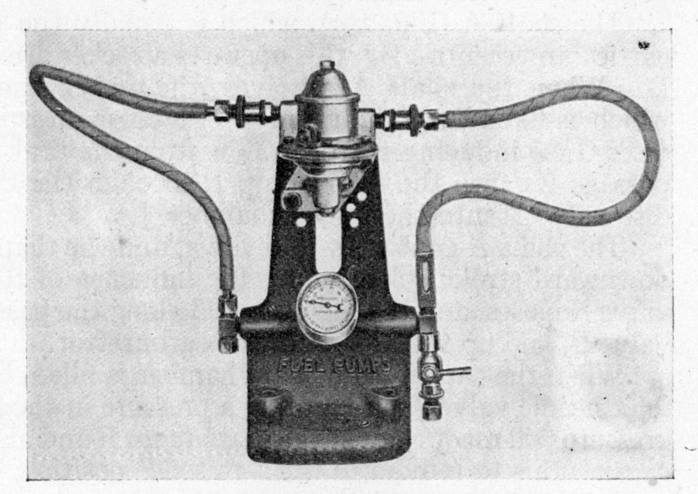

Fig. 256.—The A.C. Petrol-pump Test Stand.

THE A.C. PETROL-PUMP TEST STAND

Many unnecessary repairs can be avoided by testing all pumps before dismantling.

The use of the A.C. Petrol-pump Test and Assembly Stand (Fig. 256) will be found invaluable in all cases when the working of a pump is under suspicion. Complete instructions as to the method of using the stand are supplied with each apparatus and it is, therefore, only necessary to reiterate the following:

Before attempting repairs of any kind, mount the pump on the stand, attaching firmly with the wing nuts and bolts provided. Attach hose to inlet and outlet sides of pump, turning connections up tightly with wrench. Then actuate rocker arm by hand.

If pump will prime (i.e. commence to deliver fuel) with twenty strokes or less, then close the shut-off valve on the outlet side and work the rocker arm until $1\frac{1}{2}$ lb. to $2\frac{1}{2}$ lb. pressure is indicated on the gauge. If valves are seating properly, and there are no leaks in pump or connections, pressure will hold for several minutes before hand gradually returns to zero.

If pressure does not hold, look for leaks around diaphragm or for worn valves or punctured diaphragm. Make repair with pump mounted on stand. When completed, retest, examining for leaks.

Another useful testing device is the A.C. petrol-pump analyser which is employed for checking the performance of these pumps under actual operating conditions. The analyser mentioned will test a pump whilst the engine is running under its own power, for capacity, or petrol flow, pressure, and vacuum ; the latter test exposes the existence of any obstruction in the pipe line. The apparatus mentioned is made by Messrs. Delco-Remy & Hyatt, Ltd., 111 Grosvenor Road, London, S.W.1.

THE AMAL FUEL PUMP

The Amal fuel pump is fitted to a number of cars and commercial vehicles. It belongs to the cam-operated, flexible diaphragm type of pump, the action of which is as follows :

The shaft A (Fig. 257), which is usually the camshaft of the engine, carries an eccentric B ; this operates a rocker arm C, pivoted at the point D. When the shaft A revolves, the rocker arm C lifts the spindle E to which is fixed the diaphragm F, which is interposed between two metal discs G, so inducing petrol to flow from the tank up the pipe K through passage K1 into the filter sump L through the filter M and the suction-disc valve N into the pump chamber J.

The shaft A continues to revolve, and the diaphragm F commences its downward stroke solely under the influence of the spring H, the suction valve N closes, and the fuel is forced along the passage O, past the delivery valve P, and up the pipe R to the carburettor.

When the carburettor float chamber is filled, the float will shut off the inlet needle valve, thus creating a pressure in the pump chamber J. This pressure will react against the diaphragm F and also the spring pressure H, causing this to remain in the " raised " position.

The lever C, under these conditions, can no longer give the spindle E any movement, due to the fact that it is raised beyond the point where the lever C engages the spindle E. The lever C then simply moves backwards and forwards idly, and when this occurs the pump can no longer deliver any fuel until such time as the needle valve opens in the carburettor float chamber to admit a further supply. The pressure in the pump chamber J then falls and allows the spindle E to drop and once more come in contact with the lever C.

The spring H is set at a predetermined pressure, and this cannot be exceeded under any circumstances of the pump's operation.

The spring V is for the purpose of maintaining the rocker arm C in contact with the eccentric B to prevent noise, and it has no action on the fuel pump itself.

The filter sump L is removed for cleaning purposes by unscrewing the hexagon nut X; the filter M can then be unscrewed, cleaned, and replaced.

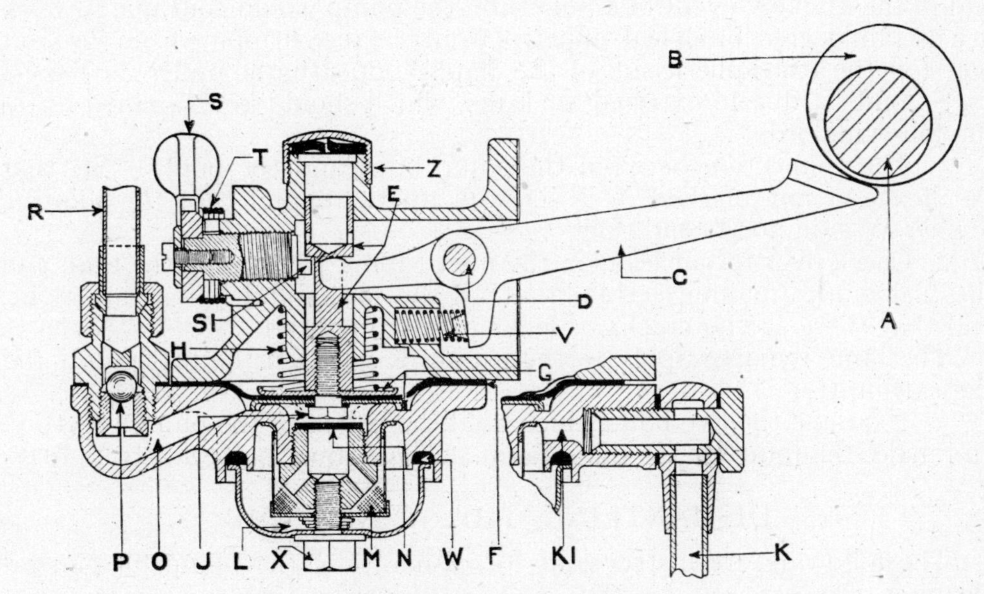

Fig. 257.—The Amal Fuel Pump.

The sump L is afterwards fitted and screwed up tightly so as to make an air-tight joint by means of the cork washer W.

The priming lever S is then operated by hand. This brings the cam of the priming lever S1 in contact with the spindle E, so working the diaphragm; about a dozen slow strokes is all that should be necessary for petrol to reach the float chamber of the carburettor. When this occurs, and the float chamber is full, the resistance to movement of the priming lever S will gradually diminish, until it is felt that it ceases to act. This means that the float chamber is full, and the diaphragm is raised under the pressure so produced in the pump chamber J and no further actuation of the priming lever is necessary.

The engine can then be started up, and the pump will continue to function in the normal manner.

The priming lever S is held back, when not in use, by the return spring T.

The inspection cover Z can be screwed off for examination of the working of the pump spindle.

POSSIBLE FAULTS

The pump can fail only for two major reasons :

Firstly—failure of movement of the diaphragm :

(*a*) Due to the spindle E not working freely up and down, which fact can be checked by removing the cover Z and turning the engine over. The float chamber must be empty or the feed pipe to it disconnected at the time.

(*b*) Or by the diaphragms having become loose on the spindle or by actual mechanical breakage, which are all very unlikely.

(*c*) The failure by rupture of the diaphragms is an unheard-of defect, and in the unlikely event of a puncture, the pump would continue to work in a certain degree, but a leak of petrol would be seen dripping from the vent hole (on the atmospheric side of the diaphragm) situated under the flange.

Secondly—due to external air leaks, which should be examined for in the following order :

1. The connection between the sump bowl and the pump. See that the hexagon nut marked X is screwed up tight, and that the jointing washer W is in good condition.

2. Check over for air leaks in the inlet tubing K between the tank and the fuel pump, making certain that all the joints and unions are tight, and that there are no cracks or leaks in the pipe itself.

The same remarks apply to the tubing R between the fuel pump and the carburettor.

3. Examine the five bolts which hold the halves of the pump together, and make the joint for the diaphragm. These must be perfectly tight.

DISMANTLING THE AMAL PUMP

The following are instructions for dismantling the pump for general cleaning purposes :

Never separate the two halves of the pump by removing the five screws unless it is necessary, even if it may be desirable to detach the whole pump from the engine for cleaning or inspection. The inlet-pipe connection K, the sump L, the filter sump M, the non-return valve N, and the delivery valve P are easily taken apart and can be flushed out with petrol (see paragraph 6).

1. For completely dismantling the pump—disconnect the fuel-pipe connections K and R from the pump. Then remove the pump in its entirety from the engine.

2. The spindle of the pump cannot be removed until the priming-lever cam arrangement S1 is screwed out : to remove this, the lever S and spring T can be lifted off by first undoing the small screw at the lever boss, then the screwed spindle with a flat on the end can be screwed out when the spindle E is lifted by depressing lever C.

The lever may be prised off with a screw-driver after unhooking the spring.

3. Next remove the split cotter-pin holding in position the lever C and pivot pin D. Tap out the pivot pin D and remove the lever and also remove the spring V.

4. Take out the securing screws from the circumference of the pump and remove bottom half containing the petrol-pipe connections and the filter itself.

5. The diaphragm F, together with the spindle E and spring H, can then be withdrawn from the pump. If fitting new diaphragms F the old ones can be removed from the spindle by unscrewing the hexagon-headed pin at the bottom end, care being taken in doing so not to bend or bruise the spindle E; when this hexagon-headed pin is removed the smaller of the two discs protecting the diaphragm can be lifted off and the diaphragms come away freely.

To hold the spindle for removing the screw W, place a bar in the cross hole of the spindle.

6. If it is desired to inspect or remove the suction valve N this can be done by removing first the filter bowl L and after that the strainer M with spring support, and then unscrew the inlet-valve seating, when the disc-type suction valve drops away. The only thing to be looked for in this connection is dirt, there being no springs of any description in this valve.

After replacing the parts see that the filter bowl seats properly on the washer W in the recess and that the bowl is tightened up firmly.

To inspect the delivery valve P the delivery connection should be unscrewed from the lower half of the pump, and the bush with screw-driver slot unscrewed from the underside, when the ball valve will fall away. Again nothing need be looked for in this valve but an accumulation of impurities.

THE S.U. PETROLIFT PETROL PUMP

This electric type of petrol pump has a hollow cylindrical electro-magnet B (Fig. 260) which, when energised electrically, draws the plunger C upwards. A pair of disc valves E and F act as non-return valves for the petrol drawn in through the pipe union at G and thence through the hole H. The pump contains an automatic electric contact for giving the plunger C its reciprocating movement. Further, when the float chamber P is filled to a certain level the float R is lifted upward and by means of the stirrup member S moves the plunger K upwards and breaks the electrical connections at A, by separating the contacts, so that the pump is put out of action. It will be observed that the pump consists of three separate compartments as follows: (1) a lower chamber containing petrol; (2) a middle chamber containing the electro-magnet and contact breaker, but no petrol; and (3) an upper chamber, with a float containing petrol that has been pumped from (1) by way of the central hollow plunger C. The outlet to the carburettor is shown at Q.

MAINTENANCE NOTES

The S.U. petrol pump is simple in construction and seldom gives any trouble. Should, however, the pump cease to function the trouble will probably be due to:

1. The pump plungers (C or K) sticking, due to dirt or grit getting between the pump plungers and the body. Often a blow on the pump with the fist is sufficient to get it working, when the dirt will pass right through. Should it not do so, the remedy is to remove the filter bowl U and foot valve Y, also the top cap of the pump and the cork float, when it will be possible to push the plunger C through the bottom, after which a clean rag can be drawn through the bore of the pump. Note when assembling the plunger of the pump that valve E is on top.

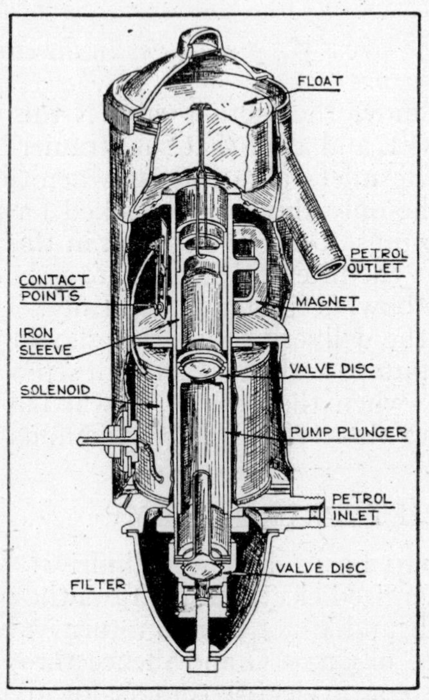

Fig. 258.—Showing, Pictorially, Principal Items of S.U. "Petrolift" Pump.

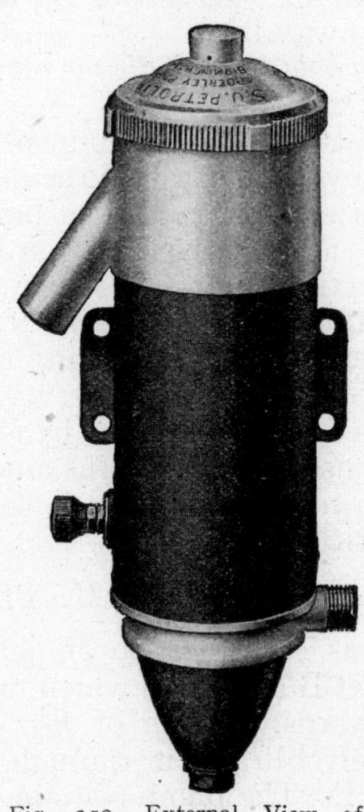

Fig. 259.—External View of "Petrolift" Pump.

If the above item is found to be in order, then,

2. First of all remove the top cap V from the pump to see if the float chamber contains petrol. If it does then the trouble is not due to the pump.

3. If the pump continues to make a pumping noise without delivering petrol, it is due to one of the following causes:

(*a*) Lack of petrol in the back tank.

(*b*) Air leak, which may be due to (1) a bad joint between the filter bowl U and the casing, in which event tightening up will generally correct. If it does not do so a new washer will have to be fitted, or (2) a loose petrol union on the suction pipe, that is to say any point between the bottom union of the pump and the back tank. The washer between the filter bowl and its bolt T should also be inspected.

(*c*) Foot valve F held up. This is a very rare source of trouble. To rectify remove the filter bowl U, filter H, and foot valve Y by means of a tommy-bar through one of the holes. The foot valve can then be cleaned. A second filter X will be found in the foot valve underneath the priming tube.

4. If the pump works very slowly without delivering petrol, it is due to :

(*a*) Blocked petrol pipe or filters, in which case the filters or pipe must be cleaned out.

(*b*) Batteries run down, in which case fill the float chamber of the pump with petrol. This will probably enable the engine to be started up by hand, and as the dynamo comes into action it will boost up the batteries sufficiently to run the pump.

5. Should the pump not work at all, providing the plunger has not stuck, the trouble will be due to :

(*a*) A bad electrical connection. To test this remove the terminal from the pump and flash the wire across the pump body. If there is a bright flash this is in order. If not, the trouble is due to the batteries being run down or bad connections somewhere in the system.

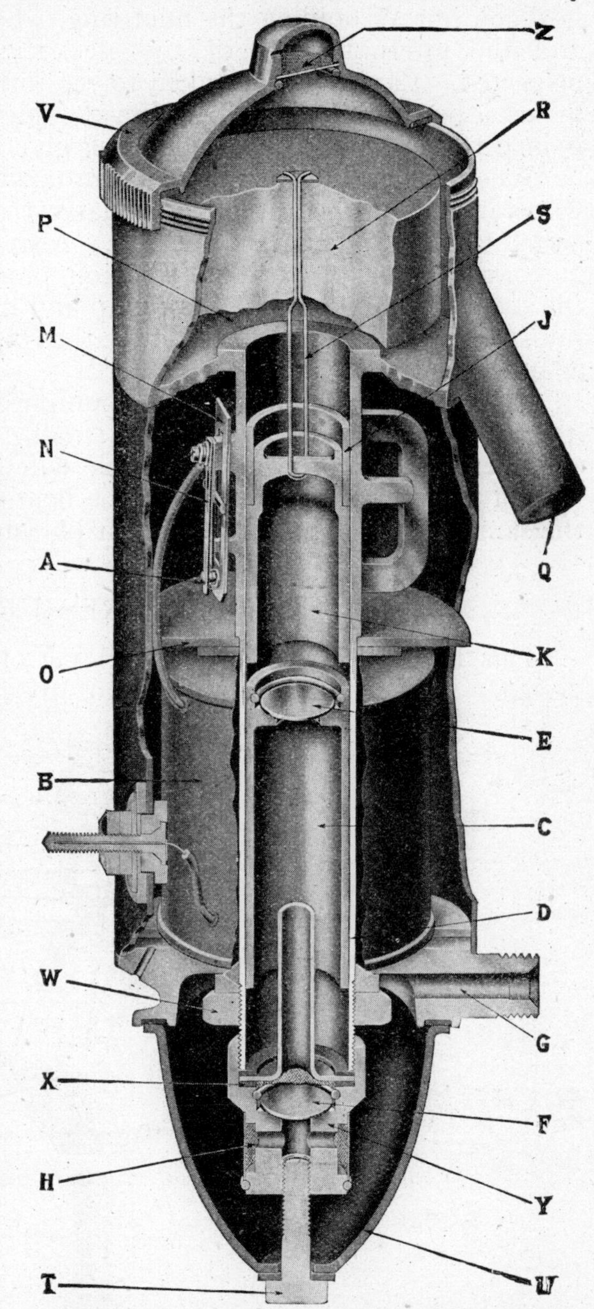

Fig. 260.—The S.U. "Petrolift" Fuel Pump, illustrating the care and maintenance points referred to in the text.

The electrical apparatus is to all intents and purposes absolutely fool-proof. Practically the only thing that can cause this to cease to function is a broken wire. If reference is made to the diagram the connections will be seen exactly. To gain access to the electrical part of the pump it will be necessary to remove filter bowl U, foot valve Y, unscrew the large hexagon nut W holding the inlet ring, when the casing can be drawn off and the internal parts of the electrical equipment and connections inspected. Care must be taken to see that the cork gland washer which makes a petrol-tight joint between the inlet ring and electrical equipment is in perfect condition. A new cork gland washer is advisable.

When the casing is removed care must also be taken to see that the wires are not broken, and particularly that the top wire does not come across the rocking contact plate M. A simple test for the contacts being in working order, providing the bottom plunger has not stuck, is to remove the cap V from the top of the pump and lift the float R up and down its full stroke. If listened for intently the rocker plate can be heard to click as it breaks the contact.

If, after being reassembled, the pump works but does not deliver petrol, it should be primed by pouring a small quantity of petrol into the top chamber. If petrol is not available a few squirts of thin oil down the tube of the pump after removing the float R and top plunger K will have the same effect. The oil used must be thin.

THE S.U. PRESSURE PUMP

This is an electrically operated petrol pump of neat and compact design. It is fitted as standard to Morris and certain other makes of British cars.

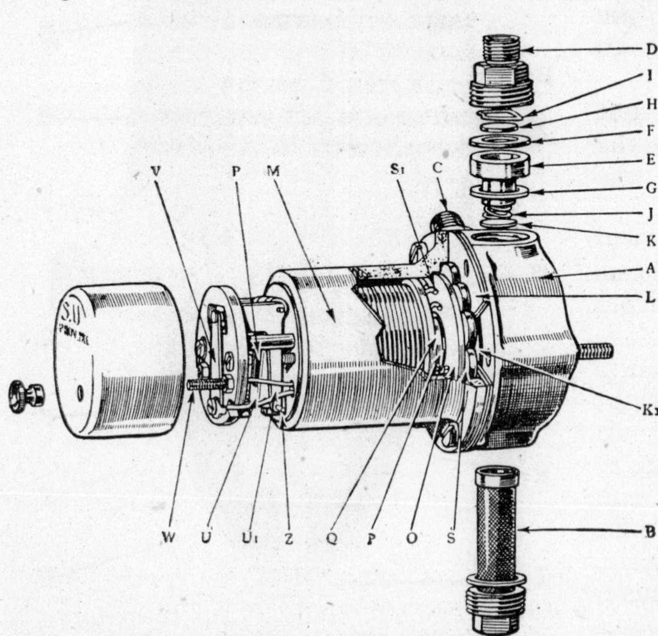

Fig. 261.—The Morris Fuel Pump (S.U. Type).

The pump is shown in part cut-away view in Fig. 261, this illustration being applicable to Morris pumps.

The S.U. pump has an electro-magnet R which attracts a steel armature O connected to the pump diaphragm L; the electrical circuit is made and broken by the movement of the armature.

The pump consists of three main assemblies—the body, the magnet assembly, and the contact breaker. The body is composed of a hollow brass stamping A into the bottom of which the filter B is screwed. The inlet union C is screwed in at an angle on one side. The outlet union D, which is screwed into the top, tightens down on to the delivery valve cage E, which is clamped between two fibre washers, F and G. In the top of the cage is the delivery valve, a thin brass disc H held in position by a spring clip I. Inserted in the bottom of the cage is a light spring J, which rests on the suction valve K, the latter being a similar disc resting on a seating machined in the body. Holes connect the space between the valves to the pumping chamber, which is a shallow depression on the forward face of the body. The space is closed by a diaphragm assembly L, which is clamped at the outside between the magnet housing M and the body, and in the centre between a brass plate K1 and the steel armature O. A bronze rod P is screwed through the centre of this and passes through the magnet core to the contact breaker, which is located at the far end.

The magnet consists of a cast-iron pot having an iron core Q, on which is wound a coil of copper wire which energises the magnet. Between the magnet housing and the armature are fitted eleven spherical-edged brass rollers S. These locate the armature centrally within the magnet at all times and allow absolute freedom of movement in a longitudinal direction.

The contact breaker consists of a small bakelite moulding carrying two rockers U and U1, which are both hinged to the moulding at one end and are connected together at the top end by two small springs arranged to give a " throw-over " action. A trunnion is fitted into the centre of the inner rocker and the bronze rod P connected to the armature is screwed into this. The outer rocker U1 is fitted with a tungsten point which makes contact with a further tungsten point on a spring blade V. This spring blade is connected to one end of the coil and the other end of the coil is connected to the terminal W. A spring, S1, is interposed between the armature and the end plate of the coil.

MAINTENANCE OF THE S.U. PUMP

The only maintenance attention called for is the occasional removal and cleaning of the filter. The latter is inserted into the bottom of the pump body and can easily be withdrawn by unscrewing its hexagon attachment screw. When removed, it should be cleaned thoroughly in petrol with a stiff brush. *A rag should never be used.*

Tracing Troubles.—Should the pump be suspected, first disconnect the pump union of the pipe from the pump to the carburettor and switch on the engine. If the pump functions, the shortage is due either to blockage of the petrol pipe to the carburettor, or possibly to the carburettor-float needle sticking up. If the pump will not function after this has been done, first remove the filter, which is held in position by the brass hexagon nut at the base of the pump, and see if this is clear. Then disconnect the petrol pipe leading to the tank and blow down this with a tyre pump to ensure the pipe being absolutely clear, and reconnect the petrol pipe.

If the pump still does not function or only works slowly, the stoppage may be due to a bad earth return. To test for this, make definite metallic contact between the brass body of the pump and the car chassis with the length of copper wire fitted. To ensure a good earth it may be necessary to scrape off a small portion of the black enamel with which the chassis is coated. If the pump then functions normally, the copper earth-wire connections should be cleaned and remade.

A bad connection in the pump itself may sometimes be traced to the nut on the terminal inside the cover not being screwed down firmly.

Should these points be found in order but the pump still does not work, the trouble is in the pump itself and the cause will be too much tension on the diaphragm or blackened contact points, the cause of which is the tensioning of the diaphragm. The remedy is to remove the cover from the contact points and pass a piece of thin card between the points when pressed together, so as to effect the necessary cleaning.

To release the tension on the diaphragm, remove the body from the base of the pump by undoing the small screws which hold these two parts together. The diaphragm itself will then be found to be adhered to the body of the pump, from which it will have to be separated. A knife will help in this operation, care being taken to prevent the rollers which support the diaphragm and act as a bearing from falling out. The body should then be replaced on to the base, and the screws put in loosely, but before finally tightening up it is advisable to stretch the diaphragm to its highest possible position. This is effected by switching on the pump and holding the contact points together while tightening the screws well up. This will effect a permanent cure.

Should a pump work intermittently or not start clicking when switched on in the morning, it is an indication that this trouble is occurring and it should be given immediate attention to obviate final stoppage on the road.

The Petrol Filter.—The filter is situated at the bottom of the pump body and is easily removed for cleaning purposes by unscrewing the hexagon plug holding it in position. It should be removed and cleaned in petrol with a stiff brush every 1,000 miles.

Cause of Noisy Pump.—If the pump becomes noisy it is usually an indication that an air leak is taking place on the suction side of the pump. Check the level of the petrol in the tank and see that it is not too low; also check all the unions and joints, making sure that the filter union and inlet unions are quite air-tight.

If the connections to the pump are in order and the trouble persists, then it is probable that an air leak has developed somewhere in the petrol-feed pipe between the tank and the pump. The best way to test whether this is so is to replace the feed pipe by a short length of temporary piping, the mouth of which can be inserted in a can of petrol. If the pump then functions properly it is obvious that a leak has developed somewhere in the feed pipe.

Failure to Feed Petrol.—Should the pump continue beating without delivering petrol, it is very probable that some dirt has become lodged under one of the valves, in which case they should be dismantled by unscrewing the top or delivery union, and lifting out the valve cage, when they can be cleaned and reassembled.

If, however, the pump struggles to pump and becomes very hot, it is probable that the pipe line has become obstructed or that the filter has become clogged.

THE ARMSTRONG-SIDDELEY PUMP

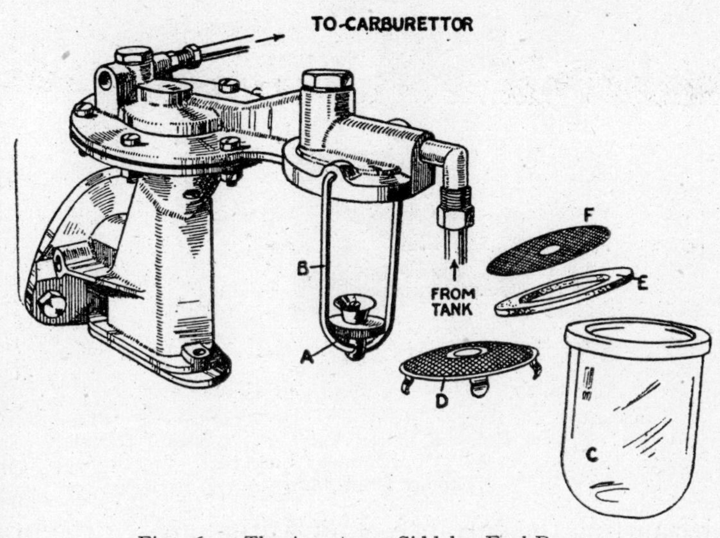

Fig. 262.—The Armstrong-Siddeley Fuel Pump.

Fig. 262 illustrates the petrol pump and filter of one model, the Armstrong - Siddeley car engine, the components being shown in the dismantled condition in order to illustrate the method of maintenance. In the illustration, the glass filter cup is shown at C, its retaining stirrup at B, and locking nut at A. The filter gauzes D and F are separated by the washer E. These filter gauzes should be dismantled and cleaned periodically, say, every 3,000 to 4,000 miles of running.

THE FORD FUEL PUMPS

The Ford cars employ the cam-operated diaphragm-type fuel pumps illustrated in Figs. 263 and 264.

In each case the main fuel tank is at the rear of the car, the level of the petrol being indicated by a gauge on the instrument panel; it is of the electric type, operated by means of a float actuating a lever which is geared to operate a variable resistance in the circuit of the indicator gauge.

The fuel pump is located on the near-side of the engine, towards the front, and is driven by an eccentric on the camshaft (see Fig. 263). It draws the petrol from the tank and supplies it to the carburettor. Being automatic in action, the pump requires little attention other than to keep it free from dirt, and all connections tight.

The construction of the pump is such as to provide a trap for sediment or water, which can be drained off by means of the drain plug on the side of the pump, after loosening the inlet-pipe union (immediately above the drain plug).

If it is desired to clean the pump screen, it may easily be reached by undoing the screw in the centre of the pump cover and removing the cover. When replacing the cover, always make sure that the cover gasket is not broken and that the cover is seating properly.

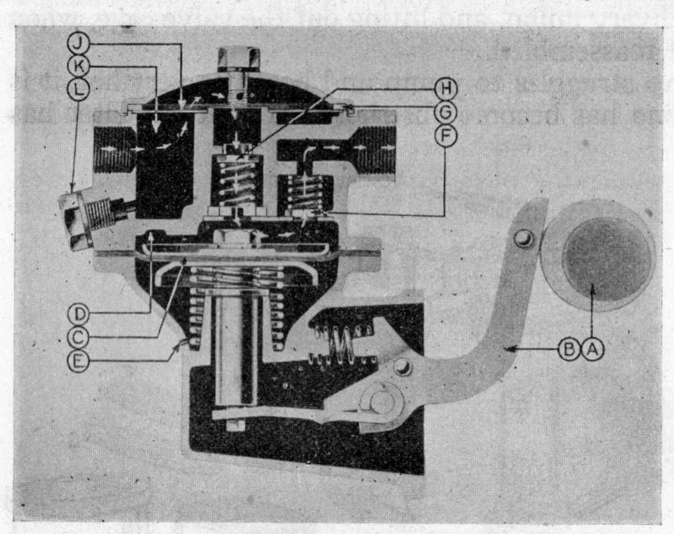

Fig. 263.—The 8-h.p. Ford Petrol Pump.

A, Camshaft. B, Rocker Arm. C, Diaphragm. D, Pump Chamber. E, Vent Hole. F, Outlet Valve. G, Gasket. H, Inlet Valve. J, Pump Screen. K, Sediment Chamber. L, Sediment Chamber Drain Plug.

Trouble.—If at any time the carburettor is not receiving sufficient petrol, one of the following is likely to be the cause:

(1) Fuel tank empty.

(2) Screen in the top chamber of the fuel pump has become fouled with sediment, in which case it should be cleaned. (See above.)

(3) The petrol pipe or its connections have a leak at some point, permitting the entrance of air to the pipe, or the prain plug on the pump is not screwed home properly. The remedy, of course, is to stop the leak, at which time the pump will prime itself and again function properly. Cranking the engine for twenty seconds with the starter should prime the pump.

(4) If at any time petrol is seeping through the small hole E shown in lower half of fuel pump (see Fig. 263) it is probably an indication of the diaphragm in the pump having become punctured. While this does not usually render the pump inoperative immediately, it is advisable to replace

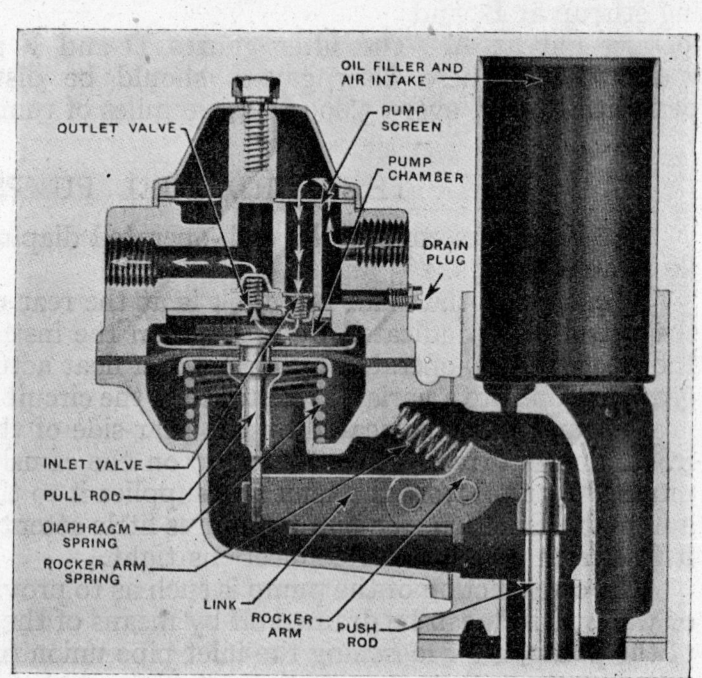

Fig. 204.—The Ford V-eight Fuel Pump.

the diaphragm as soon as possible. Ford dealers carry these parts in stock.

The Ford V-eight fuel pump is shown in Fig. 264. It is located at the top of the engine behind the carburettor, and is driven by a push rod actuated by an eccentric on the camshaft (see Fig. 264). It draws the petrol from the tank and supplies it to the carburettor. Being automatic in action, the pump requires little attention other than to keep it free from dirt and all connections tight.

The construction of the pump is such as to provide a trap for sediment or water, which can be drained off by means of the drain plug on the side of the pump, after loosening the inlet-pipe union (immediately above the drain plug).

The design of the pump is similar to that of the Ford 8-h.p. model, and the maintenance instructions are the same as for the latter model.

The later model 22-h.p. V-eight, as well as the 15-cwt. van and 25-cwt. Ford commercial vehicle, employ electric petrol pumps.

FITTING AND ADJUSTING CARBURETTORS

In view of the fact that there is a large number of different makes of carburettor fitted to motor-car and cycle engines, and that it is impossible to describe each type in detail, we shall confine our remarks to the general methods in use for fitting and adjusting carburettors. For fuller information and descriptions of typical modern carburettors the reader is referred to the footnote references.[1]

If the principles upon which the modern carburettor is designed are understood, the adjustment becomes a matter of simplicity. Moreover, the leading carburettor manufacturers always issue Instruction Manuals for their particular models of carburettor so that the garage mechanic or motorist should not experience any difficulty in making any alterations or adjustments.

Size of Carburettor

In fitting a new carburettor to an engine it is important to select the *correct size of carburettor* to suit the particular engine. It is usual to design carburettors to suit the horse-power of one cylinder, and since the inlet pipe or manifold bore governs the horse-power, carburettor sizes are expressed in terms of inlet-manifold diameters. The number of cylinders, speed of the engine, and valve diameter all govern the amount of mixture which the engine should be provided with, and some carburettor manufacturers require these particulars when supplying a new carburettor. The manufacturers usually supply tables showing the carburettor sizes for engines of different types ; in some cases the appropriate sizes of jets and choke tube are also tabulated.

As a general rule, and in the absence of more definite information,

[1] *Modern Motor Cars* (Caxton Publishing Co., Ltd.), Vol. III (Carburettors). Motor Manuals, A. W. Judge (Chapman & Hall, Ltd.), Vol. II, *Carburettors and Carburation.*

the bore of the outlet orifice of carburettor—namely, at the inlet-manifold flange—is equal to, or slightly larger than, the inlet-manifold bore.

Position of Carburettor

This is determined by the existing inlet manifold. The carburettor flange should correspond to that of the inlet manifold.

Whether the model selected is of the horizontal or vertical type will depend upon the space available, the convenience of the petrol union joints and of the controls. The petrol piping should be as direct and as simple as possible. When there is a choice of model available *the horizontal type is to be preferred,* as it has at least one angular bend less for the mixture, and gives the least loss in quantity in supplying the engine.

The carburettor should be mounted as low as possible, to ensure proper flow of the petrol when the car is inclined. The controls and petrol pipe should preferably be arranged in such a way *that the float chamber and jets can be got at* without obstruction.

The float chamber can generally be mounted in three alternative positions. The best position is with a line joining the axes of the jet (or choke) and the float chamber at right angles to the fore-and-aft line of the car—that is to say, with the float chamber outwards. In this position the level of the petrol in the jet remains unchanged when the car is on an incline.

The Induction Pipe

This should be as short and as simple as possible, of uniform diameter, and free from sudden bends or pockets which cause deposition of the fuel. The pipe should be of the same diameter or slightly smaller than the outlet diameter of the carburettor. It is important to provide good air-tight joints at the carburettor and engine ends of the inlet manifold. Special jointing materials of the graphite-coated asbestos kind, such as Hallite, are recommended for both inlet and exhaust joints. Fibre joints are also suitable for the inlet joints ; they can be used over and over again, if handled with care. A smearing of gold-size or boiled linseed oil on the surface of such a joint will ensure against air-leakage.

The carburettor will usually be supported sufficiently rigid by its engine-flange joint, but if a longer inlet pipe is employed, it may be necessary to stay the carburettor to prevent vibration.

Heating of Carburettor

With the modern grades of petrol and benzole containing a certain proportion of heavier constituents, it is necessary to supply heat to the carburettor, usually at the inlet pipe or mixture chamber, to assist in vaporising the fuel. Whenever a vertical carburettor is fitted *heating is essential.* With horizontal or "straight-through" models heating is not absolutely necessary, since the carburettor being so close to the engine becomes heated sufficiently for this purpose.

There are three alternative methods of heating, as follows: (1) by Hot Air; (2) by Hot Water; and (3) by Exhaust Gases. Of these the first is the most common, and possesses the advantage of enabling the mixture to warm up almost as soon as the engine commences to fire from the cold. It is usual to take a pipe from the main air inlet to a muff placed around the exhaust pipe, so that all the main air supply has to pass around the hot exhaust pipe.

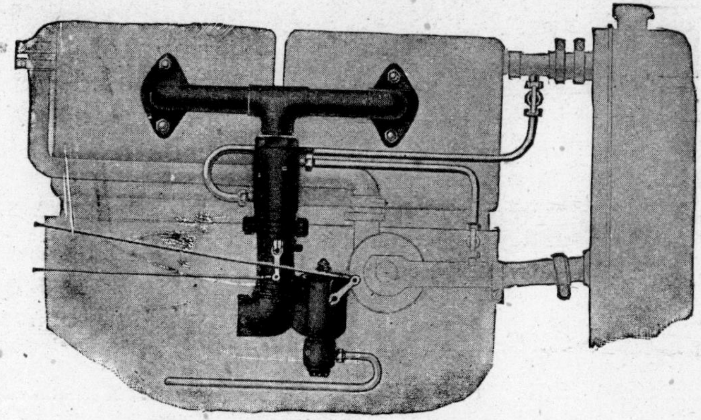

Fig. 265.—Showing Hot-water Jacket in Place.

Some makers recommend the hot-water jacketing of their carburettors by using a by-pass from the main water cooling system, as shown in Fig. 265. In arranging the hot-water pipes observe that the water inlet comes from the hottest or highest part of the radiator system, and the outlet pipe leads to the coolest or lowest part of the main cooling system.

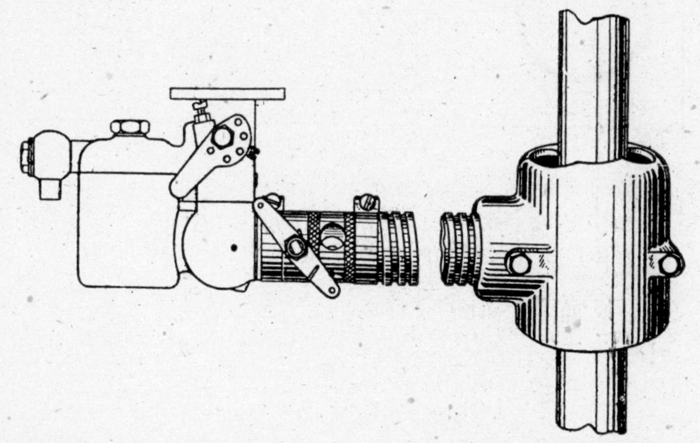

Fig. 266.—Taking Hot Air for Carburettor from around Exhaust Pipe.

When fitting a hot-air intake, Fig. 266, the use of flexible metallic tubing will be found convenient. Swivelling unions (Fig. 268) are also an advantage in some cases, for these will take up any desired direction for the hot-air pipe connection.

Exhaust-gas-jacketed carburettors are now seldom em-

Fig. 267.—Showing how Exhaust Gases are "Trapped" for Carburettor Heating.

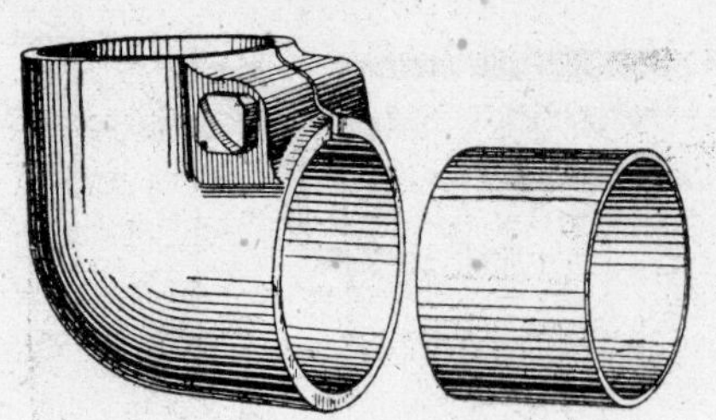

Fig. 268.—Convenient Hot-air Pipe Fittings.

ployed, except when heavy fuels such as paraffin or fuel mixtures are employed. When used, however, the method of trapping the gases, shown in Fig. 267, can be recommended.

A Variable Heating Device

In the case of hot-air systems of heating the carburettor, it is not always advisable to have the same amount of heating in summer as in winter, so that some method of varying the amount of heating may be employed with advantage. A simple but efficient method is to provide a sliding sleeve covering a portion of the hot-air intake pipe, the latter being slotted for the purpose. The sleeve is split, and sprung over the pipe. It can then be rotated or slid along so as to give different sizes of opening in the inlet pipe, thus permitting cool air to be drawn in.

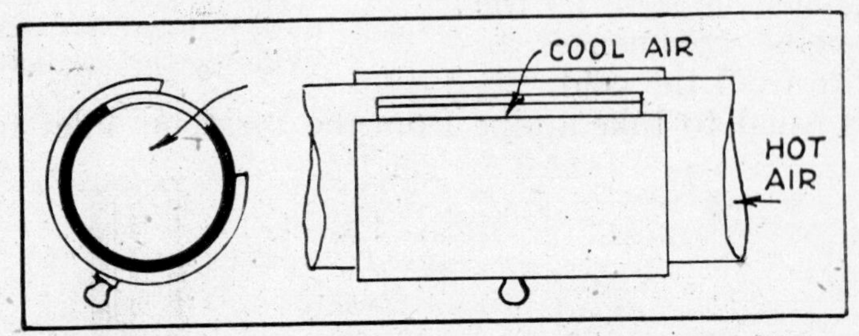

Fig. 269.—A Simple, Variable Heating Device fitted on Air Inlet Pipe.

Shape of Inlet Pipe

The actual design of the inlet pipe has a very important influence upon the running and maximum output of the engine. The leading car-engine manufacturers spend a good deal of time, and money, in experimenting with different induction systems for these reasons. It is only possible here, however, to touch upon the fringe of what is a somewhat complicated subject.

The induction pipe should provide uniform-quality mixture in equal amounts to all cylinders. It should not encourage the deposit of fuel.

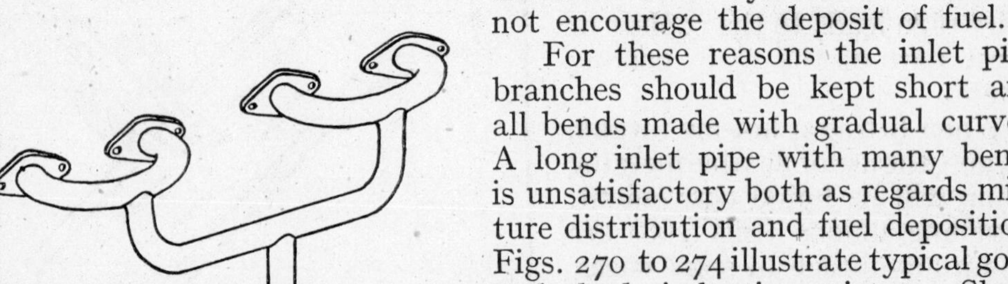

270.—Defective Induction Pipe.

For these reasons the inlet pipe branches should be kept short and all bends made with gradual curves. A long inlet pipe with many bends is unsatisfactory both as regards mixture distribution and fuel deposition. Figs. 270 to 274 illustrate typical good and bad induction pipes. Sharp bends in induction pipes cause a change of velocity (slowing down) of the mixture, leading to fuel deposit on the walls at the bend. Experience has shown that within limits, whilst pipes of different lengths have very little influence on the quantity of mixture induced or sucked through, *bends cause a very appreciable loss of charge.*

It is advisable to avoid *dips and pockets* in the induction pipe, for the same reason.

In the case of certain six- and eight-cylinder engines showing bad mixture distribution, very much better results can usually be obtained by fitting two carburettors, as shown in Fig. 274—or a dual carburettor—and separate induction pipes.

It is good practice to lag the hot air and (or the) induction pipe with

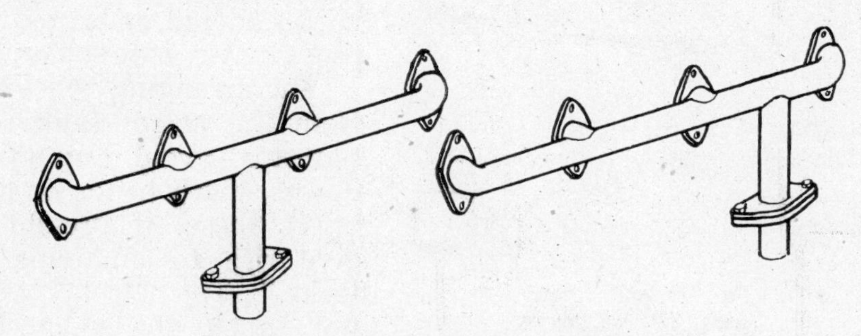

Figs. 271 and 272.—Efficient Induction Pipes.

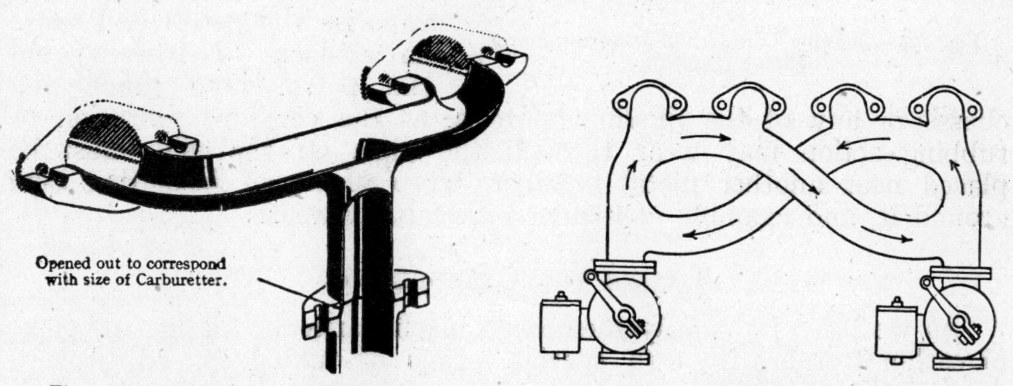

Fig. 273.—Well-designed Induction Pipe for Four-cylinder Engines.

Fig. 274.—A Double Carburettor Constant-flow Type Inlet Pipe.

asbestos string or insulating tape, in order to improve the heating of the mixture ; this applies more particularly to motor-cycle engines.

The subject of down-draught carburettors is dealt with in full, later in this section.

Petrol Filters

Although most modern cars are provided with petrol- or vacuum-tank filters to trap any sediment, it is usual to fit a gauze filter at the carburettor end ; the leading makes all have filters where the petrol supply enters the float chamber. These filters require cleaning at regular intervals, for a little water or sediment may impede the petrol flow.

If a separate filter has to be fitted, it should either be placed at the petrol-tank outlet end or close to the carburettor—never in the middle of the petrol pipe.

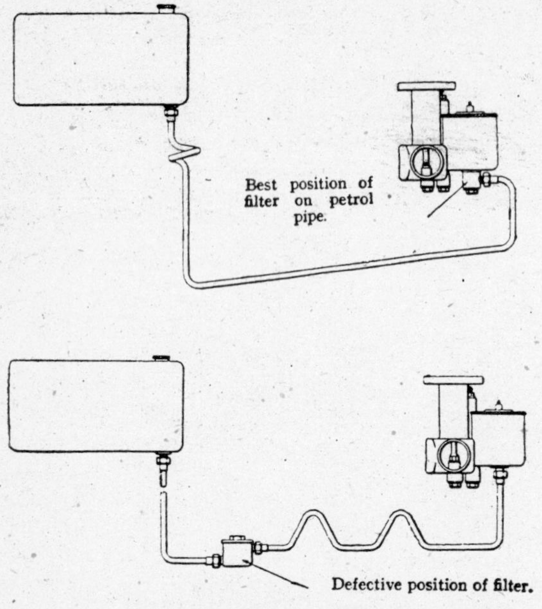

Fig. 275.—Showing Correct and Incorrect Petrol Piping (Zenith).

The Petrol Pipe

This should be made of copper. The usual size is $\frac{1}{4}$ in. to $\frac{5}{16}$ in. outside diameter by 20 S.W.G. thickness. The unions or nipples should be hard-soldered or brazed to the pipe—never soft-soldered.

In arranging the piping from the petrol tank to carburettor, avoid any ups and downs, sharp bends or flattenings; these, if present, may give rise to annoying "air-locks." The petrol pipe should not touch the exhaust pipe or silencer, for the heat will vaporise the petrol and cause an air-lock. Neither should the petrol pipe touch the chassis or any of the moving controls, as the constant vibration or rubbing action may wear through the pipe. If the pipe must be placed near another metal member, wrap plenty of insulating tape around it, and examine at regular intervals for wear.

Tuning the Carburettor

As we have previously mentioned, each particular design, or type, of carburettor has its own special means of tuning, or adjustment. As there is now a large number of different models on the market, it is obviously impossible to deal, individually, with the adjustment of each of these. We can, however, outline some general principles applicable to most types.

The result of a lengthy experience in the designing of carburettors for automobile engines has resulted in certain more or less orthodox principles being employed in their design. In most modern carburettors we find the following principal items: (1) A Main Jet; (2) a Compensating Device to enable the amount of petrol supplied by the main jet to be regulated to suit the engine speed and throttle position; (3) a Choke Tube, and (4) a Pilot, Slow-running or Starting Jet.

It is so arranged, in most cases, that the strength of the mixture—that is to say, the proportions of air and petrol—can be altered, either by changing the main jet or by substituting another size of choke tube.

Main jets are always numbered; the higher the number the greater the jet opening. The number, as a general rule, indicates the quantity of petrol of a given density the jet will pass under certain standard conditions.

The Main Jet

The *size of the main jet determines the power output* of the engine at the full-throttle opening. If too small, the power will be restricted; if too large, the fuel consumption will be excessive and carbon deposit may occur in the cylinders and exhaust pipes.

The correct size of main jet can only be determined by experiment.

To ascertain *the correct size of main jet,* in the case of a car or cycle engine, the car (or cycle) should be tested for speed on a level road. The jet which gives the greatest speed without excessive petrol consumption is the correct one. Another test is to try the car (or cycle) on a hill, which it should just be able to climb on top gear. Any improvement or falling off in pull can then be easily noted, after a change in the main jet. Too large a jet will cause a black smoky exhaust, and give rise to a pungent odour.

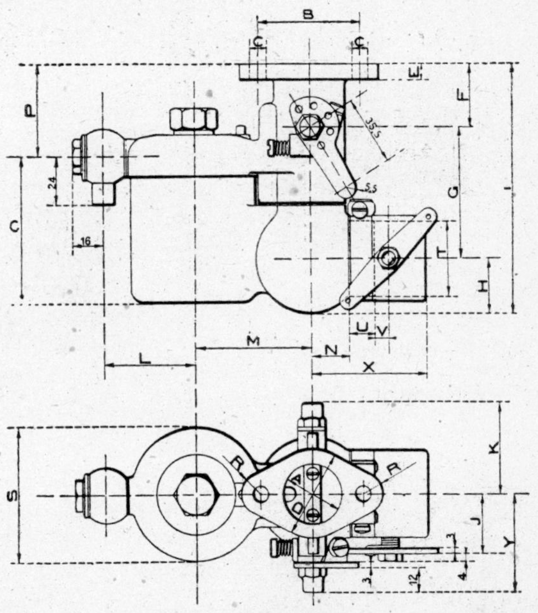

Fig. 276.—Diagram to Illustrate Method of Specifying Dimensions of Carburettor when Ordering New One.

The Compensating Device

The object of this common device to most carburettors is to maintain the mixture strength correct under most normal running conditions. With a single jet the mixture becomes richer, automatically, as the speed increases; the compensator cuts down this tendency, progressively, as the speed increases. Usually the compensator has more influence at slow speeds, as when accelerating or climbing hills slowly on top gear. The method of checking the correct size of compensator is to run the car slowly on top gear and then accelerate. If the engine pulls jerkily, it is a sign of too big a compensator; if the acceleration is poor and the engine misfires or thumps, it is a sign of too small a compensator.

We have used the term "compensator" to denote the complete compensating device. In some cases it consists of a special jet in the base of the main jet, so that our remarks may be taken to refer to in-

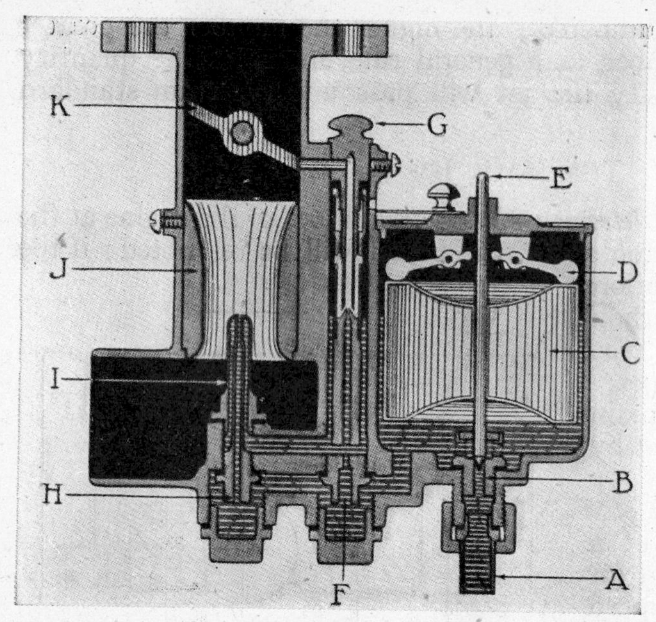

Fig. 277.—A Typical Carburettor in Section (Zenith). A, Petrol Union Nipple. B, Float-needle Seating. C, Float. D, Counterweight. E, Float Needle. F, Compensating Jet. G, Slow-running Device. H, Main Jet. I, Main-jet Cover. J, Choke Tube. K, Butterfly Throttle.

creasing or decreasing the size of this jet.

The Pilot Jet

The pilot jet is fitted to a carburettor to enable it to start and to run the engine slowly. Usually it consists of a small jet in its own choke tube, and with some adjustable means of altering the strength of mixture; the jet size or the air inlet ports may be varied for this purpose.

Referring to Fig. 278, which shows a Zenith carburettor pilot jet, it will be observed that the outlet for the mixture supplied by this jet is at U, near the throttle. It is now always arranged that when the main throttle is closed, or the accelerator released, the pilot opening to the carburettor is *not* shut off, so that the engine works solely on the pilot jet's mixture.

In Fig. 278, P is the mixture supply tube, and E the petrol inlet; A is the air opening, and V a locking screw holding the complete unit, B, in position.

In adjusting any pilot jet, first see that the throttle is closed, i.e. the throttle lever is against its stop. The engine should then start up, if everything else, including the ignition, is in order. If it fails to start, try the effect of enriching the pilot jet's mixture. In some cases (e.g. the Claudel-Hobson), the *quantity* of the mixture can be altered; this variation should be tested.

When the engine is running satisfactorily a hissing noise will usually be heard at the pilot jet; the same suction noise is evident on cranking the engine round cold.

When the engine is hot the slow-running tube should be adjusted for mixture strength, and quantity (by varying the throttle-stop position). The engine should *not* be adjusted to run dead slowly, or to labour, but rather to run at a slightly higher speed than its absolute minimum, to ensure easy starting from the cold.

The pilot mixture should be made as weak as consistent with good slow running and easy starting.

The Choke Tube

It is rarely that a change of choke tube is necessary, except when a carburettor is being fitted to another engine. The object of the choke tube is to increase the velocity of air past the main jet opening, so as to obtain sufficient suction on the jet itself.

The correct size of choke tube may be ascertained as follows: Fit the most likely size and observe the running of the engine. If the *acceleration or picking up of speed* is bad, it is a sign of *too big a choke tube.* The tests for acceleration should be made on a level road with the car running at a good speed. After travelling for a short period at this constant speed, slow down a little, and then depress the accelerator as sharply as possible and to its full extent. If the engine accelerates to its previous speed without hesitation *the choke tube is not at fault.* If, on the other hand, the engine does not respond, but falters or stops, this may be due either to the *compensator being too small* or to *the choke tube being too large.* If, after altering the compensator, the acceleration is still unsatisfactory, a smaller choke tube should be fitted.

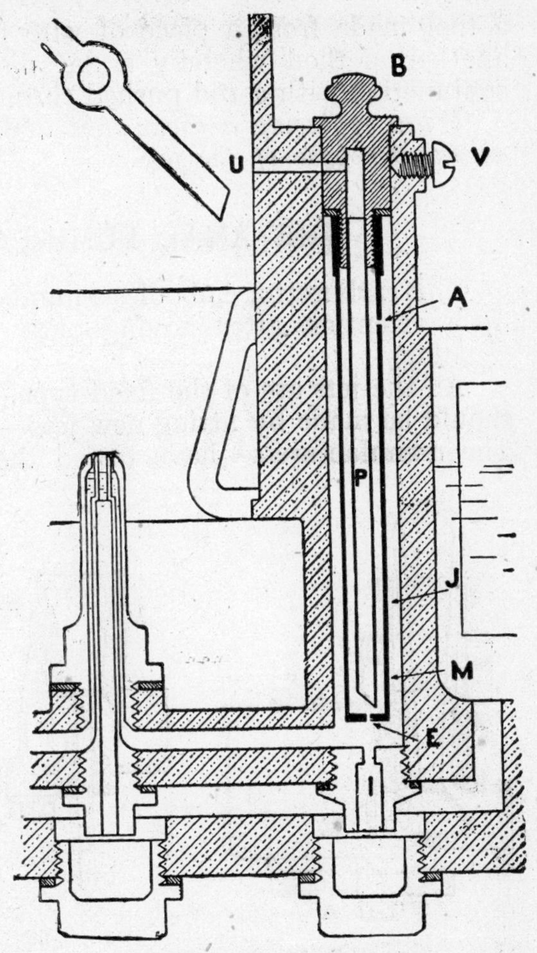

Fig. 278.—Slow-running Device.

When making any changes in choke tube in carburettors having separate choke tubes (some of the later mass-production jobs have integral chokes), small alterations in size only should be made; do not change from one choke tube to another of widely differing size.

If the *choke tube is too small,* one will usually find that the acceleration is quite good, but owing to the throttling effect on the mixture, the maximum speed on the level will be reduced; in other words the maximum power output is lowered. A larger choke and correspondingly larger jets should be fitted and the tests continued until symptoms of too large a choke are noticed.

The choke tube J (Fig. 277) is generally made a push-fit in the carburettor barrel, and is secured by a small screw through the side of the latter.

Fig. 279, A, shows the method of removing a Zenith choke tube with a tool made from a piece of wire bent to shape. Fig. 279, B, shows another method whereby a flat disc, a coin for example, is used in conjunction with a rod pushed through the jet screw hole.

When replacing a choke tube make certain the *narrowest diameter is nearest the base of the jet.*

THE AMAL PUMP-TYPE CARBURETTOR

This carburettor embodies a number of interesting features ; it requires little attention after having once been adjusted, beyond occasional cleaning.

All the jets are of the fixed type, and alterations of mixture strength should be made by fitting new jets—not by reamering out the old ones. The manufacturers[1] have tested these carburettors on most makes of car and will recommend the correct sizes of jet for any type of car.

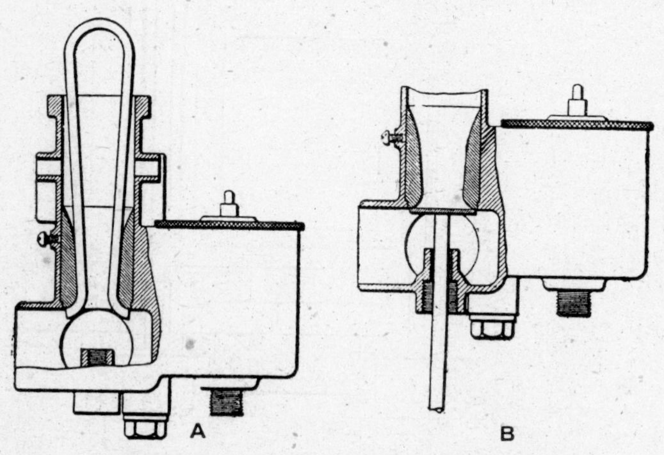

Fig. 279.—Illustrating Choke-tube Removal Methods. (A) By means of wire tool. (B) By means of flat disc and rod.

The Amal carburettor provides mixture compensation at different speeds by the special construction of the main jet alone without the introduction and complication of extra jets.

The main jet contains, besidesthe petrol orifice, an air jet which not only aids atomisation but serves also another purpose—that of compensation. When the engine speed increases under light loads, this air jet enables an increased amount of air to flow, owing to its density being lighter than that of petrol, thus automatically compensating the tendency for a greater petrol flow. The reverse state of affairs occurs under opposite conditions.

At the main jet the petrol undergoes a preliminary mixing with air, which is drawn in from the hole at the top of the main jet and through a hole in the side of the main jet into the jet chamber. The mixture then passes to the groove around the main choke ; as it issues from the choke groove through the small diffuser tubes it becomes intimately mixed with the main body of air.

Atomisation first occurs as the petrol issues from the petrol orifice into the jet chamber. This mixture then passes through the choke groove,

[1] Messrs. Amal, Ltd., Perry Bar, Birmingham.

and when it issues into the diffuser tubes it mixes with the main high-speed stream of air, thus becoming highly atomised.

With this carburettor " flat spots " are eliminated by a special arrangement, known as a " bridging jet."

As the throttle valve is opened it uncovers the bridging jet (or by-pass sleeve) which immediately has the effect of maintaining the mixture at the correct strength, the strength being regulated by the air jet and by the size of the bridging jet, thus making a flat spot impossible, ensuring quicker pick-up by the engine and smoother running.

To obtain *easy starting* from the cold the main jet is used. The throttle should be set about one-third open and the strangler valve closed; the engine will then start readily without any previous flooding.

In the case of the *Amal Vertical Pump Carburettor* (Fig. 280), this

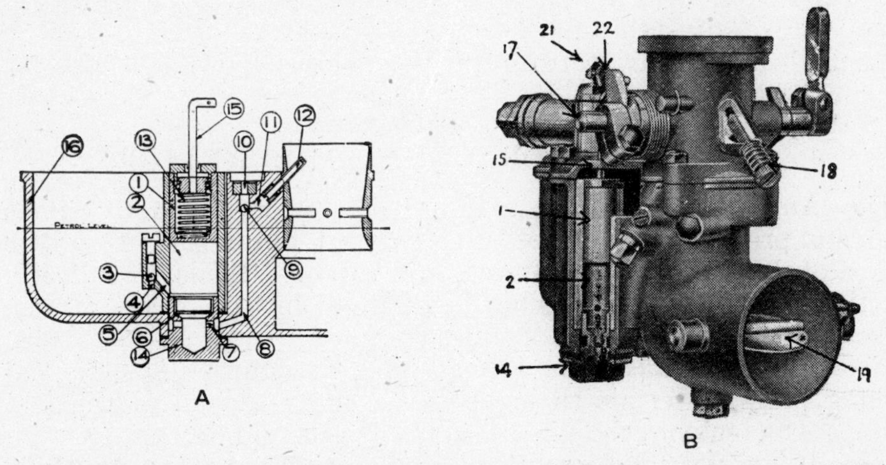

Fig. 280.—(A) Sectional View of Amal Pump Carburettor. (B) External View of same Carburettor.

resembles the standard Amal model; but it incorporates a pump, the object of which is to provide better acceleration and improved petrol economy.

When the accelerator is depressed quickly the pump forces petrol into the choke, enriches the mixture and makes up the deficiency in mixture volume, which normally would occur with a sudden large opening of the throttle at low engine revolutions. As the pump automatically enriches the mixture when quick acceleration is required, the carburettor can be set to give a weaker mixture for normal running than if the pump was not fitted.

When the throttle is opened, the pump piston 1 is depressed to the bottom of the pump chamber 2. On releasing the throttle lever the pump piston is drawn back to the top of the pump chamber. The suction created lifts the ball valve 3 from its seating and draws petrol from the float chamber 16 through the passages 4 and 5, filling the pump chamber 2.

On depressing the pump again (by quickly opening the throttle), the piston forces the petrol in the pump chamber through the filter 6 into the passage 7 and upwards along the passage 8, lifting the ball valve 9 until it rests on the upper seating 10. The petrol then passes along the passage 11, and through the pump jet 12, into the choke, where it mixes with the main air stream.

Should the throttle only be opened slowly, the pressure of petrol from the pump chamber will not be sufficient to raise the ball valve 9 as far as the upper seating, and when this happens the petrol simply flows past the seating, through passage 10, and returns to the float chamber. This latter action thus prevents the jet 12 acting as a running jet, with a consequent economy in fuel.

The action of the piston is slowed down slightly by means of a coil spring 13 attached to the piston rod and inside the pump piston. The pump piston rod 15 is actuated by a floating lever 21, in turn operated by a lever 22, adjustably fixed on the main throttle spindle. Normally the engine cannot draw petrol from the pump jet owing to the air leak through the passage 10.

AMAL DOWN-DRAUGHT CARBURETTOR

The Amal down-draught pump carburettor is exactly similar in design and principle to the type just described, but in this case advantage is taken of the weight-effect of the petrol vapour ; the latter falls into the induction pipe instead of having to be lifted into it. This results in a quicker response to throttle opening.

Tuning Instructions.—Having checked the ignition system and the sparking plugs, ascertain that the petrol filter and all of the jets are clean. The engine should be started and allowed to run until it reaches its normal temperature. Tuning should then be carried out in the following order :

(1) Obtain correct *slow-running,* or idling.
(2) Obtain correct-sized *main jet* and *choke.*
(3) Obtain correct *bridging* between *idling* and *main jets.*

To obtain correct idling.—Close throttle fully, when engine will run on idling jet. The *amount* of mixture is controlled by the idling jet ; the *strength,* or quality, is controlled by the slow-running adjusting screw. If the latter is turned in a clockwise direction it will reduce the engine speed. If the engine runs best, when idling, with the adjusting screw right in, a larger size idling jet should be fitted.

To obtain correct size of main jet and choke.—If the former is *too large,* this will be evident in excessive petrol consumption and irregular running at medium and high speeds.

If the *main jet is too small,* there will be a loss of power and occasional firing back in the carburettor ; the engine will also run harshly and on the " warm " side.

If the *choke is too large* acceleration is generally bad under all conditions; if *too small* the engine will accelerate well, but maximum road speed cannot be obtained.

To obtain correct bridging.—The engine should be allowed to idle and the throttle opened slowly until the engine is running on the main jet. If there is a point at which hesitation occurs when changing over from the idling to the main jet, when accelerating, and it is of a hunting nature, this indicates that the *bridging mixture is too rich.* To correct this, fit a larger by-pass jet.

If the hesitation is of an intermittent type, it shows that the *bridging mixture is too weak.* This can be cured by fitting a smaller by-pass jet.

Fig. 281.—The Amal Down-draught Carburettor showing Position of Jets and Controls.

16, Float Chamber.
17, Throttle Spindle.
18, Slow-running Screw.
20, Main Jet.
25, Idling Jet.
26, Bridging or By-pass Jet.
27, Air Jet.
31, Pump-jet Cover Nut.
33, Air Intake.
40, Pilot-jet Cover Nut.

MAINTENANCE OF AMAL CARBURETTORS

Generally speaking the only attention required is that of periodic cleaning, and this can be carried out without disturbing the setting of the carburettor. It is important to remember, when replacing the jets, that they should be screwed well home.

THE CLAUDEL-HOBSON CARBURETTOR

One of the most popular models of this make of carburettor is the "Z" type, so that we shall describe, briefly, its salient features and then proceed to explain its maintenance and adjustment.

The principle of this carburettor is to give normal mixture strength under all ordinary working conditions.

In this carburettor the main jet is of the submerged type, located at the base of the diffuser assembly. This is shown in Fig. 282 and consists simply of a calibrated hole K. Fig. 283 shows the actual jet.

All petrol enters the diffuser through the main jet K, through which it flows into the three concentric tubes B, N, and M. The outer tube P is an air tube only, and contains no petrol.

The tube B is a starting and slow-running tube. The holes JJ near its base admit petrol which has entered the diffuser through the main jet K. The delivery of petrol to the engine when idling by way of the slow-running jet delivery holes C is regulated by the restriction at X which is the actual slow-running jet. An air supply is drawn through the hole DD immediately above X.

In all positions of the throttle, the provision of a correct mixture falls upon the diffuser assembly.

Whilst the engine is running on tube B and the slow-running jet X, the main jet K admits more petrol than is required for slow running. Consequently, the reserve of petrol is built up in the diffuser tube N and

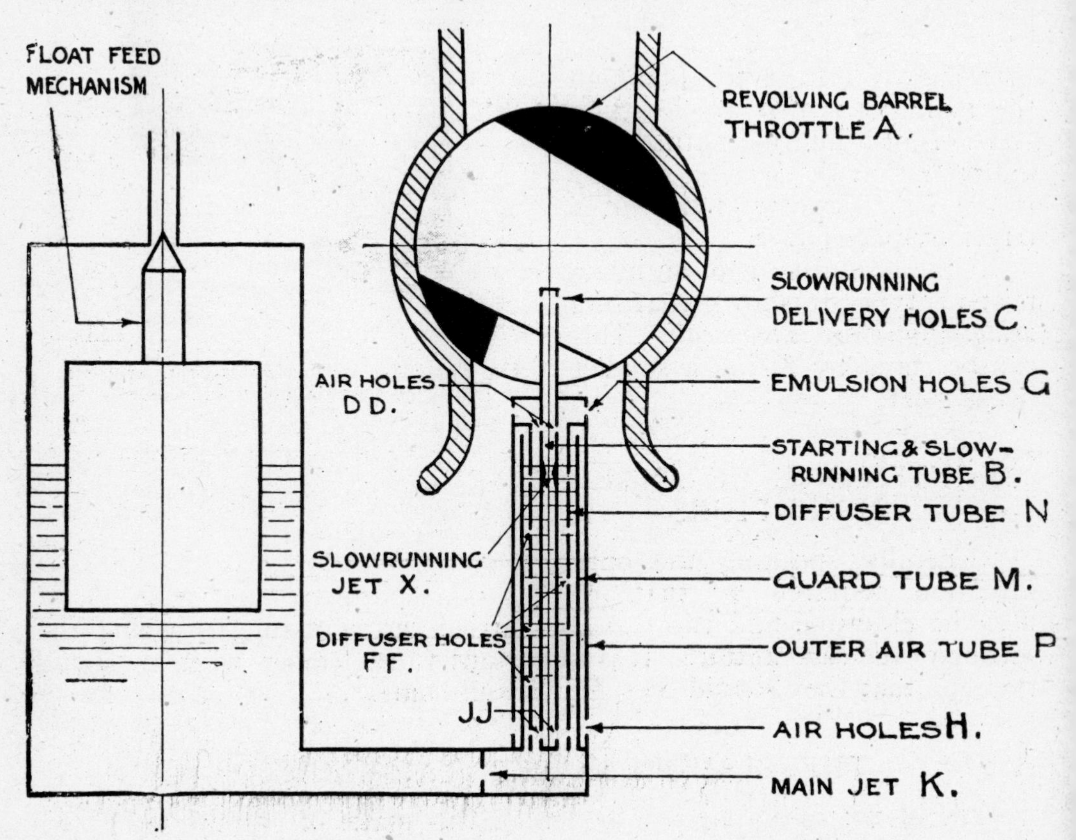

Fig. 282.—Showing the Principle of the Claudel " Z "-type Carburettor.

the guard tube M which communicate with each other by the diffuser holes FF.

When the throttle is fully opened the automatic action of the diffuser, combined with that of the power jet, provides a correct mixture at all engine speeds.

The action of the diffuser will be quite clear when the reader grasps two facts, viz.:

(1) That the level of the petrol in the tubes N and M is continually varying on the road in accordance with the engine speed and load.

(2) That the variations in the petrol level in the diffuser affect the mixture.

When the engine is idling on the slow-running jet, the main jet K admits sufficient spirit to maintain a reserve of fuel in the tubes N and M at the level set by the float-chamber mechanism.

When the throttle is opened a little, the suction begins to take effect on the emulsion holes G, and as the petrol is drawn out of the tubes N and M the level sinks. The more the throttle is opened, the lower the level becomes.

When the engine is running on full throttle, petrol will be drawn out of the tubes N and M as fast as it can enter via the main jet K so that no reserve will exist in the diffuser. As the engine slows down when the throttle is closed, the level of petrol in these tubes will mount again.

Action of the Air Holes.—When petrol is standing at its maximum level in the tubes N and M all the air holes FF are submerged in petrol. As the petrol level sinks, these holes FF are successively uncovered, commencing from the top of the tube N. Therefore, as the engine is accelerated, its suction ceases to be concentrated upon the petrol in N and M, and a portion of it is diverted to any holes FF which may be uncovered.

These holes FF are now in communication with the atmosphere, for they open into the tube M, which is open at the top to the outer air tube P, which is suitably perforated at H in communication with the annulus Y, and passage I, or the intake of the carburettor.

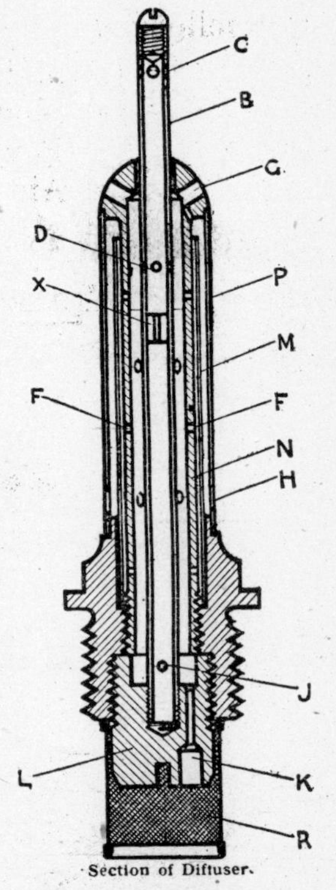

Fig. 283.—Section through Jet of Claudel-Hobson Carburettor.

In other words, whenever the engine is accelerated, the falling level of the petrol automatically diverts a proportion of the engine suction to the atmosphere, and this necessary correction prevents an excess of petrol being delivered at high engine speeds.

Similarly, when the engine is slowed down, the petrol level rises, the air holes are progressively "blanketed" from the bottom upwards by the rising reserve of petrol, and the suction is increasingly concentrated upon the petrol supply.

Throttle Barrel—The Diffuser and Jet Assembly.—The revolving barrel throttle A (Fig. 284), which is placed immediately above the head of the diffuser, is provided with a slot Z on its under side, which admits of the slow-running jet tube B being enclosed within the throttle body or mixing chamber, when in the closed positions.

The head of the diffuser consists of a ring of holes G, drilled at an angle to the lines of flow of the main air supply. These emulsion holes deliver a rich mixture of highly atomised fuel and air, as proportioned by the automatic action of the diffuser, into the main air supply.

In the closed position of the throttle, the slow-running jet is providing all the fuel required for the correct mixture, but as the throttle is opened, the emulsion holes of the diffuser come progressively under the influence of the engine depression or "suction."

Adjustments.—Adjustment of the carburettor must be confined to the following details:

(1) Main jet.
(2) Slow-running jet.
(3) Power jet.
(4) Air screw, W (Fig. 284).
(5) Throttle stop, S (Fig. 284).
(6) By-pass screw.
(7) Heating.

The petrol level is correctly set by the makers at from three to six

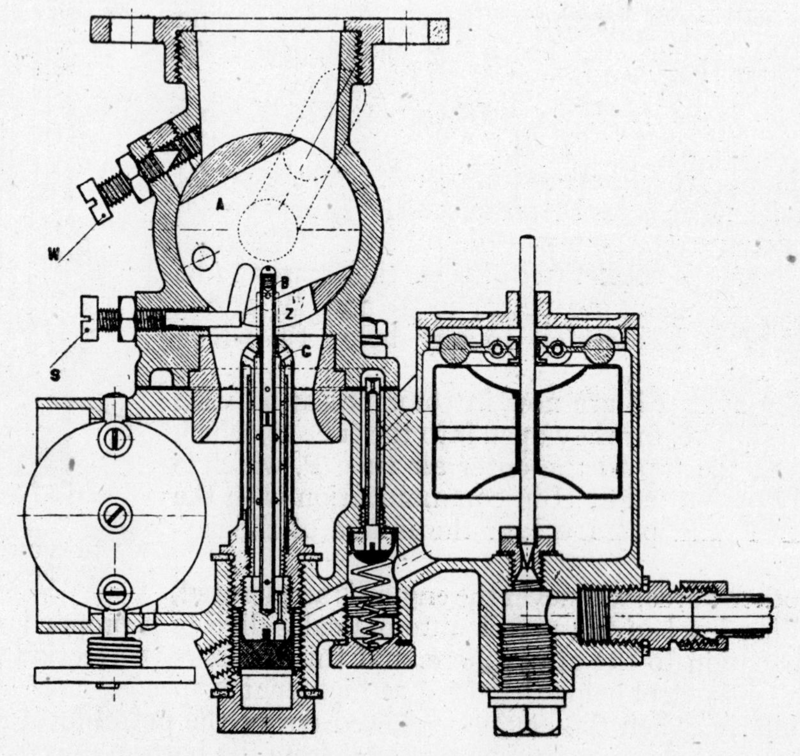

Fig. 284.—The "Z"-type Claudel-Hobson Carburettor, in Sectional View.

millimetres below the top of the guard tube. In carburettors of the "Z.P." type variations in level between these limits are not highly important.

The main jet should be set to give sufficient petrol for medium accelerations, but kept as small as possible, so that economical running may be obtained through the throttle range, irrespective of maximum power which is obtained by the extra supply of fuel, provided by the power jet which is in action at full throttle.

The method of arriving at the correct size of main jet and power jet required to give maximum power at full throttle is to test the car under load both all out on the level on top gear, and then on a hill which is sufficiently steep to considerably reduce the engine speed, without requiring the engagement of a lower gear. Full throttle must be maintained under both these conditions.

If the combination is too weak, there will be a lack of speed on the level and more especially on the hill, which will indicate the larger main or power jets are necessary. It is advisable to increase the power jet rather than the main jet if the acceleration at half throttle is satisfactory.

If jets of too large a size are fitted, the consumption may be adversely affected.

Undue richness is indicated by a black smoke and inability to accelerate immediately after changing into a lower gear.

Slow Running and Idling.—Maximum power and speed having been obtained by the use of suitable main and power jets the acceleration will almost invariably be good, and the second step is to perfect idling. The two important items in this adjustment are to work on the throttle stop, rather than the by-pass screw, and to make free use of the air screw if necessary.

In carburettors of the "Z.P." type, the air screw has no appreciable effect on the petrol consumption except in the slow-running and idling positions, though at the commencement of the adjustments the air screw should be withdrawn as far as possible without removal from the carburettor.

A hint towards diagnosing the character of any fault in the slow running may be useful at this point. If the mixture is too weak, the engine will be inclined to stop when the throttle is closed as far as possible. On the other hand, if the mixture is too strong, the engine will "hunt": that is, it will keep going, but irregularly, alternately accelerating and slowing down, instead of running smoothly and evenly on all cylinders at a very low speed.

Adjustments should be made as follows:

(1) Set the throttle stop so that the engine just continues to run. If the running is smooth and the speed low everything is in order. Should the engine "hunt," the mixture is too rich. If the engine fires irregularly, and after a minute or so stops altogether, the mixture is too weak.

(2) If the mixture is weak, screw in the air screw until the engine runs steadily.

(3) If the air screw is set right in and the mixture is still too weak, open the by-pass slightly and reset the throttle stop so that the throttle can close a little more. This will enrich the mixture, by allowing the slot in the throttle to close further around the slow-running tube.

(4) In very rare cases the above adjustments may fail to produce perfect slow running, and it may be necessary to fit a larger slow-running jet tube B.

(5) On the other hand, if the mixture is too rich, as shown by the engine tending to "hunt" when throttled down, the first step is to fit a smaller slow-running jet tube. The mixture will now be on the weak side, and adjustment will be made on the lines previously indicated.

THE BENDIX-STROMBERG CARBURETTOR

This down-draught type of carburettor[1] is fitted to some British cars and also to many American ones sold in this country. The carburettors are made in two principal models, namely, the D-36 and D-42 ones.

The DA-36 and DA-42 are identical except for the sizes of the throttle-valve body, which is larger in the case of the latter, and in general construction these carburettors follow closely the general lay-out of the

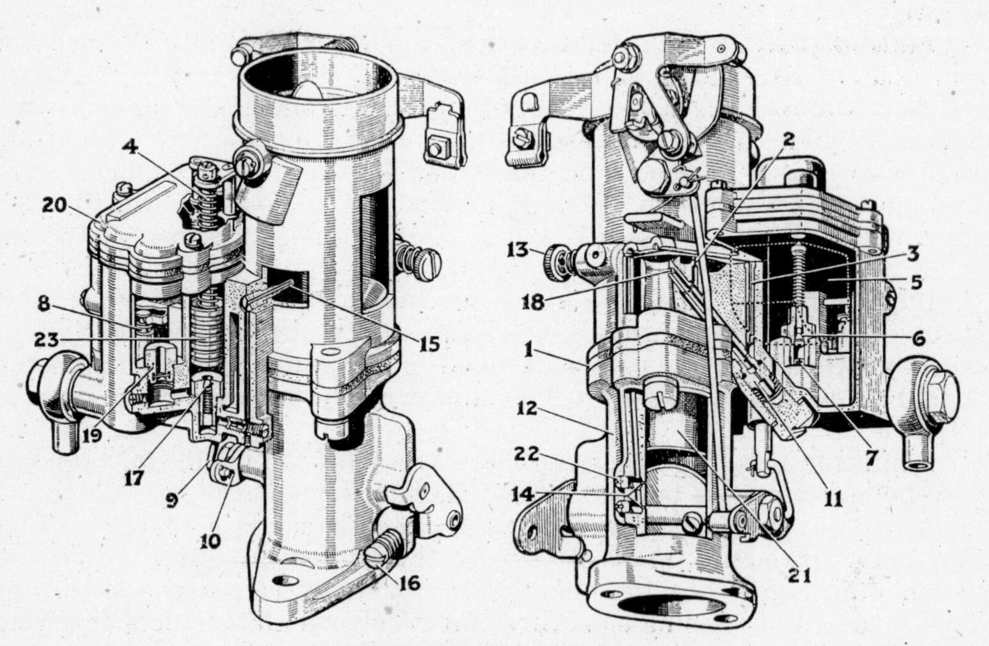

Fig. 285.—The Bendix-Stromberg Carburettor.

1, Main Body Gasket.
2, Air Bleed.
3, Idle Tube.
4, Pump Spring.
5, Float.
6, Economiser Valve.
7, By-pass Jet.
8, Needle Valve.
9, Pump Link.
10, Holes-pump Lever.
11, Metering Jet.
12, Throttle-valve Body.
13, Idling Air Screw.
14, Idle-discharge Holes.
15, Pump-discharge Jet.
16, Throttle-stop Screw.
17, Delivery-ball Valve.
18, Main-discharge Jet.
19, Check-disc Valve.
20, Float-chamber Cover.
21, Venturi Tube.
22, Plugs.
23, Pump Piston.

D series, being composed of a die-cast metal main body and cast-iron throttle-valve body, the latter being a safeguard against warping under the influence of heat. The chief points of difference between these and the earlier models lie in the size of the float chamber and float—which are larger in the new series—and the separation of the economiser valve and acceleraton pump into two separate and distinct systems so that each may be tuned to any degree without influencing the other in any way.

Fig. 285 shows the carburettor in section. The float-chamber cover (20) is detachable, and is held in place by three small screws. The main body is split across horizontally at (1), the joint being held by

[1] Marketed by Bendix, Ltd., Birmingham.

two screws. It is necessary to split the body here in order to change the venturi tube (21).

The Stromberg systems of mixture correction by air bleed and the idle lay-out are retained together with the economiser valve, ensuring the delivery of lean economical mixtures at part-throttle running.

The operation of the carburettor will be clearly understood on reference to the illustration. Fuel flows into the float chamber via the needle valve (8), and the level is maintained at the required height by the float (5). At normal driving speeds at part throttle fuel flows through the metering jet (11), and passing up the emulsion passage or discharge jet (18) becomes mixed with air entering via the air bleed (2), and is discharged into the air stream at (18). Since full throttle demands a richer mixture for power, the action of opening the throttle fully forces open the economiser valve (6), when the required amount of extra fuel is permitted to meter through the by-pass jet (7), thus enriching the mixture to the desired degree.

The fuel for idling and small throttle openings is taken from the delivery side of the main metering jet, and is metered by the restriction at the base of the idle tube (3). After being drawn past the restriction, the fuel passes up the idle tube, along the horizontal passage, when it meets air admitted by the idling air screw (13), and thence down to the two idle-discharge holes in the throttle-valve body (12).

The prompt and rapid acceleration so characteristic of the Bendix-Stromberg carburettor is made possible by the action of the accelerating pump, which delivers a small and governed quantity of fuel into the air stream when the throttle is suddenly opened. The operation of the pump is extremely simple and is trouble-free in service. When the throttle is closed, the pump piston is drawn up and the cylinder is charged with fuel through the check-disc valve (19). On the throttle being opened suddenly the piston descends and compresses the fuel in the cylinder, closing the check valve (19) and opening the delivery-ball valve (17), through which the fuel is forced on its way to discharge via the pump-discharge jet (15).

Easy starting is ensured by the Bendix-Stromberg automatic " Varie Flow " strangler valve, which, when the strangler knob is pushed in slightly after the initial start, opens and closes in accordance to the engine suction, thus putting only the required degree of depression upon the jets to ensure the correct mixture, and rendering over-strangling or choking impossible. A still further safeguard in this respect is the incorporation of an auxiliary disc-relief valve in the strangler valve itself, which operates in the event of the engine being run with the strangler knob right out.

Additional refinement in the form of the Bendix-Stromberg " Fast Idle " may be incorporated, which obviates the necessity for hand or foot control of the throttle when starting. This operates by mechanical linkage between the strangler mechanism and the throttle, so that when the strangler knob is pulled out for starting the throttle is automatically held open sufficiently to give an engine speed that will not stall at low temperatures. The "Fast Idle" functions over the whole range of the strangler movement, and only goes out of action when the strangler valve is open in the running position.

This series of models is also designed for use in conjunction with the Bendix-Stromberg "Auto-choke," which is a completely automatic thermostatically controlled device governing the mixture strength over the cold-starting and warming-up period, thus eliminating all hand manipulation of the strangler when starting and getting away.

ADJUSTING THE CARBURETTOR

(1) *Idling and Low Speeds.*—This must be carried out with the engine well warmed up. With the hand throttle in the closed position, adjust the throttle-stop screw (16) to give the desired engine speed. The idling air screw (13) controls the strength of the idling mixture, and the screw should be turned in and out until the position is found where the engine rhythm is most regular. Screwing *in* gives a *richer* mixture, and screwing *out* a *weaker* one. If a satisfactory adjustment cannot be obtained with any setting of the air screw, the idle-discharge holes (14) should be inspected by removing the plugs (22). The idle tube (3) may be removed for inspection by taking off the float-chamber cover.

(2) *Part Throttle and High Speeds.*—The main metering jet should be of a size sufficient to pass the required amount of fuel for smooth running at speeds from about 15 m.p.h. up to 45–50 m.p.h., at which point the economiser valve will open. The size of the economiser or by-pass jet (7) is governed by the amount of extra fuel required to bring the mixture up to full throttle strength and is usually about 40 per cent. smaller in diameter than the metering jet.

(3) *Acceleration Pump Adjustment.*—The quantity of fuel delivered by the pump is controlled by the size of the pump-discharge jet (15), and the *duration* of the charge by the spring (4).

The stroke of the pump may be altered by changing the link (9) from one of the two holes (10) to another, the hole nearest the throttle spindle giving the less discharge and vice versa. Normally the link is in the farthest hole, which may be termed the winter setting. If the pump discharge appear excessive during the summer months, the link should be moved into the second hole. It is inadvisable to attempt any other readjustment of the pump without first consulting the makers.

(4) *Float Level.*—The standard setting of the fuel level in the float chamber is $\frac{9}{16}$ in. below the top face of the float chamber, and is easily examined by removing the float-chamber cover, when the height of the fuel level may be measured. It should be unnecessary to make any alteration unless special fuels are being used or the carburettor has been handled roughly. When necessary, the level can be corrected by carefully bending the float arm where it meets the float. Bending the float up will raise the level, and vice versa.

DIAGNOSIS OF FAULTS

The functioning of the carburettor is so intimately connected with other elements of engine operation that engine troubles are often difficult to diagnose, and the carburettor is only too often blamed for faults for which it is not responsible. When trouble ensues in the shape of the engine misfiring, refusing to start, developing high fuel consumption, etc., after previous good performances, the trouble can usually be located more quickly by following an orderly system of investigation covering the different elements which are essential to engine operation, as indicated by the following :

1. Make certain that fuel is reaching the float chamber and thereafter the engine cylinders.
2. Ascertain whether the ignition is functioning. Detach a wire from plug and hold about $\frac{3}{16}$ in. away from metal of cylinder while the engine is turned over.
3. Check the compression of each cylinder by turning the engine over by the starting handle with the ignition switched off and the throttle wide open.
4. Check ignition timing and ascertain whether it is in accordance with maker's setting.

In cases when the carburettor itself is under suspicion, the following points should be checked :

Loss of Maximum Speed.—Check throttle valve for full opening, and check economiser valve (6) for stoppage. In order to extract the latter it is necessary to remove float-chamber cover, withdraw split pin from link (9), slip out link, and withdraw pump piston (23), when the economiser valve may be unscrewed and withdrawn.

Flat Spot at Small Throttle Opening.—15 to 20 m.p.h.—Adjust idling to give more regular engine rhythm. If flat spot is still evident, examine idle holes (14) and idle tube (3) for stoppage.

" *Flat Spot at Half Throttle.*—Withdraw metering jet (11) and examine for stoppage. Check accelerating pump for stoppage. If throttle can be held at the flat spot and the running is continually uncertain, a larger metering jet should be fitted.

High Petrol Consumption.—Check jets and float level for correct setting. If setting is correct and carburettor proved at fault the most probable cause is a sticking or leaking economiser valve, which permits flow of fuel at part throttle to the detriment of economy. Remove economiser valve and examine for foreign matter, which may be removed by blowing through valve orifice.

THE FORD CARBURETTORS

The carburettors employed on Ford cars are of special design, being of the down-draught type, automatic in action, and providing a correctly balanced air and petrol mixture at all speeds.

Fig. 286 illustrates the carburettor used on the 8-h.p. cars.

The quantity of petrol entering the carburettor from the fuel pump is governed by means of a float and valve so designed as to maintain a correct fuel level at all times. The float level should never be altered for any reason.

The volume of gas mixture entering the inlet manifold is controlled by the opening and closing of the throttle valve by means of the accelerator pedal, according to the speed desired by the driver.

The carburettor jet sizes are fixed and are selected to give the most satisfactory operation over the entire range of engine speed; nothing is to be gained by interfering with them.

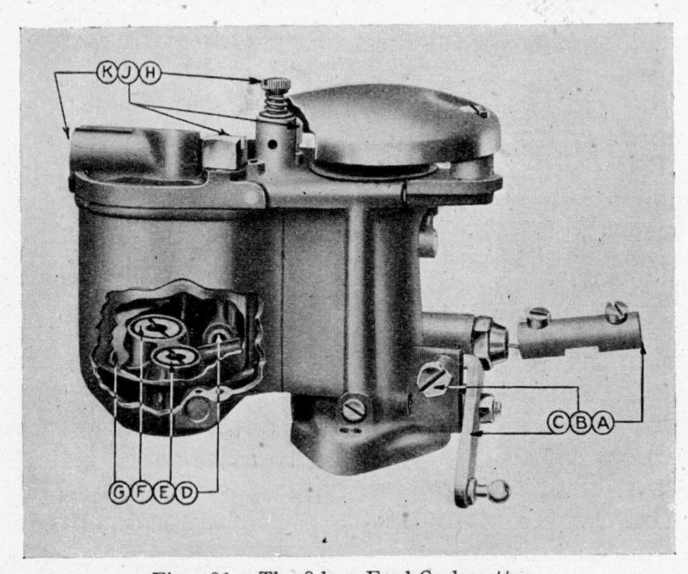

Fig. 286.—The 8-h.p. Ford Carburettor.

A, Starting Control. B, Throttle-adjusting Screw. C, Throttle Lever. D, Starting Jet. E, Main Jet. F, Compensating Jet. G, Float. H, Air-adjusting Screw. J, Float-chamber Screws. K, Petrol Inlet.

The only thing likely to affect the operation of the carburettor is the presence of dirt or water in the float chamber or jets. Should it become necessary to obtain access to the jets for cleaning purposes, this may be done by undoing the two square-headed screws on top of the float chamber (see Fig. 286) when the float-chamber bowl, complete with the jets, can be removed. The main and compensating jets will be found in the bottom of the float chamber, the slow-running jet is located on the rear edge of the bowl at the top and the starting jet on the outside of the float chamber in front of the starting device. These jets are all provided with screwdriver slots, permitting easy removal, and should be cleared by blowing through them. Never use a pin or piece of wire for clearing, as this will destroy the accurately calibrated orifices and upset the operation of the carburettor. Under no circumstances should the emulsion block (the die-cast plate held by three screws to the rear face of the float chamber and carrying the nozzle which projects into the venturi tube) be removed, as it is most essential that this should make an air-tight joint with the bowl.

The carburettor is equipped with a special starting device, which enables the mixture to be enriched sufficiently to ensure easy starting from cold, while at the same time preventing any possibility of raw petrol being drawn down into the cylinders.

The device is actuated by a control located in the centre of the dashboard and need only be used when the engine is cold.

The control should be pulled out and turned clockwise until the engine has warmed up. It should be released by turning anti-clockwise as soon as the engine shows signs of "hunting" or stopping due to over-richness.

Never depress the accelerator pedal when starting. The slow-running position of the throttle obtained when the engine is warm, in accordance with the instructions above, is the best position for starting with either a hot or a cold engine.

Slow-running Adjustment.—The only adjustments required are to the throttle-adjusting screw and the air-adjusting screw for idling speeds (see Fig. 286).

The approximate settings are:

Air-adjusting Screws.—One-half to one full turn open.

Throttle-adjusting Screw.—Screwed in about ½ to 1½ turns after the set-screw touches throttle lever.

The best adjustment is about ¾ turn open.

To obtain the exact settings for the individual engine, proceed as follows:

When engine is warm, turn throttle-adjusting screw so that engine will run sufficiently fast to prevent stalling. The air-adjusting screw should next be turned in or out until engine runs evenly; the throttle screw may now be readjusted if engine is running too fast, followed by a further readjustment of the air-adjusting screw. These operations should be repeated until idling speed is satisfactory.

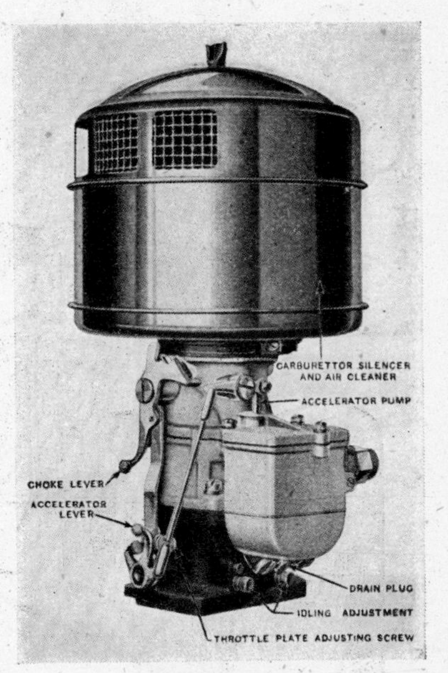

Fig. 287.—The Ford V-eight Carburettor.

Do not expect a new engine which is stiff to idle perfectly at low speeds, or to "rock" on compression when stopped.

The V-eight carburettor is shown in Fig. 287. It is of the dual down-draught type with acceleration pump and bleeder-valve choke, and is automatic in action.

This carburettor is adjusted at the worksbefore the car leaves the manufacturers, so that, with the exception of the idling adjustment, it will remain correct, unless tampered with.

The idling adjustment should be regulated after the car has been run in.

This can be done by means of the idling-adjusting screws shown in Fig. 287, the engine speed being set to that equivalent to 5 m.p.h. on top gear. Have the engine well warmed up and make sure there are no air leaks at the intake manifold, windscreen wiper, or distributor vacuum-brake connections.

The full idling adjusting valves control the quantity of mixture for slow-speed running.

Turning the screws out increases the quantity of mixture and therefore the speed. Adjust one side of the carburettor at a time. Turn the valve in slowly until the engine begins to "lag"; then slowly turn it out until the engine begins to "roll." Finally, very slowly, turn the valve in until the engine runs quite smoothly.

Then repeat the procedure for the other side of the carburettor. It may be necessary after making these adjustments to reduce the engine speed to 5 m.p.h. by means of the idling-adjustment screw.

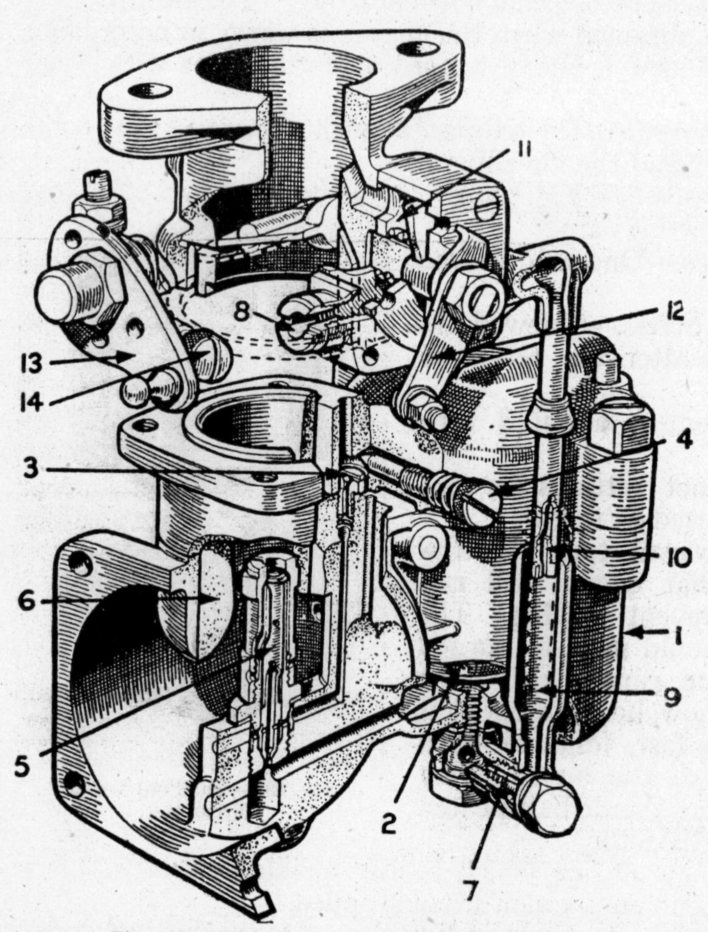

Fig. 288.—Solex Vertical "Starter" Carburettor.

1, Float Chamber.
2, Float.
3, Pilot Jet.
4, Air Adjustment for Pilot Jet.
5, Main Jet.
6, Choke.
7, Starter Petrol Jet.
8, Starter Air Jet.
9, Well.
10, Dip Tube.
11, Starter Mixing Chamber.
12, Starter Control Lever.
13, Throttle Control Lever.
14, Throttle Adjusting Screw.

THE SOLEX VERTICAL-TYPE CARBURETTOR

Fig. 288 shows the Solex carburettor as fitted to certain types of car engine.

The dismantling of this carburettor is a simple operation, it only being necessary to unscrew the two square-headed screws to enable the float chamber complete with its floats and jets to be removed.

Carburettor troubles likely to be experienced are as follows:

(*a*) *Choked Jets*, caused by water or dirt entering from the tank. To avoid this as far as possible the petrol passes through a filter before entering the carburettor. Choked jets will cause irregular running or stopping altogether.

In such cases the petrol supply should first be shut off. Then, dismantle the carburettor by unscrewing the square-headed screws previously mentioned, and take off the top of the float chamber; the jets are then accessible. These should be removed with the aid of a small spanner. When cleaning the jets, do not in any circumstances pass anything through the holes, or the sizes of the jets may be altered and the satisfactory running of the engine effected.

(*b*) *Punctured Float.*—This affects the petrol level and causes flooding when the engine is stationary; in this case a new float should be fitted.

Adjustments.—When the carburettor is dismantled do not use undue force when unscrewing and also when replacing the main jet. Further, in the case of the float chamber make sure that the main and pilot jets register correctly and do not use undue force when tightening the retaining screws.

An adjustment is provided on the pilot jet for regulating the mixture; this only affects the engine when idling or when starting on the main carburettor. Too rich a mixture will result in uneven running and deposit soot on the plugs.

Too weak a mixture will also cause uneven running and have a tendency to cause frequent misfiring.

The adjustment takes the form of a spring-tensioned milled and slotted screw, and is fitted on the side of the carburettor close to the float chamber. Provided the pilot jet is of the correct size, therefore, the screw should be turned in a clockwise direction to enrich the mixture, and in the reverse one to weaken it. If it is impossible to obtain satisfactory results by means of this adjustment, the pilot jet should be changed for a smaller or larger size.

THE SOLEX CARBURETTOR ADJUSTMENTS

Fig. 289 shows the Solex carburettor as used on cars and commercial vehicles, the particular model shown being the Type MOVT, suitable for six-cylinder engines. The information given is, however, applicable to most other types.

ADJUSTMENT

Idling.—Adjustment for idling should be carried out with the engine only moderately warm; if adjusted when the engine is hot, there will be some difficulty in starting from cold. Closed-throttle running is affected to a considerable extent by the idling adjustment.

Too rich a mixture is recognised (*a*) by a rhythmic surge or " hunt " which the engine develops when warm; (*b*) by a certain amount of petrol dropping from the carburettor when the throttle is opened and the engine stops, after having been idling for some time; (*c*) by a heavy coating of soot being deposited on the plug points.

Insufficient petrol is recognised by an irregular misfire when idling, and difficulty in starting.

Do not alter the idling jet unless absolutely necessary. Adjust for idling by means of the knurled nut W, Fig. 290. By rotating this

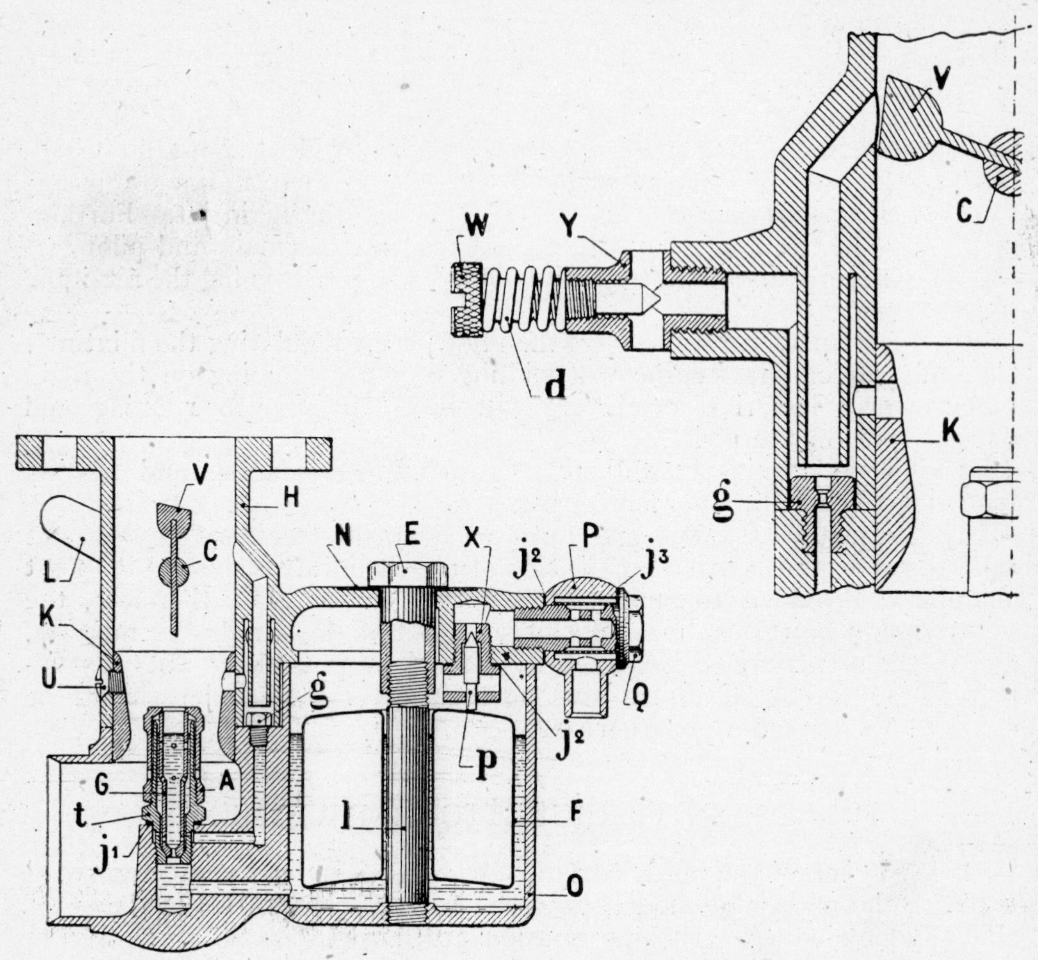

Fig. 289.—Sections of the Solex Carburettor, Type MOVT.

G, Main Jet.
g, Auxiliary Jet.
t, Main-jet Carrier.
F, Float.
A, Main-jet Cap.
K, Choke Tube.
P, Swivelling-filter Union.
U, Choke-tube Fixing Screw.
j[1], Main-jet Carrier Washer.
j[2], Needle-valve and Petrol-union Washer.
L, Throttle Lever.
j[3], Large Swivelling-union Washer.
p, Needle.
V, Throttle.
Q, Filter Union-assembling Nut.
H, Body of the Carburettor.
O, Float Chamber of the Carburettor.
X, Needle-valve Seating.
C, Throttle Spindle.
E, Dismounting Nut.
I, Central Pillar.
N, Nameplate.
W, Idling-adjusting Screw.
d, Control Spring for W.
Y, Idling-mixture Air Inlet.
K, Choke Tube.

screw outwards, a slight air leak is produced in the slow-running passage which reduces the mixture strength in the vaporiser.

By careful regulation absolute correctness of mixture can be obtained.

Adjust for slow running on throttle stop S, Fig. 290.

Adjustment for Power.—This can only be carried out with the engine hot. A slightly better power output can be obtained by the use of a slightly larger main jet than that supplied as standard. Do not increase beyond this and do not use a reamer.

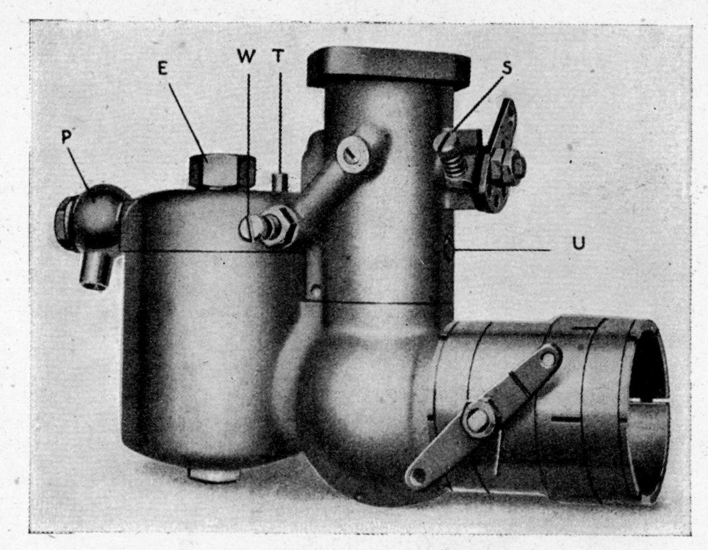

Fig. 290.—The Solex Carburettor as fitted to Leyland Engines.

E, Clamp Nut for Top Half.
T, Tickler.
P, Petrol Filter.
S, Throttle Stop.
W, Idling Adjustment.
U, Choke-tube Securing Screw.

Any tendency for the mixture to be on the weak side is generally indicated by "popping back" in the carburettor on full throttle. (*Note.*—This condition may also hold when the engine is cold.)

SOLEX DOWN-DRAUGHT SELF-STARTING CARBURETTOR

This carburettor follows the usual Solex method of operation and embodies a starting device to regulate, automatically, the richness of the mixture in inverse proportion to the temperature and speed of the engine; it takes the form of a separate small complete carburettor which is also used for slow-running purposes.

The carburettor, in certain models, has an acceleration pump, but this is not a standard fitting; the pump in question is shown in section in Fig. 292.

THE SOLEX THERMOSTARTER CARBURETTOR

This is an easy-starting carburettor having a heat-controlled rich mixture starting jet and air supply, constituting a special small carburettor quite independent of the main carburettor. The automatic thermostarter is made of two main parts: the *Starter*, that is to say the special apparatus for starting and running; and the *Thermostat* which automatically controls the opening and closing of the starter, according to the temperature of the engine.

The combination of these two elements achieves by automatic means, and independently of the driver, the correct entry and subsequent withdrawal of the starter device in conformity with the needs of the engine.

Briefly the operation of the carburettor, shown in Fig. 293, is as follows:
The jet G*s* feeds the starter-well jet and provides a high-velocity air stream for atomising the petrol. This starting mixture passes into the carburettor via the inclined port shown on the right, just above the throttle. Distortion of the bimetallic strip B at a set temperature bends it to close the aperture O, i.e. the end of the connecting pipe between the thermostat and the starter unit. The latter unit is all ready to function when it is desired to start the engine. When the thermostat actuates the starter unitthe latter is pushed out of action immediately. To compromise for the hot and cold conditions of the engine a carburettor setting must be used suitable for when the engine is cold and during the warming-up process. The pilot jet is for idling and is fed via the main carburettor jet. The output of the pilot jet cannot overlap that of the main jet.

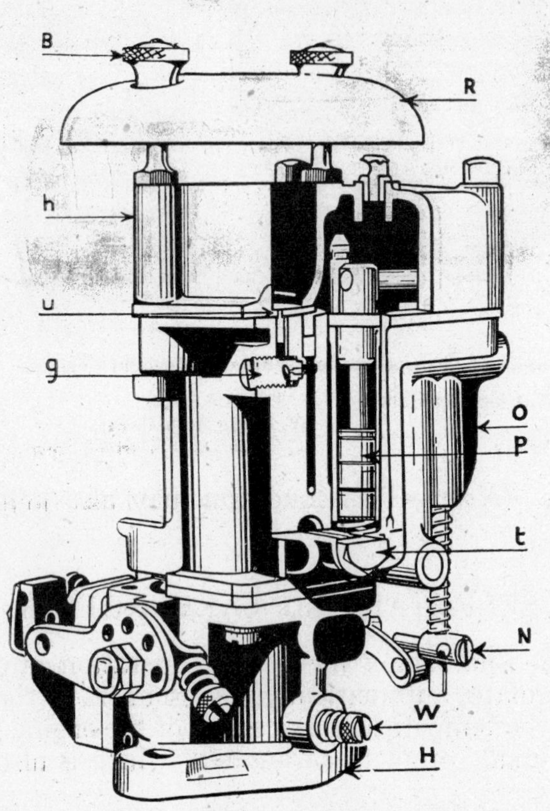

Fig. 291.—The Solex Down-draught Self-starting Carburettor.

B, Air-bell Fixing Nut. *g*, Pilot Jet. H, Flange of the Carburettor. *h*, Float-chamber Cover. N, Pump-rod Adjusting Nut. O, Float Chamber of the Carburettor. *p*, Pump Piston. R, Air Bell. *t*, Main Jet Carrier. *u*, Air Bleed. W, Slow-running Volume-control Screw.

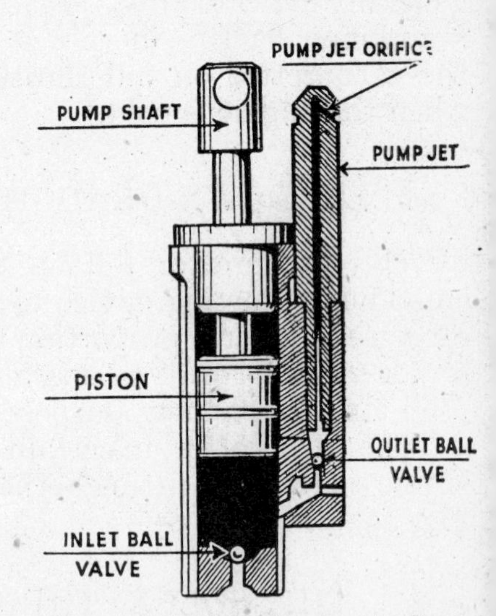

Fig. 292.—The Solex Acceleration Pump.

THE THERMOSTATIC BOX

In this box, made of non-corrodible metal, and fixed on the exhaust pipe, is the thermostat, which is made up of a "bimetal strip," one end of which is fixed and the other equipped with a valve C_2 (Fig. 293). A spring-load anchorage forces the "bimetal strip" into contact with adjustment screw H, which acts as a fulcrum. The valve C_2 is placed in front of an orifice at the end of the tube and when open puts the starter in communication with the thermostat.

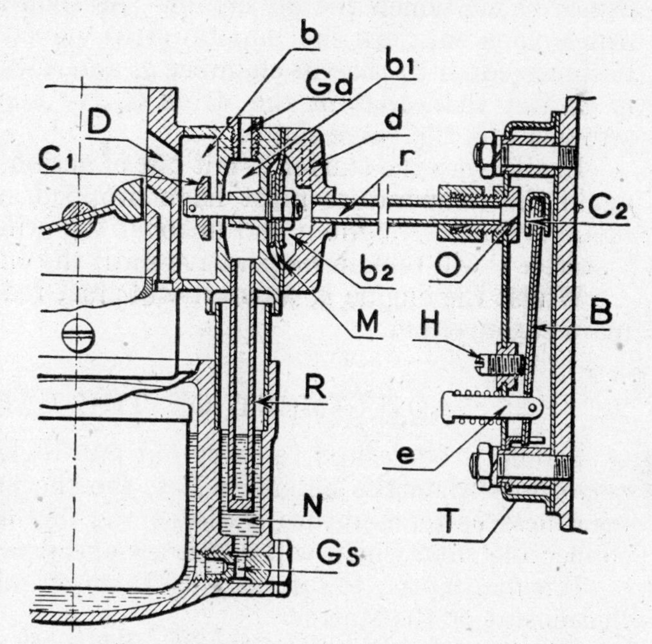

Fig. 293.—A Section of the Solex Thermostarter showing the position of the Bimetal Strip B when the Engine is cold and the Orifice O therefore open. *b*, Vacuum Chamber. b_1, Vacuum Chamber. b_2, Vacuum Chamber. B, Bimetal Strip. C_1, Starter Valve. C_2, Bimetal Strip Valve. D, Mixture Supply Port. *d*, Vacuum Balance Tube. *e*, Thermostat Spring Anchorage. G*a*, Air Jet. G*s*, Petrol Jet. H, Bimetal Strip Fulcrum Screw. M, Membrane of Valve C. N, Starter Well. O, Control Orifice. R, Dip Tube. *r*, Starter and Thermostatic Union Pipe. T, Thermostatic Box.

The "bimetal strip" is the actuating element of the thermostat: it is made up of two stainless metals, having different expansion coefficients, which are welded together along their whole length.

When this is heated it is bent by the action of the different expansions of the two metals.

When it is cold, and consequently straight, the valve C_2 is removed from the orifice O (Fig. 293), but on a certain predetermined temperature being reached, the distortion of the strip forces the valve C_2 into contact with the orifice O (Fig. 294) and puts the starter out of action.

The action of the starter is controlled by the movement of the valve C_1, which is operated via its stem by the membrane M. This membrane M is in effect the expanding wall of a chamber b_2 to which s transimitted the suction of the engne, through the tube *d*, and which is also connected to the thermostarter box by the union tube *r*. When the engine is started, either by hand or by the electric motor, the vacuum created in the chamber *b* via the tube D causes the valve C_1 to open. The chamber b_1 is then subjected to the engine suction and the starter works normally.

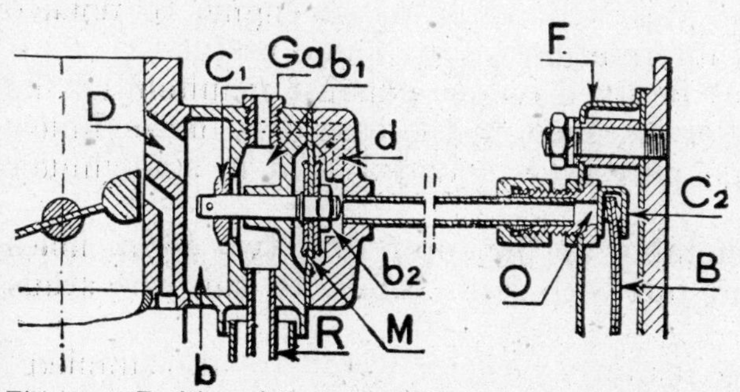

Fig. 294.—Position of the Bimetal Strip B when the Engine is hot; the Orifice O, it will be seen, is here closed by the Valve C_2.

At the same time, however, the chamber b_2 is similarly put into depression by the suction of the engine through the tube *d*; this action, however, is very weak owing to the excess leakage through the relief orifice O via which the air enters. As soon as the engine is warm, the orifice O is shut by the bimetal strip valve, the vacuum in chamber b_2 becomes equal to that in chamber *b*, and, as the surface of membrane M is greater than that of the valve C, the suction on the former is the stronger and the valve shuts.

In this way the starter is put out of action, and before it can operate again the temperature must have dropped sufficiently to allow the bimetal strip to straighten and uncover the orifice O. In other words, the "starter" will remain inoperative until the engine cools down.

Whilst the engine is warm it will start readily on the pilot jet of the main carburettor.

ADJUSTMENT OF THE CARBURETTOR

Should it be desired to carry out any regulations to the starter air or petrol jets when the engine is hot, the thermostat can be put in action regardless of temperature by loosening one of the joints on the copper connecting tube which will admit air and prevent thermostatic cut-off.

It is inadvisable to tamper with the internal arrangements either of the thermostat or the starter.

If either should refuse to respond to the above adjustment or the temperature alterations as effected by the use, or otherwise, of "distance washers" between the thermostatic box and the exhaust manifold, it is best to return them to the makers for attention fully assembled.

FITTING THE THERMOSTARTER CARBURETTOR

This carburettor is made in various sizes from 26 mm. to 40 mm., the larger single and double air-jet sizes (40 mm.) being suitable for commercial vehicles.

In regard to the fitting of this carburettor to an engine to replace an existing type the following information will be found useful.

The thermostatic box must be fixed on the exhaust manifold at the hottest part of the latter. (For instance, in the case of a four-cylinder engine, it is generally between port leads 3 and 4, and in six-cylinder motors between 4 and 5.)

Choose a flat portion, preferably at the top; drill two $\frac{13}{64}$-in. holes 104 mm. between centres and tap with $\frac{1}{4}$-in. B.S.F. to suit the studs supplied with the equipment.

For very hot pipes interpose distance washers, which are also supplied.

The 4 × 6 mm. copper tube provided with bi-cone nipples normally about 16 in. long will then be suitably bent, fitted to join up the thermostatic box and the starter cover plate as illustrated, care being taken that there is no air leakage at the joints, which would interfere with the action of the thermostat.

THE SOLEX GOVERNOR THERMOSTARTER CARBURETTOR

This commercial-vehicle carburettor has a governor device for limiting the engine speed to a predetermined maximum value, above which it is not possible for the engine to operate.

In most respects it resembles the standard Solex carburettor, but it has, in addition, a sealed governor device.

Fig. 295 shows the carburettor in sectional view, whilst the throttle tube and its " exploded " parts are given in Fig. 296.

The governor has no mechanical connections whatsoever to any driving shafts. It operates on the velocity principle, the closing of the throttle sufficiently to cause the engine speed to remain constant being accomplished by reason of the velocity of the ingoing air stream taking effect on the inclined face of the butterfly type of throttle.

This is shown at (1), Fig. 295. It will be seen that the throttle is mounted eccentrically on the spindle, i.e. the " tail," or lower half, is longer than the " head." Thus air pressure on the head has the closing effect mentioned.

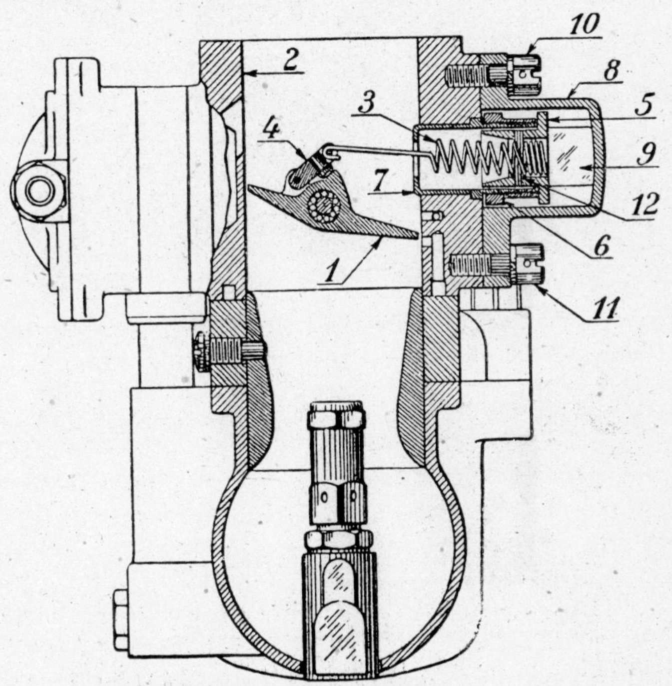

Fig. 295.—The Vertical Model Solex Governor Thermostarter Carburettor. 1, Butterfly. 2, Throttle Chamber. 3, Governor Spring. 4, Spring-link Anchorage. 5, Spring-regulating Sleeve. 6, Tension Nut. 7, Threaded Guide for Tension Screw. 8, Locking Cover. 9, Cover Guide. 10-11, Fixing Screws. 12, Steel Peg.

Resisting the closing effort of the air charge is a coil spring (3), anchored to the throttle. Since the pressure of the air charge on the throttle—or butterfly—or vane—(they are all the same thing)—increases as the engine speed rises it will be clear that by adjusting the pull of the spring to any required tension, the throttle will start to close when the pressure of the air charge, and therefore the engine revolutions, reaches an equivalent value.

In order that the throttle shall be properly sensitive to the opposing forces of air pressure and spring tension, it floats on a hardened and ground spindle on needle roller-bearings. The spindle in turn operates in substantial bronze bearings with full provision for taking end thrust. It is coupled to the accelerator in the usual way, but the throttle is free to rotate on it independently. This free movement is limited by a simple drive, of dog formation, between spindle and throttle. The result is that the throttle is always positively closed by the dog when the accelerator pedal is released, but on pressing it down again the throttle is opened by spring (3) as the dog drive recedes from it. Sufficient lost motion is allowed for throttle movement on the spindle during governing, so that the driver's foot can always be kept right down on the pedal, and the governor, meantime, will operate freely, controlled only by the speed of the engine.

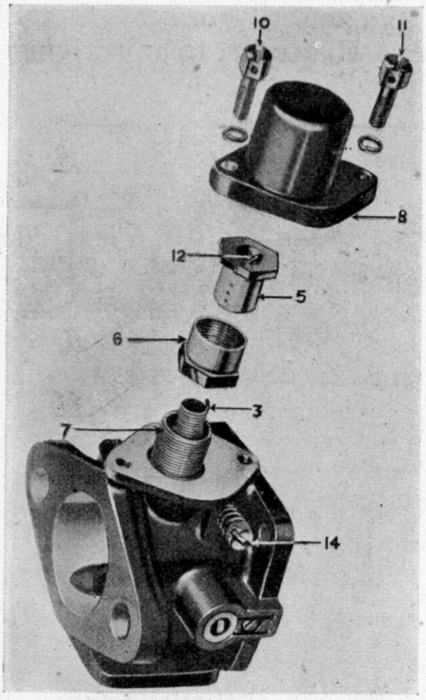

Fig. 296.—Exploded View of Throttle Tube and its Component Parts. 3, Governor Spring. 5, Spring-regulating Sleeve. 6, Tension Nut. 7, Threaded Guide for 6. 8, Locking Cover. 10, Fixing Screw. 11, Fixing Screw. 12, Peg through 5. 14, Slow-running Adjustment Screw.

The outer anchorage of spring 3 consists of a steel peg 12 housed in a sleeve 5 and passing through the spring coils. The sleeve itself has no lateral fixing device, but the inner face of its hexagon abuts against the outer one of the tension nut 6, as shown in the cross-sectional view. This member is threaded, and screws on to the housing 7. By screwing 6 out or in, therefore, sleeve 5 will also move with it, and increase or decrease, as the case may be, the tension of the spring.

Here, then, is the means of adjusting to one's needs the speed to which the engine shall be governed.

This alone is not sufficient. The governor, in action, would probably "hunt" or "surge," because the air pressure on the throttle would tend to overclose it; the speed would then fall, the spring take control, open the throttle, again too far, and thus set up a continuous cycle of opening and closing. Elimination of this undesirable feature is by control of the "rate" of the spring.

Every spring has a natural rate of vibration, or, as the radio enthusiast would term it, "frequency."

This rate can be varied by increasing or decreasing the number of its coils, and this adjustment is used on the Solex instrument to match up the spring rate to the pulsational action of the air charge on the throttle at the particular engine speed selected.

The sleeve 5, if revolved, will cause the peg 12 to be screwed along the spring, thus altering the number of coils between peg and spring hook. These, which are the ones in action, are the only ones that matter, those on the outer side, farthest from the throttle, being "dead."

The successful tuning of a Solex governor carburettor, therefore, centres in the adjustment of spring-regulating sleeve 5 and tension nut 6.

An important adjunct to steady and sensitive governing lies in the method of attaching the spring hook to the throttle. Referring again to Fig. 295, a link 4 is seen, pivoted to the throttle at its one end. The other extremity houses a bronze roller, over which the spring is hooked, this roller, of course, affording a wear-free anchorage for it. A small boss, or distance piece, fixed in the lower face of the link, is shown as preventing it from meeting the platform-shaped lip on the throttle, which lies immediately below the link. The action of this simple mechanism is rather subtle. With the throttle fully open, the link and spring are in a straight line. As, however, the throttle closes, a point is reached where the boss of the link touches the platform-shaped lip, and from that point onwards the increasing upward tilt given to the outer end of the link results in progressively increased loading of the spring.

ACTION OF THE GOVERNOR

Having in mind the construction of the various parts, especially link 4, sleeve 5, and nut 6, we can picture briefly the sequence of events.

On depressing the accelerator pedal, the dog drive on the spindle allows the throttle to open fully under the influence of the spring.

The pressure of the air charge on the tail of the throttle is at first very light and does not move it. As the selected governed speed is approached, however, the throttle commences to close and the pressure builds up very rapidly indeed as this closing movement progresses.

A correspondingly sharp increase in the build-up of spring resistance is called for, without having to alter the already determined tension at the full open-throttle position, and this is provided by the link 4 and its boss, as already described.

In this way the throttle remains wide open until immediately before the governing speed is reached, so that pick-up is not restricted. Then the whole of the closure takes place over the smallest possible number of engine revolutions.

ADJUSTING THE GOVERNOR CARBURETTOR

The sleeve 5 should not be rotated alone, since it alters both the spring rate and spring tension. A certain amount of idle movement of the hexagon is present, viz. about one-third of a facet either way. This represents the " rock " of the spring hook in the grooved pulley. After any adjustment of sleeve 5, therefore, take care to see that it rests, when released from the hand, midway through this idle movement. In this way a twofold benefit results : the spring hook does not bind sideways in the pulley groove, and also the sleeve will not rotate under the influence of the spring when the load is removed.

Before replacing the governor cap note that both hexagons must be in line to allow the locking flats inside the cap to pass over them.

Cases occasionally occur where the sleeve adjustment brings it outwards so far that it fouls the cap. Sometimes, too, the opposite condition is reached, where the tension nut comes up against the face of the carburettor, whilst yet more clockwise rotation, to lower the engine speed, is required. Correction for both the conditions is obtained by altering the position of peg 12 in the sleeve to another pair of locating holes. There are four positions in all, as shown in Fig. 295. Select one nearer the hexagon in the first case, and farther from it in the second.

This alteration is not by any means difficult, but, if preferred, spare sleeves can be supplied by the makers with the peg in any desired position.

Examination will show that the peg is tilted at an angle in relation to the bore of the sleeve. This tilt matches the pitch of the spring coils. To avoid error when rethreading the sleeve on to the spring, it is most important to see that the tilt lines up with, instead of opposes, the pitch of the spring. To ensure this, all that is necessary is to make quite certain that the end of the peg which is canted *towards* the spring is fitted first into the coils.

After completing adjustments required, replace the cap and secure it by the screws 10 and 11, and their spring washers. It should be sealed also by passing a wire through the drilled heads of the screws and securing the wire with a lead seal, so as to make it secure against unauthorised tampering.

THE S.U. CONTROLLABLE-JET CARBURETTOR

This well-known automatic carburettor is fitted as standard to many motor cars, so that the following information on its adjustment and the troubles likely to occur will no doubt be useful to the owner-driver and garage engineer.

The S.U. carburettor has a suction-operated piston (Fig. 297) which moves up and down under the influence of the inlet-pipe suction effect. The piston has a tapered needle at its lower end, the needle in question dipping into the petrol jet (Figs. 297 and 298); the movement of the piston therefore controls the amount of petrol drawn from the jet, and hence regulates the mixture strength.

Adjustments

In connection with the adjustment of the carburettor it is essential that this should be done by means of the jet and jet-adjusting nut so that when the engine is running slowly the correct mixture is obtained, i.e. it should fire evenly. This adjustment not only regulates the mixture for idling, but also for the whole range of speeds.

If incorrectly adjusted the performance will be poor and the petrol consumption heavy.

When considering the fitting of this type of carburettor it should be remembered that *a larger needle will give a weaker mixture* over the whole running-speed range and *a smaller needle a stronger mixture.*

To adjust the carburettor proceed as follows:

Run the engine until it attains its normal running temperature.

Adjust the jet to such a position that the engine idles on the correct mixture. An easy way to do this is to screw the jet-adjusting nut up higher than its normal position and then adjust the jet correctly; as the jet-adjusting nut actually only acts as a stop to prevent the jet from

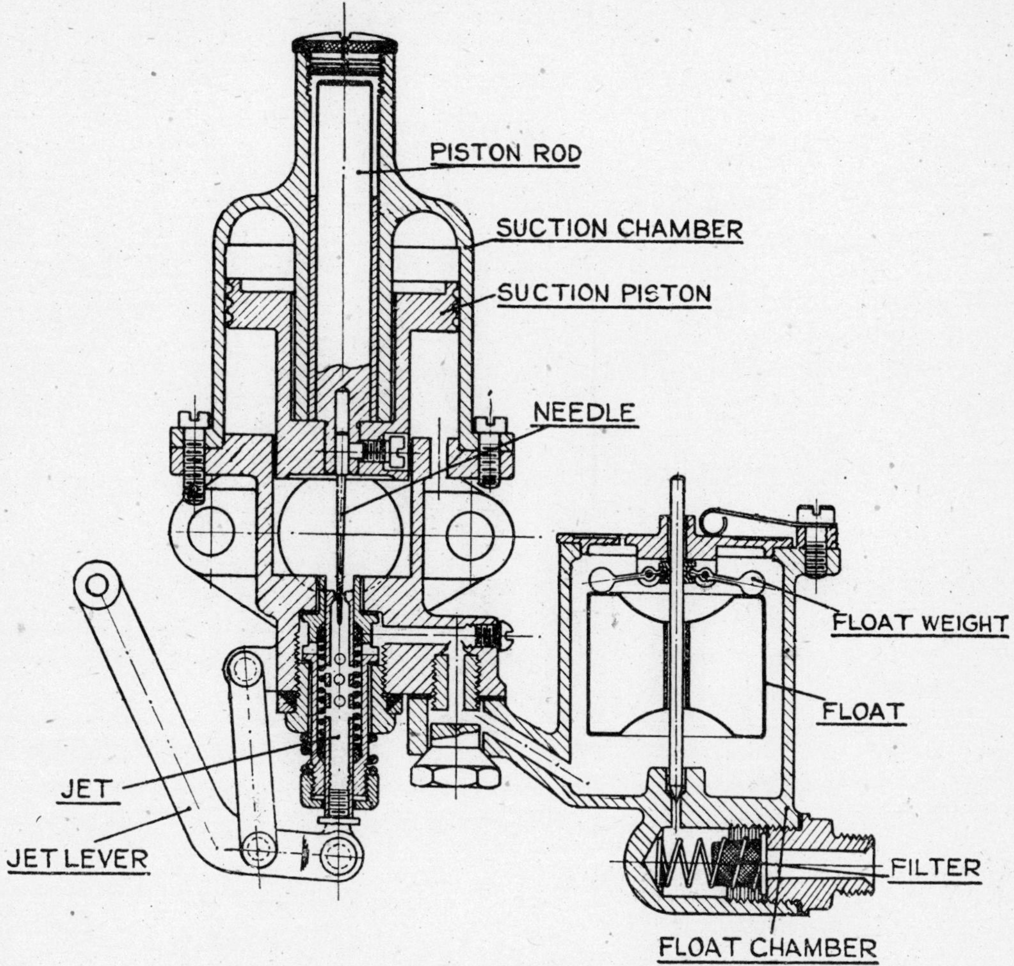

Fig. 297.—Sectional View of S.U. Carburettor (Petrol Entry at Base).

coming beyond its correct position, it can then be screwed down until it butts up against the jet head. This will be the normal running position, with the mixture control set at weak.

A simple way to test for strong mixture when the engine is idling is to lift the piston up slightly, say $\frac{1}{32}$ in., and if when this is done the engine runs faster, the mixture is too strong.

If the road performance is not satisfactory, a larger or smaller needle will be necessary as the case may be. The jet control will be found to be helpful in determining whether more or less petrol is required.

These are the only possible adjustments that can be made to the carburettor, and it is of no use whatever trying to adjust the carburettor in any other manner.

Should it be necessary to change the needle, this can be done by removing the two screws holding the suction chamber in position, the suction chamber can then be lifted off and the piston removed. At the side of the piston will be seen a set-screw. When this is slacked off, the needle can be withdrawn and the new needle replaced. The position of the needle is with its shoulder flush with the face of the piston. When

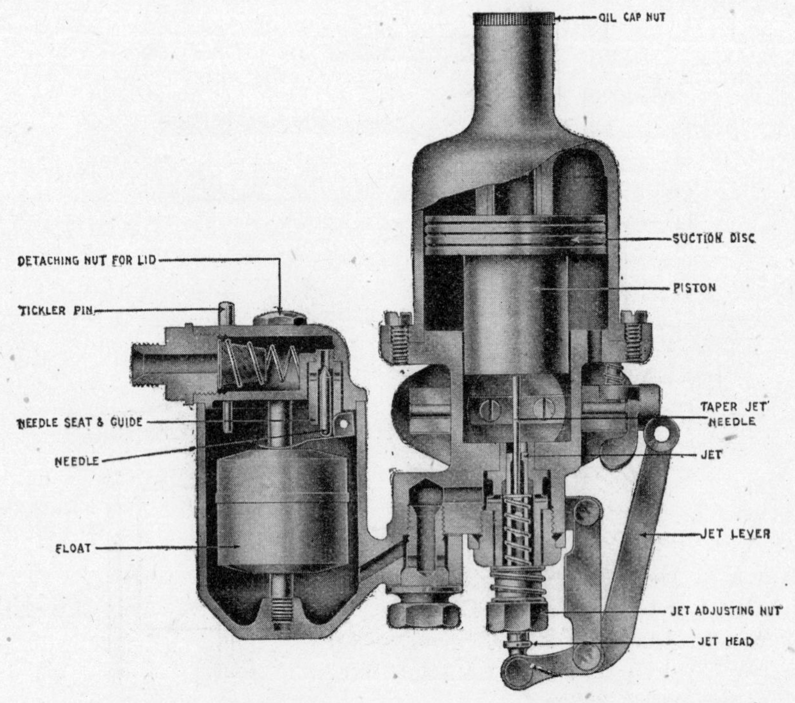

Fig. 298.—Pictorial Sectional View of the S.U. Controllable-jet Carburettor (Petrol Entry at Top).

replacing, care should be taken that the keyway at the side of the piston registers with the key in the body. Great care should also be taken to see that all machined faces and parts are kept scrupulously clean.

There are a number of faults that will cause an engine to run badly, but if the trouble is due to the carburettor it can only be one of the following points :

(A) Piston sticking.
(B) Dirt or water in the carburettor.
(C) Float chamber flooding.

(A) *Piston Sticking.*—The suction piston comprises the piston, forming the choke, the needle, and suction disc; into this is inserted the hardened and ground piston rod which works in the bearing of the suction chamber.

The piston rod running in the bearing is the only part which is in actual contact with any other part—the suction piston and needle having clearance fit, and consequently do not cause sticking. If this does occur the trouble must be looked for in the piston rod and its bearing. A sticking piston can be ascertained in a few seconds by inserting a finger in the air intake and lifting the piston, which should come up quite freely and fall right on to its seat with a click when released; if it does not, it will probably be found that the piston rod is sticky or dry.

To free this remove the oil-cap nut from the top of the suction chamber, pour in a few drops of paraffin, and work the piston up and down with the finger until free. A few drops of thin oil such as bicycle or sewing-machine oil should then be dropped in, but under no circumstances should a heavy-bodied lubricant such as engine oil be used. No oil must be used on any other part of the suction chamber.

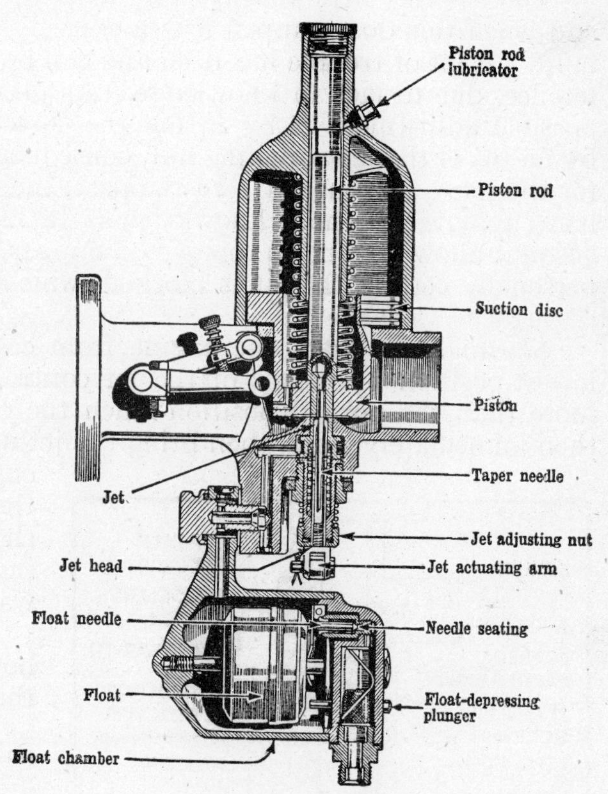

Fig. 299.—Arrangement of S.U. Carburettor on later Models of Morris Cars.

(B) *Dirt or Water in the Carburettor.*—When this is suspected lift the piston with something small, such as a pencil. The jet can then be seen. Flood the carburettor by depressing tickler pin and watch the jet; if the petrol does not flow through freely there is a blockage. To remedy this start the engine, open the throttle, block up the air inlet momentarily without shutting the throttle; keep throttle open until the engine starts to race. This trouble seldom arises with the S.U. carburettor owing to the size of the jet and the petrol ways. When it does happen, the above method will nearly always clear it. Should it not do so, the only alternative is to remove the jet, but this, however, *should on no account* be done unless it is *absolutely necessary,* as when refitting it has to be carefully centred to the needle, and it is practically impossible to assemble this part correctly unless it is first thoroughly understood how this is carried out.

(C) *Float Chamber Flooding.*—This can be seen by the petrol flowing over the float chamber and dripping from the air inlet, and is generally caused by grit between the float-chamber needle and its guide; this can be removed by depressing tickler pin, which allows the incoming petrol to wash the grit through the guide and into float chamber.

If the above instructions are carefully read it will be realised that the S.U. carburettor is very simple when thoroughly understood, but if it is not, it promptly appears to become an extremely complicated piece of mechanism.

There is very little that is likely to go wrong with the S.U. carburettor, and when this does happen it is a perfectly simple matter to rectify the fault. A lot of trouble has been and can be caused by unnecessary interference, due to lack of knowledge. As previously pointed out, the only possible adjustment is by fitting the correct needle adjusted for idling by means of the jet-adjusting nut, consequently there is no need whatever for the jet to be touched. In the past, the chief trouble has been the jet being removed without knowledge as to recentring it; therefore, on no account allow anyone to remove or tamper with this part unless you are personally certain that it is blocked, which, after all, is a very unlikely occurrence.

Starting.—To start the engine from cold bring the jet down to its lowest position by means of the jet control; open the throttle slightly more than the normal position when the engine is hot, the engine will then immediately start, then bring the jet up to such a position that the engine will fire evenly. It can then be driven away, but the jet should be brought up, weakening the mixture as the engine warms up.

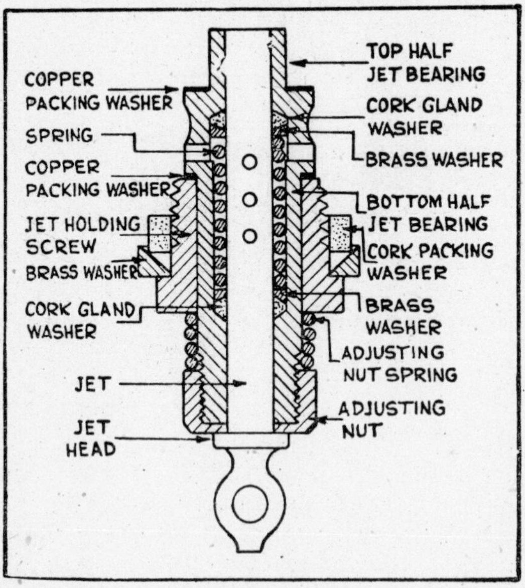

Fig. 300.—Showing Details of the S.U. Carburettor Jet Head and Gland.

To start when the engine is hot it is unnecessary to enrich the mixture, and the jet should be right up or in the position which gives the weakest or normal mixture.

Centring the Jet.—Should it be essential to remove the jet, this can be done by unscrewing the jet-holding screw (this is the large hexagon screw which fits into the body at the back of the jet (see Fig. 300). It must be understood that the needle is very nearly as large as the jet, and yet must not touch it. When assembling it is therefore necessary to carefully centre the jet to the needle, which is done as follows:

First screw the jet-adjusting nut to its top position and move the jet right up until the jet head is up against this, then refit the jet, taking care that the jet parts are assembled in the correct position. When this is done, feel if the piston is perfectly free by lifting it up with the finger. If it is not, slacken the jet screw and try again. It may be necessary to slacken the screw several times before the piston falls perfectly freely. When this has been done bring the jet-adjusting nut back to its *original* position. Experience shows that a very large percentage of carburettors that are returned for correction have had the jet removed and not centred correctly to the needle. It is quite easy when removing the piston to bend the needle, in which case it will bind on the jet and thus cause the piston to stick. The test for a bent needle (providing the jet is not out of centre) is to remove it from the piston and refit the suction chamber into the body of the carburettor and see if the piston falls freely.

THE ZENITH "U"-TYPE CARBURETTOR

This well-known carburettor has been fitted to several makes of car, and as there is a large number of cars now on the road using this type of carburettor, the following notes on its dismantling, tuning, starting, and general adjustment will no doubt be useful.

Dismantling for Cleaning.—The bottom half of the carburettor can be taken away by loosening the winged spanner A (Fig. 301), and swinging the stirrup D to one side, when the bottom portion will come away in the hand.

It is then only necessary to disconnect the strangler wire in order to lift the bowl of the carburettor right away from the engine.

Parts that might need cleaning are as follows: main jet, compensating jet, slow-running jet, and petrol filter.

To remove the jets it is necessary to detach the winged spanner A from the bottom of the stirrup, as this acts as a jet key as well.

This key is pushed on to the bottom of the stirrup and held by spring-loaded balls so that a sharp pull will detach it from the carburettor proper.

The hexagon in it is then used for removing the plugs

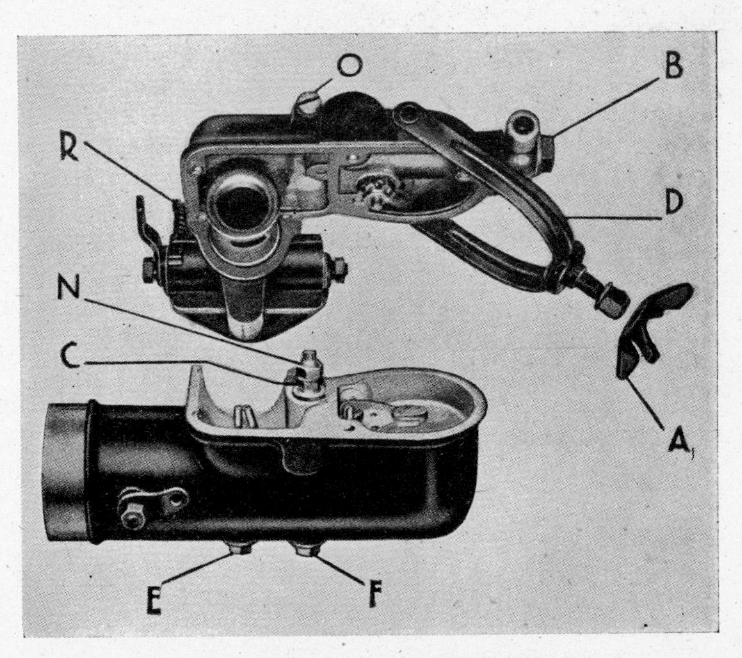

Fig. 301.—The Zenith "U"-type Carburettor.

E and F and the jets can then be unscrewed and removed by means of the squared end of one of the prongs of the jet key.

The petrol filter is removed from the top portion by means of an ordinary spanner.

When the nut B is unscrewed the whole filter tube can be withdrawn from the carburettor.

At the end of the tube is a screw, and when this screw is undone the gauze filter tube can be slipped off and washed in petrol. When replacing take care not to damage it.

These are the only parts of the carburettor that need cleaning now and again.

Do not clean the jets by passing a wire through them—this may enlarge the orifice—clean out by blowing or washing in petrol.

For cars used overseas, sometimes it may be necessary to make adjustments to suit the climate. The adjustment consists of determining the correct size of the choke tube, which is held in position by a small screw, main jet, compensating jet, slow-running jet, and capacity tube.

Starting.—The procedure recommended when starting from cold is as follows :

First completely close the air strangler in the intake of the carburettor by extending the control on the dash, open the throttle about one-third on the hand control, and turn the engine over a few times with the ignition switched off, which will have the effect of priming the cylinders, and freeing the pistons, etc.

Then open the strangler a small amount (the exact degree will soon be found after a few experiments), when, on switching on and again turning the engine over, it should start readily and continue to run, after which the strangler should be gradually released as the engine warms up.

Difficulty can be caused by the strangler not closing properly, so that the control wire should be examined. The slow-running jet N may be choked up—take this out and clean it. The slow-running adjusting screw O may be adjusted too weakly, screw this slightly in a clockwise direction.

The stop screw R regulates the opening of the throttle and therefore controls the quantity of mixture for slow running. It may be necessary in the course of time to adjust the throttle-stop screw to compensate for the slight wear between the end of it and the throttle lever. A slight right turn of R (half a turn will probably be ample) will suffice.

The screw O regulates the quality of the mixture. If it is found in spite of screwing this as far as it will go to the right, so that the needle is on its seating, that the slow running is still poor, then a size larger slow-running jet N should be tried. On the contrary, if it is necessary to unscrew the screw O by three complete turns and the mixture is still too rich, try a smaller jet N.

If the carburettor has been removed for any reason, it is essential when it is replaced that there should be no air leakage between the carburettor and the cylinders, that the two halves of the carburettor should be clamped snugly together, and that the slow-running jet is not choked up.

Poor Acceleration.—In the winter time this may very often be due to the engine not getting sufficiently hot.

If in spite of the engine being thoroughly hot the acceleration is bad, then see to the following points: slow-running adjustment is too weak—try the screw O in a richer position.

The compensating jet is too small—try one size larger.

The capacity tube also has an effect on the acceleration, as it regulates the quantity of petrol standing in reserve for acceleration.

If a weak spot is noticed when the throttle is opened from low speeds, then a larger capacity tube should be tried, and vice versa.

The capacity tube can be removed by unscrewing the slow-running jet N and then the slow-running tube C, when the capacity tube will fall out if the bowl is turned upside down.

The new tube is simply dropped into the carburettor and is not held in any way.

Lack of Power and Speed.—If this is due to the carburettor, it is probably owing to the main jet being partially choked, or being a little too small, and the size larger should be tried. In this respect, however, care should be taken to make sure the lack of speed is not due to the ignition being retarded or to an insufficient supply of petrol from the tank.

Make sure also that the strangler valve opens fully, as if this sticks in a partially closed position it will restrict the speed of the car, and increase the consumption of petrol.

THE ZENITH "V"-TYPE CARBURETTOR

This is a later model than the "U" and "H" types. It embodies an automatic starting device with an original atomisation and distribution principle.

This carburettor is made in three models, viz. the vertical, horizontal, and down-draught. In connection with the working principle this may be explained, briefly, as follows:

From the tank the petrol passes through the union A (Fig. 304), the filter, and the needle seating into the float chamber. The float rises, and when reaching a certain predetermined height will push the needle on to its seating, thus regulating the petrol flow.

The float chamber contains the main jet 1, compensating jet 2, compensating well 3, slow-running jet 4, and to carburettors fitted with the auto-starting device, starter jet (Fig. 302).

The petrol will then flow through the main and compensating jets and also rise in the compensating well.

From the jets the petrol flows along to separate channels into a common channel in the emulsion block 5, which is attached to the float chamber.

The petrol in the compensating well is in direct communication with the air and with the emulsion block, consequently all the petrol from the jets and well is now centred in one channel in the emulsion block.

This channel leads to a nozzle 6 that projects directly into the choke tube.

A special jet 4 is provided for slow running, and the petrol is drawn through this slow-running jet into a channel which leads to the engine side of the throttle. The petrol is atomised immediately on leaving the jet by air entering the carburettor at the base of the adjusting screw F.

Starting.—To obtain an easy start from the cold, the air strangler should be closed, by extending the control on the dash. Then, with the throttle also closed, the engine should be cranked over a few times. Then, open the throttle about $\frac{1}{8}$ in., using the hand control, and open the air strangler slightly. The engine will then start if the ignition is switched on and the starter again used. When the engine commences to "fire" regularly release the strangler to the "full-open" position.

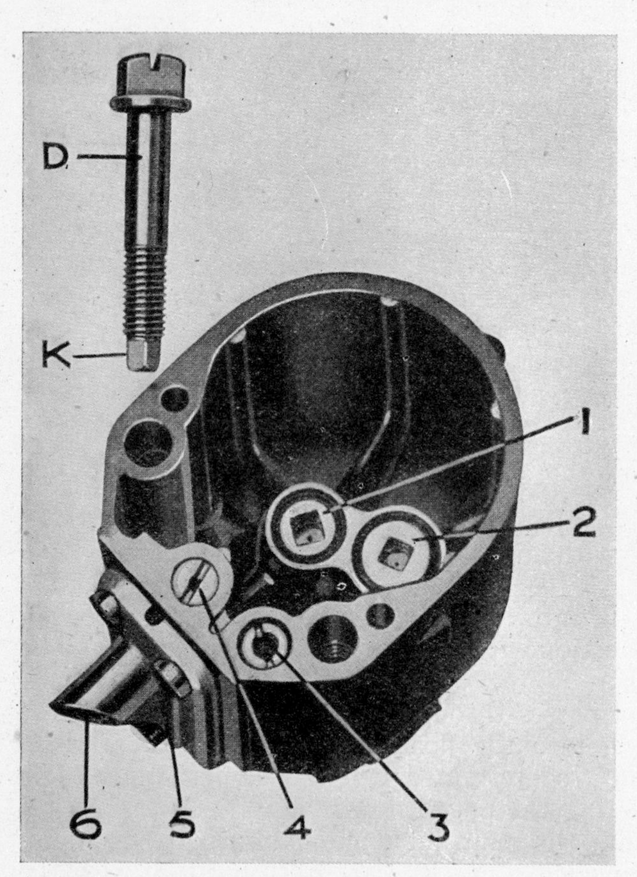

Fig. 302.—Showing Jet Chamber of Zenith "V"-type Carburettor.

Adjustments to Carburettor.—In the case of standard-model cars the carburettor has the most suitable adjustment for the engine's best performance. If, however, this has become altered, as when the engine has been dismantled for overhaul, the following procedure should be observed:

Slow Running.—Slow running is adjusted by means of the stop screw E (Fig. 304) and the air-regulating screw F.

Speed of Tick-over.—The top screw E determines the speed of the slow running, i.e. it adjusts the opening position of the throttle. To increase the slow-running speed the stop screw must be turned in a clock-wise direction. A turn in the opposite direction will give a slower tick-over.

Richness of Slow-running Mixture.—The richness of the slow-running mixture is adjusted by the air-regulating screw F. Should the engine refuse to tick-over for any length of time, or stall on deceleration, it is a sign that the slow-running mixture is weak. To overcome this the mixture should be made richer by turning the regulating screw in a clockwise direction. If the engine is inclined to "hunt" when running slowly the mixture is too rich and must be weakened by turning the air-regulating screw F in an anti-clockwise direction.

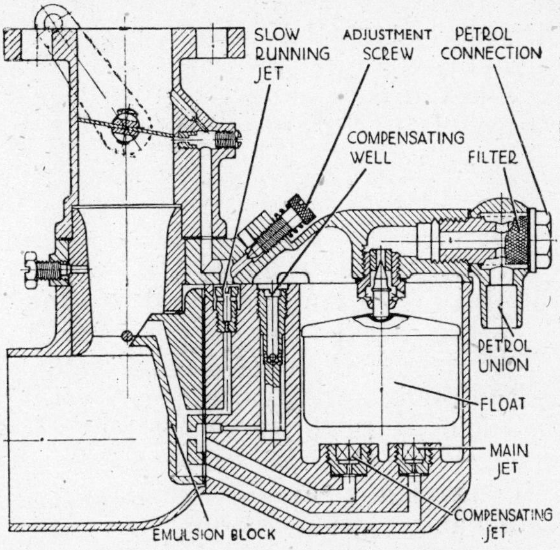

Fig. 303.—Sectional View of "V"-type Carburettor (Vertical Model).

Dismantling the Carburettor.—The bowl of the carburettor can be removed by taking out the holding-down screws D. The hand should be placed underneath the bowl during this operation, for when the screws are removed the bowl will drop into the hand, and any petrol that is contained in the bowl can then be emptied back into the tank. On turning the bowl upside down the float will slide out and reveal the main and compensating jets at the bottom of the bowl.

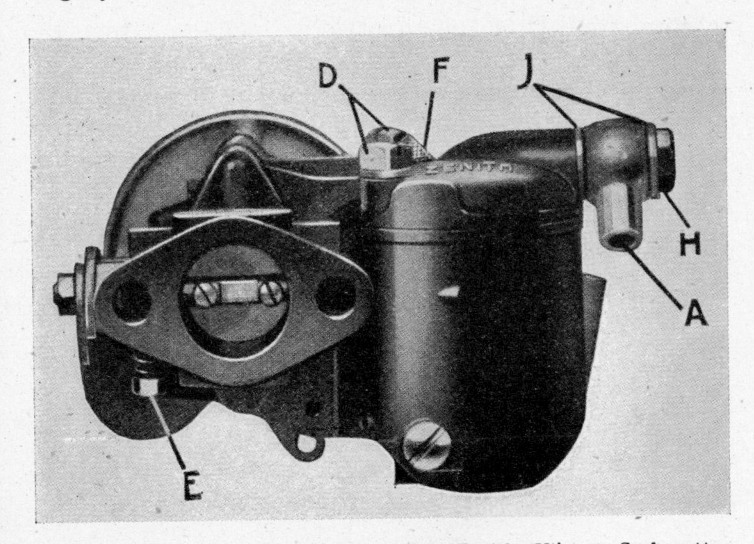

Fig. 304.—Illustrating the Regulation of the Zenith "V"-type Carburettor (Horizontal Model).

The Jets.—The jets should be removed occasionally and be thoroughly cleaned. The holding-down screws D are milled at the end to fit into the jets. When the bottom end is placed into the jets a spanner applied to the head of the screw will enable the jets to be removed.

When cleaning the jets it is not advisable to pass anything through them that is liable to damage them. The most satisfactory and effective method is to blow through the jets and wash them in petrol. This will remove any obstruction and leave the jets undamaged.

The sizes of all jets in the Zenith carburettor run in fives and the larger the number the larger the jet.

The Filter.—The petrol is filtered on entering the carburettor and the filter should be cleaned from time to time. To remove the filter unscrew the petrol connection H (Fig. 304) and pull the filter out of its chamber. The filter gauze can then be thoroughly cleaned with petrol.

When reassembling the filter care must be taken to see that the washers J are correctly replaced.

"V"-TYPE CARBURETTOR STARTING DEVICES

These carburettors are made in several models having different starting devices; the latter include the Strangler (Semi-automatic and Fully-automatic), the Air-valve, and Dip-tube methods.

Stranglers.—To provide the required rich starting mixture some "V"-type carburettors have a strangler flap inserted in the air intake. When the control from the dash is operated the flap closes the air intake, and upon the engine being turned over the depression is directed entirely upon the jets of the carburettor.

Consequently, a very rich mixture is supplied and the engine starts readily and continues to run.

It is often advantageous to give the engine one or two turns with the strangler closed and ignition "off." Then switch "on" and again turn the engine over by starter or handle.

Most stranglers are inter-connected with the throttle, so that the latter is automatically opened the correct amount when the strangler is closed. If this is not so it is recommended that the throttle is opened slightly by the hand control.

Semi-automatic Strangler.—This type of strangler has the ordinary rigid flap (*a*), having in it an opening (*c*) covered by a diaphragm (*e*) as shown in Fig. 305. This will remain closed during the initial firing, but as the engine

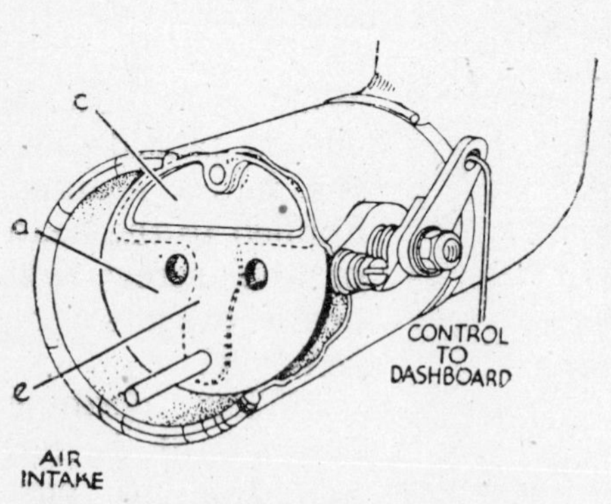

Fig. 305.—Semi-automatic Air Strangler.

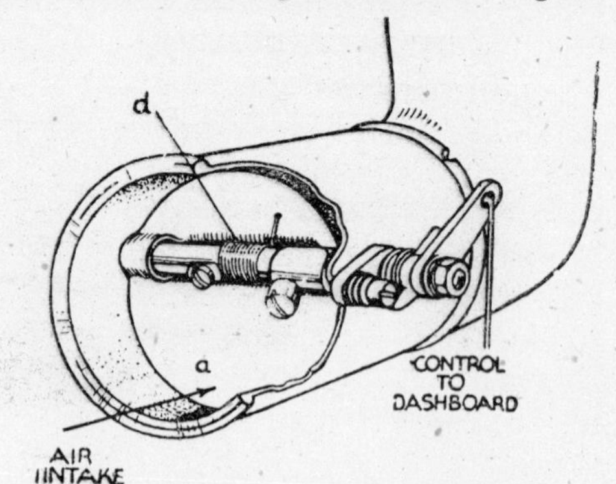

Fig. 306.—Fully-automatic Air Strangler.

speed increases, because of the general thinning of oil, easing of bearings, pistons, etc., the extra depression will cause the diaphragm to open.

Air is thus admitted and the desired weakening effect obtained.

Fully-automatic Strangler.—As shown in Fig. 306, the strangler flap (*a*) is free to move on an offset spindle and is only held closed by the spring shown. When the extra depression is created, after the engine has started, the tension of the spring (*d*) is overcome and the flap opens to admit air to give the necessary weakening effect and provide varying volume. These stranglers give a buzzing noise which acts as a warning note that the strangler is in operation.

The Automatic Air Valve.—Referring to Fig. 307, when the control on the dash is operated, the main valve 21 is pulled off its seating, uncovering the drilling 22 on the engine side of the throttle. The engine should now be turned over a few times with the switch " off." Now switch on the ignition and turn the engine over again. During this time *the throttle must be closed to the idling position.* Consequently, upon the engine being turned, a strong depression is created at the outlet 22. This will result in petrol being drawn from the passage 19, and air from the venturi 23. Depression will also be directed on the starting jet 18 and petrol will be drawn through this part from the float chamber. The passage of the petrol from the starting jet 18 can be traced up the channel 19 across the air valve 20 along the communication tube 24 into the venturi 23. Here the petrol will be met by air entering the venturi, and will be broken up to form a rich starting mixture. This mixture will then be drawn into the engine via the channel 22. The size of starting jet and venturi are such that this mixture of petrol and air is correct to ensure the mixture will now fire. Immediately it does so the suction or depression at 22 will increase. This extra depression is apparent throughout the channels of the starting device, and will result in the air valve 20 being drawn off its seating. The stem of the air valve is " stepped " so that when it is drawn into its housing there will be a space around the end of the stem. Air will be drawn through this space with the result that a certain amount of the depression on the starting jet 18 is released. Consequently, less petrol will be drawn through this jet, and the starting mixture is at once weakened. Further, the additional air supplied will result in the engine turning at a speed considerably in excess of normal idling.

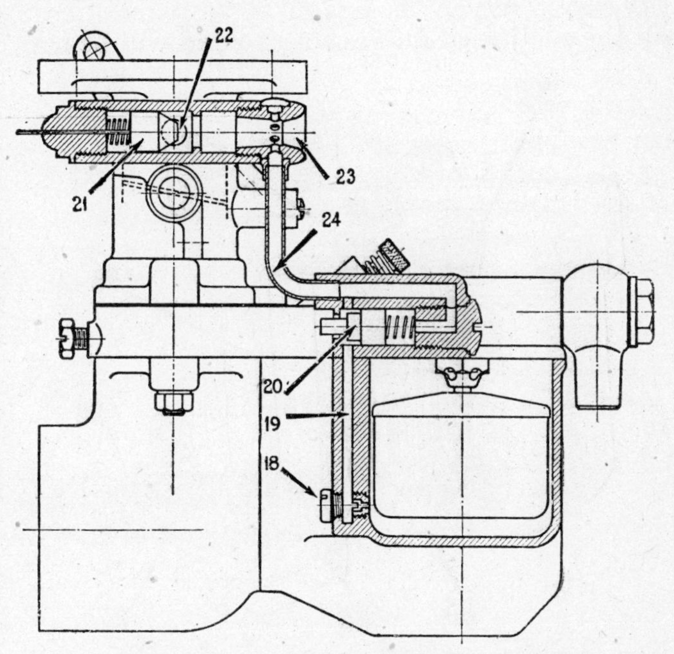

Fig. 307.—Action of Zenith Automatic Air Valve.

Automatic Starting Device (Dip Tube).—Some models of the " V "-type carburettor are fitted with a starting device similar to that shown in Fig. 308. Actually, this shows a down-draught carburettor, but exactly the same principles apply to other models.

To start the engine from cold the automatic starting-device control on the dashboard is operated, resulting in the main valve 26 being drawn off its seating to the position shown in the drawing. With the ignition switched on, the engine should now be turned over by means of the starter, ensuring at the same time the throttle is not depressed. *It is essential that the throttle should not be opened beyond the normal idling position for starting purposes.* When the engine is rotated with the throttle in this position, all the suction or depression created will be concentrated on the outlet 27 on the engine side of the throttle. This depression will be apparent at the venturi 28, and in the communication tube 33, which will result in air being drawn through the venturi, and petrol from the dip tube 31.

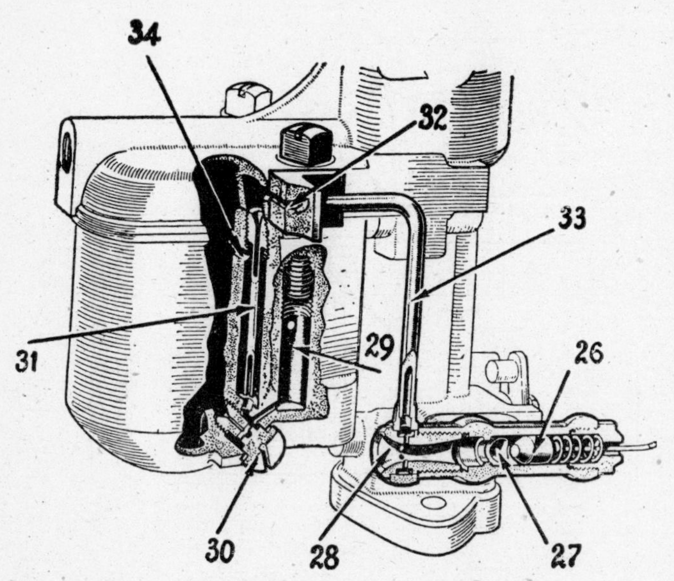

Fig. 308.—Automatic Starting Device (Dip Tube).

The petrol is drawn from the dip tube through the control jet at the top. It then passes across the connection 32, down the communication tube 33, to the throat of the venturi 28. There, the petrol is met by air entering the venturi and is broken up to form a rich starting mixture; the latter then passes into the induction pipe through the drilling 27. This rich mixture is required only for a short period. Automatic weakening off is ensured by air from 34 mixing with petrol issuing from the starting jet 30 as soon as the fuel jn the dip-tube well and reserve well 29 has been exhausted; the mixture thus becomes weakened.

THE ZENITH "V"-TYPE DOWN-DRAUGHT CARBURETTOR

This carburettor is made in several models, of which the Type 36 VI-2 is a typical one; the general principles are the same for all of these models, which differ only in detail design, dimensions, and arrangement.

The Type 36 VI-2 is a recent model embodying an acceleration pump and economy device together with the latest instant-starting device.

Petrol enters the carburettor at the union 1 (Fig. 309) and passing through a gauze filter 14 reaches the needle and seating 13. Unless the float 2 is already lifted against the needle by petrol in the float chamber 3 the petrol will continue its course past the needle into the float chamber. It will continue to flow until the various passages are filled and the petrol reaches a predetermined level which causes the float to lift against the needle, pushing it on to its seating. This prevents more petrol entering and causing the carburettor to flood.

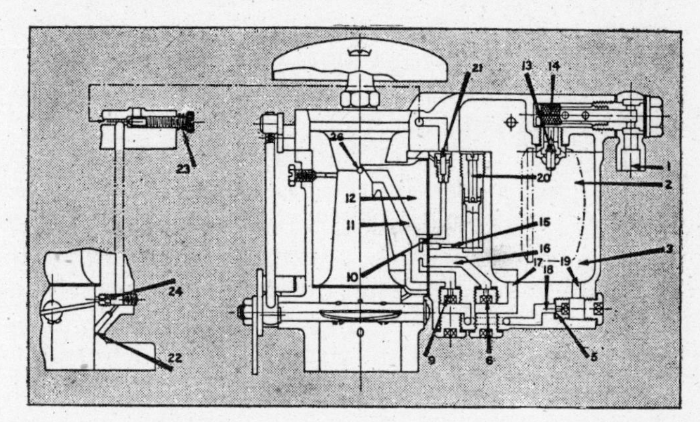

Fig. 309.

Petrol will have entered the passage 18 in the base of the bowl by passing through the outlet 19 and economy jet 5. It will then have passed through the main jet 9 into the main channel 11 in the emulsion block 12. Here it will remain at the predetermined height, which is just below the emulsion-block outlet.

The petrol will have also passed through 17 to the compensating jet 6. From the compensating jet the fuel passes along the passage 16 above it and joins the petrol from the main jet in the common channel 11.

From the main channel in the emulsion block, petrol will pass into the slow-running jet drilling via the passage 10.

Similarly the well of the capacity tube 20 will be filled to the petrol level by the fuel flowing from the emulsion block through passage 15.

Fig. 310.—The Zenith "V"-type Down-draught Carburettor.

It has now been observed how the petrol reaches the jets and channels. The fuel will occupy the positions described all the time the engine is stationary and there is a supply of petrol from the tank or pump.

Starting.—The automatic starting-device control on the dashboard is operated, resulting in the main valve 7 (Fig. 310) being drawn off its seating. When the engine is turned with the throttle in its idling position the suction will be concentrated upon the outlet 6 on the engine side of the throttle. This suction will be apparent at the venturi 4 and in the communication tube 9, which will result in air being drawn through the venturi and petrol from the dip tube 8.

Petrol is drawn up the dip tube, across the connection 1, and into the venturi by means of the holes 5. There it is met by air entering the venturi as previously explained in the section on "V"-type carburettor-starting devices. The mixture passes into the induction pipe through the drilling 5. The rich mixture thus induced is only required for a short period. There is a drilling from the float chamber into the dip-tube well that allows air to pass, and as soon as the fuel in this well and the reserve well 2 has been exhausted efficient weakening off is assured by the air now being admitted. This air will be drawn up the dip tube 8 with petrol now being supplied direct from the starting jet 3.

Consequently the mixture is automatically weakened and the engine will continue to run at a fair speed without hunting or showing signs of an unduly rich mixture. This is the ideal arrangement for starting an engine from cold. A very rich mixture is only necessary for the initial firing, after which the starting device provides a more normal mixture and causes the engine to run at a speed that promotes rapid warming up and circulation of the lubricating oil, thereby minimising cylinder wear. At no time is neat petrol entering the engine.

If necessary, the car can now be driven away immediately with the starting device still in action. As soon as the engine has reached its normal working temperature it will be found that the starting control can be released. The valve 7 will then return to its seating and the device will be inoperative.

Main Carburettors.—The engine is now working on the main carburettor only. With the throttle closed down to the idling position, the mixture will be supplied from the slow-running jet 21 (Fig. 309).

With the starting-device valve closed and the throttle only just open, the depression will be concentrated on the outlet 22, which will in turn be directed on the slow-running jet 21. Consequently petrol will be drawn from the well beneath the jet, measured on passing through, and meet air entering at the base of the adjustment screw 23. The amount of air mixing with the petrol from the slow-running jet is controlled by this air-adjustment screw 23.

At the throttle edge there is a further outlet 24 which breaks into the slow-running passage. Upon the throttle being opened from the idling position this will give an additional mixture to ensure progressive get-away from slow running—this explains the title of " progression jet " for that part situated at 24.

With the throttle opened still further the depression will be concentrated on the nozzle of the emulsion block which projects into the narrowest part of the choke tube. This will first result in petrol being drawn from the passages 11, 15, and 16, so that the source of petrol supply is eventually through the main and compensating jets 9 and 6. It will be observed that the petrol in the well of the capacity tube 20 has been consumed, and, as the top of the well is open to the atmosphere, petrol issuing from the main and compensating jets is now under atmospheric pressure. As a result, petrol drawn from the jets will be broken up in the main channel 11 by air from the capacity tube. This mixture will then be drawn from the emulsion-block nozzle into the choke tube.

It is essential that this mixture should be distributed completely across the choke tube in all directions. To obtain this even distribution a small circular bar, 25, has been placed across the choke tube at right angles to the emulsion-block nozzle. Air rushing from the intake will strike the bar and create a vacuum on the side facing the engine. The petrol-air mixture leaving the emulsion block will run along the bar, filling up the vacuum and then proceed past the throttle valve into the induction pipe.

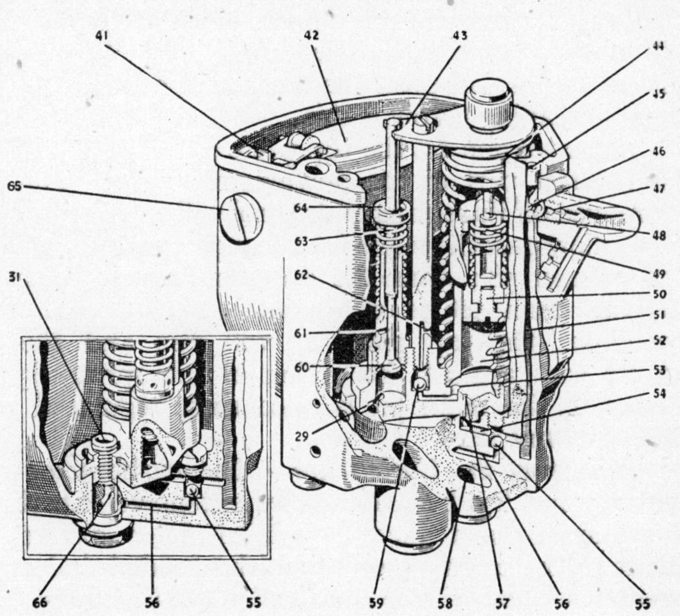

Fig. 311.—Zenith Acceleration Pump and Economy Device.

It will be realised that as soon as petrol in the float chamber falls below the predetermined level the float will fall, permitting the needle 13 to drop, and petrol will pass into the chamber through the seating.

Acceleration Pump and Economy Device.—To ensure powerful acceleration without detrimental effect to the consumption figures an ingenious pump and economy device is incorporated in the bowl of the carburettor. This device is operated by an interconnection between the throttle movement and plunger in the pump. As the throttle is opened so will the pump be operated automatically. The movement of the throttle is transferred by means of the interconnection mechanism to the top of the pump piston. The arm forces down the pump against the action of the outer spring 44 (Fig. 311), this will depress the inner piston 48 and the plunger will be forced down by the inside spring 49. The petrol in the chamber 52 will be driven through the outlet 57 along the passage 54, up channel 51, through the pump jet 47, and so from the emulsion-block nozzle into the choke tube.

A leak is provided for any excess petrol from the pump; the outlet for this from the pump chamber is at 53. It will then pass the ball valve 59 and return to the float chamber of the carburettor by outlet 62.

When the throttle is closed the outer spring 44 will force the piston back to its top or inoperative position. This will cause petrol to be drawn into the top of the fixing stud 31, where a small dome filter is arranged, and out through the holes 66 at the stud base. There the petrol passes through another filter and along the passage 56. The ball valve 55 will be lifted and petrol will continue its course along the channel 54, through 57 into the pump chamber 52. The ball valve 55 will fall back on to its seating and act as a non-return valve. Similarly the ball valve 59 prevents the pump leak becoming an inlet channel. A further ball valve is situated at 46 near to the pump jet. When petrol is pumped up the channel 51 it will push the ball valve against the air inlet 45 and prevent petrol escaping through this.

An extension on the top plate 43 of the pump strikes the shoulder 64 on the last part of the downward stroke. This causes the valve 60 to be moved off its seating and petrol will at once enter from the float chamber at 61, flow past the valve 60, through the opening 29, and so into the main-jet channel 58; thus the economy jet is by-passed and the full effect of the main jet is obtained. As soon as the throttle commences to close, the top plate 43 will rise and the valve 60 will return to its seat against the action of the spring 63, so that the supply of petrol to the main jet is once more regulated by passing first through the economy jet.

Adjusting the Carburettor.—The carburettor is delivered with a jet setting that has been found by extensive experimental work to be most suitable for the engine to which it is fitted, consequently very little adjustment to the carburettor should be needed, indeed the user will find that greater service will be obtained from the carburettor if adjustments are made only when absolutely necessary. Adjustment to the slow-running mixture is the only likely alteration, apart from an occasional cleaning of the jets, float-chamber bowl, filter gauze, etc. When trouble is experienced with the engine do not assume that it is always due to the carburettor. If satisfied that the instrument is completely free from dirt, do not be tempted to alter the carburettor until all other possible causes of trouble, such as sparking plugs, timing of ignition, valves, etc., have been investigated.

Slow-running Adjustment.—The slow running is adjusted by means of the throttle-stop screw and the air-regulating screw.

The stop screw determines the speed of slow running, i.e. it adjusts the throttle position for idling. To increase the slow-running speed the stop screw must be turned in a clockwise direction. If turned with opposite rotation a slower tick-over will be given.

The richness of the slow-running mixture is adjusted by the air-regulating screw. Should the engine refuse to tick over for any length of time or stall on deceleration the slow-running jet may be choked and should be cleaned. After examination reset the slow running by means of the throttle and air-adjustment screws. If the engine is inclined to hunt when running slowly the mixture is too rich and must be weakened by turning the air-regulating screw in an anti-clockwise direction. The best position for the slow-running air screw from the point of view of pick-up is *within three turns* of the full home position. A size of slow-running jet must be decided upon that will permit even tick-over with this setting of the screw.

There are factors quite apart from the carburettor that have a considerable influence on the slow running, i.e. slow running when the engine is out of gear and the car is stationary. These factors include non-air-tight joints, worn valve guides, valves not seating, ignition too far advanced, incorrect setting of sparking-plug points. Such details must always be given consideration when slow running is irregular. The carburettor only should not be suspected.

Removing the Carburettor Bowl.—The bowl is readily removed by releasing the fixing bolts shown in Fig. 310.

The hand should be placed beneath the bowl during this operation so that when the bolts are removed the bowl will drop into the hand. (Economy note: Petrol in the bowl can then be emptied back into the tank.)

The jets should be removed occasionally and thoroughly cleaned. One of the fixing bolts is squared at the end to fit into the jet covers and jets. When the bottom end of the bolt is placed in the squared recesses a spanner applied to the head of the bolt will enable the jets to be removed.

When *cleaning the jets* do not pass anything through them that is likely to damage the carefully calibrated orifices. The most satisfactory and efficient method is to blow through them and wash them in petrol—this should remove any obstruction and will leave the jets undamaged. The sizes of all jets in Zenith carburettors are clearly numbered and the larger the jet the greater the number. The *slow-running jet* is provided with a screw-driver slot to enable it to be removed. This applies also to the screw holding the *capacity tube*. Upon removing the screw and inverting the bowl the capacity tube will fall out. To remove the *float* remove the large-headed screw 65. The complete *pump and economy device* mechanism can be taken out by unscrewing the plug 66. This will enable the two filters to be cleaned and the pump and economy attachment can be removed by pulling out the unit from the inside of the bowl. The *emulsion block* is held to the side of the bowl by three screws, and the removal of these will enable the block to be taken off and the pump jet 47 inspected. Particular care should be taken not to damage the gasket beneath the block. Upon replacing, locate the bottom screw first and then tighten all screws evenly.

The *starting jet* 3 is taken from the carburettor by means of a screw-driver. This also applies to the *progression jet* 24, but in this case the cover must be removed first and care taken that it is replaced after inspection.

THE AUSTIN DOWN-DRAUGHT CARBURETTOR

The Zenith "V"-type down-draught carburettor is fitted to the sports model Austin Seven, Ten-Four, and Light Six sports models, and the Sixteen with Hayes transmission. On the latter three cars there is no hand-throttle control, but the strangler control is connected to the throttle lever to give the required throttle opening for warming-up or fast idling, with a suitable amount of strangling. The connection between the throttle control and the strangler has an adjustment which enables the throttle opening and strangler position to be adjusted relatively if necessary. Incidentally, the down-draught carburettors with which we are now concerned all have a buzzer device incorporated in the strangler valve, which gives audible warning when the engine is running with the strangler fully or partially closed.

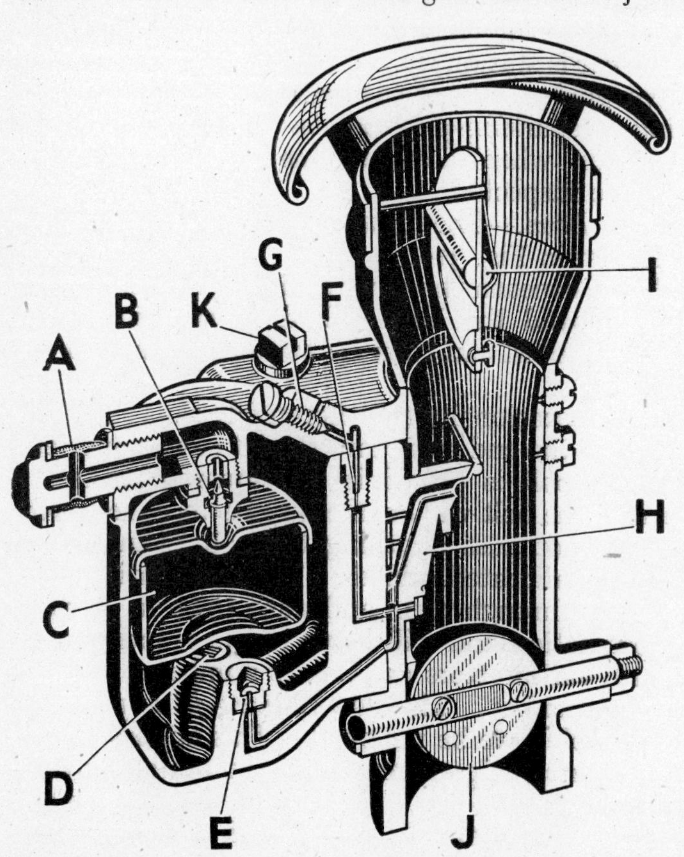

Fig. 312.—The Austin Down-draught Carburettor.

Fig. 312 shows a sectional view of the Zenith down-draught carburettor fitted on the Austin Seven and Ten-Four sports models. The petrol enters through the union at A, at which point a filter gauze is fitted. B is the needle valve operated by the float C. D and E are the main and compensating jets, F the slow-running jet, and G the slow-running adjustment. H is the emulsion block from which the petrol emerges into the induction bore, I is the strangler, and J the throttle. One of the two screws which secure the float chamber to the main casting is shown at K.

In making slow-running adjustments it should be borne in mind that other factors, quite apart from those arising in the carburettor, influence the slow running of an engine. Chief among them is the ignition, which may be too far advanced or erratic, due to dirt, incorrect adjustment, worn parts or bad insulation. Equally, for satisfactory slow running the plug gaps must be set correctly. Air leaks from worn valve guides, or faulty gaskets, or from any of the induction-joint washers, as well as badly seated valves, can also affect the slow running. These are points to be investigated in addition to the carburettor adjustments.

Apart from the slow-running adjustments, no other alteration need be made to the standard setting of the carburettor. The jet and choke sizes are determined, as a result of extensive tests, to give the best all-round performance, and any alteration made to improve one feature of the engine's behaviour will almost of necessity impair others. If the setting has been inadvertently altered, it should be restored.

CARBURETTOR TUNING AND TESTING

Although the modern petrol engine will run on a relatively wide range of petrol-air mixture proportions, it will only run efficiently on an extremely limited range. It is therefore desirable to tune, or adjust, each carburettor so as to give the best petrol economy consistent with good power output. The following information may help those who have to deal with carburettor adjustment on automobiles :

(1) The greatest power output is obtained by using a mixture on the rich side, namely, from 11 to 13 parts of air to 1 part petrol, by weight.

(2) For perfect combustion the mixture proportions are about 15 parts of air to 1 part petrol. The power output is about 5 to 7 per cent. less than in (1).

(3) For the greatest fuel economy, a weaker mixture of 16 to 17 parts air to 1 part petrol should be used. This gives the greatest mileage per gallon of petrol, but does not yield the greatest power, by about 10 to 15 per cent.

(4) Very rich mixtures (8 to 11) result in excessive carbon formation; this is evident by excessive fuel consumption, overheating and clouds of black smoke—due to carbon dust—from the exhaust. The exhaust will have a pungent odour.

(5) Weak mixtures result in sluggish running and bad pulling. If too weak, the combustion is so slow that the mixture is still burning when the inlet valve is opening, and firing or "popping" back into the carburettor may occur.

(6) *A rich mixture* will give a *bright yellowish exhaust flame*, whereas a weak mixture gives a *less intense whitish* or bluish white flame.

(7) A weak mixture gives bad starting, poor acceleration, and the inability to run the engine slowly.

Test for Rich Mixture

We have already indicated one or two methods of testing for rich mixtures, but the fuel-consumption test is probably the best practical one for carburettor-tuning purposes. It is a well-known fact that each class of motor car gives a certain mileage per gallon, depending upon its weight and engine horse-power. This information may safely be taken as a criterion for making comparative tests of fuel consumptions or mixture strengths. Since it is now the practice to fit engines of certain horse-power in cars of certain weights, we may for present purposes define the average petrol consumption as being dependent only on the horse-power of the engine in the case of modern cars. The following table shows the petrol consumptions for engines of various R.A.C. horse-power ratings, for average speeds (viz. 25 to 35 m.p.h.) and on good flat roads :

Fig. 313.—A useful Graduated Tank for Petrol-consumption Tests (M.E.).

PETROL CONSUMPTIONS OF DIFFERENT ENGINES

Rated Horse-power.	Petrol Consumption in Miles per Gallon.
5 to 7	45 to 40
7 „ 10	40 „ 34
10 „ 11	34 „ 32
11 „ 13	32 „ 30
13 „ 15	30 „ 27
15 „ 20	27 „ 23
20 „ 25	23 „ 19
25 „ 30	19 „ 17
30 „ 40	16 „ 14

On wet or gritty roads the consumptions will be higher. Similarly, at higher speeds than 35 m.p.h., on the indirect gears, with partially deflated tyres, and in head winds, there will be a greater fuel consumption.

A well-designed engine should give a petrol consumption of not more than about one-half a pint per brake horse-power per hour.

It is easy to fit a small measuring-tank device on the dash-board to check the fuel consumption, or for more accurate results to use one of the special fuel-measuring devices on the market, e.g. the Gallometer. If the petrol tank is filled to a certain mark on the gauge before starting a fuel-consumption test, and the mileage-recorder reading taken both before and after the road test, the quantity of petrol used can readily be ascertained by noting the exact quantity required to fill the petrol tank to the same fuel-gauge reading; the car should, of course, be on level ground when the gauge readings are taken.[1]

[1] Full details of fuel- and carburettor-testing methods are given in *The Testing of High-speed Internal Combustion Engines*, A. W. Judge (Chapman & Hall, Ltd.).

Fig. 430 illustrates the M.E. fuel-consumption measuring tank, which is provided with a calibrated petrol gauge for the purpose.

FUEL-CONSUMPTION TESTING APPARATUS

Tests of the fuel consumption of a motor vehicle can conveniently be carried out on the road under actual driving conditions with the Zenith Mileage Tester shown in Fig. 314.

This apparatus consists of an accurately graduated glass vessel of $\frac{1}{10}$-gallon capacity, an electric fuel pump, and a three-way petrol cock mounted as a single unit and arranged for attachment to the driver's off-side side window. The apparatus weighs 9 lb. In regard to its installation, the tester is hooked over the glass of the near-side front door, and the bottom pressed against the glass so that the vacuum cups adhere to the glass holding the tester rigid.

The two rubber pipes from tester are then slipped through the windscreen and under the side of the bonnet, or they can be passed through any convenient orifice in the floor boards, taking care they are not pinched or pass too close to the exhaust pipe *en route*.

The petrol pipe from the vacuum or main tank to the carburettor is then disconnected at the carburettor. The necessary unions to suit the carburettor fitted to the car are then selected and attached to the two rubber pipes. The pipe leading from the glass bulb in the tester is then connected to the carburettor, whilst the other one from the pump is connected to the pipe from the tank.

Cars having a mechanical or electric fuel pump feeding directly to the carburettor should have the pipe disconnected at the carburettor so that the tester is fitted in between the pump and the carburettor.

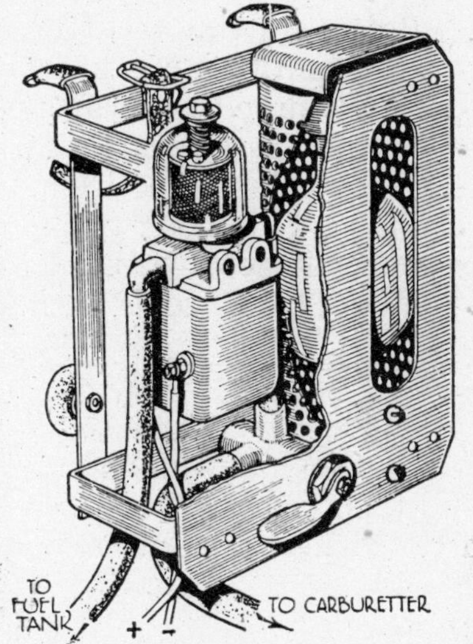

Fig. 314.—Zenith Mileage Tester.

The wires from the electric fuel pump are then attached to the electric system by clamping the insulated clip to any live point, and earthing the other wire by clipping it on to any convenient part of the frame such as the brake handle.

The pump is supplied for either 12-volt or 6-volt systems, but the 12-volt is supplied if no voltage is specified.

Method of Operation.—When the handle of the three-way cock, which is clearly visible from the front of the tester, is placed in a vertical position the petrol is pumped direct from the tank to the carburettor, and consequently it is possible to drive the car as long as one wishes.

When the tap handle is turned to the right, petrol is not only pumped direct from the tank to the carburettor but also to the glass bulb.

As soon as this fills up to the graduated mark on the top the handle is turned back to the vertical position.

During this period the carburettor has continued to receive its normal supply of petrol, but we now have the graduated glass full of petrol ready for the test.

At the predetermined moment the tap handle is turned to the left; this immediately shuts off the supply from the main tank to the carburettor, which can then only get its supply from the graduated bulb.

Immediately this is emptied the tap is turned to the vertical position again.

This means that any number of consumption tests can be taken without stopping the car, and readings obtained under all conditions.

Making a Test.—When all connections have been completed the instruction plate should be read carefully. The tester control valve is first placed in the "to run until ready to test" position. Engine is started and warmed up. (This can be done on the road while driving out of heavy traffic.)

Before starting test, the tap handle is placed in the "to run and fill" position, until bulb is filled beyond the upper graduation mark. Handle is then returned to former position.

As soon as the car is travelling at proper speed, tap handle is turned to the "to test" position. As fuel passes the upper graduation mark, read the speedometer trip mileage. As fuel passes lower graduation mark, read speedometer trip mileage again.

The distance covered, multiplied by ten, is the actual miles per gallon obtained.

FAULTS IN CARBURETTORS

In the following notes, the more common defects in carburettors, and their remedies, will be considered; in each case the symptom will be denoted first and the remedy afterwards.

(1) Bad Starting

Assuming that the ignition system and the valve timing are in order, and the trouble is due to faulty carburation, the causes may include:

(*a*) Air leaks at carburettor joints or along worn valve stems. These may be cured by remaking the joints or binding with insulating tape, by fitting new valves and (or) guides, or by using one of the valve-stem sealers on the market, e.g. the S.U. or "Flexigas" type of valve-stem sealers.

(*b*) The *pilot or slow-running jet may be choked* or set to give too weak a mixture.

(*c*) There may be a *starvation of petrol* due to air-lock in piping, or to insufficient fuel in tank or float chamber (due to a leakage). Test by trying to flood carburettor and attempting to start engine.

(*d*) *Too much air.*—Shut off the main air valve, or strangler, and try starting again. In some cases it is possible to obtain a start in cold weather by placing a rag over the main air-supply inlet.

(*e*) *Throttle-lever stop incorrectly adjusted.*—If the throttle is opened too much, there will not be sufficient suction on the pilot jet to give the correct amount of petrol for starting. In some cases the throttle stop may be found set to shut the throttle too far, and thus prevent sufficient mixture from being drawn up.

(*f*) *In cold weather,* owing to poor vaporisation and fuel deposition, starting may be difficult. If a hot wet rag be wrapped around the carburettor a start can often be obtained. A piece of iron in the shape of a horse-shoe, heated and held against the mixing-chamber part of carburettor, will often give an easy start. Engines prone to bad starting may often be cured by *filling the radiator with hot water,* or by leaving one of *the special radiator lamps* of the miner's safety-lamp type under the bonnet for a few hours beforehand.

Although, theoretically, it should not be necessary with modern carburettors to "flood" them, in practice this usually helps in starting engines in cold weather.

(2) Popping Back in Carburettor

This may occur as a back-fire in carburettor at any or all speeds. It is due to too weak a mixture. Check by flooding the carburettor—by depressing float button—and note whether the popping ceases. It is usually due to a stoppage of petrol, which may be caused by *a choked petrol pipe, jet or filter,* by *running out of petrol,* or by *water in the float chamber.* It is usually necessary to dismantle the carburettor to eliminate this trouble.

Pre-ignition may also give rise to similar symptoms, so that in the case of an excessively hot engine this likelihood must be taken into account.

(3) Excessive Fuel Consumption

This is due, in general, either to *too large a jet* or to *leakage of petrol in the fuel feed system.* Before attempting to alter jet size examine all unions and pipes for signs of leakage, more particularly at the carburettor. If the *fuel level is too high* leakage will occur when the engine is stationary. *A faulty needle valve* will cause the petrol to drip from the carburettor. It is always a good plan to turn off the petrol at the tank when not using the car. *Dirt on the needle valve seating* will also cause *flooding. One or other of the jets not screwed tightly* on its seating is another possible cause. Sometimes the jet base plugs are the source of petrol leakage.

(4) Petrol Drips from Carburettor

In addition to the possible causes mentioned in (3), this may be due to *insufficient heating of the mixture. A punctured float* is another cause of petrol leakage.

(5) Engine Will Not Run Slowly

The chief cause for this is usually an incorrect setting of the pilot jet or throttle-lever stop. Try, first, altering the position of the latter, shutting it off little by little until, when the engine is hot, it just runs slowly. If this is not satisfactory the jet size should be increased.

Air leakages past the valve stems, or at the carburettor or inlet manifold joints, will also prevent an engine from running slowly.

We have assumed in the above remarks that the ignition is working correctly and the valves correctly adjusted for clearance at the tappets. If the valve seats are in poor condition or the compression is bad, the engine will not run very slowly.

(6) Engine Will Not Accelerate Well

Lack of acceleration, or pick-up, as we have previously mentioned, is generally due to one of the following causes : (*a*) Too small a main jet. (*b*) Too large a choke tube. (*c*) Compensating device not adjusted correctly ; if a well-jet compensating device, the jet may be too large so as to cause hunting, or jerky running. Apart from carburation causes, poor acceleration may be due to badly fitting pistons and rings causing a loss of compression, or to incorrectly adjusted valves and bad seatings.

(7) Engine Will Not Give Full Power

The probable cause may be (*a*) *Too weak a mixture* at full throttle ; test by fitting larger jet. (*b*) *Too rich a mixture* ; test by fuel consumption and by noting whether exhaust is black and pungent. (*c*) *Too small a carburettor* for size of engine. (*d*) *The accelerator not opening throttle to its full extent* ; this is a common cause, and one which should therefore be checked from time to time. (*e*) *Water or dirt in float chamber* ; this will usually give rise to " popping " in the carburettor.

(8) Hunting at Most Engine Speeds

This is caused by (*a*) A loose throttle connection, causing the throttle to rock a little ; sometimes, in the case of a butterfly throttle, the latter becomes loose on its spindle. (*b*) Too large a compensating jet. (*c*) Partial stoppage of petrol due to partly choked petrol pipe or filter.

(9) Progressive Falling Off in Efficiency of Running

Many carburettors contain *certain working mechanical parts* for controlling the mixture strength; for example, suction-operated pistons controlling the jets, choke-tube area, or air intake. In time *these parts wear* and the efficiency of operation falls off. The only remedy in such cases is to fit new parts.

Carburation Fault-finding Table

The following tabular method of ascertaining carburation faults and their causes is due to the Zenith Carburettor Co., Ltd.

CARBURETTOR FAULTS AND THEIR REMEDIES

DEFECT.	CAUSE.	REMEDY.
The engine will only run slowly and at low speeds. As soon as one accelerates, there is popping back in the carburettor. At the same time, the petrol in the float chamber is at its normal level.	*The main jet is stopped up.*	Remove the plug. Dismount the jet with the special key supplied with each instrument. Unstop it by blowing through it, then replace it. Replace the plug.
There is popping back, the engine misses and finally stops.	*The petrol does not get to the carburettor.*	See that there is some petrol in the tank.
There is no petrol or not enough petrol in the float chamber.	*The filter is obstructed.*	If the filter is dirty, dismount it and clean it. If the petrol supply is from an autovac, see that the latter is not empty. To do this, close the petrol tap at the outlet of the autovac. Dismount the petrol pipe to the carburettor. On opening the tap, the petrol should flow; if not, the autovac is empty. Verify also if the suction pipe going from the carburettor or inlet pipe to the autovac is quite air-tight. If it is air-tight, the autovac needs repairing.
The engine runs well at high speed, but as soon as it runs slowly there is popping back in the carburettor. The engine, if made to run slowly, stops.	*Compensator blocked up.*	Same operation as for a stopped-up main jet. The compensator is under the lower plug.
Impossible to start from cold, either with or without the mixture control. When hot, the engine works quite normally when the throttle is opened, but, when put back to slow running, quickly stops.	*Slow-running tube blocked up.*	Dismount the slow-running jet. Blow in the orifice and if possible work the part up and down in the petrol, keeping the head above. If necessary, a thin piece of wire can be used; for example, a small piece of copper wire as used in electric-lighting wire.
The carburettor leaks when not in action.	*Needle seating loose.*	Tighten the seating nut under the float chamber.
	Main-jet plug or compensator plug unscrewed or not screwed up tight enough. *Fixing screws of the diffuser bracket not screwed tightly enough.*	Tighten the two screws at the foot of the diffuser tube bracket
	Vehicle slopes too much.	On a steep incline or if the vehicle slopes too much on a hill, the carburettor may leak. Avoid stopping under these conditions, or else shut off the petrol during the stop.
	Dirt on needle seating.	Clean out float chamber.

DEFECT.	CAUSE.	REMEDY.
There is a strong smell of petrol and the engine jerks.	*Some dirt has got between the needle and the seating, preventing the regulation of the petrol supply.* *This comes in too great a quantity and floods the carburettor.* *In pressure-fed vehicles, this indicates too high a pressure for the carburettor, or, the tank being almost empty, the petrol arrives in the carburettor mixed with air and makes the needle work erratically, which produces the same phenomenon.*	Turn off the petrol. Remove the float-chamber cover. Clean the float chamber and the filter. Lower the pressure as soon as it gets above the 2 lb. mark and use a special needle seating *for pressure-fed carburettors.* Refill the tank.
Popping back takes place in the carburettor after running at high speed. For example, on the flat or on a hill after running with the throttle fully open for several miles. The petrol supply is correct.	*Pre-ignition.*	This phenomenon exists especially on engines where the compression is higher than the average, but it also occurs on standard engines which are very dirty or on which the sparking plugs are defective. A very common defect. Clean the cylinders with an oxygen blow-pipe. Change the plugs.

MISCELLANEOUS USEFUL CARBURETTOR NOTES

(1) *Jets*.—It is always advisable to carry one or two spare jets. An engine usually requires different (larger) jets for winter than for summer running.

Never attempt to open out a jet; a very small increase in the jet diameter may cause an excessive petrol consumption. See that the jets are seated correctly.

(2) *Float*.—The float level should be checked at intervals, since wear in the float-needle mechanism occurs in the course of time.

If the float punctures—as in rare instances it does—you can get your vehicle home by turning the petrol tap off sufficiently to just feed the jets so as to keep the engine running.

(3) *Petrol Tubing*.—If this fractures on the road a temporary repair can be made by using rubber tubing over the crack. Failing this, smear well with yellow soap and bind with ordinary or insulating tape.

(4) *Two-stroke Carburettors*.—Carburettors for two-stroke engines require rather finer adjustment than for four-stroke ones; the permissible range of mixture variation is less in the former case. If the *mixture is too weak, four-stroking will occur*; a larger jet is then indicated. In the case of two-stroke engines using the "petroil" (i.e. petrol and oil mixture) system of lubrication, it is important to keep the float chamber and filter clean. The effect of an accumulation of heavy oily matter in the carburettor is to cause misfiring and also starting difficulty.

(5) *Air Leaks*.—A very frequent cause of poor running at low speeds and of difficult starting is that of air leaks past the valve stems and guides. A shaking of the valve in its guide or a bright area on the valve stem may be taken as an indication of wear. The correct remedy is

to fit new valves and guides, but a temporary expedient is that of using a valve-stem sealer such as the S.U. or "Flexigas."

(6) *Starting*.—To start an engine which has bad air leaks, open the throttle a little more than is usual in normal cases, inject petrol (preferably of the lighter density grade) into each cylinder through the sparking plugs, or into the inlet manifold, crank the engine a few turns by hand, and then switch on and crank again; keep the engine speed up until engine begins to warm. A piece of soft rag, felt, or sponge soaked in petrol and placed in or near the main air inlet during the preliminary cranking operation will also help matters.

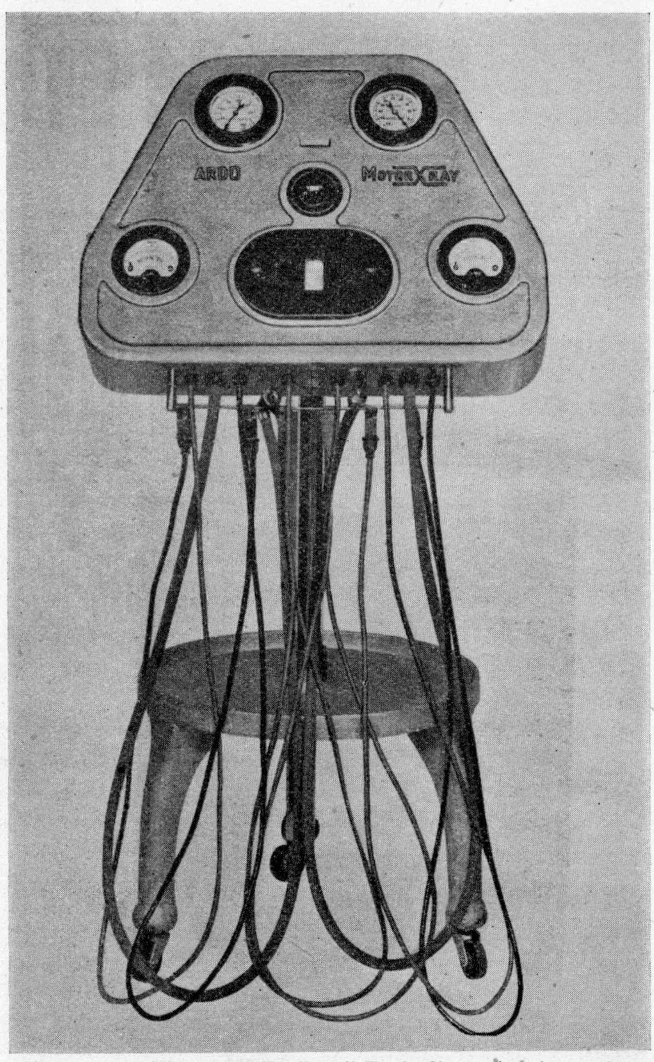

Fig. 315.—" The Motor-Ex-Ray " Fault-diagnosing Apparatus.

MOTOR-ENGINE FAULT DIAGNOSERS

A new type of apparatus that has come into favour in large garages and motor engineering works, where cars have to be inspected, faults diagnosed and remedied, is a combination of several instruments, chiefly electrical and pneumatic, conveniently arranged with switches or connections so that the operator can carry out a series of tests upon an engine, rapidly and reliably; these tests are made with the engine in its chassis.

Once the operator has been instructed in the use of such an apparatus, he can readily ascertain engine faults and can also tune up engines, without any high degree of skill or experience.

Fig. 315 shows a typical British instrument, known as the "Motor-Ex-Ray," which has a series of grouped dials and the necessary electric cable and air-line connections to enable a series of tests to be carried out on an engine. The instruments consist of a voltmeter, ammeter, pressure gauge, and vacuum gauge. The apparatus in question enables the following items to be dealt with. It (1) Reports immediately the condition of valves, whether sticking or burnt, etc., and timing. (2) Checks carburettor setting. (3) Records the amount of compression in each cylinder. Shows any loss, and locates its cause, whether in pistons, rings, cylinders, valves, or gaskets. (4) Reports condition and amount of back pressure present in complete exhaust system. (5) Gives complete H.T. condition of the coil, calibrated against number of pounds compression in the motor, in any circumstances of load or speed. (6) Shows any high or low speed missing due to points or worn distributor shaft, etc. (7) Complete tests of magneto. (8) Fouled or worn-out plugs which test O.K. outside. (9) Checks autovac system. (10) Checks short circuits in distributor head and H.T. wire.

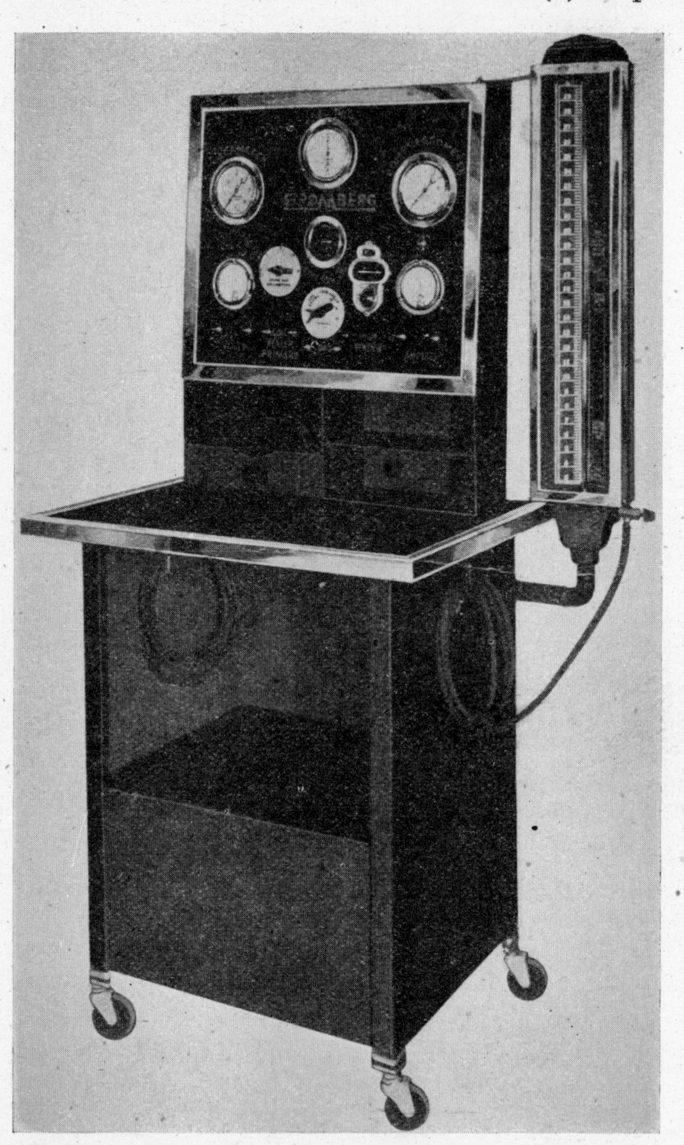

Fig. 316.—The Stromberg Motoscope and Mercury Vacameter.

In addition, it enables a wide range of tests to be made on the battery, dynamo, cut-out, lamps, and starting motor. The output of the dynamo can be checked and the charging rate tested after making third-brush adjustments.

Another, rather more elaborate, testing plant is the Stromberg Motoscope and Mercury Vacameter combination unit shown in Fig. 316.

It consists of a cabinet having a group of instruments and controls which are connected to the engine by suitable electric leads and pipes.

The makers issue definite instructions on the methods of making the various tests with this apparatus, the methods in question being quite simple to execute, so that no scientific knowledge is called for. The operator need only be properly trained in the *use* of this tester.

The Stromberg Motoscope Model O mounted on steel bench is an excellent engine-trouble tracer, and will quickly reveal defects in the spark plug, coil or magneto, distributor unit, ignition cable, carburettor, sticking valves, valve leaks, and valve springs, etc. It can be used for timing valves and ignition, gaskets—head and intake—synchronising breaker points rings and compression, booster brake test, clogged silencer, back pressure, fuel pump, vacuum tank, etc.

The Stromberg Mercury Vacameter or Master Engine Tester is a satisfactory instrument for the adjustment of carburettors and synchronisation of the ignition with the carburation for carburettor idling and high-speed adjustments, mixture tests, valve tests—timing, leaky and sticky valves, vacuum-gauge testing, ignition synchronising distributor test and timing, intake, manifold, gasket, and for compression tests.

The instrument actually makes it possible for the service station to increase the petrol mileage and give its customers smoother engine performance. Unlike the old-style vacuum gauge, this precision instrument gives an accurate indication of the troubles that cause a poor vacuum in the manifold leading to the carburettor.

Built to primary standards and with a mercury column that reads in full inches, its visibility as well as its sensitivity enables good results to be obtained.

The overall length of the metal case which contains the Vacameter itself is 40½ in., with 6¼ in. wide, depth 2 in.

These instruments are marketed by Messrs. Brown Bros., Ltd., Great Eastern Street, London, E.C.2.

CHAPTER VII

THE CLUTCH

THE function of the clutch being to connect or to disconnect the engine's crankshaft with, or from, the gear box and transmission, it follows that the clutch should perform this operation smoothly, surely, and quietly. The amount of pedal movement, or pressure, should not be inconveniently large. Further, the clutch should operate for long periods without the necessity of adjustment or renewal of the friction surfaces. Having outlined the desirable features of automobile clutches, we can pass on to a consideration of the usual clutch troubles and their remedies.

CLUTCH TROUBLES

The modern motor-vehicle clutch, having passed through a series of development stages, during which any weaknesses have been detected and remedied, seldom gives trouble in its earlier periods of usage, but only after two or more years of hard use. There are, however, many cases of neglect or misuse by negligent and careless drivers, who race their engines every time they wish to engage the clutch, and who let the latter in with a jerk every time. The same type of individual seldom gives attention to such items as clutch dressing, or lubrication, or clutch adjustment, with the result that sooner or later he experiences trouble.

It is evident that the penalty of neglect and misuse is paid for by frequently recurring clutch troubles.

In order to obtain the best running results, and the longest life, it can be stated that the clutch should always be engaged very gently whenever starting off or changing gears ; it should also be lubricated, or dressed, in accordance with the manufacturer's instructions ; further, it should be examined every few thousand miles for wear in the friction surfaces, as shown by the increased idle movement of the clutch pedal ; wear in the clutch-operating mechanism is another contributory cause.

TYPES OF CLUTCH

There are several different types of clutch in present use, the principal being as follows : (1) The External Cone Clutch, lined with leather or fabric material ; (2) the Internal Cone Clutch, lined with leather or fabric material ; (3) the Single-plate Dry Clutch ; (4) the Cork-insert Clutch (lubricated) ; (5) the Multiple-plate Clutch (lubricated) ; and the Semi-centrifugal and fully Centrifugal types of Plate Clutches. The hydraulic clutch, including the type known as the "Fluid Flywheel" is also included under this heading.

Each type of clutch has its own minor troubles, peculiar to its design, but there are certain troubles common to all types, namely: (a) Clutch Slip; (b) Clutch Fierceness, or Harshness; (c) Clutch Chatter; and (d) Clutch Spin.

SLIPPING OF VARIOUS TYPES OF CLUTCHES

No matter what the design of clutch, it is prone to slip at times; some types, of course, much more so than others. Before considering special kinds of clutches and their peculiarities, it will be as well to mention the symptoms associated with clutch slip. A slipping clutch can readily be detected by running the car on top gear, throttled down to about six to eight miles an hour, and gently applying either the foot or hand brake. If the engine shows a decided tendency to stop, or labours heavily, there is certainly no clutch slip. If, on the other hand, the speed of the engine is but little affected by the application of the brakes, the clutch is slipping.

Another indication is when the engine is started, from rest, on low gear, on an incline. Here, the power transmitted through the clutch is almost a maximum, and therefore we have a strong test of the gripping action of the clutch. If the car takes an appreciable time to move off when the clutch is actually released (to engage), this is a sure sign that it is slipping.

Another test for this trouble is when climbing a steep hill on a lower gear; if the engine races when the accelerator pedal is depressed, without a corresponding increase in the speed of the car, there is no doubt about the clutch slipping. The chief causes of clutch slip are as follows: (1) oil or grease on the friction surfaces; (2) badly adjusted or broken clutch pressure spring; (3) badly adjusted clutch stop—which does not permit full engagement of the gripping surfaces; (4) worn friction surfaces.

A *common driving fault*, leading ultimately to clutch slip, is that of driving continuously with the foot on the clutch pedal, so that the latter is always more or less depressed, allowing a slight slipping, and therefore a wearing action.

CONE CLUTCHES

Although this type of clutch has been replaced to a large extent by the single- and multiple-plate types, there are still a number of cone clutches in use on vehicles built a few years ago.

Many of the earlier designs of cone clutch were faulty, the usual defects being too small a diameter—and therefore excessive forces on the friction material—incorrect angle of the cone surface, and insufficient surface or area of material.

Slipping of a leather-faced cone clutch may be caused by a badly worn clutch leather, which results in the clutch not bedding sufficiently; in some cases the stops prevent the worn leather from fully engaging with the metal surface of the other clutch member.

Oil or grease on the leather will cause slipping. If there is a leakage of oil from the crankshaft journal, at the flywheel end, or from the engine side of the gear box, this will cause slipping, since the effect of a lubricant on leather is to reduce its coefficient of friction.

Broken or insufficiently tensioned clutch spring will also tend to cause slipping.

Another frequent cause of the slipping trouble is the glazing of the surface of the leather due to dust or grease accumulation. If there is a formation of dirt on the front (squared) or spigot end of the clutch shaft, this will sometimes limit the travel of the latter and thus prevent the clutch from engaging properly with its opposing member.

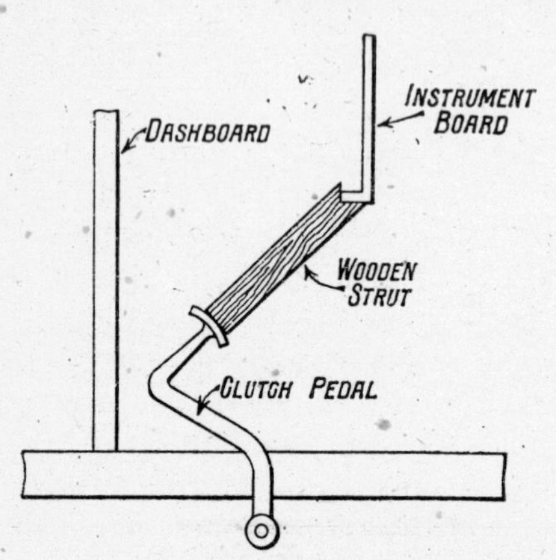

Fig. 317.—Showing Method of Holding Clutch Depressed.

REMEDIES FOR SLIPPING CLUTCHES

The common cure for a slipping leather type of clutch is to depress the clutch pedal as far as it will go—after the footboards have been removed—and to wedge or block it in this position. This can easily be done by cutting a piece of wood to fit between the end of the depressed pedal and the instrument board, or front seat, as shown in Fig. 317. Special screw devices are also sold for clutch-depression purposes.

The clutch leather will then be clear of the metal surface of its opposing member, and petrol can be squirted in between the two as the inner member (carrying the clutch leather) is rotated by hand. There is usually not much room between the leather and metal when the clutch is fully depressed, so that a scrubbing brush of wire cannot be inserted. A useful device can be made from a strip of tinned iron for inserting between the leather and metal, so as to scrape or roughen the surface of the former to allow the petrol to dissolve the oil or grease on it. Fig. 318 shows a suitable form of home-made clutch tool for this purpose. The serrated bent-over portion should have a maximum length of 2 or 3 millimetres only, since there is little clearance between the clutch members. The tool can conveniently be made from a piece of steel or tinned iron strip of 1 in. by 18 S.W.G. section. A loop is formed at one end for operating the tool.

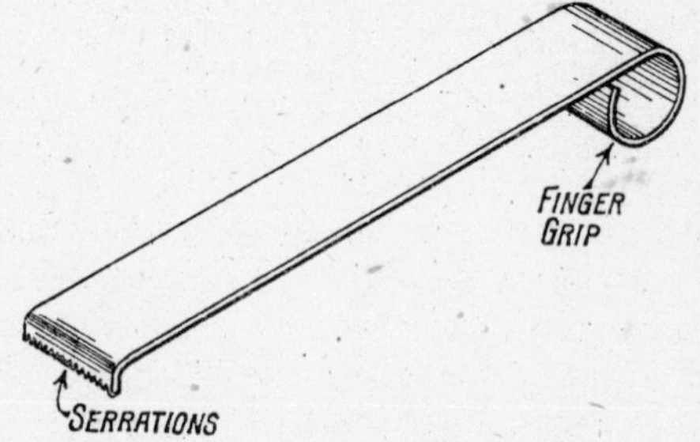

Fig. 318.—A useful Clutch Tool.

After the leather has been well washed and scraped, the clutch should be left in its depressed condition for several hours, to allow the petrol to drain away and dry off.

In an emergency, when on the road, slipping can often be prevented by inserting Fuller's earth or French chalk between the leather and metal.

On no account should the ordinary belt-dressing materials, used in engineers' workshops to prevent machinery belting from slipping, be used; these materials include powdered resin, powdered sulphur, and certain patented "belt-slip" preventing compounds.

In some designs of clutch, special leather expanders are inserted between the leather and the metal of its support, and if these clutch expanders are not properly adjusted slipping may be caused; a further reference to these expanders will be made later.

SLIPPING OF DISC-TYPE CLUTCHES

The usual causes of slip of these clutches are excessive wear of the clutch-disc friction linings or facings, oil or grease on these linings, an improperly adjusted clutch pedal, or a broken clutch spring; insufficient tension of the clutch springs is another possible cause. Bent or worn clutch discs will often cause slipping also.

The dry-plate type of clutch occasionally becomes coated with an accumulation of oil or grease—usually as the result of careless lubrication of the clutch spigot or to leakage from the crankcase; the surface becomes glazed and slipping occurs. If the friction surfaces are badly worn, the rivets may engage with the other moving metal plates and slipping will then occur.

The cure in this case consists in depressing the clutch, using for preference the device shown in Fig. 317, and thoroughly scraping the friction surfaces, using plenty of petrol. If the clutch can readily be dismantled, the friction surfaces can be well brushed with a stout bristle or a wire brush, using ordinary petrol to brush the dirt away.

CURES FOR FIERCE CLUTCHES (LEATHER)

The surface of the leather should first be treated, by depressing the clutch, scraping the surface with a scraper of the type shown in Fig. 318, and well flushing with petrol or benzole. After this has been drained away, and the leather is dry, dress the surface either with *collan oil,* or *neat's-foot oil,* so as to soften the leather and to preserve it. It is better to apply these oils hot, so as to penetrate the leather more quickly.

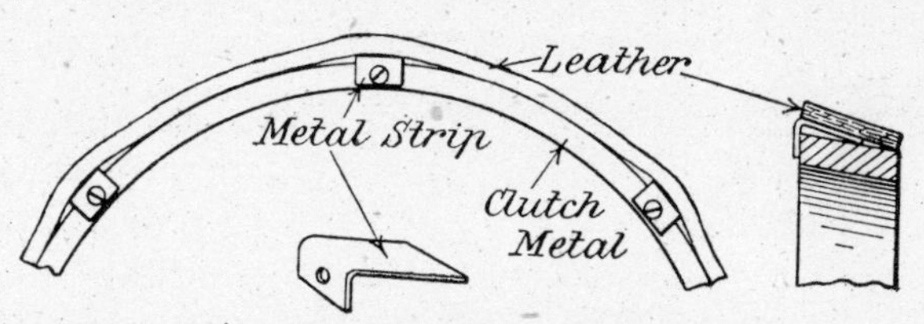

Fig. 319.—A useful Method of Preventing Clutch Fierceness, by Using Expanders.

A plunger type of squirt may be used to inject the oil into the space between the inner and outer clutch members.

The oil dressing should be worked into the surface of the leather thoroughly, using a flat metal strip for this purpose ; the inner member should be rotated during this operation. Leave the clutch depressed for several hours, to allow the dressing to soak in.

On no account use mineral oil for dressing the leather ; for this reason ordinary lubricating oils should not be employed, although *pure castor oil* can be used when no other suitable oil is available.

A good expedient for a consistently bad clutch, as regards fierceness, is to use clutch-leather expanders, consisting of six or eight strips of tinned iron or copper inserted at equal intervals between the inner surface of the leather and the metal surface of the cone to which it is attached. This results in the hitherto truly conical leather surface being broken up into a series of slight ridges, or bumps, thus reducing the contact area, and curing the fierceness (Fig. 319).

A suitable type of strip is one measuring $\frac{1}{4}$ in. to $\frac{3}{8}$ in. wide, by 18 to 20 S.W.G. thick, and of length equal to the width of the clutch leather.

In the case of some cars, special adjustable spring-loaded plungers are arranged at intervals around the inner clutch member, so that they press on the inside surface of the leather, through appropriate holes in the clutch metal.

Fig. 320 illustrates a typical example of such a clutch with its plunger expanders. Only one plunger is shown of the five fitted around the periphery.

The *spigot, or clutch pilot bearing*, should be well lubricated when the clutch leather is dressed, or clutch expanders fitted.

To adjust the plunger type of clutch expander, the split-pins should be removed, and the plunger screw given a turn in the proper direction to force it against the leather. Do not adjust too tightly against the leather or slipping and burning may occur.

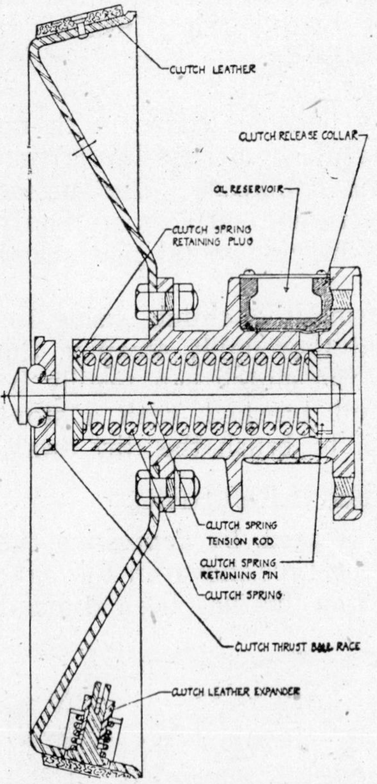

Fig. 320.—Illustrating Spring-loaded Clutch Leather Depressors for Preventing Fierceness.

CLUTCH-PEDAL ADJUSTMENT

When overhauling the clutch, make certain that the clutch-operating pedal is properly adjusted. There should only be a small amount of idle movement, or free travel, of the pedal before the clutch commences to disengage, and when the clutch pedal is partially depressed—but before it reaches the footboard—the clutch should be fully disengaged. The clearances for the Borg & Beck clutches are given later. The clutch pedal should never require depressing as far as the footboard to disengage the clutch. On the other hand, when it is released, there should be proper positive engagement, and no slipping. If, when the clutch pedal is released, slipping or dragging occurs, it may be a sign that the clutch-pedal stop requires adjustment, so as to allow the pedal to move farther backwards, i.e. towards the driver.

Each make of car has its own provision for clutch-pedal adjustment, and in this respect the manufacturer's handbooks of instructions should be consulted. It can, however, be taken for a fact that adjustments are almost invariably provided and can readily be found if the clutch mechanism be examined. Later, we shall consider a few typical examples of car, and describe the clutch adjustments.

FERODO CONE CLUTCHES

The use of Ferodo fabric in place of leather for cone clutches necessitates a change in the angle of the cone. The coefficient of friction being higher, a somewhat greater cone angle is required. In the case of leather cone clutches the average cone angle is about $12\frac{1}{2}^\circ$, for Ferodo from 12° to 15° is usual ; an angle of 18° can, however, be used without serious end thrust. The same remarks on the care of clutches as in the case of leather types apply, except that it is unnecessary to dress Ferodo material—only to keep it clean and free from glazing.

WORN CLUTCH LININGS

After a clutch has been in use for some considerable time, the friction material will be found to have worn appreciably ; usually this occurs after 25,000 to 40,000 miles of road running. The result of such wear is that the clutch sinks more deeply into the flywheel member, bringing the clutch pedal nearer the footboard, with certain designs.

In most cases an adjustment is provided to bring the clutch pedal back to its original position.

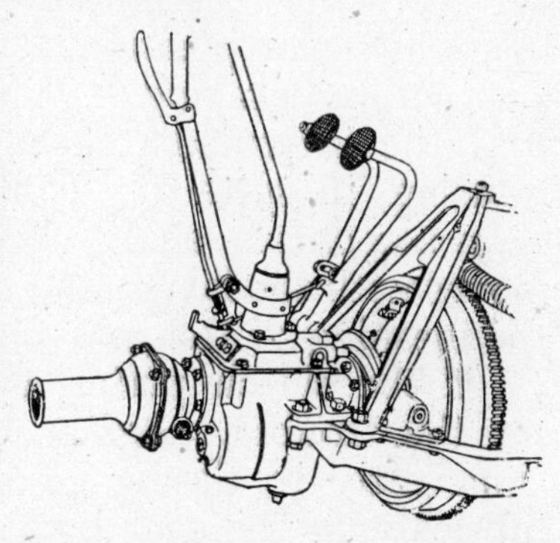

Fig. 321.—A Typical Gear-box Unit, showing Clutch-pedal Adjustment.

A typical method of accomplishing this is shown in Fig. 321. There the clutch-pedal lever is provided with a slot, and is distinct from the clutch-operating lever ; the latter is connected to the former by means of the bolt shown, which engages with the slotted portion of the clutch-pedal lever. In this way the position of the clutch pedal can be altered relatively to the clutch-operating lever. In other examples there is an adjustable link between the clutch pedal and the clutch-depressing lever or fork—usually of the screwed type—whereby the length of the link can be altered so as to take up any wear in the linings.

BROKEN CLUTCH SPRING

It is rarely that one comes across cases of broken clutch springs, but when these do occur they are apparent by a slipping tendency of the clutch, and in the clutch pedal not returning to the engaged position when the foot is released. If, when the clutch is slipping badly, no resistance is felt when the foot is removed from the clutch pedal, this points to the case of a broken spring.

STICKY OR DRAGGING CLUTCH

Cases occasionally occur of a clutch which does not release properly when the pedal is depressed. The usual causes of dragging clutches include (1) wrongly adjusted clutch pedal, which does not permit enough axial travel of the clutch to ensure disengagement; (2) gummy or sticky clutch surfaces, which cause a drag between the two sets of plates or the two surfaces; (3) worn spigot bearings; (4) bent clutch plates; (5) clutch discs not sliding freely on the castellated shaft or hub keys; (6) too thick a lubricating oil in the case of plate clutches of the "wet" type; (7) excessively thin oil in the transmission. The clutch should be thoroughly washed out with petrol and new lubricant inserted, in the case of plate clutches. Cone clutches should be washed and dressed in the manner previously prescribed. If, in the case of plate clutches, this treatment does not cure the trouble, the clutch should be dismantled for careful examination to detect bent plates, a worn spigot bearing, or unlubricated parts.

GEAR ENGAGEMENT DIFFICULT—SPINNING CLUTCH

It is not uncommon, even in the more recent cars, to come across cases where it is difficult to engage the lowest gear when starting off. On depressing the clutch pedal and moving the gear lever from neutral to its low-gear position, it is often found to be impossible to engage the gear without grating or grinding of the gear teeth. This means, of course, that the intermediate shaft between the engine and gear box is still rotating, in spite of the fact that the clutch pedal is depressed. The gear-box clutch shaft, which is connected to the one clutch member, moves with the latter, and so this shaft rotates in the gear box, preventing the meshing of the gear pinions.

If the clutch plates, or cone surfaces, are sticky, this may account for the trouble. Again, the clutch pedal may not depress the clutch sufficiently to disengage the surfaces. A thin lubricant, or a lack of lubricant in the gear box, will also encourage the rotation of the clutch or intermediate shaft.

If the car is fitted with a clutch stop, and many modern clutches are, or brake, this will effectively obviate clutch spin on disengagement; in many cases it is a simple matter to fit a clutch brake. All that is necessary is a piece of spring steel or hard brass of appreciable stiffness, one end of which is provided with a pad of leather, wood, fibre, or Ferodo, and the other affixed to a convenient part of the chassis frame (Fig. 322). The friction pad is so arranged that it is clear of the clutch-shaft cone, or disc, when the clutch is engaged, but comes into contact with the cone or disc when the latter is disengaged; the friction pad acts as a brake, to prevent the clutch member in question from spinning. A clutch brake is a useful asset not only in connection with the silent engagement of the low gear when starting from rest, but also when changing gear on the road, for it quickly stops the clutch from spinning, and leaves the gears in the correct positions, or with the correct speeds for meshing. In some cases the use of a *thicker lubricant in the gear box* will prevent clutch spinning by introducing more friction to the rotating gears.

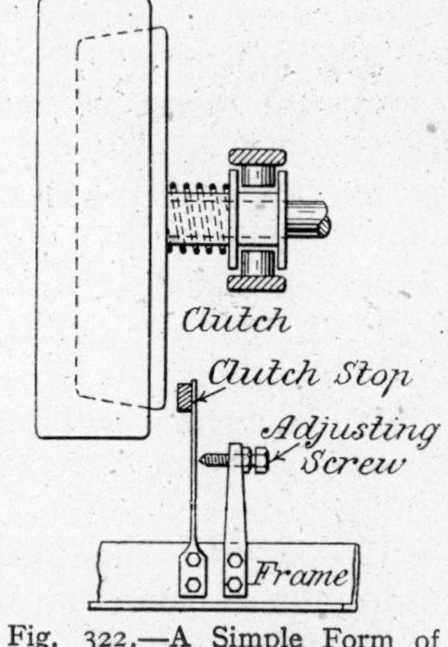

Fig. 322.—A Simple Form of Clutch Stop, to Prevent Spinning.

In the case of "wet" single- or multiple-plate clutch, the *degree of viscosity of the lubricant used* in the clutch is very important. If too thick, the plates will tend to stick and the gear shaft will continue to turn after the clutch is depressed. In such cases of spinning of the clutch, the lubricant should be drained out, and the plates washed with petrol or paraffin; after this has been drained away, the correct grade of oil recommended by the makers of the car, or clutch, should be introduced.

Too thin a lubricating oil may result in fierceness of action and in more rapid wear of the friction surfaces.

WORN PLATE CLUTCHES—RELINING

After a considerable period of usage, or when a car has been constantly used by a driver who makes a practice of slipping the clutch on top gear, of starting off in top or in second gear, or of *constantly resting his foot on the clutch pedal on long journeys*, the clutch lining, or friction material, may be found to have worn down so that the clutch will not function satisfactorily.

In most cases it will be found that the material has worn so thin that the rivet heads are level with the surface, and are actually making contact with the metal of the other clutch member. This not only causes slipping, but may lead to noisy operation.

The relining of a plate clutch is not a difficult matter, but there is one proper method of carrying out this work, and it is necessary to employ suitable tools for the purpose.

The following notes are based upon the practice recommended by Messrs. Ferodo, Ltd., the manufacturers of the well-known brake and clutch linings.

The new clutch linings are supplied ready moulded and to the correct dimensions as a rule; otherwise they must be cut from flat or strip material. The die-pressed correctly shaped linings are much more convenient to work with, and should always be obtained, if possible.

Having punched out the old rivets, and stripped the lining off, clean the metal surface to which the fabric is to be attached, and clear out the rivet holes. Next fix the new lining temporarily in position by means of two or more metal cramps; the holes in the linings to take the rivets can then be drilled, using an ordinary drill brace and a sharp twist drill, which should be a fairly easy fit in the holes in the shoe; these then act as guides for the drill.

The lining can be removed when all the holes have been drilled in it, and held firmly, yet lightly—to avoid damage or deformation—in a vice for the purpose of countersinking the holes in the working face of the lining to receive the head of the rivet. It is best to use a Slocombe centre drill for this purpose, but an ordinary sharp twist drill of the same diameter as the head of the rivet can be used as an alternative.

It is important not to countersink the clutch lining too deeply, or there will not be sufficient material for the rivet to hold to. Tubular aluminium or copper rivets are best for fixing the linings of *plate clutches*; such rivets can be obtained from the makers of the friction linings.

When the rivet is inserted in the lining it should be tapped lightly home, and its shank should project about $\frac{1}{8}$ in. beyond the metal of the clutch cone; this is just sufficient to allow it to be riveted or beaded over.

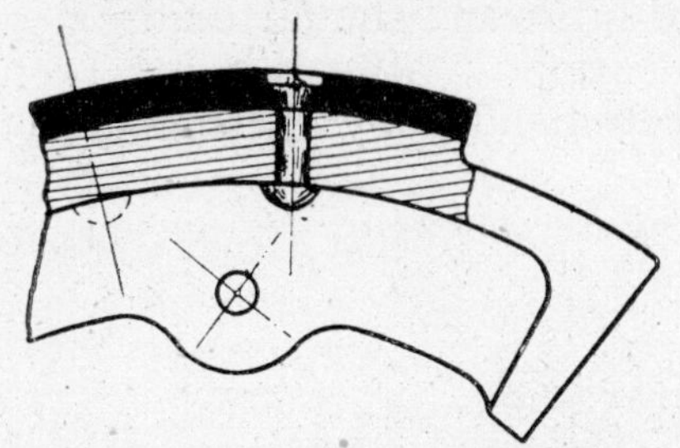

Fig. 323.—Showing Method of Sinking Rivet in Clutch or Brake Material.

In riveting, commence from the centre and work both ways to the ends; if the holes have been accurately drilled they will coincide with the holes in the shoes and each rivet can be driven in in turn.

There is *one important point* to note when drilling the clutch lining—namely, to mark the position of the lining on the plate before drilling, so that it can be replaced in exactly the same position.

When closing the rivets it is important to back them up, using a short length of round steel bar with a flat end for this purpose. The diameter of the bar should be the same as that of the rivet head; the bar should be held firmly in a vice. If the rivet head is slightly below the surface of the lining the head is easily located by the depression formed in the lining. When all the rivets have been closed up any threads of fabric left by the drill may be removed by filing, so as to leave a smooth finished surface.

Most amateurs can successfully undertake the relining of a clutch plate with the replacement linings now obtainable.

CLUTCH-LINING RIVETING TOOL

In addition to the usual solid copper and aluminium rivets used for holding the friction material to the clutch plate, tubular rivets made of copper are also employed. Fig. 324 shows a convenient shape of riveting tool for this type of tubular rivet, developed by Messrs. Raybestos, Ltd. The head of the rivet is held against a " dolly " fixed in the vice, whilst the punch, which has a double curvature on its riveting face, is applied to the other end of the tubular rivet. The object of coning the nose of the punch is to ensure that the rivet stem is spread evenly in all directions over the friction material in its vicinity.

The tool shown in the lower illustration is a countersink drill, with a pilot shank for use on brake shoes, to countersink the rivet holes.

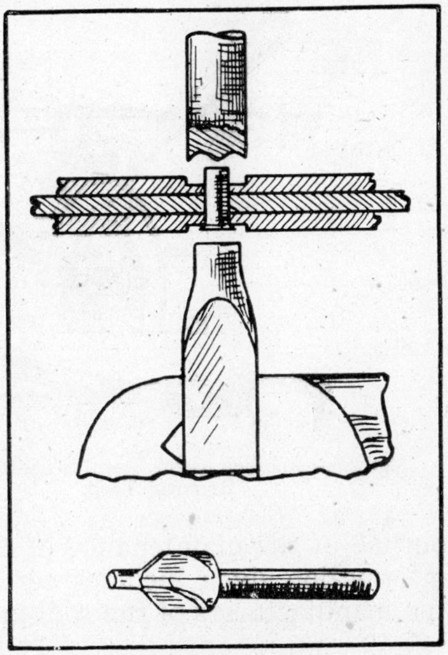

Fig. 324.—The Raybestos Clutch-lining Riveting Tool.

REMOVAL OF THE SPRINGS

In the case of exposed clutches of the cone type—that is to say, where the engine and gear box are separate and the unit construction is not employed—little difficulty is experienced in the removal of the clutch springs, since they can be got at readily. Similarly in the replacement of these springs it is not difficult to compress them, either by hand or with a makeshift tool or lever device. Often a long screw with a tube at one end can be made to exert pressure on the spring, sufficient to enter the nut.

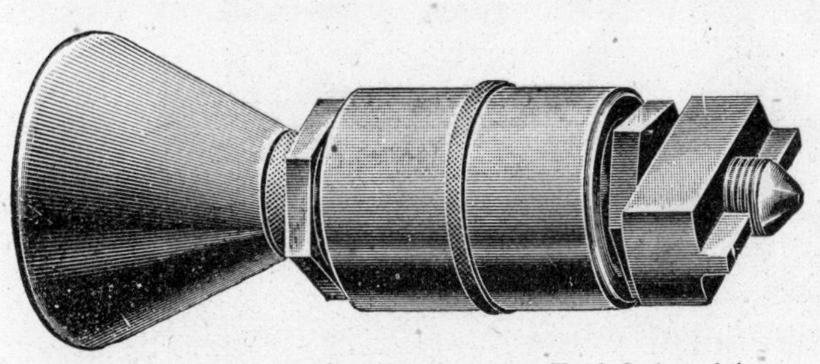

Fig. 325.—A Convenient Clutch-spring Tool designed for Morris Clutches (Brown Bros.).

In the case of enclosed clutches, some manufacturers now supply special clutch-spring compressing devices, to enable the springs to be compressed, and held there whilst the nuts are removed, or replaced, as the case may be.

We illustrate a neat finger-operated device (Fig. 325), known as the " Millennium," which has been designed for the removal of the clutch springs of Morris clutches. The knurled screws are adjusted so that the clutch spring is compressed sufficiently to enable the cotter to be withdrawn from its slot.

Fig. 326 illustrates another type of clutch-spring compressor which takes its purchase on the back of the clutch plate, and uses a toggle-lever action to exert the necessary force to close the spring sufficiently to allow the nut to be screwed on. This is an easy tool to use, and the removal or replacement of the springs can be quickly undertaken.

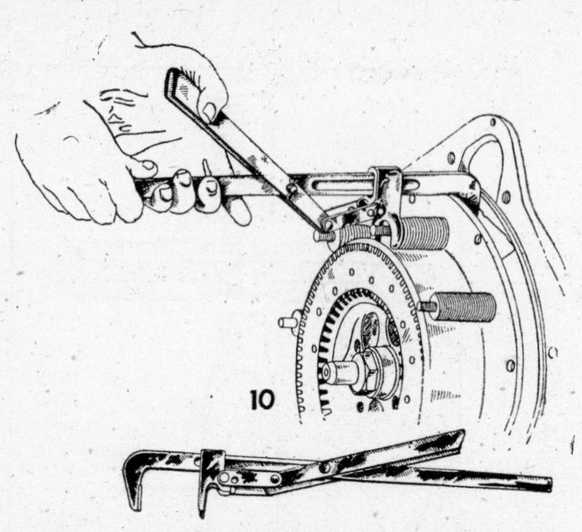

Fig. 326.—Another useful Form of Clutch-spring Removal Tool.

CARE OF PLATE CLUTCHES

Since the greater number of clutches in use for automobile work are of the plate type—the cone clutch being gradually superseded by this type—a brief outline of the maintenance of this pattern of clutch will be given. The information given includes certain instructions and advice tendered by the manufacturers of the well-known Ferodo clutch and brake linings.

Fig. 327.—A Typical Multiple-plate Clutch Dismantled.

The ordinary single- and multiple-plate clutch does not require very much attention, and will operate for relatively long periods without giving trouble.

The dry-plate clutch, as its name implies, does not require any lubricant; its ideal working conditions are clean, dry surfaces and accurate alignment.

It is therefore essential that no lubricant or dressing should be used, and that the clutch or clutch-pit design should aim at the rigid exclusion of dirt in any form.

The clutch should be inspected about once every 10,000 miles or so, and if any dirt or dust—due to abraded materials or otherwise—is observed, it should be dismantled and cleaned thoroughly.

It is advisable, of course, at this juncture to lubricate the joints and pins of internal levers and other moving portions, which may not be readily accessible from the outside. The thrust-release ball-races naturally require lubrication from time to time.

It is not from normal use that any trouble or difficulty may be expected, but plate clutches are susceptible to misuse, and this occasionally arises of gross and entirely unnecessary character. Since in engagement they are particularly smooth and easy, these characteristics are sometimes taken undue advantage of, and cars are driven for long periods in traffic with the clutch partially engaged with friction surfaces slipping at considerable speed against each other. In this way, undue heat and wear arise, detrimental to both linings and metal surfaces. To some extent, the fore-mentioned conditions are incidental, but they can be very much overdone, and cases arise where even high-carbon-steel discs have scored and buckled through being raised to red heat—there is no occasion for any misuse of this kind, and it should be noted that when very low speed is required, it is very much better to change down into low gear and run the engine slowly with the clutch fully engaged than to travel along in top gear with a partial clutch engagement, for this following additional reason. Some varieties of moulded composition linings are more susceptible to the effect of heat than woven asbestos fabrics, and lose some of their "grip" when raised to high temperatures—it is generally due to this cause that clutches slip when fully engaged. In such instances, it is worse than useless to change into low gear and race the engine as drivers sometimes do in their endeavour to re-establish the temporary loss of driving power. The only thing to do is to run the engine as slowly as possible to get the car out of the way of traffic, then let it rest with engine running and clutch disengaged; in a very few minutes the parts will cool down and the car can then be driven as usual. On the other hand, if a small amount of lubricant has accidentally reached the working friction surfaces and causes slip, it may be removed by running the engine at high speed, letting the clutch in and out until it is "felt" that the oil or grease has been dissipated. If lubrication is excessive, nothing remains but a thorough cleansing with petrol, naphtha, or other solvent of grease—paraffin is not recommended.

After a certain period of service the friction linings may be reduced by wear, so that the extension of the clamping plate ceases and does not allow the full pressure of the springs to act against the linings. In such cases, the amount of slipping will noticeably and gradually increase, and finally the clutch will cease to function at all. For this condition, only one thing remains to be done, i.e. renew the linings.

FLEXIBLE CLUTCH PLATES

In order to provide smoother engagement and take-up of the drive when declutching, it is now the general practice to fit flexible clutch plates instead of plain ones of the solid pattern. There is a variety of such clutch plates on the market, but the majority employ the same principle, viz. in providing radial and circular slits in order to obtain flexibility in a fore and aft direction, i.e. perpendicular to the plane of the clutch plate. The Borg & Beck clutches described in this chapter utilise the flexible and also the shock-absorbing types of clutch plate.

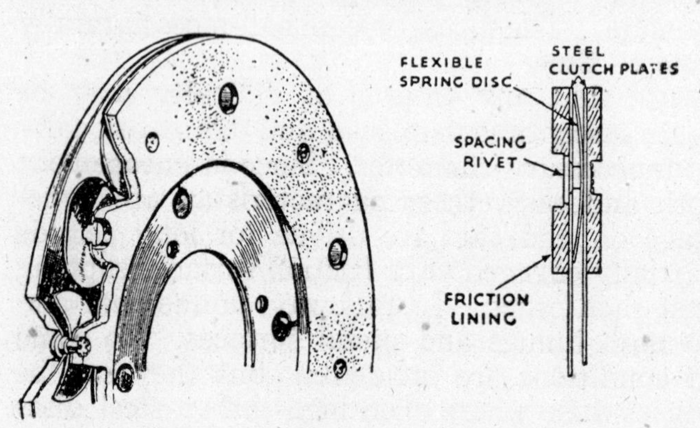

Fig. 328.—Flexible-type Clutch Plate.

The Newton & Bennett clutch plate shown in Fig. 328 obtains its flexibility by means of dished spring-steel washers each of which is held in place by means of a rivet; the latter also serves to hold the friction material to the plate. These slightly curved washers are arranged with their curvatures alternately in one direction and then the other. As a result, when the clutch is engaging, the washers are flattened out by the clutch-spring load so that the drive is taken up more gradually than with a solid plate clutch. A further advantage is that the slots and holes in the two plates enable air to circulate and thus to cool the friction surfaces.

MAINTENANCE AND ADJUSTMENT INSTRUCTIONS

Having outlined the more important service information in connection with automobile clutches, we cannot do better than describe a few typical cases taken from ordinary motor-car practice. In this way the reader will not only become conversant with the different designs and clutch details, but will learn a good deal about the essentials of clutches from their maintenance adjustment and repair. Although it is impossible to cover every type of clutch in use, yet it will be possible to apply the general principles of maintenance and the methods outlined to practically any example which the motor engineer is likely to encounter.

We shall commence with an example of a cork-insert type of plate clutch, namely, the familiar Morris clutch illustrated in Figs. 329 and 330. This clutch provides four friction surfaces. The driving surfaces comprise (1) the rear face of the flywheel, (2) and (3) both faces of a floating plate, (4) the forward face of the clutch pressure plate. Six clutch-driving pins pass through the flywheel, the floating plate, and the pressure plate, all of which consequently revolve with the engine.

The driven surfaces comprise a double line of cork inserts in two steel plates, the plates themselves being mounted on a toothed driving hub keyed on to the driving shaft carrying the direct drive, i.e. top speed, one plate being between the flywheel and the floating plate, the other between the floating plate and pressure plate.

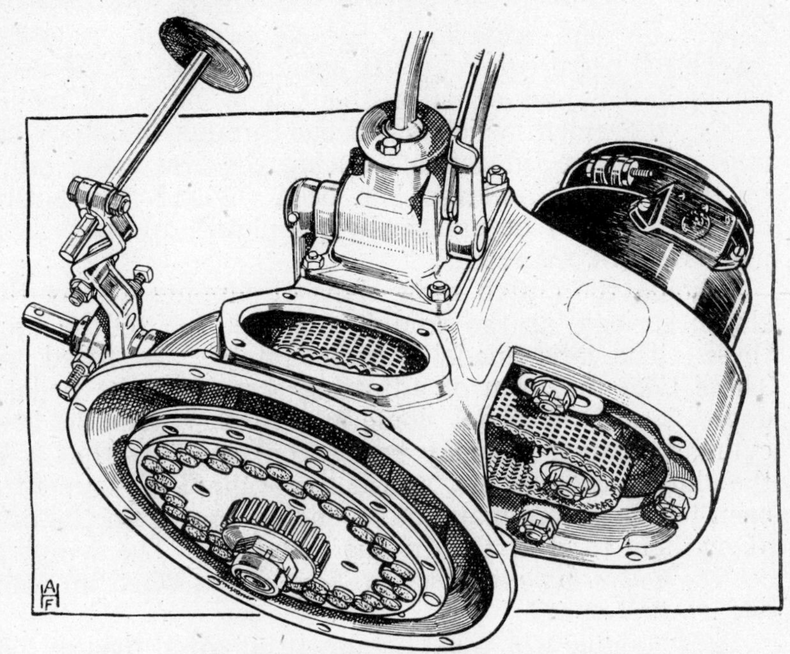

Fig. 329.—The Morris Clutch, Gear Box, and Dynamotor Drive.

Driving pressure for the clutch is derived from helical springs on the driving pins outside the pressure plate. The general construction of the clutch is given in Fig. 330.

The clutch must run in oil. Persistent slipping of the clutch must not be resorted to.

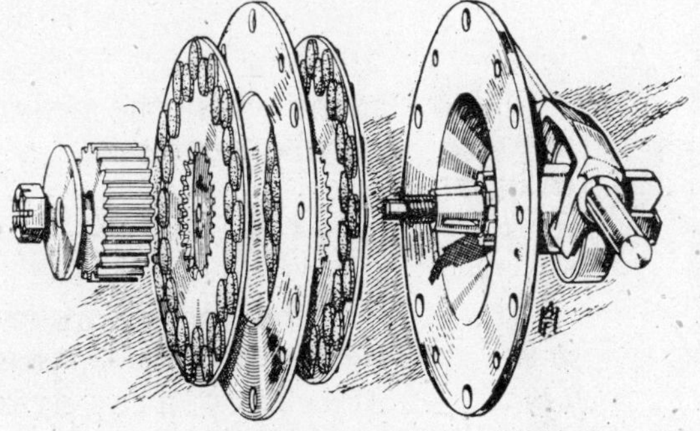

Fig. 330.—The Morris Cork-insert Plate Clutch.

Owing to its granular structure, cork consolidates considerably under pressure. The effect of this in the clutches under consideration is to allow the pressure plate to take up a position closer to the engine flywheel, and as this plate carries the withdrawal hub with which the withdrawal fork engages, and which is attached to the clutch pedal, a corresponding movement takes place in the pedal itself, causing it to come forward and project into the body of the car. There is a possibility that when this happens the clutch pedal may move to such an extent that it touches on the bottom of the slot cut for it in the footboard. Assuming that this has occurred, it will be seen at once that some of the useful tension of the clutch springs will be dissipated at this point instead of being concentrated in keeping the driving and driven plates of the clutch in close contact. The more pressure there is on the footboard the less pressure is available in the clutch, and consequently there is a danger of slip occurring. Special provision is made in the hub of the clutch pedal, whereby the exact position of the pedal in the car can be regulated, and an adjustment here must be made to compensate for any movement which may occur through the above cause. The point is of particular importance during the first 2,000 miles of running, as by the time this mileage has been covered the natural consolidation of the corks will be practically completed, and very little further movement is to be expected.

Should the clutch show signs of slipping at any time, examine the clutch springs, as the trouble may be due to the breakage of one of these. The later model Morris clutches are fitted with *clutch stops.* These take the form of adjusting screws in the pedal arms which, on depression of the pedal, come into contact with the boss formed on the cylinder casting. It may happen on new cars that a slight swelling of the clutch corks occurs, and if the original adjustment of the screw has been too fine there may not be enough travel on the driven members to allow them to clear the driving members. The symptom of this is that *grating noises always occur in the gear box* when an attempt is made to engage first speed.

The trouble will quickly cure itself after the car has been in use a certain time, but it can at once be remedied by giving the adjustment screw two or three turns, bringing the head of it nearer to the pedal arm and thus allowing more movement when the pedal is fully depressed.

Fig. 331.—The Morris Eight Clutch Components.

THE MORRIS EIGHT CLUTCH

The Morris Eight car employs the single-plate dry clutch illustrated in "exploded" view in Fig. 331 and in part cut-away assembled view in Fig. 332.

This clutch runs dry, so that if *persistent slipping* occurs this is an indication of oil having found its way into the clutch compartment;

in this event the cause of the oil leakage is either the engine or gear box—most probably the latter.

If the clutch is allowed to slip continuously the centre driven plate very quickly becomes excessively hot, and the heat and friction will very soon destroy the surface of the fabric facings.

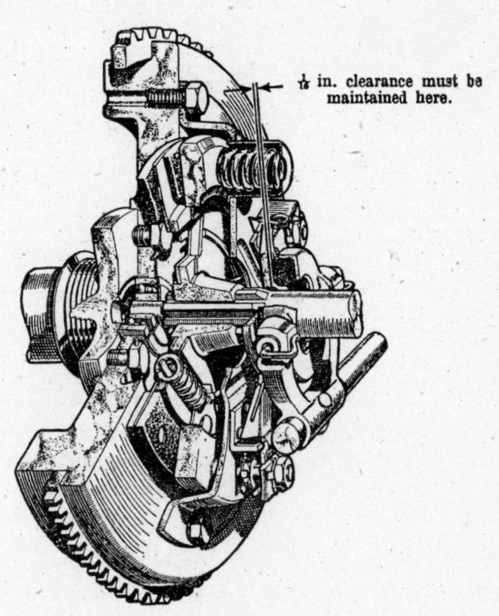

Fig. 332.—The Morris Eight Clutch Assembly.

Morris Eight clutches are correctly adjusted at the Works before the car is delivered. In the early life of the car, however, a certain amount of bedding down of the friction surfaces takes place, which will permit the pressure plate to take up a position nearer the withdrawal mechanism, and thus reduce the necessary clearance between the withdrawal-lever plate and the thrust-bearing. If this clearance is completely taken up, the clutch cannot be fully engaged and clutch slip is produced, which rapidly wears the friction lining and further aggravates the trouble.

The maintenance of an adequate clearance between the thrust bearing and the release-lever plate is an absolute necessity and is the only service attention required by this type of clutch.

The minimum clearance between the withdrawal-lever plate and the face of the thrust bearing is $\frac{1}{16}$ in., which gives a free movement of $\frac{1}{2}$ in. at the clutch pedal.

When the clutch-pedal movement approaches this figure, it is essential to make use of the adjustment provided at the base of the clutch pedal, so that it has ample clearance.

The adjustment consists of a slotted quadrant lever with serrated face, to which the clutch-pedal arm is held by a bolt. Slackening the locking nut enables the clutch pedal to be moved into the desired position, and it is to be noted that the serrated washer between the pedal and the quadrant lever has its serrations offset, so that the adjustment to the extent of half a serration can be obtained by rotating this washer half a revolution.

Take care to tighten up the lock nut after adjusting.

In addition, see that there is not excessive pedal travel, as this will put undue strain on the carbon thrust block. There should not be more than $1\frac{1}{4}$ in. clearance between the pedal arm and its stop on the clutch housing when the pedal is held lightly with the carbon block in contact with the thrust ring. Need for this adjustment is shown when *the engine tends to stop if the clutch pedal is fully depressed.*

Fig. 333.—The Austin Seven Flywheel and Clutch Cover.

A, Flywheel Cover. B, Flywheel showing top dead-centre mark for Nos. 1 and 4 cylinders. C, Clutch-ring lubricator.

The thrust bearing consists of a solid carbon block and it *does not require any lubrication*, but may be damaged if there is too much clutch-pedal travel.

THE AUSTIN SEVEN CLUTCH

The clutch used is of the single-plate dry type. The clutch surfaces must be kept free from oil or grease, otherwise slipping will occur.

The operating ring must be lubricated lightly through the oil hole provided; this is shown at C in Fig. 333. The regular periods for oiling, when the car is in use, are weekly ones.

The oiler can be seen from the driving seat when the rubber mat has been turned back. Press the clutch pedal down a little and the oiler will move forwards to facilitate lubrication.

THE FORD 8-H.P. CLUTCH

This clutch is of the single-plate dry type operated by foot pedal on conventional lines.

The maintenance of this clutch and the method of adjustment are illustrated in Fig. 334. The clutch is also shown sectionally, in Plate facing p. 374.

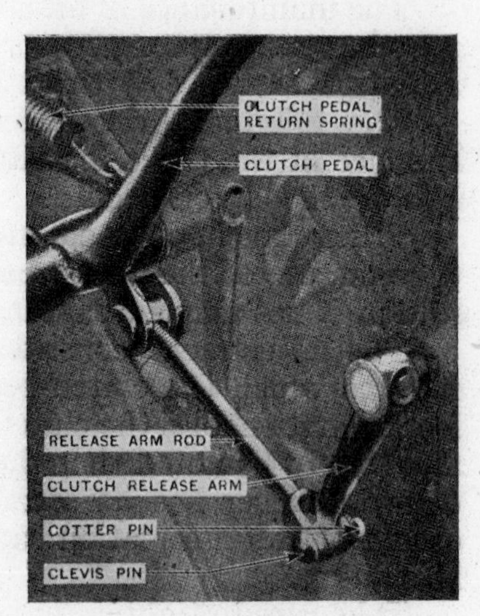

Fig. 334.—Ford Eight Clutch Adjustment.

The clearance between the clutch-release bearing and the clutch-operating fork must be maintained at all times and is indicated by the amount of free movement of the clutch pedal. As the clutch-disc facings become worn, it will be necessary to adjust this clearance. The correct adjustment is when the clutch pedal has 1 in. free movement. This adjustment is easily made by removing the clevis pin (see Fig. 334) and turning the release-arm rod. Screwing out the rod towards the front of the car, by increasing its length, will increase the clutch-pedal free movement. After making the adjustment, be sure to replace the clevis pin and cotter pin.

The clutch springs are set to the required pressure before the car leaves the factory, and under no circumstances should any attempt be made to adjust the pressure by interfering with the setting of the clutch-release fingers.

The *clutch-release bearing* is lubricated by means of a grease cup which is accessible through an opening in the floor immediately in front of the gear box, and connected by a flexible tube to the bearing. The cup should be refilled with grease and then screwed down as far as it will go, once every 1,000 miles.

THE AUSTIN TWELVE CLUTCH

In the case of the Austin Twelve clutch, shown in Fig. 335, the method of taking up the wear is indicated on the illustration. The adjustment should be such as to allow at least ½ in. free movement of the clutch pedal with the fingers.

Lack of this free movement will prevent the clutch from proper engagement owing to the pedal touching the floor, and clutch slip will therefore result.

The adjustment is obtained by slackening the locking bolt E (Fig. 335)

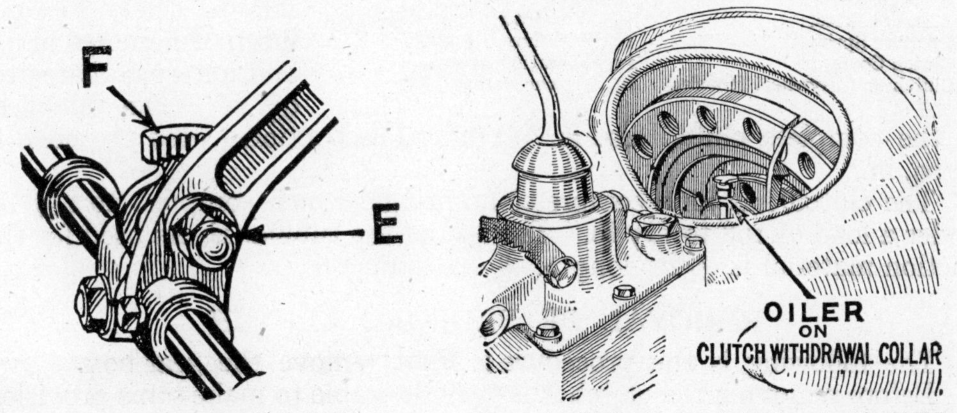

Fig. 335.—Adjustment of Austin Twelve Clutch.

Fig. 336.—Method of Lubricating Austin Clutch Withdrawal Race and Sleeve.

and setting the pedal forward, towards the front of the car, one or two notches on the quadrant F attached to the clutch-operating shaft; then tighten up the locking bolt.

Fig. 336 shows the upper part of the gear-box and clutch-housing casting of the Austin 12-h.p. car, to illustrate the method of lubrication of the clutch-withdrawal race and sleeve. The clutch in question is of the single-plate type.

To lubricate the withdrawal thrust race and the sleeve, the floor-boards should be removed, and lubricant (engine oil) introduced through the spring-lid oiler, situated in the opening over the clutch. This operation should be repeated once every month. Care is necessary to avoid over-lubrication, for any excess of oil may get between the clutch plates and cause them to slip.

DISMANTLING A PLATE CLUTCH

The methods of dismantling plate clutches is similar for most designs, although certain details in different makes may vary. In order, therefore, to explain the methods employed we have taken the case of the well-known Bedford commercial-vehicle clutch and give the procedure adopted, step by step. The inspection and re-assembly of this clutch are afterwards dealt with in a similar manner.

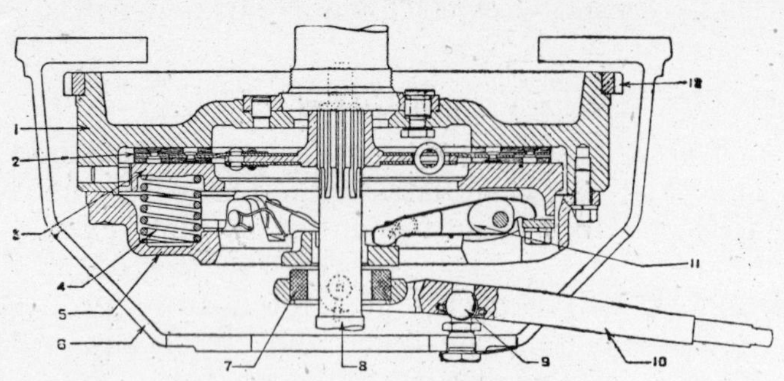

Fig. 337.—Bedford Clutch Assembly.

1, Flywheel.
2, Friction Plate.
3, Pressure Plate.
4, Pressure Springs.
5, Clutch Cover.
6, Clutch and Flywheel Housing.
7, Withdrawal Bearing.
8, Clutch Shaft.
9, Withdrawal-lever Fulcrum.
10, Withdrawal Lever.
11, Operating Levers.
12, Flywheel-ring Gear.

The clutch on this widely used vehicle is of the single-disc pattern and is shown in Fig. 337. The dimensions of the clutch lining are as follows: thickness, $\frac{1}{8}$ in.; internal diameter, $6\frac{1}{8}$ in., and external diameter, $9\frac{7}{8}$ in. The thickness of the complete clutch disc is ·354 in. The frictional area provided is 96 sq. in.

The clutch has nine compression springs, which compress to $1\frac{35}{64}$ in. under a load of 108 to 117 lb. The size of the tubular rivets used for the friction material is $\frac{7}{32}$ in. long $\times$ $\frac{9}{64}$ in. diameter.

REMOVAL OF BEDFORD CLUTCH

The following is the procedure: First remove the gear box.

Before removing the clutch it is very desirable to make some provision for the fact that when the clutch-cover bolts are unscrewed from the flywheel, the pressure of the clutch springs, acting through the medium of the clutch levers, will have the effect of throwing out the withdrawal sleeve at the back of the clutch, and this will be found to prohibit the removal of the assembly except with considerable difficulty, due to the temporarily increased depth of the clutch from back to front.

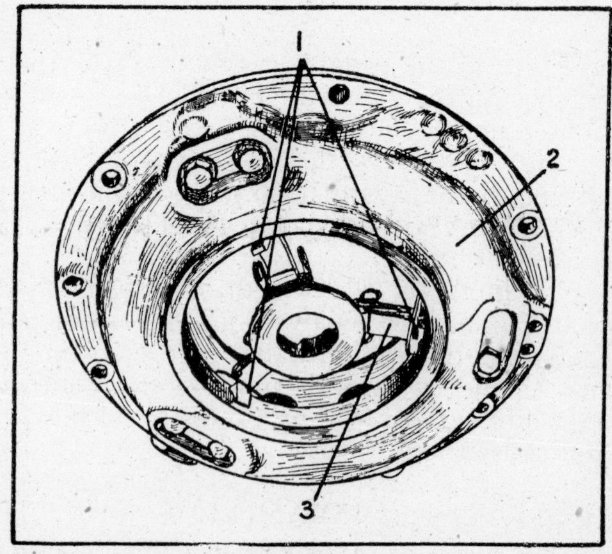

Fig. 338.—Method of Introducing Packing into Clutch when Removing.

1, Packings. 2, Clutch Cover. 3, Clutch-pressure Levers.

Three packing pieces, therefore, should be made up for this purpose and these will be found a valuable accessory when handling clutch repairs. The packing pieces should be cut if possible from $\frac{1}{2}$ in. by $\frac{3}{4}$ in. angle iron and should be $\frac{3}{8}$ in. wide, the $\frac{1}{2}$-in. side being drilled with a small hole capable of accommodating a length of wire or string.

Reference to Fig. 338 will show how these packings should be introduced into the clutch. The $\frac{3}{4}$-in. side of each packing should be inserted between the levers and the cover and pushed home as far as it will go, the clutch pedal being pushed down with the hand, so as to depress the levers and provide the requisite clearance for their insertion.

After the clutch pedal has been used for this purpose, the necessary dismantling can be proceeded with.

Remove clutch fork and withdrawal-bearing assembly.

Remove the clutch inspection cover on the top of the clutch housing.

Mark the cover and flywheel to ensure reassembly in the same relative positions as previously. This is important.

Unscrew, evenly, the six set-screws attaching the clutch cover to the flywheel, withdraw the clutch cover and pressure-plate assembly complete from the flywheel, and lower through the bottom side of the clutch housing.

Lift out the clutch disc.

If an examination of the clutch face in the flywheel shows that this is scored, the flywheel should also be removed for skimming.

TO DISMANTLE

N.B.—The clutch must be dismantled for renewal of the clutch cover, pressure plate, or levers.

Remove the three special springs at the inner ends of the clutch levers by drawing one end out of the small hole into which it is inserted in the withdrawal sleeve and lift off the withdrawal sleeve.

Mark the clutch cover and pressure plate to ensure reassembly in the same relative positions as formerly. This is important.

Place the cover and pressure-plate assembly under a press, the clutch cover upwards, and apply light pressure to the cover through the medium of a bar placed across its top face.

Remove the three special packing pieces inserted between levers and cover.

Undo the six bolts attaching the clutch-lever withdrawal plates to the pressure plate, particularly noting the location and quantity of any shims which are found under the plates, as these must be replaced in the same position as formerly when reassembling the clutch.

Relieve the pressure on the press, remove the assembly to the bench, and lift the clutch cover off the pressure plate.

Turn the clutch cover over and remove the three levers from the cover. The method of carrying this out is quite straightforward, but the operator should particularly note the method of assembly of the three special springs close up to the fulcrum pins, which are fitted for the purpose of preventing the clutch levers rattling.

TO INSPECT

Inspect the clutch face of the flywheel and pressure plate and if scored these should be skimmed up in a lathe. With regard to the flywheel, the necessity for skimming will entail the removal of the three dowels fitted inside the flywheel rim which drive the pressure plate. These may be driven out from the outside of the flywheel rim.

Where a cut of appreciable depth has to be made across the flywheel face, it is very important to note that a cut of corresponding depth must be taken across the machined face to which the clutch cover is bolted, as otherwise it is impracticable to set the clutch adjustment correctly when the whole clutch is reassembled, without the use of an unnecessarily large number of shims under the lever-withdrawal plates.

Check for seized or stiff levers on their pins or for excessive wear on the tips of the levers. In cases where the amount of wear is small, it will be found satisfactory to stone down the tips of the levers, but if excessive, the levers must be renewed. Similarly, excessive wear in the lever holes or on the shank of the lever pins must be rectified by renewal.

Check the clutch springs for weakness or fracture. To do this, place all the springs on a surface plate and lay a straight-edge across them ; discard all short springs.

Inspect for *excessive wear in withdrawal-sleeve slots.*

Inspect the clutch-disc assembly for *worn linings or excessive wear in the splines.* The latter may be checked by inserting the front end of a new gear-box main-drive gear into the clutch hub and testing for play.

With worn linings, the service engineer must decide whether to replace the linings only or the clutch-disc assembly entirely.

If the *clutch-disc hub splines show excessive wear,* a new disc assembly should be fitted.

Inspect the *clutch-spigot bearing* in the crankshaft for wear ; if any appreciable wear is found, renew the bearing. It is a good plan to *lubricate this spigot bearing* whilst the clutch is removed, with a high melting-point grease.

Check the *pressure plate in the flywheel* and make sure by trial that the plate moves freely on the flywheel dowels and on its outer diameter in the flywheel without appreciable play.

Clutch "judder" is often due to the fact that the pressure plate is not free on these locations and hence tends to engage jerkily when the clutch pedal is released.

It is important to keep the clutch in balance. For this purpose the clutch assembly should not be more than 1 in. ounce out of balance ; i.e. no more than a weight of 1 oz. at a radius of 1 in.

REASSEMBLING THE BEDFORD CLUTCH

In connection with the reassembly of the clutch, reference should be made to Figs. 337 and 339. Lubricate the lever pins and lever sparingly with graphite grease and reassemble the levers to the clutch cover. The special springs which are fitted between the levers and the clutch cover should be so fitted that the straight portion of the spring lies across the back of the levers, i.e. facing the operator when looking at the back of the clutch.

Place the withdrawal sleeve in position over the inner ends of the levers, machined face upwards, and introduce the special springs at this end so that the coils of the springs tend to *close up* when the withdrawal bearing is depressed. It will be seen that it is possible to fit these springs the wrong way round, so that the coils relax under these conditions and some of the value of the springs is thereby lost.

Fig. 339.—Clutch, and Method of Checking Withdrawal Sleeve Face.

1, Dial Indicator.
2, Clutch-pressure Lever Spring, Outer.
3, Clutch-withdrawal Sleeve.
4, Clutch-pressure Lever Spring, Inner.
5, Clutch-pressure lever.
6, Clutch-pressure Lever Withdrawal Plate.
7, Clutch Cover.
8, Clutch-cover Bolt.
9, Withdrawal-plate Screw.

Place the main-clutch springs in position around the back face of the pressure plate.

Place the clutch cover over the pressure plate with the location marks matched up and bolt down the withdrawal plates over the ends of the levers, taking great care to ensure that the shims under the plates are replaced in the same position as formerly.

At this stage it is very desirable that the rear face of the clutch withdrawal sleeve be checked to ensure that it runs true, or is, in other words, square with the back face of the clutch cover. It will be appreciated that the shims under the clutch-cover plates affect this condition and are fitted for the purpose.

To carry out this check, it is essential for the flywheel to be removed, and even though removal may in some cases be undertaken specially for this purpose, the additional time involved is well spent. To ensure accurate results the repairer should machine in the lathe a disc corresponding in thickness, internal and external diameters to a complete clutch-disc assembly; it will be found that a discarded pressure plate forms a very suitable basis from which to machine this disc. If conditions do not permit of this being done, a new clutch-disc assembly from parts stock may be used, but owing to minor variations of thickness over the linings which are inevitable in such a disc, the results will not be of such a high standard as would be obtained with a specially made disc.

The disc should be placed in the flywheel and the clutch cover together with the pressure plate bolted up after it, care being taken to tighten the cover bolts evenly. A discarded piston or some similar form of distance piece which has dead true top and bottom faces should then be placed in the centre of a surface plate and the flywheel front face which bolts to the crankshaft flange placed upon it. A dial indicator supported in a scribing block should be used for checking over the face of the withdrawal sleeve, noting that the sleeve should be pressed firmly on to the lever tips before checking. Fig. 339 illustrates the method of checking.

The maximum variation in height between any two points on the withdrawal-sleeve face must not be more than ·003 in. Having fulfilled the necessary conditions, the cover may then be unbolted from the flywheel to allow of removal of the special disc used for checking.

The clutch is then ready for replacement.

TO REPLACE THE CLUTCH

Place the clutch disc in the flywheel with the longer side of the hub boss to the front.

Place the cover and pressure-plate assembly under a press and apply pressure to the withdrawal sleeve until it is possible to reinsert the packing pieces between the levers and the cover.

Push the clutch cover and pressure-plate assembly up into the clutch housing and locate the pressure plate on the flywheel dowels in the same relative position as before, so that the marks made by the mechanic on the flywheel and clutch cover line up.

Replace the clutch-cover set-screws.

Replace clutch fork and withdrawal-bearing assembly.

Replace clutch-top inspection cover.

Depress the clutch pedal and remove the special packings between the levers and the cover.

Before attempting to replace the gear box it is necessary to centralise the clutch disc, as the diameter of this is smaller than the internal diameter of the flywheel and it is therefore likely that when bolting up the clutch cover the disc may become "sandwiched" between the pressure plate and flywheel, in an eccentric position.

BEDFORD CLUTCH TROUBLES AND THEIR CAUSES

The following are the probable causes of the clutch troubles which may be likely to arise after long periods of service :

CLUTCH FIERCE

1. Broken pressure plate.
2. Pressure plate does not slide freely on dowels.
3. Flywheel out of truth.
4. Clutch disc faulty.
5. Clutch linings badly worn.
6. Pedal sticking.

CLUTCH SLIPS

1. Clutch linings badly worn.
2. Clutch springs weak.
3. Clutch-pedal adjustment incorrectly set.
4. Broken pressure plate.

CLUTCH JUDDERS

1. Pressure plate does not slide freely on dowels or in flywheel.
2. Clutch-lever plates incorrectly shimmed.
3. Broken pressure plate.
4. Clutch linings badly worn.

CLUTCH SPINS WHEN RELEASED

1. Clutch-lever plates incorrectly shimmed.
2. Faulty clutch-spigot bearing.
3. Faulty clutch disc.

EXCESSIVE WEAR ON WITHDRAWAL BEARING

1. Clutch-pedal adjustment incorrectly set.
2. Driver rides clutch pedal.

THE LEYLAND SINGLE-PLATE CLUTCH

A typical example of a well-designed heavy-duty clutch of the commercial-vehicle type is shown in Fig. 340. The clutch in question is that fitted to Leyland vehicles, e.g. the "Tiger," "Titan," and "Buffalo" chassis.

The arrangement of the clutch is such that no internal adjustment is required except when resetting to obtain the full amount of pedal movement. This adjustment is effected by means of a hand nut on the clutch pedal, accessible through the cab floorboards.

The arrangement of the clutch is shown in Fig. 340. The clutch disc consists of a sheet-steel disc guaranteed true, to which are riveted, by means of hollow brass rivets, the two friction linings.

To prevent any possibility of clutch slip in service a heavy spring pressure is used, the total load on the clutch being 1,440 lb. in the case of passenger and light goods machines, and 1,860 lb. in the case of heavy goods machines. An exceptionally large wearing surface is provided, the total area of the friction linings being 252 sq. in.

The clutch cover plate, A, Fig. 340, is spigoted into the flywheel, the set-screws B being so pitched that the plate can only be replaced in one position to avoid the possibility of inadvertently replacing with the T.D.C. line in the wrong position.

The clutch unit is carried on the cover plate A and on an extension tube C, bolted to the plate, is carried the withdrawal race assembly.

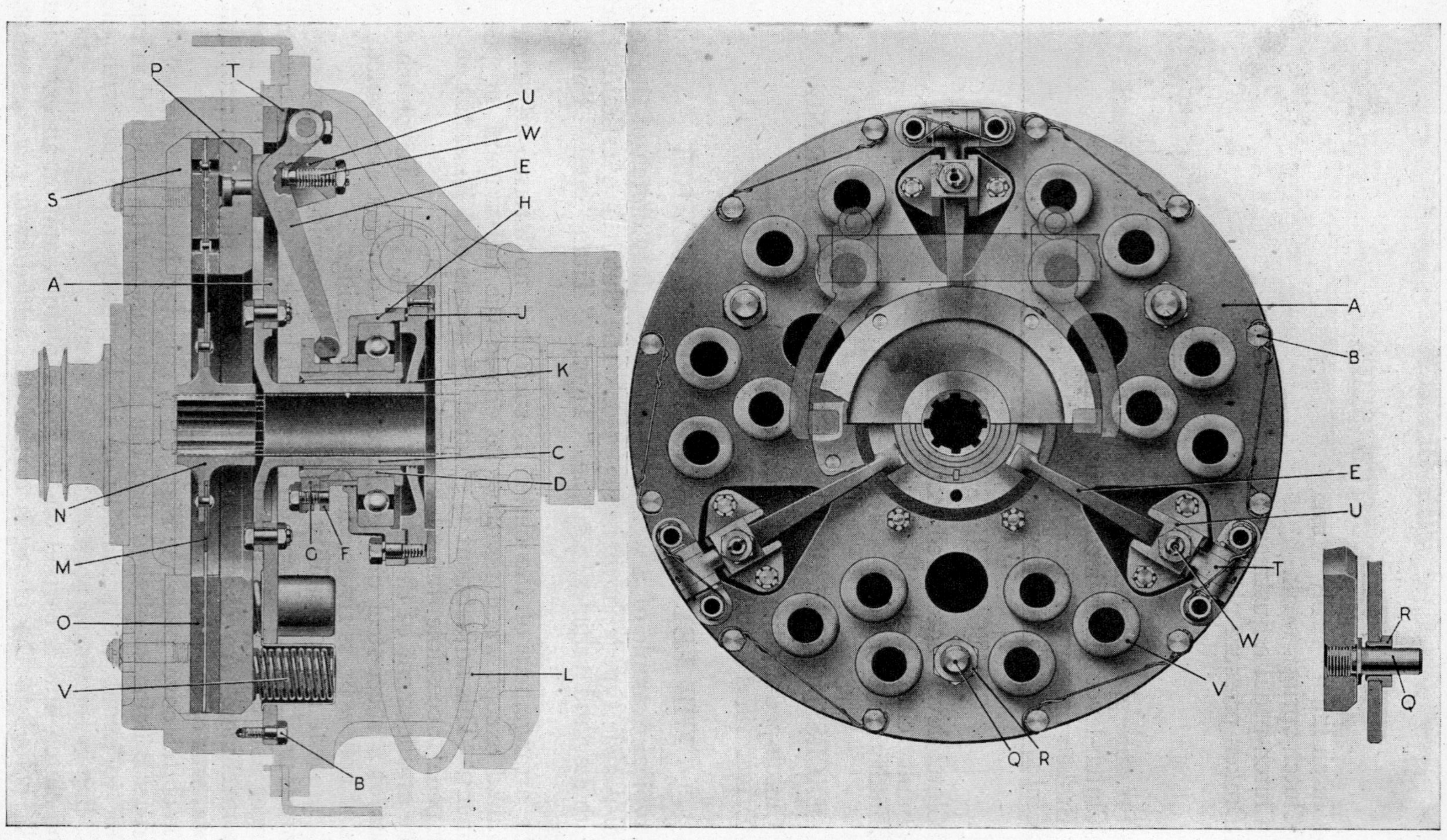

Fig. 340.—The Leyland " Titan " Plate Clutch in Side-sectional and End Views.

The inner sleeve D is bushed and free to slide endways on the tube C, rotation of the sleeve with the withdrawal levers E being effected by the pad ends of the fingers locating in slots formed in the flange F on the outer sleeve, which is keyed to the inner sleeve. The ball-race and outer sleeve are locked on the inner sleeve by the screwed collar G, the collar being locked to the flange F by a set-screw and tab washer. The outer ring of the ball-race is a press fit in the housing H which totally encloses the ball-race. Oil loss from the housing is prevented by a cork-and-linen joint at J and oil-retaining grooves at K. Lubrication of the withdrawal race is effected by means of a flexible pipe, L, which connects the housing with a Tecalemit nipple of the lubrication battery.

It is important that after the withdrawal assembly has been down for inspection the cork-and-linen joint J is replaced, a new one being fitted if the original one is damaged.

A friction ring is riveted to the rear face of the withdrawal race housing, and this, being prevented from rotating by the toggle levers, is utilised as the fixed member of the clutch stop.

The clutch disc M is riveted to the hub N, and has riveted to it the friction linings O. The splined hub is mounted on the extension of the combined shaft and pinion, the end of this shaft being centralised in the flywheel by a ball-race. The end of the shaft is well tapered to allow easy entry when replacing the gear-box unit. The ball-race is retained in the flywheel by means of a sheet-metal cover attached to the flywheel by set-screws; a paper packing is fitted between the cover and the flywheel, loss of grease from the spigot recess being thus prevented.

The clutch pressure plate, P, made from a special alloy cast-iron, is located on the cover plate by dowel pegs, Q, screwed and riveted in the pressure plate; these pegs locate in bushes, R, screwed and riveted into the cover plate. *It is essential that the pegs should have a clearance of $\frac{1}{16}$ in. in the bushes* R. It should also be noted that when new bushes, R, are fitted and the clutch relined, a clearance of at least $\frac{3}{32}$ in. should be allowed between the bush and the shoulder on the dowel peg Q. The bushes must be filed after riveting over, if necessary, to obtain this clearance. When the clutch linings are new the pegs Q should project $\frac{3}{4}$ in. through the bushes R; when this projection is reduced to $\frac{1}{8}$ in. the lining is completely worn out, it is therefore advisable to reline at $\frac{1}{4}$-in. projection.

An insert, S, secured by four studs in the flywheel ensures that replacement can be effected without damaging the flywheel. The withdrawal levers E, operated by the withdrawal collar, pivot on three fulcrum pins carried in the fulcrum brackets, T, secured on the cover plate by special nuts which also retain the pins in the brackets.

These levers, E, pass through the lifting brackets U, a hardened pad in the lever bearing on the hardened end of the adjusting set-screws.

Eighteen springs, V, supply the necessary pressure at the clutch faces; in the case of heavy goods vehicles double concentric springs are used. All holes in the pressure plate which come in contact with the friction linings are carefully rounded off to prevent damage to the disc, and when plates are removed for skimming up these radii must be well defined.

The housing of the clutch-withdrawal race is utilised as the fixed member of the clutch stop, the rear face being lined with friction lining. This engages with a disc fitted on the clutch shaft which is the spinning member. The clutch should be adjusted so that when the clutch is normally disengaged the clutch stop faces do not come in contact.

NORMAL CLUTCH ADJUSTMENT

Ordinary adjustment on all models is effected by means of the hand-nut on the clutch pedal. As wear occurs on the linings, the tips of the withdrawal levers will come nearer to the clutch cover A, Fig. 340. When these levers have taken up the maximum position further life can be obtained from the clutch lining by resetting the adjusting screws W on the lifting brackets U. When resetting by means of these adjusting screws, it will be necessary to unscrew the hand nut to bring the clutch-withdrawal race into its correct position—that is, within $\frac{1}{2}$ in. of the clutch stop face.

It is essential that there should always be approximately 1 *in. of free travel on the clutch pedal, when the clutch is in engagement.* It should be noted that when adjusting the clutch by means of the hand nut, the nut should be "unscrewed" to give the necessary clearance.

In case of clutch slip :

(1) See that the pedal is not fouling the floorboards.
(2) See that the pedal lever is free.
(3) See that the three withdrawal levers are clear and bearing evenly.
(4) Wash out the disc with petrol.
(5) Burn the clutch by slipping.

THE LEYLAND CLUTCH PEDAL

A clutch-pedal stop is now fitted to all vehicles. This stop takes the form of an adjusting screw in the pedal arm which, on depression of the pedal, comes into contact with a boss formed on the cylinder casting. Occasionally it may happen on absolutely new cars that slight swelling of the clutch material occurs, and if the original adjustment of the screw has been very fine there may not be sufficient travel on the driven members of the clutch to allow them to clear the driving members. The symptom of this is that grating noise always occurs in the gear box when an attempt is made to engage first speed. The trouble will speedily right itself when the car has had a little use, but can be immediately remedied by giving the adjusting screw two or three turns, bringing the head of it nearer to the pedal arm and thus allowing more movement when the pedal is fully depressed.

THE MEADOWS CLUTCH

In view of the different cars which have been fitted with the Meadows type of single-plate clutch, it may be of interest to give some particulars of this clutch—shown in Fig. 341—and to point out its method of adjustment and maintenance.

The most popular form is the 14-in. diameter model, but a 16-in. type is used on larger engines.

These plate clutches are of the single dry-plate type. Pressure is applied by 12 springs equally disposed round the circle, giving a total pressure of 1,500 lb., according to spring-adjustment conditions. An adjustment for wear of the friction linings is provided by fine-threaded screws, the nuts on which form the abutment for the three clutch-actuating levers. These linings are of exceptional width. A self-contained thrust bearing is provided for the withdrawal and this bearing is mounted on the hub of the back plate so that there is no relative movement to cause wear. The clutch hub is splined to S.A.E. Standard No. 10 C. 1½ in. diameter, 10 splines, to suit standard types four-speed gear-box stem pinion (primary shaft).

The driven member is a hardened and ground steel plate mounted on a hardened-steel hub, and is as light as is consistent with strength. A clutch stop is fitted on the primary shaft. Wear of the friction rings until they are down to the rivet heads is automatically taken up and does not affect the drive, but only the position of the clutch pedal. This is compensated for by the adjustment on the back-plate studs.

When the clutch pedal is released the sliding sleeve should always occupy the same position in relation to the flywheel. This position, of course, is altered by wear.

In making any adjustment the important point to note is that when the abutment ends of the three clutch-operating levers are in contact with the nuts on the back-plate studs and the lower ends are engaged in the sliding sleeve, this sleeve should engage with equal contact on each lever end. A feeler gauge should be employed in setting the nuts to the upper end of the levers.

The nuts have a fine thread and three slots and the studs are cross-drilled so that not more than a 30° movement need be made. If this fine adjustment is carefully made so that the pressure is uniform over the whole surface of the friction rings, a perfectly sweet clutch engagement will result.

MAINTENANCE POINTS

This clutch is very smooth, will transmit the full torque of the engine under all conditions without tendency to slip, gives no trouble, is easily relined and is practically everlasting, as all the parts, including the flywheel, are made from steel stampings.

Do not slip clutch excessively instead of changing gear. With the

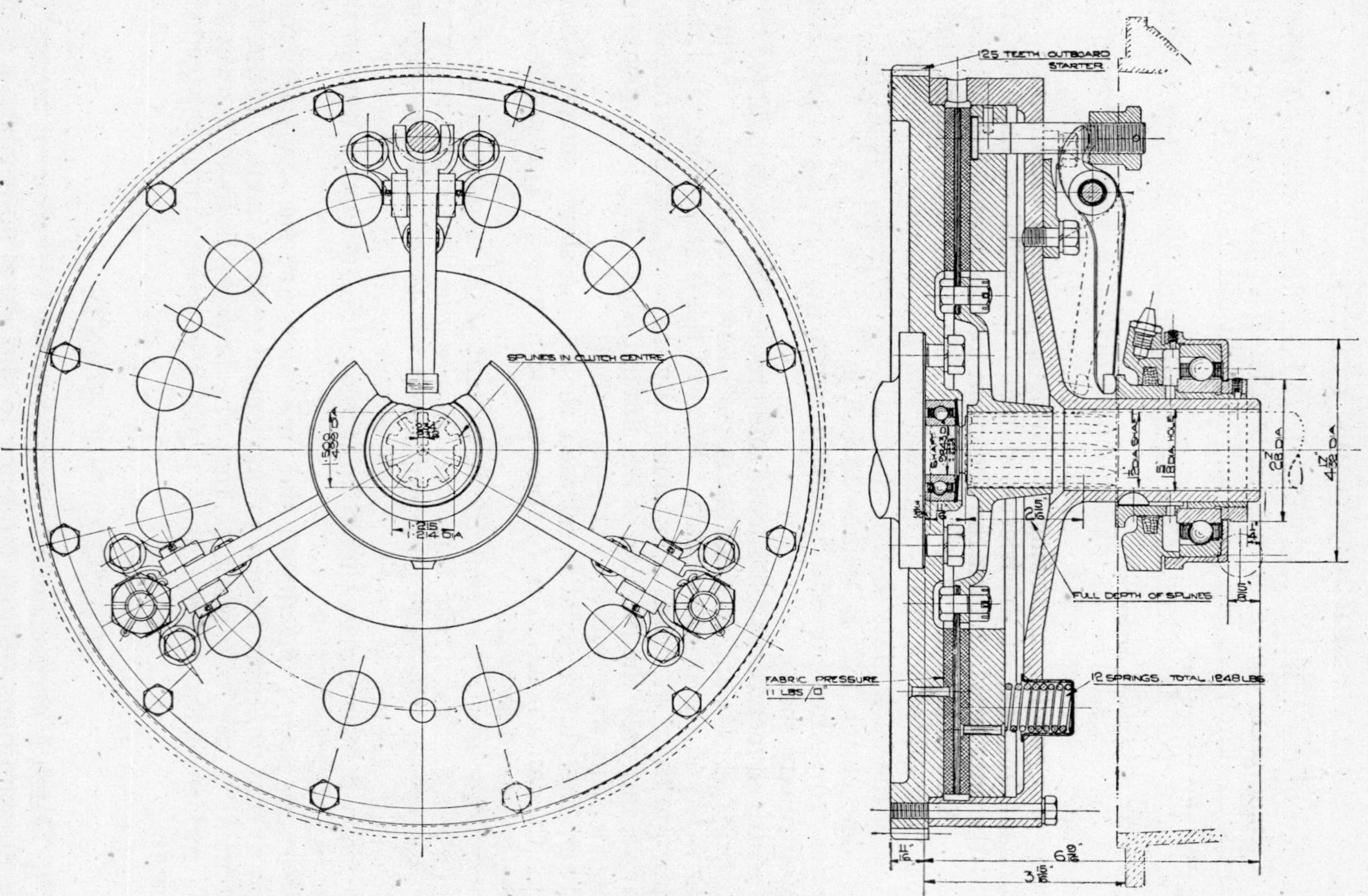

Fig. 341.—The Meadows Clutch.

easy-changing four-speed gear box such as the Meadows type, there is no excuse for this and it is not good for the clutch.

Do not drive with foot on clutch pedal, as this clutch is very light in operation owing to its great leverage.

If clutch slips, examine at once to see if friction rings are worn down to the rivet heads ; a slipping clutch means an overheated engine.

If the clutch does not disengage freely and gear change is difficult, wash out with paraffin.

The Singer car dry single-plate clutch is shown in Fig. 342. When

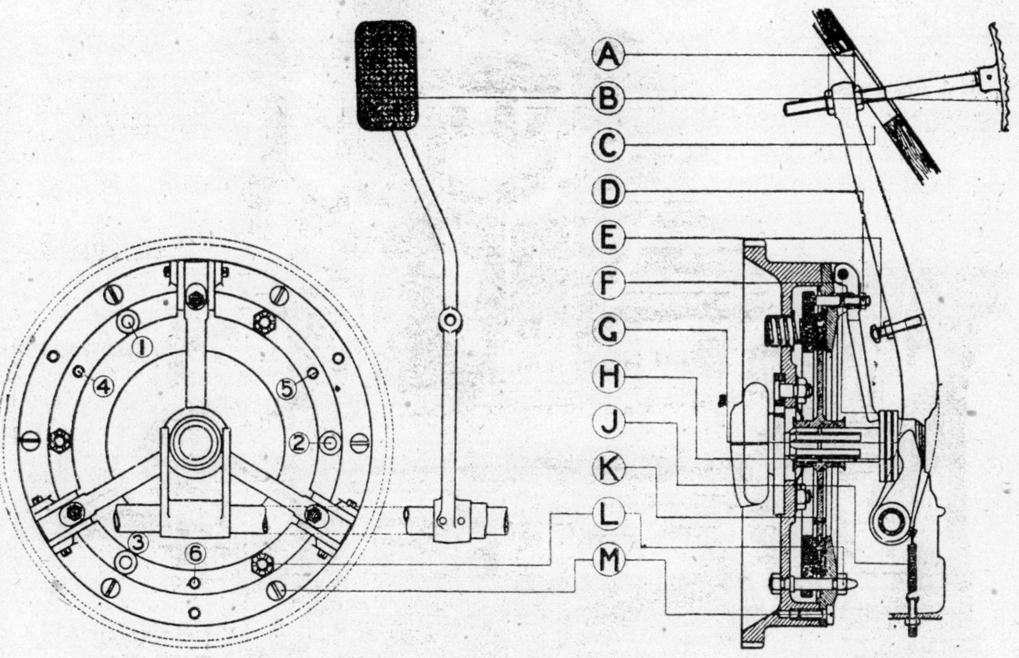

Fig. 342.—Illustrating Adjustments and Maintenance of Dry Single-plate Clutch.

the car has been in use for a lengthy period, the clutch may show a tendency to slip. This will probably be due to the taking up of the clearance originally allowed at points F, Fig. 342, as a result of wear in the fabric linings. A clearance of $\frac{1}{32}$ in. must be maintained between lever and thrust race F, by means of screw and lock nut D. It is also important that there should always be clearance at points C and G. The clutch-pedal stop E stops on engine arm to prevent excessive clutch movement, and should need no further adjustment. The spring J brings pedal out of engagement with the thrust race. The pedal pad B can be adjusted by unscrewing nuts A, screwing up pad to the desired position and locking up nuts again. The thrust race H is normally lubricated from the gear box, but should occasionally be covered with a film of grease. In the case of fierce clutches, it is permissible to insert a small quantity of thin machine oil through holes 1, 2, and 3 (left-hand illustration). Thick oil must not be used.

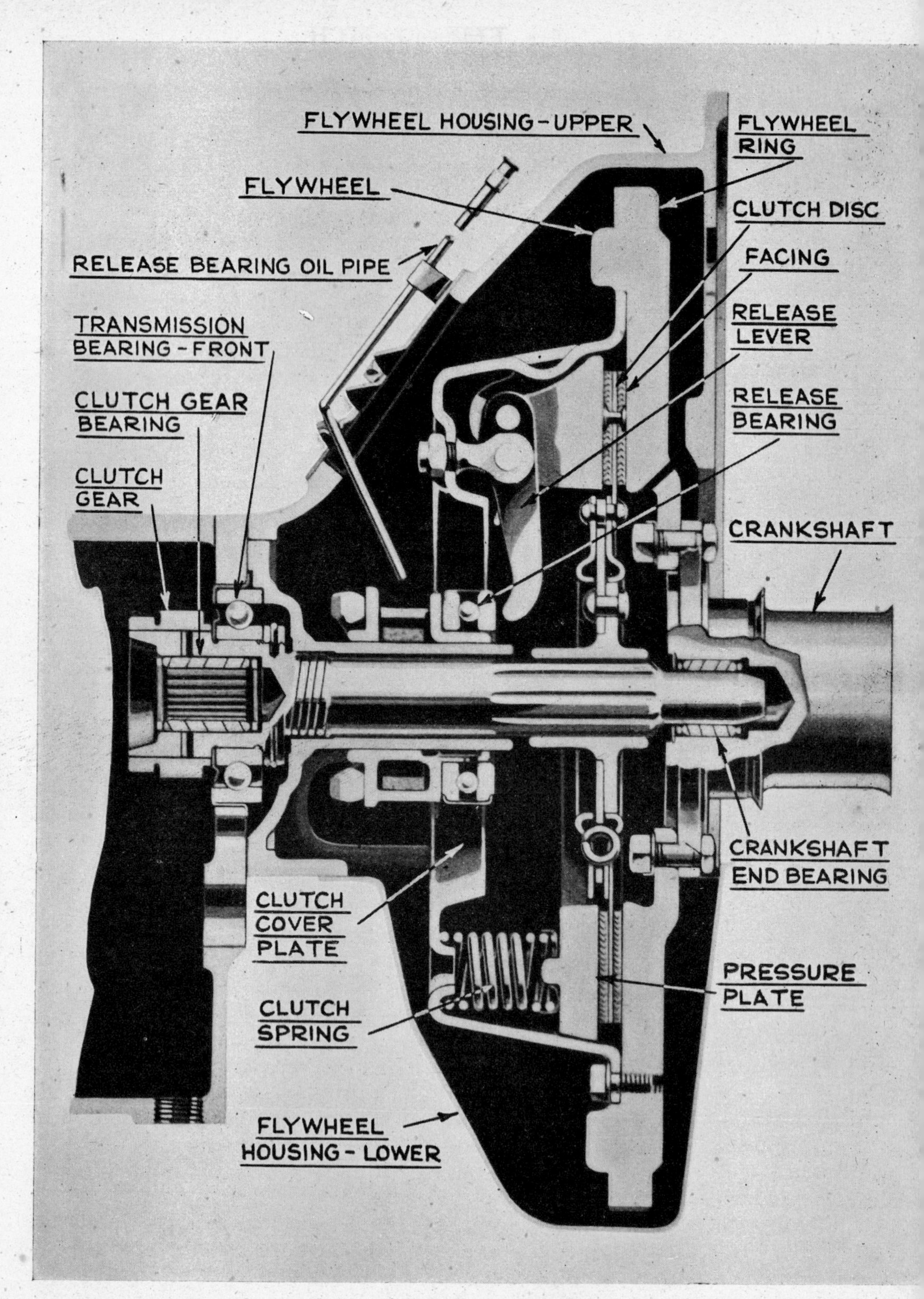

Fig. 343.—A Typical Dry Single-plate Clutch, showing various Components and Items of Maintenance.

To Dismantle Clutch.—This is best effected by the following sequence of operations :

(1) Remove screws M and screw three of them into holes 1, 2, and 3 to preserve concentricity of clutch plates. (2) Withdraw split-pins and unscrew three nuts L, and draw off clutch complete. (3) If new fabric linings are required, take out the three screws M from holes 1, 2, and 3 and the clutch plates K will be released.

To Reassemble the Clutch.—(1) Assemble the clutch plates with three screws M in holes 1 2, and 3. (2) Insert this assembly into flywheel, screw the remaining three screws M equidistantly into the outer ring of holes in the clutch. Screw up nuts L and put in split-pins. (3) Remove the three screws M from holes 1, 2, and 3 and screw into holes 4, 5, and 6, which will force the back plate against the springs, and thus allow the centre plate to float for centring purposes. (4) Replace gear box. (5) Remove screws M from holes 4, 5, and 6 and insert into the remaining outer holes in clutch plate. (6) Adjust the clutch to previous instructions.

MULTIPLE-PLATE CLUTCHES

The Morris six-cylinder engine car clutch is shown in Fig. 344 in an " exploded " view.

The clutch provides four friction surfaces. The driving surfaces comprise (*a*) the rear face of a pressure plate, (*b* and *c*) both faces of a floating plate, (*d*) the forward face of the flywheel cover plate. Eight clutch driving pins pass through the flywheel, the floating plate, the pressure plate, and the cover plate, all of which consequently revolve with the engine.

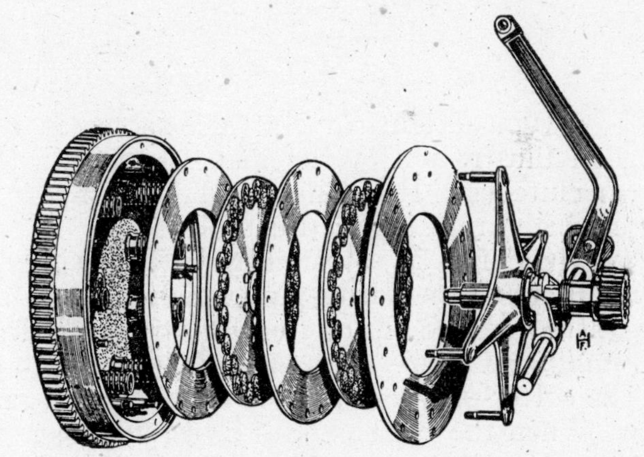

Fig. 344.—Showing Components of the Morris Multiple-plate Clutch.

The driven surfaces comprise a double line of cork insets in two duralumin plates, the plates themselves being mounted on a splined driving hub engaging the driven shaft, one plate being between the pressure plate and the floating plate, the other between the floating plate and cover plate.

Driving pressure for the clutch is derived from helical springs housed between the flywheel and the pressure plate.

The clutch must run in oil. Persistent slipping of the clutch should not be encouraged.

Owing to its granular structure, cork consolidates considerably under pressure. The effect of this, in the clutches under consideration, is to allow the pressure plate to take up a position closer to the engine flywheel cover plate, and as this plate is connected with the withdrawal spider with which the withdrawal fork engages, and which in turn is attached to the clutch pedal, a corresponding movement takes place in the pedal itself, causing it to come upwards and project into the body of the car. There is a possibility that when this happens the clutch pedal may move to such an extent that it touches on the bottom of the slot cut for it in the footboard. Assuming that this has occurred, it will be at once seen that some of the useful tension of the clutch springs will be dissipated at this point instead of being concentrated in keeping the driving and driven plates of the clutch in close contact. The more pressure there is on the footboard the less pressure is available in the clutch, and consequently there is a danger of slipping. Special provision is made at the bottom of the clutch pedal whereby the exact position of the pedal in the car can be regulated, and an adjustment here must be made to compensate for any movement which may occur through the above cause. This point is of particular importance during the first 2,000 miles of running, as by the time this mileage has been covered the natural consolidation of the corks will be practically completed, and very little further movement is to be expected.

The clearance between the pedal and its stop should be set to approximately $1\frac{3}{4}$ in., and there should be at least $\frac{3}{8}$ in. to $\frac{1}{2}$ in. clearance between the pedal arm and floorboard.

A LIGHT-CAR PLATE CLUTCH

A typical light-car clutch is shown in Fig. 345. This will serve as a good illustration of the method of adjustment of these smaller model car clutches. It belongs to the single-disc fabric-faced type, the springs of which are readily adjustable.

The clutch is adjusted in the following manner :

Remove the cotter-pins which lock the spring nuts A, when the latter can be screwed up or slacked off as required. Care must be taken *that equal turns are given to the nuts* in order to equalise the spring pressures. The cotter-pins should then be replaced.

When the car has been in use for a lengthy period, the original clearance allowed between the clutch fork and withdrawal ball-race housing at B may have disappeared, due to wear in the fabric clutch facings, thus causing the clutch to slip. A minimum clearance of $\frac{1}{32}$ in. must be maintained between these points, which can be effected by slacking off the set-screw C the desired amount and then tightening up the lock nut.

Clutch and brake-pedal adjustment may be carried out by slacking off nut D and screwing foot pads in or out as required, afterwards relocking nut D.

In regard to the clutch lubrication, the clutch pressure plate moves on three driving studs, E, which should be lubricated every 500 miles.

The centre driven plate sliding on the constant-pinion spline shaft at F and the clutch-withdrawal ball-race at G should be also lubricated after the same period.

The hole G is normally concealed by the clutch fork, but by pressing down the clutch pedal this is exposed to view.

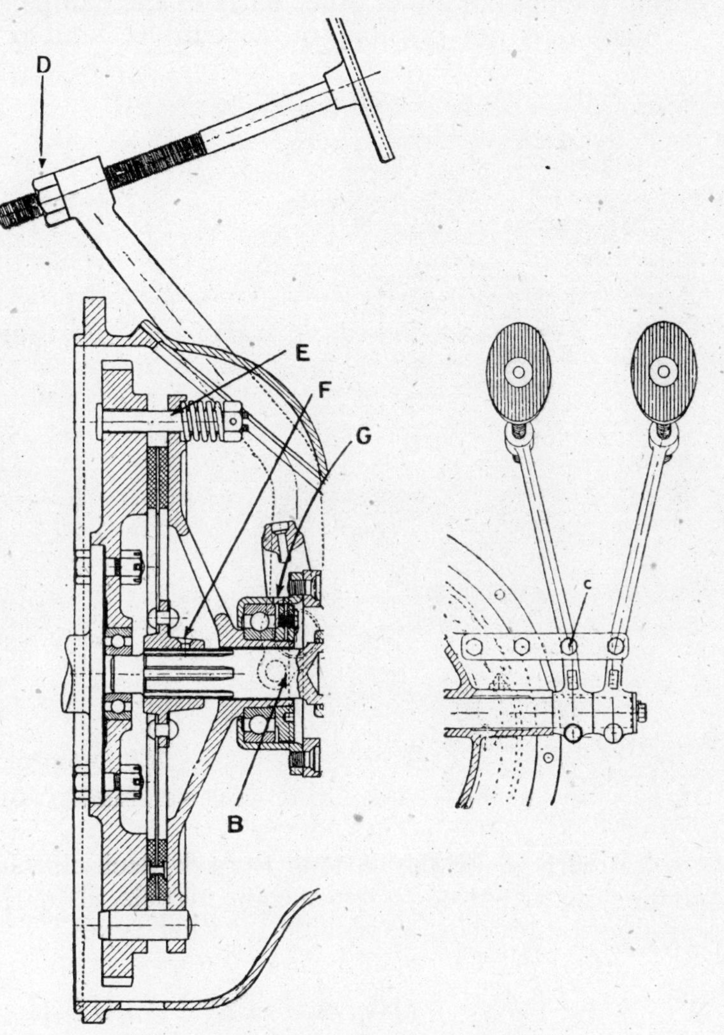

Fig. 345.—A Typical Light-car Plate Clutch.

THE BORG & BECK CLUTCHES

These clutches, which are now widely used on cars and commercial vehicles of different makes, are available in several models and sizes, suitable for either "open" or "unit" construction and with release bearings of either the graphite or ball-bearing type. The clutches are of the single-plate pattern with a central steel plate having rings of frictional material on each side. Sometimes the plate is of solid construction and is riveted on to the splined member engaging with the gear-box main shaft; in other cases it is of the flexible-plate pattern shown in Fig. 346 (right).

This clutch plate combines the full-contact cushion feature of the "plain" or "rigid" type driven plate with a coil-spring vibration dampener of improved construction. The purpose of the dampener is to eliminate or break up torsional vibrations originating either in the engine or transmission system and thus prevent what is commonly called "Transmission Noise, or Rattle." The use of half-round lock wires to retain the coil springs in slots, which are formed in both the enlarged hub flange and the driven members, permits the use of much larger springs than formerly possible and in most cases these large springs are capable of transmitting the entire torque of the engine without danger of breakage during the normal life of other parts of the dampener and plate.

Since it is not possible, on account of limited space considerations,

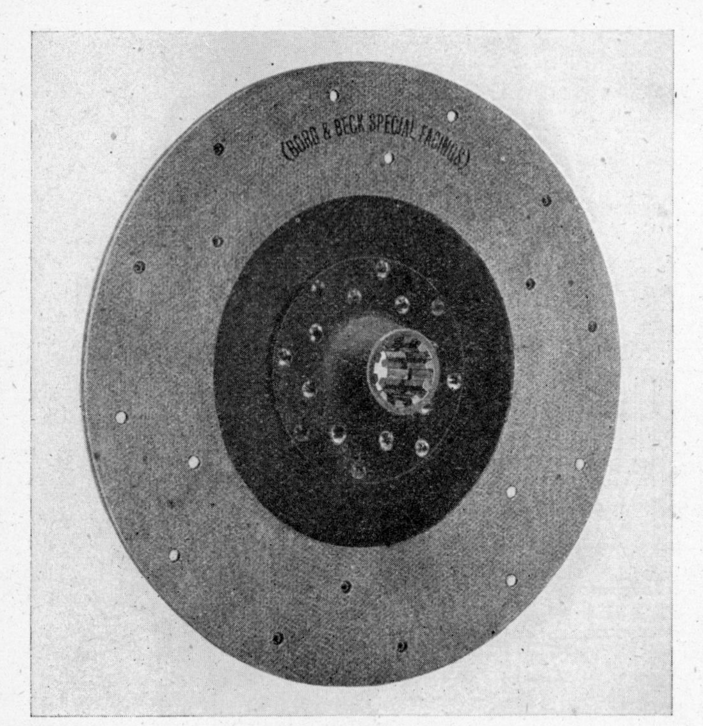

Fig. 346.—Types of Clutch Plate. Left, Solid Pattern. Right, Flexible Pattern.

to deal with all of the various Borg & Beck clutch models here we shall confine our attention to two specific models, although much of the general information given is applicable to other types.

THE A.G.-TYPE CLUTCH

The clutch (Fig. 347) is of the single-plate dry-disc type, no adjustment for wear being provided in the clutch itself. An individual adjustment is provided for locating each lever in manufacturing, but the adjusting nut is locked in place by means of special tag-lock washer, and should never be disturbed, unless the clutch is dismantled for replacement of parts.

A graphite release bearing (7) is used, mounted in a cup (8) attached to throw-out fork, and a release plate (10) is attached to inner ends of release levers (12) by means of retainer springs (11). Release is accomplished by moving release bearing forward against the release plate (10). The release levers are pivoted on knife-edge fulcrums (13) mounted upon clutch cover (4) and at their outer ends shoulder studs (15) extend through holes and are fitted with adjusting nuts (16) by which each lever is located in correct position. The outer or shorter ends of the release levers engage the bearing plate (17) carried upon the shoulder studs (15) attached to pressure-plate lugs, and thus the pressure plate (18) is pulled away from

Fig. 347.—Borg & Beck (Type A.G.) Clutch.

the driven plate (3) compressing the several small coil springs (5) which are assembled between the pressure plate and the clutch cover (4).

When the foot pressure is removed from clutch pedal the clutch springs force the pressure plate forward against the driven plate, gradually and smoothly applying the power of the engine to the rear wheels.

As the clutch facings wear, the pressure plate moves closer to the flywheel face and the outer or shorter ends of the release levers follow. This causes the inner or longer ends of the levers to travel farther towards the gear-box and decreases the clearance between the release-lever plate and the release bearing. The effect on clutch pedal is to decrease the clearance or free travel under toe board, which is the distance clutch pedal moves down away from the underside of toe board before release bearing comes in contact with release-lever plate. Some free movement must always be maintained to prevent clutch pedal riding against underside of the toe board and causing clutch to slip. This free movement is restored by adjusting the clutch pedal.

TO ADJUST CLUTCH PEDAL

All cars are provided with one or more adjustments on the clutch pedal or pedal shaft, and these should be adjusted in accordance with instructions supplied by the car manufacturer. In general, proceed as follows, referring to Fig. 348.

Adjust the pedal away from the underside of the toe board until clearance or free movement is approximately $\frac{3}{4}$ in. (Fig. 349). The pedal pad should come in contact with the top of the toe board when pedal is pressed down. If it does not move that far, making it necessary to spring pedal to make pad touch toe board, further adjustment is necessary. These instructions apply where the vehicle manufacturers do not provide a pedal stop.

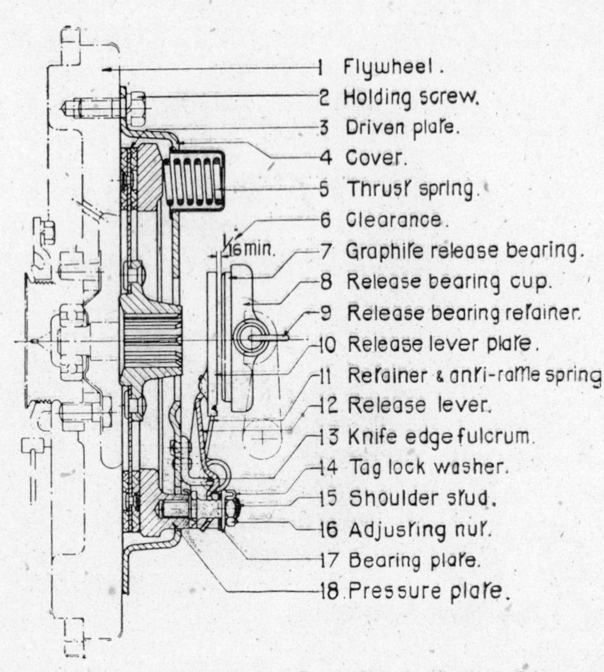

Fig. 348.—The Borg & Beck Clutch (Type A.G.).

When this adjustment has been made, a minimum clearance of $\frac{1}{16}$ in. (6) (Fig. 348) between graphite release bearing and release-lever plate *should* be obtained.

Press pedal down and note distance release bearing travels after it comes in contact with release plate. To obtain a clean release, the lever plate should be pushed towards the flywheel $\frac{1}{4}$ in. for $6\frac{1}{4}$-in. A types. If it does not travel that distance move pedal up, bearing in mind that pedal pad must touch toe board as above when pressed down for full clutch release.

No other adjustment is necessary. *Do not* turn the adjusting nuts (16),

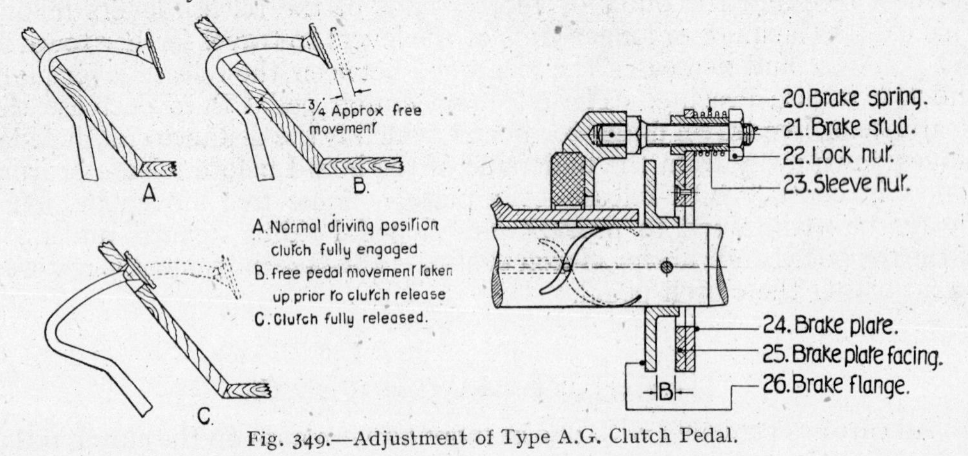

Fig. 349.—Adjustment of Type A.G. Clutch Pedal.

because that will throw pressure plate out of position and cause clutch to chatter.

A clutch brake is provided when required, by fitting to the clutch shaft a flange (26) Fig. 349 (right-hand diagram) which, when the clutch pedal is depressed, is brought into contact with a brake plate (24) fitted with renewable facings (25) and carried by the release-bearing housing.

The brake plate is carried by sleeve nuts (23) working on studs (21) fitted to the release-bearing housing and is held in position by springs (20) secured by the nuts (22) which lock the sleeve nuts (23).

With the clutch in the engaged position, the distance (B) Fig. 349 (right-hand diagram) between the brake-plate facing and the flange should be maintained at $\frac{3}{8}$ in. in the 12R type and $\frac{7}{16}$ in. in the 14R, 14R2, and 16R types. Any adjustment necessary can be made by adjusting the sleeve nuts (23) after slacking off the lock nuts (22), care being taken to tighten up the lock nuts after adjustment.

SERVICING THE BORG & BECK CLUTCH (TYPE A.G.)

To remove clutch from the flywheel (1) it is necessary to remove the holding screws (2) (Fig. 348). Loosen each of holding screws a turn or two at a time until the spring pressure is relieved (this should be carefully done to prevent springing the flanged edge of cover). The screws can then be removed and the complete clutch lifted off the flywheel, all parts except driven plate (3) (Fig. 348) being assembled to the cover.

If it is found necessary to replace parts of the cover assembly it can be dismantled, reassembled, and adjusted with the aid of an arbor press or drill press as follows :

1. After first straightening the bent-up arms of tag-lock washer (14), place the cover on the bed of the press with wooden blocks under the

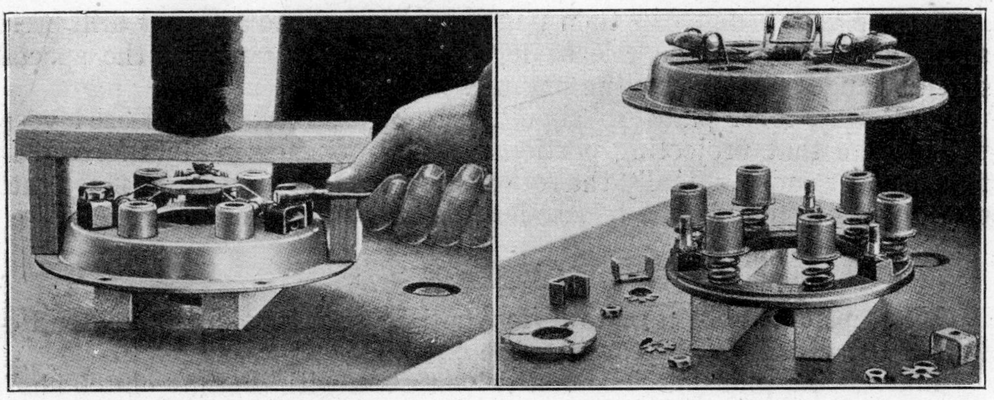

Fig. 350.—Showing the Use of Wood Blocks in Dismantling Clutch.

Fig. 351.—Reassembling the Clutch.

pressure plate so arranged that cover is left free to move down. Place three blocks of wood to form a bridge, the legs of which should rest on the outer rim of clutch cover as shown in Fig. 350.

2. Compress the cover with the spindle of the press and holding it

under compression, remove the adjusting nuts (16) (Fig. 348) and then slowly release the pressure to prevent the springs from flying out.

3. The cover can then be lifted off and all parts will be available for inspection. It is advisable to replace any parts which show wear.

TO REASSEMBLE CLUTCH

1. Lay the pressure plate (18) (Fig. 348) on the block in the press and place the springs on it in a vertical position, seating them on the small bosses on the pressure plate, afterwards placing spring cups over their outer ends as shown in Fig. 351.

2. The levers (12) can then be mounted on the knife-edge fulcrums (13) by slipping the inner ends of release levers under the retainer spring (11) taking care that the release levers are properly seated (see Fig. 351). It is advisable to wipe the short end of the lever and the knife-edge fulcrums with a little graphite moistened with oil, as this will help to eliminate friction within the clutch.

3. The cover can then be laid on top of the assembled parts, as shown in Fig. 351, taking care that machined portions of pressure-plate lugs are directly underneath the slots formed in clutch cover.

4. The three blocks of wood to form a bridge should then be placed in the same position as previously and the assembly slowly compressed, the pressure-plate lugs being guided through the slots formed in clutch cover. Care must be taken that the thrust springs remain correctly in their seats on the pressure plate.

5. Holding the clutch under compression, the bearing plate (17) and tag-lock washer (14) are then placed in position on shoulder stud (15) (refer Fig. 348), adjusting nut (16) can then be screwed down on the shoulder stud until the nut is flush with top of stud.

6. The clutch unit can then be removed from the arbor or drill press and final setting of the release levers obtained by use of the special service gauge supplied by the manufacturers.

7. Release-lever plate (10) should then be assembled to release levers, taking care that projecting portions properly engage in slots formed in release-lever ends. Finally the retaining springs (11) should be fitted into the grooves formed in the release-lever plate as indicated in Fig. 348.

CAUTION

When placing driven plate in flywheel be sure that chamfered end of hub of the drive plate is towards the outside.

Line up the pilot bearings and driven plate with dummy clutch shaft before tightening clutch-cover holding screws. Tighten holding screws before pulling out dummy shaft.

THE LONG CLUTCH TYPE 9 C.F.

This is a unit type of clutch used in passenger and commercial vehicles. It will transmit 150 lb. ft. torque (maximum). The clutch-release lever

Fig. 352.—Long Type (9 C.F.) Borg & Beck Clutch.

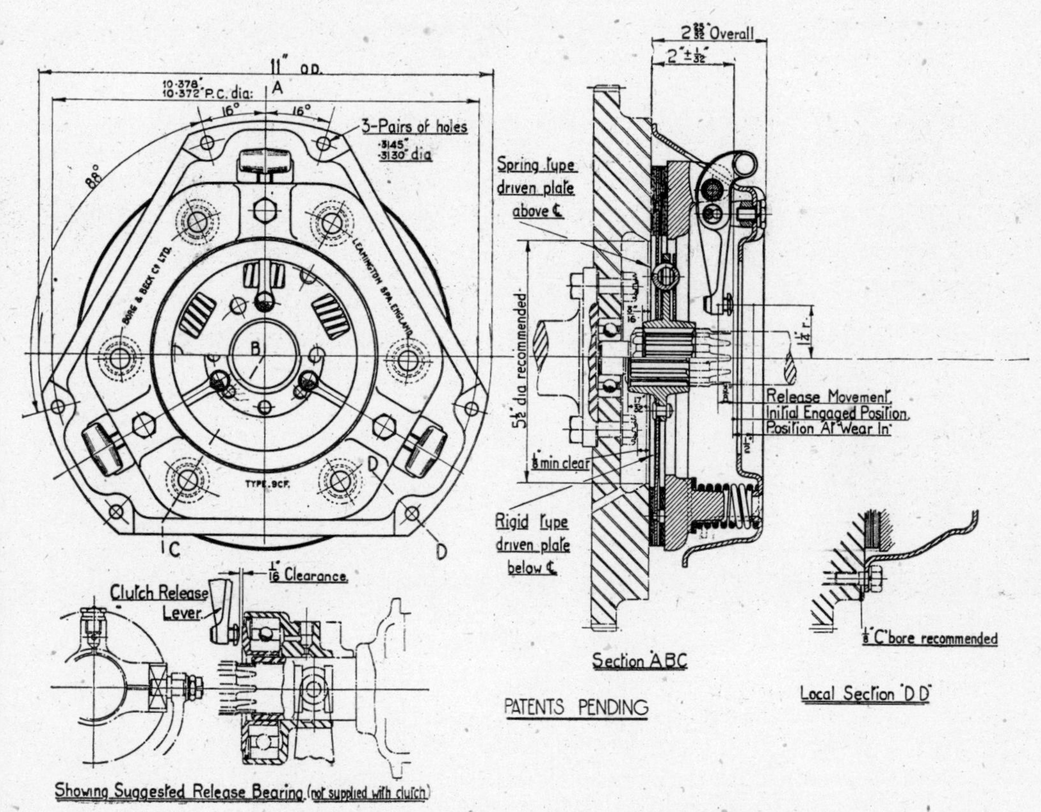

Fig. 353.—The Long Type (9 C.F.) Borg & Beck Clutch.

ratio is 3·9 to 1. The release-bearing travel to release clutch is $\frac{3}{8}$ in. (minimum).

The release-pedal ratio is 8 or 10 to 1.

The pressure required to release the clutch is about 250 lb. on the release bearing.

The total weight of the clutch is 14 lb. 8 oz., and radius of gyration, 3·45 in. This clutch is suitable for speeds up to 5,000 r.p.m. It has a flexible-type friction disc plate, as shown in Fig. 352 and three release toggle levers. A sectional view of the clutch is given in Fig. 353.

THE BORG & BECK TYPE R CLUTCHES

These heavier pattern clutches are of the single-disc type, a sectional view being given in Fig. 354 and photographs of the four-lever toggle assembly in Figs. 355 and 356.

The release-lever sleeve (12) in the case of the ball-bearing type, or

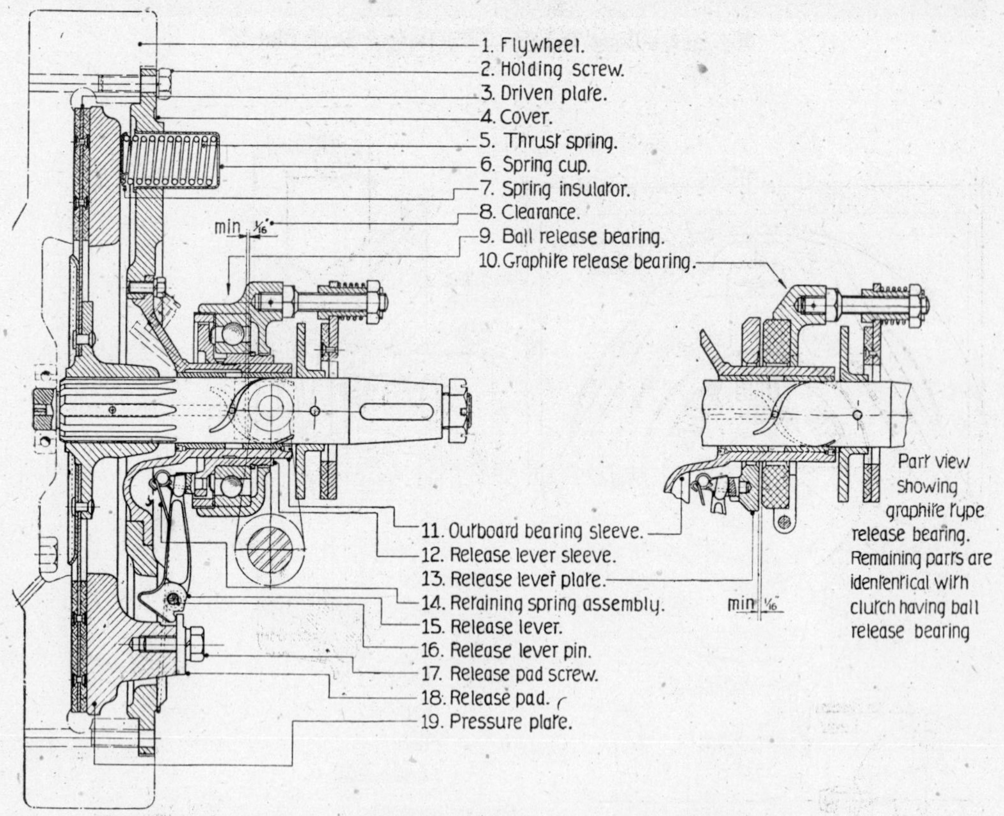

Fig. 354.—The Heavy (Type R) Borg & Beck Clutch.

the release-lever plate (13) in the case of the graphite-bearing type, is held in contact with the inner ends of the release levers (15) by means of the retaining-spring assembly (14). The release levers are mounted on pins (16) carried in lugs formed on the clutch cover (4), the pins being locked in position by coils formed in the retaining-spring assembly. The outer ends of the levers bear against release pads (18) which are secured to lugs on the pressure plate (19) by means of release pad screws (17). A number of coil springs (5), carried in spring cups (6), are fitted between the cover and the pressure plate, thus providing the necessary driving pressure. Spring insulators (7) are fitted between the springs

Fig. 355.—Part-sectioned Type R Borg & Beck Clutch.

and the pressure plate to protect the springs should the pressure plate become excessively heated.

When the clutch pedal is pressed down the release bearing in turn pushes the inner ends of the release levers forward. The outer ends of the release levers moving to the rear pull the pressure plate away from the driven-plate assembly (3), permitting a positive, clean release.

When the foot pressure is removed from the clutch pedal, the clutch springs force the pressure plate forward against the driven plate, gradually and smoothly applying the power of the motor to the rear wheels.

To allow full engagement of the clutch, it is essential that there shall be some free movement between the pedal mechanism and the pressure-plate actuating mechanism when the clutch is in the engaged position.

Fig. 356.—External View of Type R Borg & Beck Clutch.

To ensure this, a clearance of not less than $\frac{1}{16}$ in. must be provided between the pedal-lever arms and the trunnion pads on the release-bearing cover in the case of the ball-bearing type, or between the faces of the bearing and the release-lever plate in the graphite-bearing type.

As the clutch facings wear, the pressure plate moves closer to the fly-wheel face and the outer or shorter ends of the release levers follow. This causes the inner or longer ends of the levers to travel farther towards the gear box and decreases the release-bearing clearance and free pedal movement (or clearance under the toe board) referred to above. This free movement must be restored by adjustment of the clutch pedal.

ADJUSTING CLUTCH PEDAL

All cars are provided with one or more adjustments on the clutch pedal or pedal shaft, and these should be adjusted in accordance with instructions supplied by the car manufacturer. In general, proceed as follows, referring to Fig. 354.

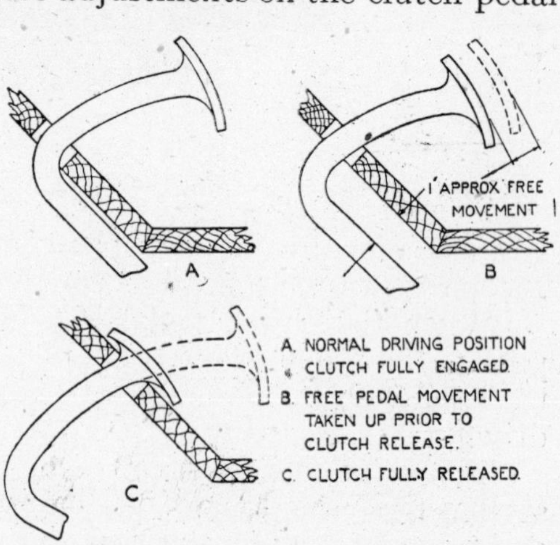

Adjust the pedal away from the underside of the toe board until the free movement is approximately 1 in. (Fig. 357), this corresponding to a clearance at the release bearing of not less than $\frac{1}{16}$ in. (see 8, Fig. 354).

Press pedal down and note distance release bearing travels after the release-bearing clearance has been taken up. To obtain a clean release, the inner ends of the levers should be pushed towards the fly wheel $\frac{1}{2}$ in. for 12R and $\frac{9}{16}$ in. for 14R and 16R units.

1" APPROX FREE MOVEMENT

A. NORMAL DRIVING POSITION CLUTCH FULLY ENGAGED.
B. FREE PEDAL MOVEMENT TAKEN UP PRIOR TO CLUTCH RELEASE.
C. CLUTCH FULLY RELEASED.

Fig. 357.—Adjustment of Type R Clutch.

When release-lever plate has travelled this amount and no more, pedal should be in contact with pedal stop, if provided, or alternatively pedal pad should be down to toe board so that no further travel is possible. If such is not the case the pedal must be moved down, or the stop adjusted so that this condition is obtained, since overtravel of the release bearing leads to close coiling of the thrust springs and brings undue stress on the internal parts of the clutch.

No other adjustment is necessary in the 12R and 14R types. *Do not* turn the screws (17), because that will throw pressure plate out of position and cause clutch to chatter.

The wearing thickness of the facings of the 14R2 and 16R types is greater than that of the 12R and 14R types, and provision is made to accommodate the wear by readjusting the clutch when the facings are half-worn.

When the facings are half-worn the release bearing will have moved away from the flywheel approximately $\frac{1}{2}$ in. from its initial engaged position. The position of the mechanism should then be readjusted to its initial engaged position by reversing the pressure-plate release pads (18), these pads being provided with a step which, when the pads are in the engaged position, allows the outer ends of the levers to move the requisite distance farther from the flywheel.

When this adjustment for facing wear is made, it will be necessary to readjust the clutch pedal, taking care that the minimum release-bearing clearance of $\frac{1}{16}$ in. is maintained.

SERVICING THE TYPE R CLUTCHES

To remove clutch from the flywheel (1) it is necessary to remove the holding screws (2) (Fig. 354). *Do not disturb* release-pad screw (17). Loosen each of holding screws a turn or two at a time until the spring pressure is relieved. The screws can then be removed and the complete clutch lifted off the flywheel, all parts except driven plate (3) (Fig. 354) being assembled to the cover.

If it is found necessary to replace parts of the cover assembly it can be dismantled and reassembled with the aid of an arbor press or drill press as follows:

1. Disconnect the retaining-spring assemblies (14) from the release-lever plate (13) or sleeve (12) and remove the release-bearing mechanism.
2. Place the cover on the bed of the press with wooden blocks under the pressure plate, so arranged that cover is left free to move down. Place three blocks of wood to form a bridge, the legs of which should rest on the outer rim of clutch cover, making sure the wood blocks clear the outboard-bearing sleeve (11) if so fitted.
3. Compress the cover with the spindle of the press, and holding it under compression remove the release-pad screws (17) and then slowly release the pressure to prevent the springs from flying out.
4. The cover can then be lifted off and all parts will be available for inspection. It is advisable to replace any parts which show wear.

TO REASSEMBLE CLUTCH

1. Lay the pressure plate (19) (Fig. 354) on the block in the press and place the insulators (7) and springs on it in a vertical position, seating them in the small grooves on the pressure plate, afterwards placing spring cups over their outer ends.

2. The levers (15) can then be mounted on the cover (4) by inserting the pin (16), afterwards locking same in position by means of retaining-spring assembly (14). It is advisable to wipe both ends of the lever and the pin (16) with a little graphite moistened with oil, as this will help to eliminate friction within the clutch.

3. The cover can then be laid on top of the assembled parts, taking care that machined portions of pressure-plate lugs are directly underneath the slots formed in clutch cover.

4. The three blocks of wood to form a bridge should be then placed in the same position as previously and the assembly slowly compressed, the pressure-plate lugs being guided through the slots formed in clutch cover. Care must be taken that the thrust springs remain correctly in their seats on the pressure plate.

5. Holding the clutch under compression the release pad (18) and lock washer are then placed in position so that screws (17) can be securely screwed hard down in pressure-plate lug (refer to Fig. 354).

6. The clutch unit can then be removed from the arbor or drill press and remainder of release mechanism added.

7. Finally the retaining springs (14) should be fitted into the holes drilled in the release-lever sleeve (12) or release-lever plate (13) as indicated in Fig. 354.

Note.—When placing driven plate in flywheel, be sure that chamfered end of hub of the drive plate is towards the outside.

Line up the pilot bearing and driven plate with dummy clutch shaft on unit-construction type before tightening clutch-cover holding screws. Tighten holding screws before pulling out dummy shaft.

The following precautions should be observed :

Do not under any circumstances let gear box hang in clutch assembly during removing or refitting of gear box to engine.

Do not drive with foot on clutch pedal.

Do not slip clutch excessively instead of changing gears, as this causes rapid wear of clutch facings.

Do not put oil, grease, or paraffin in the clutch. Keep facings dry and free from oil.

CHECKING CLUTCHES FOR MISALIGNMENT

It is important to ensure that clutches should be correctly lined up, as misalignment causes rapid wear on the splines of the clutch, puts undue stress on the driven member, and may result in the hub breaking loose from the plate. It is also responsible for worn retractor collars and levers and may be the cause of fierce chattering or dragging.

If considerable backlash occurs or if the clutch drags it is advisable to remove the gear box and clutch and to check the flywheel housing with a dial indicator as shown in Fig. 358.

Mounting A as shown by Fig. 358 for flat flywheels and mounting B

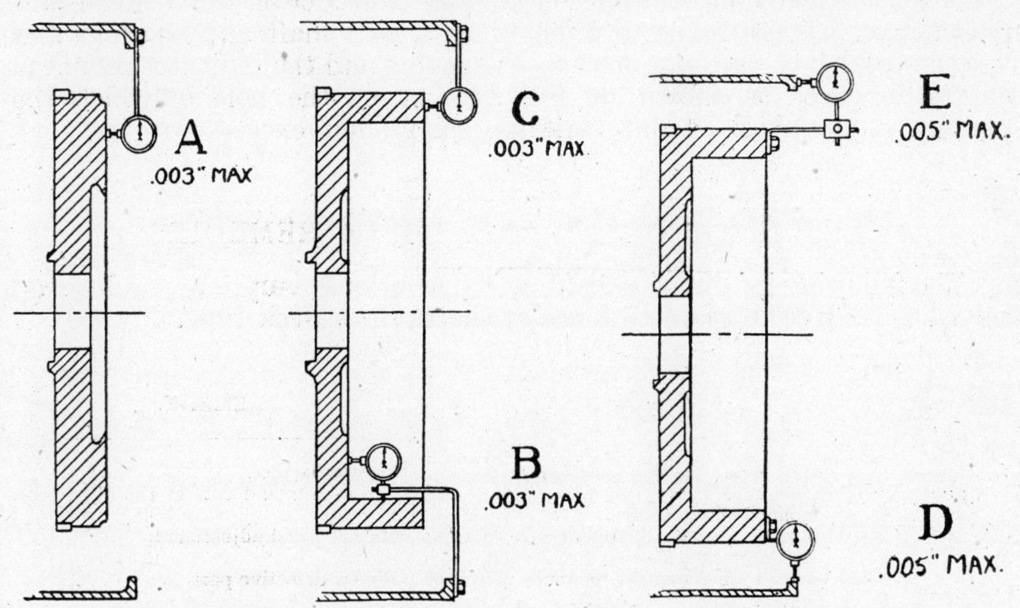

Fig. 358.—Illustrating the Various Methods of Checking Clutches for Misalignment.

as shown by Fig. 358 for recessed type of flywheel are used to determine run-out on friction face of flywheel and should not exceed ·003 in. Proper machining of this face is a necessity to satisfactory operation of the clutch. Mounting C as shown by Fig. 358 shows correct method of checking rear face of flywheel. Run-out should not exceed ·003 in., as the clutch cover is mounted on this surface.

When the gear-box bell housing is centred by the inside diameter of the engine housing it is essential that this be concentric with the flywheel, and run-out should not exceed ·005 in. Fig. 358 shows mounting of indicator for this check. (Refer to mounting D.)

It is also important that the rear face of the engine housing be parallel with the flywheel face, and this run-out, as indicated by mounting E, Fig. 358, should not exceed ·005 in.

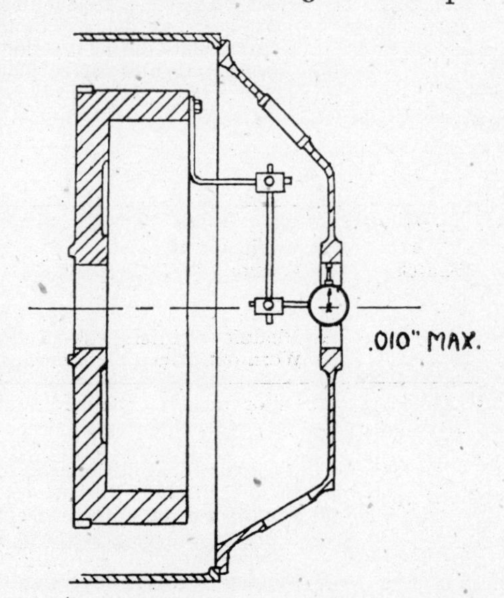

Fig. 359.—Method of Checking Misalignment when Dowel Pins are used for Locating Bell Housing.

If the run-out of either of these faces exceeds ·005 in. they should be remachined to correct this. The use of shims to correct such error should be discouraged, as proper machining is the only permanent cure.

The engine should be turned over slowly by hand to obtain readings.

When the gear-box bell housing is located by dowel pins instead of a pilot flange, it is advisable to remove the clutch shaft and bearings and with the gear-box case mounted on the engine and the indicator mounted on the flywheel, as shown by Fig. 359, check the hole in which the bearing is mounted. Total variation should not exceed ·010 in.

CLUTCH TROUBLES AND THEIR REMEDIES

The following information relates to the various symptoms, causes, and remedies relative to plate clutches of the Borg & Beck type.

SYMPTOM.	CAUSE.	REMEDY.
1. Drag or Spin.	(*a*) Oil or grease on the driven-plate facings.	Fit new facings.
	(*b*) Misalignment between the engine and splined clutch shaft.	Check over and correct the alignment.
	(*c*) Improper pedal adjustment not allowing full movement to release bearing.	Correct pedal adjustment.
	(*d*) Warped or damaged pressure plate or clutch cover.	Renew defective part.
	(*e*) Driven-plate hub binding on splined shaft.	Clean up splines and lubricate with small quantity of "Gredag" or similar lubricant.
	(*f*) Pilot bearing or bushing of clutch shaft binding.	Renew or lubricate pilot bearing.
	(*g*) Distorted driven plate due to the weight of the gear box being allowed to hang in clutch plate during erection.	Fit new driven-plate assembly.
	(*h*) Broken facings of driven plate.	New facings required.
	(*j*) Dirt or foreign matter in the clutch.	Disassemble clutch from flywheel and clean out the unit with dry rag, also see that all working parts are free. *Caution :* Never use petrol or paraffin for cleaning out clutch.
2. Fierceness or Snatch.	(*a*) Oil or grease on driven-plate facings.	Fit new facings.
	(*b*) Misalignment.	Check over and correct the alignment.
	(*c*) Binding of release levers on eyebolt pins.	Work in small quantity of penetrating oil, taking care to avoid oiling up the driven-plate facings.
	(*d*) Binding of clutch-pedal mechanism.	Free and lubricate bearings.
	(*e*) Worn-out driven-plate facings.	New facings required.
3. Slip.	(*a*) Oil or grease on the driven-plate facings.	Fit new facings.
	(*b*) Weak thrust springs. If excessive slip is allowed to occur, the heat generated will soften the springs and add to the trouble.	Fit new thrust springs.
	(*c*) Binding of clutch-pedal mechanism.	Free and lubricate bearings.
	(*d*) Improper pedal adjustment or pedal fouling floorboards, so preventing full engagement.	Correct the pedal adjustment.
	(*e*) Binding of release levers on eyebolt pins.	Work in small quantity of penetrating oil, taking care to avoid oiling up of the driven-plate facings.

SYMPTOM.	CAUSE.	REMEDY.
4. Judder.	(*a*) Oil or grease or foreign matter on the driven-plate facings.	Fit new facings.
	(*b*) Misalignment.	Check over and correct alignment.
	(*c*) Pressure plate out of parallel with flywheel face.	Fit new eyebolts and reset.
	(*d*) Contact area of friction facings not evenly distributed. Note that friction facing surface will not show 100 per cent. contact until the clutch has been in use for some time, but the contact area actually showing should be evenly distributed round the friction facings.	Fit new driven-plate assembly.
	(*e*) Bent splined shaft or buckled driven plate. (*f*) Release-bearing fork out of true.	Fit new shaft or driven-plate assembly.
5. Rattle.	(*a*) Damaged driven plate. (*b*) Worn parts in release mechanism. (*c*) Excessive back-lash in transmission. (*d*) Wear in transmission bearings. (*e*) Bent splined shaft. (*f*) Graphite release bearing loose on throw-out fork. (*g*) Release-bearing fork out of true.	Fit new parts as necessary.
6. Tick or Knock.	(*a*) Hub splines badly worn due to misalignment.	Check and correct alignment.
	(*b*) Worn pilot bearings.	Fit new driven-plate assembly or pilot bearing.
7. Fracture of Driven Plate.	(*a*) Misalignment distorts the plate and causes it to break or tear round the hub.	Check and correct alignment.
	(*b*) If the gear box during assembly or dis-assembly be allowed to hang with the shaft in the hub, the driven plate may be distorted, leading to drag, metal fatigue, and breakage.	Fit new driven-plate assembly.
8. Abnormal Facing Wear.	Usually produced by overloading and by the excessive slip starting associated with overloading.	In the hands of the operator.

THE SEMI-CENTRIFUGAL CLUTCH

A new type of plate clutch which has been introduced in more recent model cars, which of the Ford V-eight and Vauxhall 25 are typical examples, has certain definite advantages over the conventional pattern dry-plate clutch, from the points of view of light-operating clutch-pedal pressure and freedom from slip under full-load conditions. The clutch in question employs the ordinary foot-pedal release mechanism, but has much lighter plate springs than usual. In order to obtain sufficient plate pressure at all speeds above the idling speed, the clutch is fitted with weighted hinged levers so arranged that as the engine speed increases the centrifugal forces on these weighted arms causes them to press more and more upon the clutch plates, thus giving greater pressures as the speed rises.

The principle of the semi-centrifugal clutch is illustrated by the typical clutch design shown in Fig. 360[1] (diagrams 1, 2, and 3).

[1] Courtesy of *English Mechanics*.

A is the flywheel, and B is the clutch-pressure ring. Between the two the flexible discs C is held, when the clutch is in engagement by the six compression springs D, one of which is shown in the sectional view. These springs are held by a cover plate E bolted to the flywheel by studs, the cover plate being of pressed-steel plate and of no great weight. It carries bosses F, which project inside and form bearings for the operating levers G.

These levers form a particular and an important feature of the clutch and its operation. They are pivoted to the bosses F on two rollers, as shown at H, which are pocketed in a hardened bush. The lever (only one of which is shown in our view) is again pivoted on a needle bearing in the lug which is integral with the heavy pressure plate B. The inward end of the levers G rest against a thrust bearing J, which is moved inwardly to release the clutch by the forked lever K coupled to the clutch pedal.

The important feature of the clutch is the bob weight L which constitutes the outward end of the lever G, and is an integral part of it.

As the speed of the engine increases, the centrifugal force, acting on this weight, tends to throw it outwards, away from the centre of rotation, and in that way increases the pressure on the pressure ring B, so acting as an increment to the pressure of the clutch springs D and increasing the pressure between the flywheel and the pressure ring, thus gripping the driven plate more firmly. It will be seen that the clutch is, to that extent, self-acting, but in such a way that, as the engine speed decreases when throttling to change gear, the pressure on the clutch is automatically reduced and the foot pressure required to disengage the clutch to that extent similarly reduced.

Two forms of central (driven) plates are available. The first is the simple plate, Diagram 1, riveted to the sliding member M on splines on the primary gear shaft. This plate is made flexible at its outer circumference by slots machined in it. It thus beds down easily, under all conditions between the fabric linings on the flywheel surface and the surface of the pressure plate.

In a further modification (shown in Diagrams 2 and 3) this plate is duplicated. Its place is taken by a central rigid plate N of small diameter formed on the spined sliding boss M on the splined end of the gear shaft, and the actual pressure plate C is fitted around the boss but not attached to it. Another thin plate O, complementary to plate C, is similarly fitted on the outside of the central plate N, rigid with the boss.

The driving connection with the central rigid plate N and the actual pressure plate C and its complementary plate O, is by means of six inserted compression springs P which fit in slots in all three plates. These are shown in the part end view of the clutch, Diagram 3.

The effect of the intervention of these springs between the rigid plate (which is part of the sliding boss on the gear shaft) and the driven plate of the clutch, is to give an elastic take-up of the drive. After the clutch has been engaged the engine power cannot be transmitted to the central

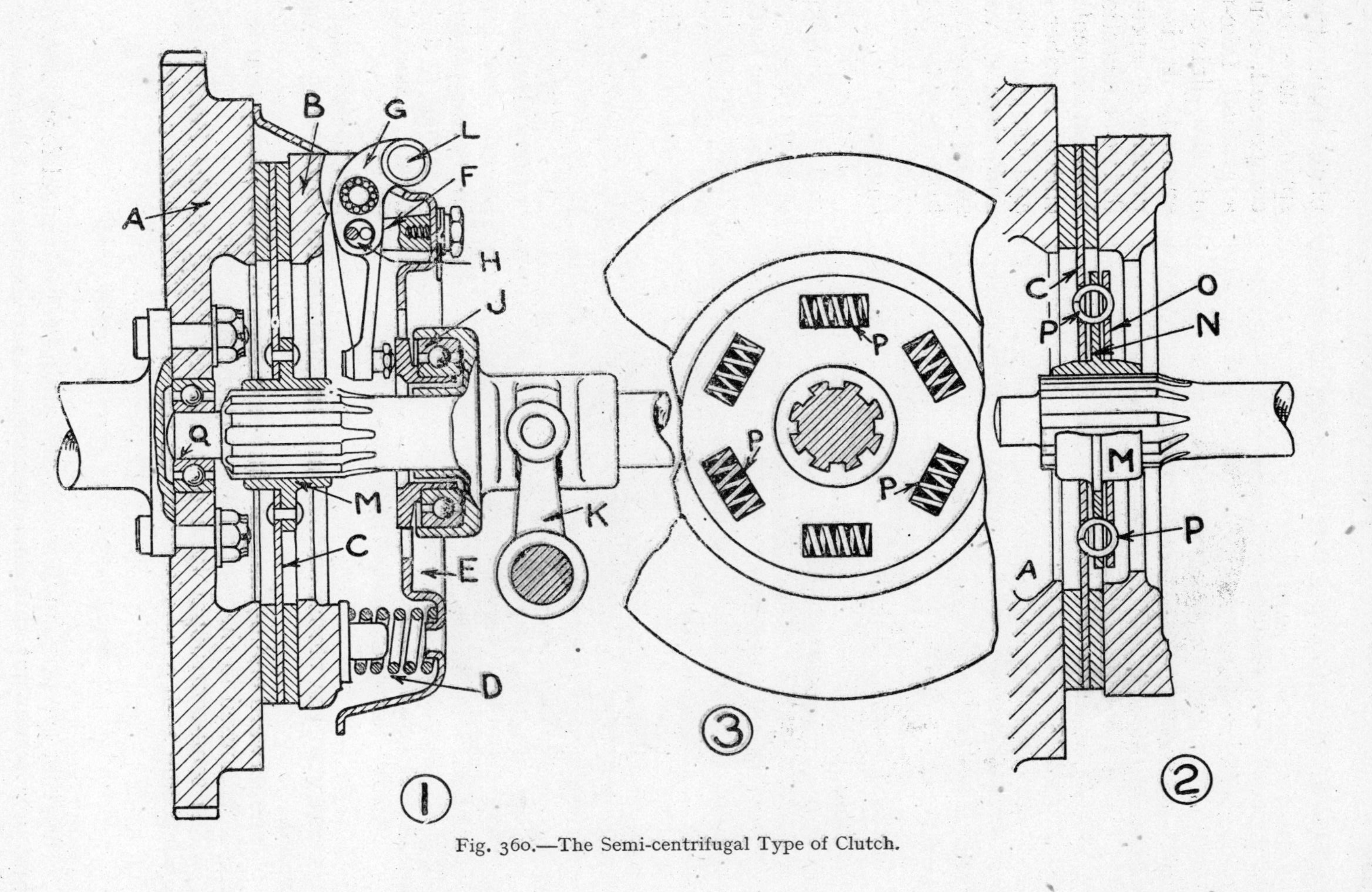

Fig. 360.—The Semi-centrifugal Type of Clutch.

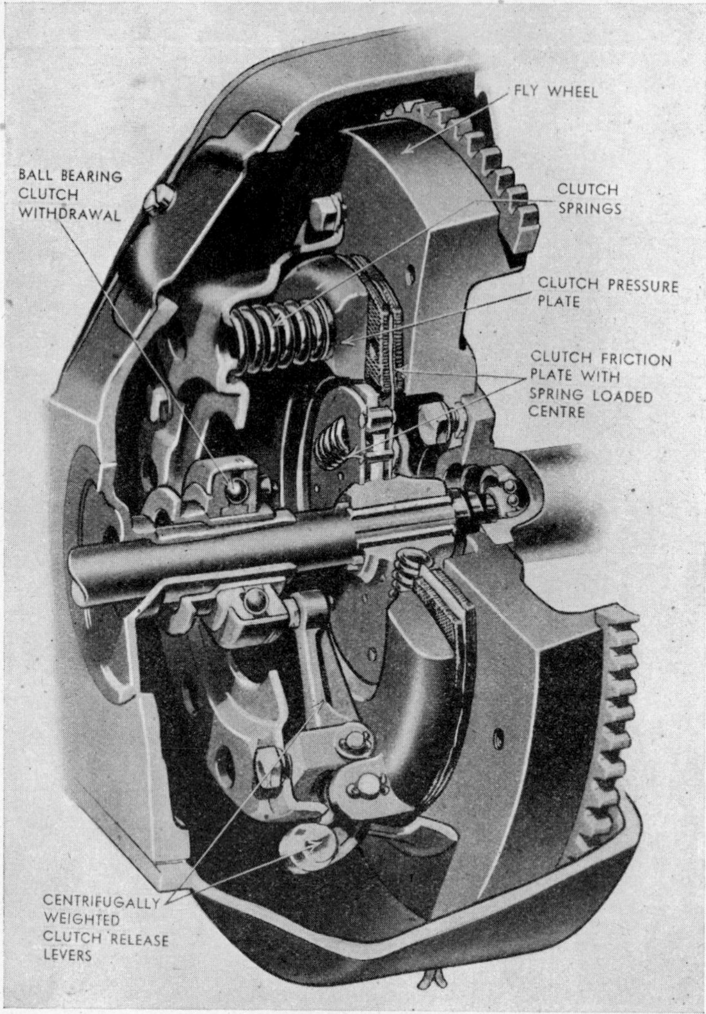

Fig. 361.—The 25-h.p. Vauxhall Semi-centrifugal Clutch.

plate until these springs have been compressed. Hence a gradual take-up of the drive is ensured. It is in practice a spring-drive connection, between the central clutch member C and the gear shaft, and gives a very smooth non-shock, take-up of the load when the clutch is engaged.

It will be seen that the clutching pressure upon the driven plate in this clutch is progressive, due to the centrifugal action of weights L, and increases as the speed increases, so that slipping is entirely eliminated. At the same time the spring pressure is normal at times when declutching is required. No adjustment is necessary to the clutch springs, and in practice no adjustment is provided.

The forward end of the gear shaft is carried in a ball steady bearing Q which is housed in the central recess in the flywheel.

The semi-centrifugal type of clutch employed in the Ford V-eight 22-h.p. and 30-h.p. cars is shown on the left in Plate facing p. 376.

THE CENTRIFUGAL CLUTCH

Another type of clutch which also uses the centrifugal force principle but in a somewhat different manner is that known as the centrifugal clutch.

Whilst the semi-centrifugal type relies on foot pressure to release or disengage the clutch, with centrifugal action to increase the pressure between the friction surfaces after engagement, the fully centrifugal type dispenses with foot pressure and effects engagement and disengagement automatically.

The clutch is so designed that when the engine is idling, at about 500 to 600 r.p.m., compression springs within it separate the driving and driven-clutch surfaces so that no drive is transmitted to the gear-box main shaft.

When, however, the engine speed increases as by the operation of depressing the accelerator pedal, the weighted arms of the clutch tend to fly outwards under centrifugal action and in doing so force the clutch surfaces together, so that the drive is taken up and, as the engine speed increases, the plates are forced together more and more firmly.

A typical clutch of the centrifugal class is the Newton automatic clutch, the principle of which is shown in Fig. 362, as fitted to Riley and other makes of car. This contains six weights and twelve springs in all.

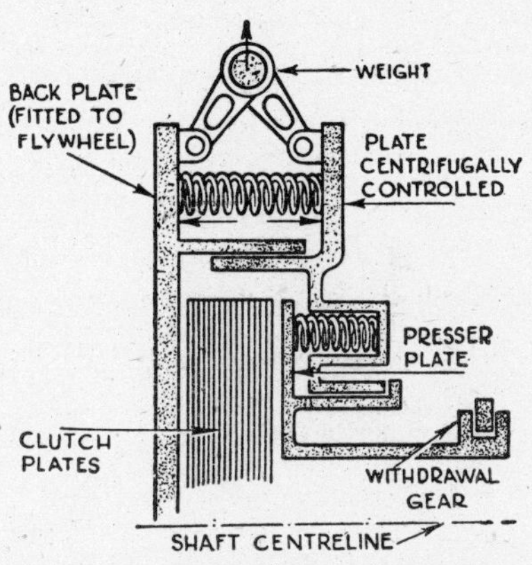

Fig. 362.—The Newton Automatic Centrifugal Clutch.

A number of frictional clutch plates is arranged between a presser plate and a back plate fitted to the engine flywheel. The springs which normally hold the presser plate in contact are mounted on a third plate, which, within limits, can slide endwise under the control of the centrifugal force created by the weights. A second set of springs A tends to keep the back plate and the controlled plate apart. At low speeds these springs have their own way and no pressure is exerted upon the driving plates.

In connection with the adjustment of semi-centrifugal clutches, there are no adjustments on the clutch members, such as the screws, springs, etc. The only adjustment provided is the connecting link between the clutch pedal and clutch-operating lever on the outside of the clutch housing. The usual clutch-pedal idle movement is of the order, 1 in. to $1\frac{1}{2}$ in.

As the speed increases, the centrifugal forces gradually move the controlled plate towards the back plate, overcoming the outward pressure of the springs A. An increasing nipping effect is then produced by the presser plate until, eventually, the full force of the main springs B is exerted. At this point the controlled plate comes against a stop, limiting further movement, so that, no matter how great the centrifugal force may eventually become, the clutch plates only experience the normal spring load. From this it also follows that the presser plate can be withdrawn by the pedal at any time.

There are certain refinements not mentioned in the description given ;

including an oil dashpot which is fitted in order to give a smooth engagement.

The weights employed are of a few ounces each, whilst the clutch itself is of compact dimensions ; thus a 14-h.p. car clutch would not exceed 12 in. in outside diameter.

The Newton clutch requires *very little in the matter of maintenance*, for it is designed with a view to any wear being taken up automatically by the inner springs, which are built up by about $\frac{5}{32}$ in. This means that the clutch will still work in a satisfactory manner up to $\frac{5}{32}$ in. wear on the friction material of the discs. An advantage of this clutch is that it requires no clutch pedal, for it is engaged automatically by accelerating the engine and disengaged by taking the foot off the accelerator, in a similar manner to the fluid flywheel, which is described later in this chapter.

THE DAIMLER FLUID FLYWHEEL

This transmission device takes the place of both the clutch and the flywheel of the ordinary car's transmission. It resembles an ordinary enclosed plate clutch, but actually consists of two parts only, one of which is a flywheel or driving member, and the other the driven member. Both the driving and driven members are of saucer-like section and are divided into a large number of cells by radial webs. A small gap separates the driven member from the driving member so that the latter can rotate freely. The driving member is of cylindrical construction so that the driven member is enclosed within it and the whole compartment is filled with a special oil.

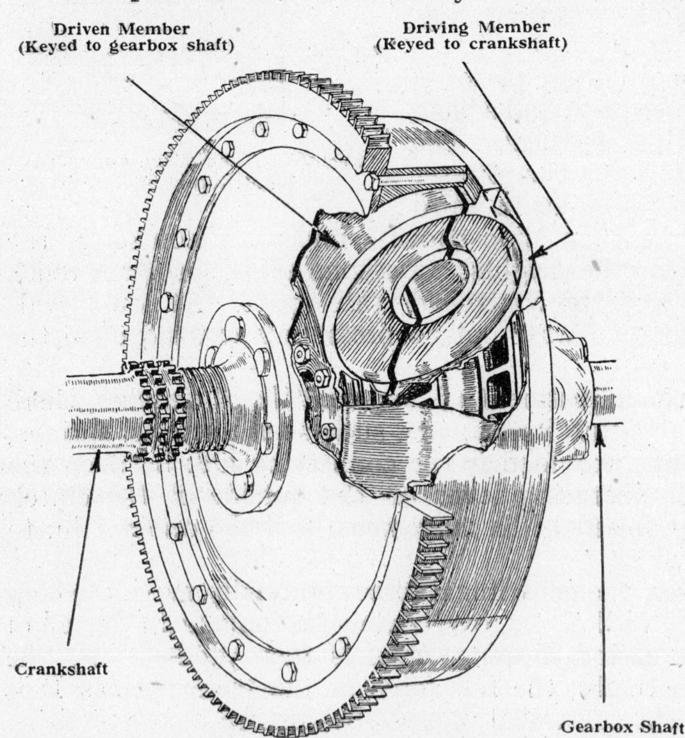

Fig. 363.—The Daimler Fluid Flywheel.

The fluid flywheel transmits power in the following manner. Assuming the car to be stationary and the engine started, the rotation of the driving member by the engine causes the oil in its cells to flow towards their outside periphery. From here, as the "driven" member is yet stationary, the oil flows past the outside periphery of its cells, through them, and past their inside periphery to the inside periphery of the driving-member cells, and from there back again to the outside periphery. In other words, the oil starts on a circulatory motion between the cells of the driving and driven members.

In passing from the webs of the driving to those of the driven member, the oil is retarded in velocity and, therefore, releases kinetic energy

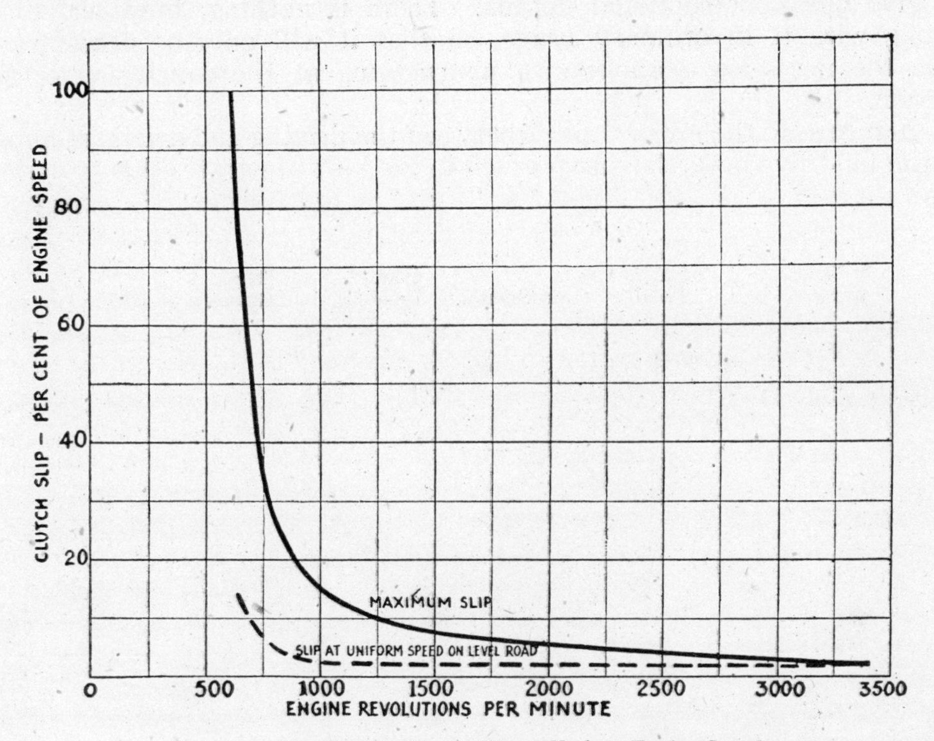

Fig. 364.—Showing the Clutch Slip at Various Engine Speeds.

which sets the driven member in motion. Since, even when the driven member has attained full speed, the load on it causes it to lag behind the driving member, the centrifugal forces in the latter are always larger than those in the driven member, so that the circulatory motion of the oil, and therefore the transmission of power from one to the other, are always kept up.

At *ordinary speeds* the oil needs but little retardation to develop the driving torque, hence the lag, or "slip," between the driving and driven members is insignificant.

At *low engine speeds*, however, the "slip" is so great that there is no drive, or torque, communicated to the gear-box mainshaft member; the "slip" in this case is therefore 100 per cent. The engine-driven member therefore revolves and the main gear shaft remains stationary, so that we have the same condition as when an ordinary car engine is running with the gear lever in neutral. At engine speeds below about 600 r.p.m. there is no power communicated to the "driven" or gear-shaft member.

The essential feature of the "slip" is that it diminishes so rapidly as the car begins to move that exceedingly smooth starting and low running speed is obtained without any prejudice to normal running efficiency.

The Daimler fluid flywheel is a patented invention, and we are unable to give any constructional details. There is nothing, however, to go wrong with it in ordinary usage, so that it will only be necessary to give the necessary maintenance instructions at the conclusion of this section.

In regard to the lay or "slip" between the driving and driven members of the fluid flywheel, the curve given in Fig. 361 illustrates this at various engine speeds. The full line is the "slip" under full-throttle conditions,

Fig. 365.—Showing the Daimler Fluid Flywheel and Pre-selective Gear Box in Chassis.

while the dotted line shows the normal amount of "slip" existing when the car is travelling at a steady speed on a level road. The important point to note is that while the "slip" at very low engine speeds (on full throttle) can be 100 per cent.—as it is when starting off—it falls off exceedingly rapidly but smoothly, with increasing speed, a characteristic not hitherto equalled with any form of hydraulic or electrical transmission. As soon as the car is travelling at a normal speed, the "slip" is of the order of 2 per cent. only. In other words, the normal running efficiency of the fluid flywheel is 98 per cent., which is considerably greater than that of a good gear box (even the heat generated is so insignificant as to be easily dissipated by the rotation on direct drive) or rear axle.

MAINTENANCE OF THE FLUID FLYWHEEL

The fluid flywheel requires no attention other than occasionally to top up with fluid to the required level. To refill, turn the engine until one of the filling plugs is at its top position, as shown in Fig. 365. Now, remove the plug by means of the special spanner provided in the tool kit of the car and fill (using the specially shaped filler also provided for this purpose) to the level of the filler hole with the special flywheel-fluid mixture provided by the Daimler Company or any of its depots.

After filling, replace the plug and screw it up tightly. It should be emphasised that this topping up is only required at very infrequent intervals. Further, only a small quantity of the fluid is necessary to restore the level.

In the rather improbable event of any internal trouble occurring with the fluid flywheel it should be returned to the makers for expert examination and repair.

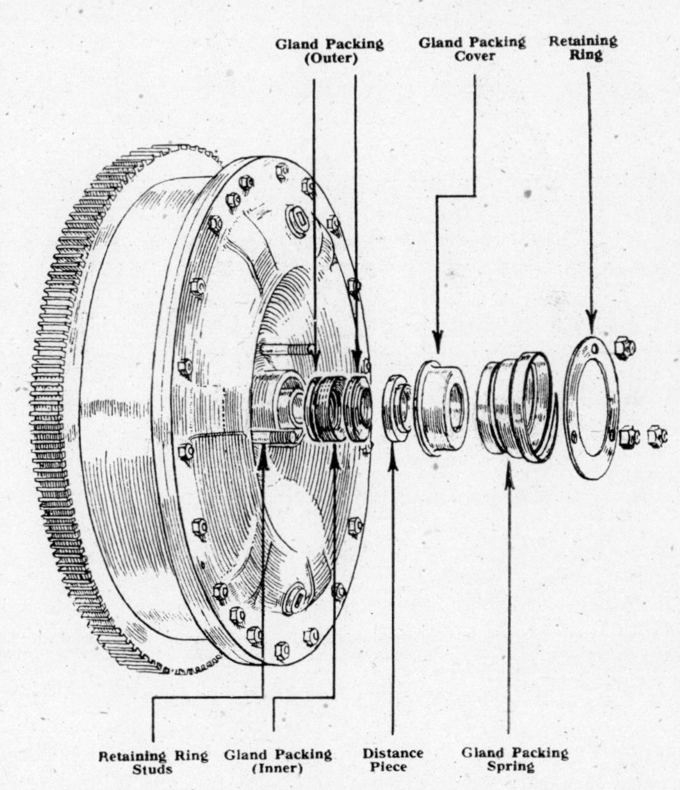

Fig. 366.—Illustrating Maintenance of the Lanchester and Daimler Fluid Flywheels.

FLUID-FLYWHEEL LEAKAGE AND ITS CURE

In the event of leakage of fluid from the flywheel casing, after long periods of service, the gland packing should be replaced. The method of doing this, in the case of the Lanchester "10" and Daimler "15," is illustrated in Fig. 366.

In order to replace the gland packing it is necessary to withdraw the gear box so that access can be obtained to the centre of the flywheel. The procedure is then as follows :

First, dismantle the universal joint at the rear of the gear box. Then detach the selector rod from the selector lever. Next, undo the bolts on the gear-box flange and rubber support beneath gear box, and withdraw the complete gear box from the splined runner shaft on the flywheel. Having gained access to the flywheel, turn until one of the filler plugs is at the bottom. Remove the plug and drain off the oil into a pan. Then, undo the three nuts holding the retaining ring (see Fig. 366). Finally, withdraw in turn, the gland packing ring, gland packing cover, distance piece, and the three gland packings.

After renewing the three packing pieces, reassemble in the reverse

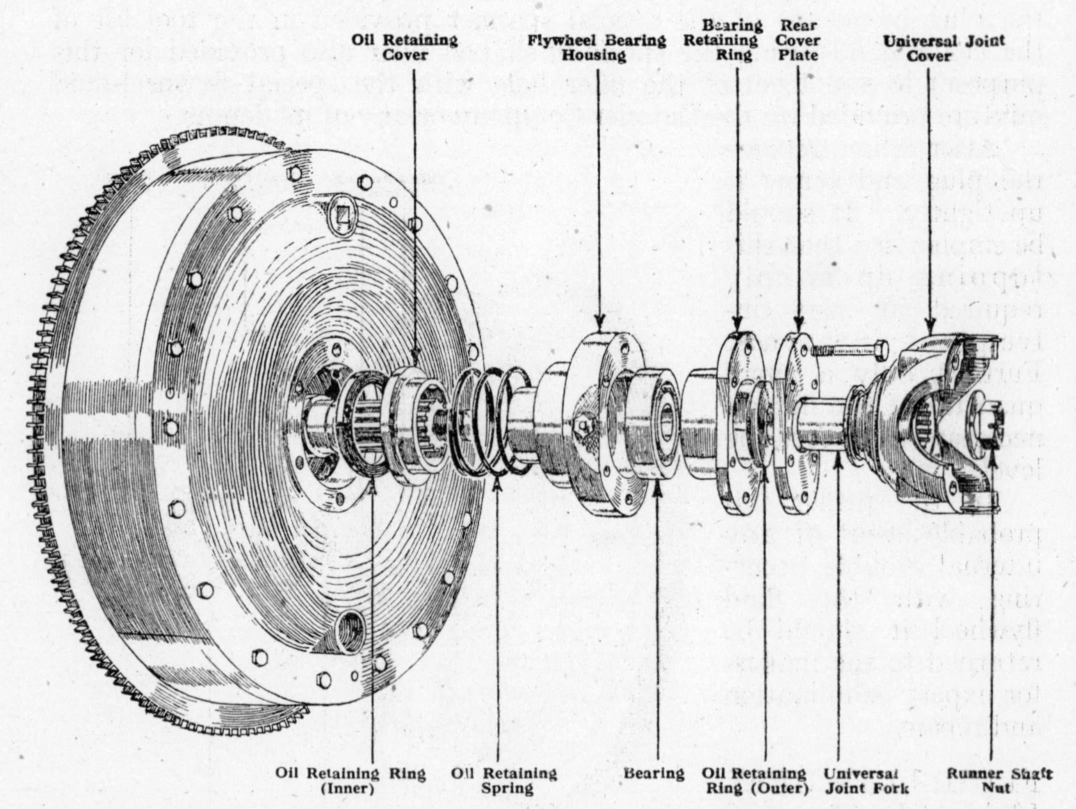

Fig. 367.—Illustrating Maintenance of the Fluid Flywheels fitted to the larger-model Daimler Cars.

order to that previously described and refill the flywheel casing in the ordinary way.

Care should be taken to ensure that the universal joint behind the gear box is properly lubricated on reassembling.

In the case of the larger Daimler cars, of 20 h.p. and over, a somewhat different design of shaft is employed between the flywheel and gear box.

The procedure in this case is illustrated by reference to Fig. 367 and is as follows :

First drain the fluid from the flywheel as previously described. The universal coupling should then be dismantled and the back half, together with the shaft, dropped so that the front half may be withdrawn from the splined runner shaft after removing the runner-shaft nut and its washer. Continue as given below :

1. Undo the bolts holding the rear cover plate in position and remove cover plate.

2. Withdraw the bearing-retaining plate. The oil-retaining ring situated within this plate need not be removed as it is unlikely that this needs replacing.

3. Withdraw the bearing housing complete with bearing.

4. Remove the oil-retaining spring, oil-retaining cover, and the inner oil-retaining ring.

After replacing the inner oil-retaining ring reassemble in the opposite order to that given above, making sure that the rear cover-plate bolts are tight. A good-quality liquid packing, such as "Holdfast," should be used between the bearing housing and flywheel casing, also between the bearing-retaining plate and cover plate. The universal coupling should be refilled with high melting-point bearing grease before reassembly. Finally lubricate the flywheel bearing by means of the grease gun, and refill the flywheel with fresh fluid.

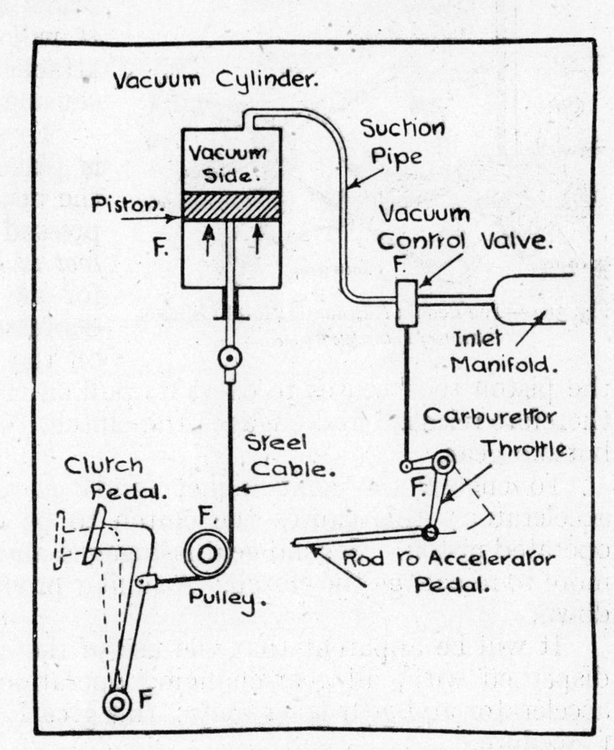

Fig. 368.—Illustrating Principle of the Bendix Automatic Clutch Control.

THE BENDIX AUTOMATIC CLUTCH CONTROL

This device, which is fitted to several makes of car, is for the purpose of dispensing with the foot operation of the clutch pedal so that the only foot control, other than the brake pedal, is the accelerator. The latter automatically operates the clutch control, whilst it regulates the engine speed and output. The Bendix device can be fitted to existing cars, as it is only necessary to make connections to the accelerator and clutch pedals and to take a suction-pipe connection to the inlet pipe.

The principle employed is that of utilising the partial vacuum in the inlet manifold for operating a clutch-operating piston which can move in a cylinder under vacuum (or atmospheric) control. The pressure on this piston is the means of supply for the automatic clutch disengagement, when required.

The accelerator pedal is connected to a vacuum-control valve in such a way that when the accelerator is depressed the control valve shuts off the supply of vacuum to the cylinder of the clutch-operating piston, so that the clutch is released and is therefore returned (by its own clutch springs) to the fully engaged position.

Assuming that one wishes to start the car from rest, with the gear lever in neutral and the engine just idling, it will be apparent that since the accelerator pedal has been left disengaged or untouched, the control valve will be open to the vacuum supply so that the piston will be "sucked" up the cylinder, under the influence of the atmospheric pressure below and the inlet suction above. It will therefore pull on the cable attached to the clutch pedal, thus causing the clutch to be disengaged.

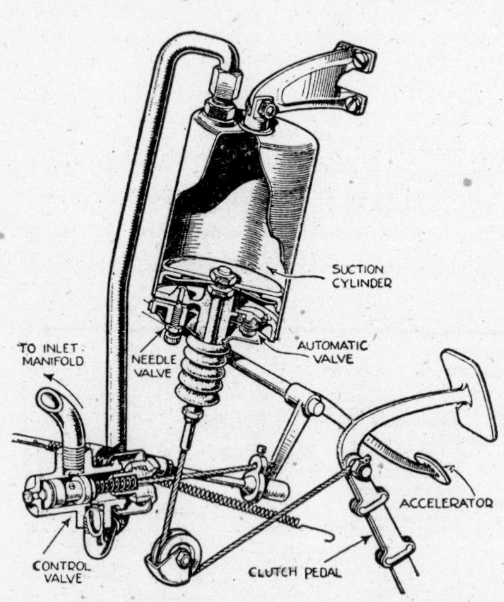

Fig. 369.—The Bendix Automatic Clutch Control. (Courtesy *Automobile Engineer.*)

To start the car, the gear lever is placed in 1st (bottom) gear and the accelerator pedal is slowly depressed with one foot. *The other foot is kept clear of the clutch pedal*, for as soon as the accelerator is depressed the control valve shuts off the vacuum to the cylinder and the piston then ceases to exert its pull on the clutch pedal ; the latter is therefore released and engages the clutch. The car then moves away in bottom gear.

To engage the next higher (2nd) gear, the foot is taken off the accelerator ; this causes the clutch to be disengaged by the vacuum-operated piston. Second gear is engaged and the accelerator pressed once more to re-engage the clutch. A similar process is employed for changing down.

It will be apparent that the use of the clutch pedal by the driver is dispensed with, all gear-changing operations being carried out by the accelerator and gear lever only ; this greatly simplifies the gear-changing procedure.

In connection with the re-engagement of the clutch, when the accelerator is depressed it is, of course, necessary for this to be done gradually—not with a sudden jerk. In order to accomplish this, in addition to the automatic valve arranged on the atmospheric side of the piston, there is an adjustable needle valve shown in Fig. 369, so that as the piston descends there will be a certain resistance due to the leakage of the air through the needle valve.

From the foregoing account it will be evident that the Bendix clutch control renders car driving easier and tends to save the driver a certain amount of fatigue.

In addition, it *also gives a free-wheeling effect,* for if the accelerator is released, as when pulling-up or descending a hill, the clutch is automatically disengaged, so that the engine is disconnected from the gear box and rest of the transmission.

Further, if by any chance the engine should " stall " when the car is

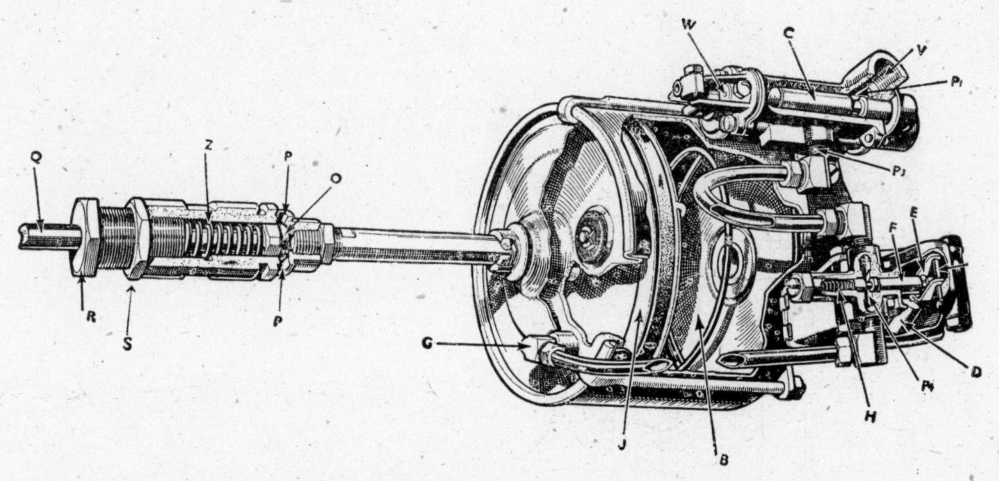

Fig. 370.—The Bendix Clutch Control on one model Morris Car.

B, Power Cylinder. C, Dashboard Control Plunger. D, Pendulum. F, Pendulum Valve Plunger. J, Piston. O, Spring-loaded Valve. P, Air Holes. Q, Connecting Rod. R, Adjusting Sleeve. S, Lock Nut. V, Connection to Induction Pipe.

descending a hill, the vacuum in the inlet pipe will cease to exist, and the clutch will therefore be released by the piston, since the latter will have no vacuum supply above it. The transmission will then be connected to the engine and will motor the latter around until it starts firing, when it will automatically be disconnected from the transmission, by the vacuum-operated piston.

The Bendix automatic clutch control is made by Messrs. Bendix, Ltd., Tyseley, Birmingham, who publish an instruction booklet giving full particulars of the method of adjusting and servicing this mechanism.

THE TALBOT TRAFFIC CLUTCH

The Talbot cars, except the lower-priced " 65 " one, are fitted with a special form of centrifugally operated clutch, known as the " traffic clutch."

In brief, the function of the Talbot " Traffic Clutch " is to allow complete disconnection between engine and gear box at all speeds below 600 engine revolutions per minute. Above this speed the clutch gradually takes up the drive until solid engagement is obtained at approximately 900 engine revolutions per minute. Between these two speeds the clutch slip decreases in proportion to the rapidity with which the engine reaches the higher speed.

As will be seen from Fig. 371, and also from the description of the clutch, there is incorporated in the device a "reversed" free-wheel, the object of which being to ensure that whenever the road wheels are turning and

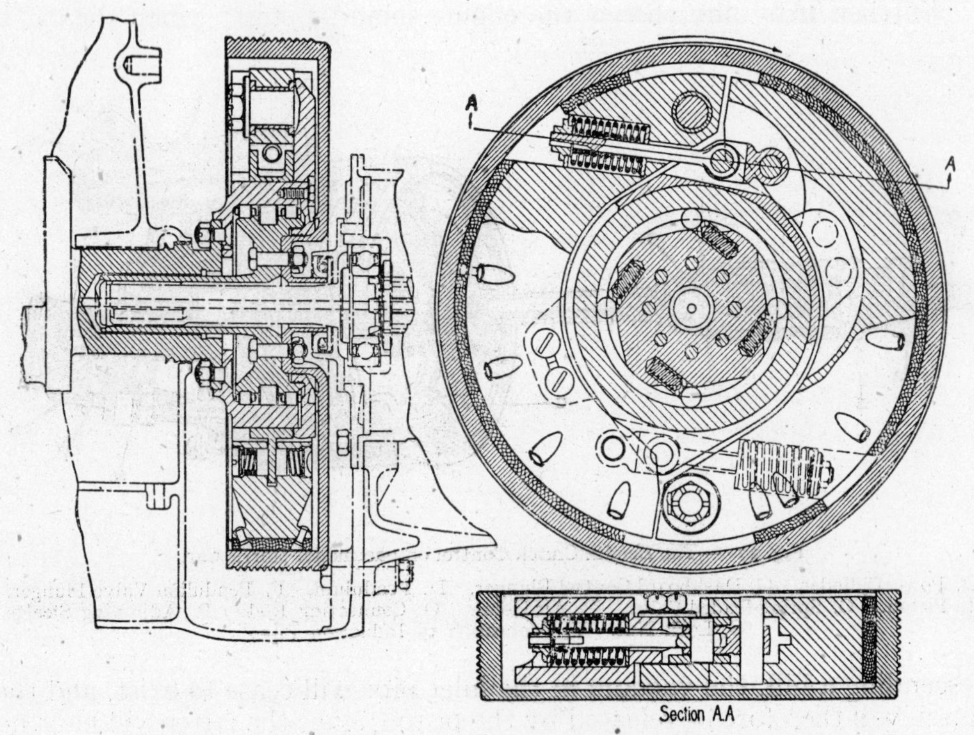

Fig. 371.—The Talbot Traffic Clutch in Side and Front Sectional Views.
(Courtesy *Automobile Engineer*.)

a gear is engaged, there will be solid engagement between the road wheels and the engine. As soon as the road wheels cease to turn, and the engine speed is reduced to below 600 r.p.m., there is disconnection between the two. Thus, if the accelerator is released while the car is moving, the full decelerating qualities of the engine are retained. Also, this device prevents the stalling of the engine through an improperly adjusted slow-running jet on the carburettor, as often happens with systems which allow the road wheels to over-run the engine.

Another advantage of this reversed free-wheel is that the full braking effect of the engine is retained when leaving the car on a hill with a gear engaged to assist the brakes.

A brief description of the construction of the unit is as follows :

Bolted to the end of the crankshaft is a member which forms the outer race of the free-wheel, and of a large double-row roller-bearing. It also has attached to it a member pivoted to which are two steel shoes on which the friction linings are riveted. The shoes are pivoted at their leading ends, and their trailing ends are linked to an annular member which surrounds the outer roller-race, and which is free to rotate slightly as the shoes expand under the action of centrifugal force. To these links the leading ends of the shoes are also connected by another link, surrounding the stem of which are two coil springs acting on a spring cap screwed on the end of the stem. Thus, when the engine is running and the shoes rotating, centrifugal force tends to make them expand against the springs, whilst

Fig. 372.—Showing the Components of the Talbot Traffic Clutch.

the arrangement of links is such that the expansion of the two shoes is bound to be identical, as if one tends to lag behind the other it will be expanded by the floating of the annular member to which the links are attached.

Surrounding the shoes is a ribbed steel drum which is bolted to the inner member of the free-wheel, the latter having its centre extended in a hub-like formation to engage with splines on the end of the gear-box driving shaft. The shaft, however, does not actually support this driven member of the clutch and driving member of the free-wheel, as the support necessary for it is afforded by the two rows of rollers lying between the races formed by the inner and outer portion of the free-wheel.

Between these two rows of rollers there are four larger rollers spaced 90°, and the inner member of the free-wheel has formed on it between the races of the smaller rollers four cam tracks which give a wedging action

Fig. 373.—Components and Assembly of Talbot Traffic Clutch.

of the four large rollers between the inner and outer members of the free-wheel, the rollers being held out into constant engagement with the outer member by means of small spring-loaded plungers. As has already been mentioned, the free-wheel is not fitted in order to allow the car to " coast " but to prevent it so doing should the clutch shoes be out of engagement with their drum, and it should be remembered that the inner member of the free-wheel is the driving member. Thus, when the car is over-running the engine at speeds below the main clutch full-engagement speed (900 r.p.m.), as when slowly descending a hill with the accelerator released, the road wheels transmit power through the back axle, propeller shaft, and gear box to the inner member of the free-wheel which is driven through the splines on the end of the gear-box shaft, and therefore the inner member drives its outer member through the four large rollers and, as the outer member is rigidly attached to the crankshaft, the engine also is driven.

The speed at which the clutch shoes come into operation can be controlled by adjustment of the nut on the link connecting each shoe to the annular member. To prevent a knock occurring in the coupling as a result of the shoes coming into contact with the drum too quickly, a damping device is incorporated in the sides of the shoes. These dampers press against lugs on the annular member and give the necessary damping acting.

CHAPTER VIII

THE GEAR BOX

THE modern gear box is one of the most reliable pieces of mechanism of the car, and seldom gives trouble. For this reason very few people trouble to ascertain the likely causes of trouble which may eventually occur.

Naturally a good deal depends upon the manner in which the car has been driven and looked after, and gear-box trouble may therefore be experienced much earlier when there is neglect. For example, the irresponsible amateur owner-driver may forget that the gear box requires periodical lubrication, or that constant clashing of the gears will in time lead to badly worn gear teeth and to noisy operation.

It can, however, be stated that with reasonable care and attention the well-designed gear box will not require mechanical attention under about 25,000 to 40,000 miles.

In dealing with the subject of gear-box maintenance and repairs, we shall commence with the more simple items and conclude with some definite examples, from actual modern practice, of typical gear boxes, and their maintenance, etc.

The principal items with which the mechanic is likely to be concerned in connection with gear boxes may be enumerated as follows: (1) *Lubrication and Replenishment*; (2) *Worn Teeth*; (3) *Worn Bearings*; (4) *Leakage of Lubricant.* Other troubles, less likely to occur, include *Slackness in Gear Shifters, Non-alignment of Gear Striker, Gears Slipping Out of Mesh, Non-alignment of Gear Box after Dismantling and Re-assembling.*

Before proceeding with the subject of lubrication, it is proposed to give some typical gear-box diagrams, showing the internal arrangements and constructions, and the accepted notations—that is to say, the names by which the various parts and components are known in the trade; this will no doubt assist the student and novice in obtaining a better conception of the gear box.

GEAR-BOX CONSTRUCTION

There are two principal types of ordinary gear box in common use, namely (1), the plain or sliding dog, or sliding gear-wheel type, sometimes referred to as the "crash change" gear box and (2) the synchro-mesh or "easy change" type. We shall deal first with the former pattern of gear box, since there is still a large number of commercial vehicles and cars in service, fitted with this kind of gear box. Special transmissions, including the pre-selective gear box, will be dealt with later.

The synchro-mesh gear box is dealt with later in this chapter.

Fig. 374 illustrates a typical three-speed gear box, with multiple-plate clutch and flywheel complete. The various items are annotated,

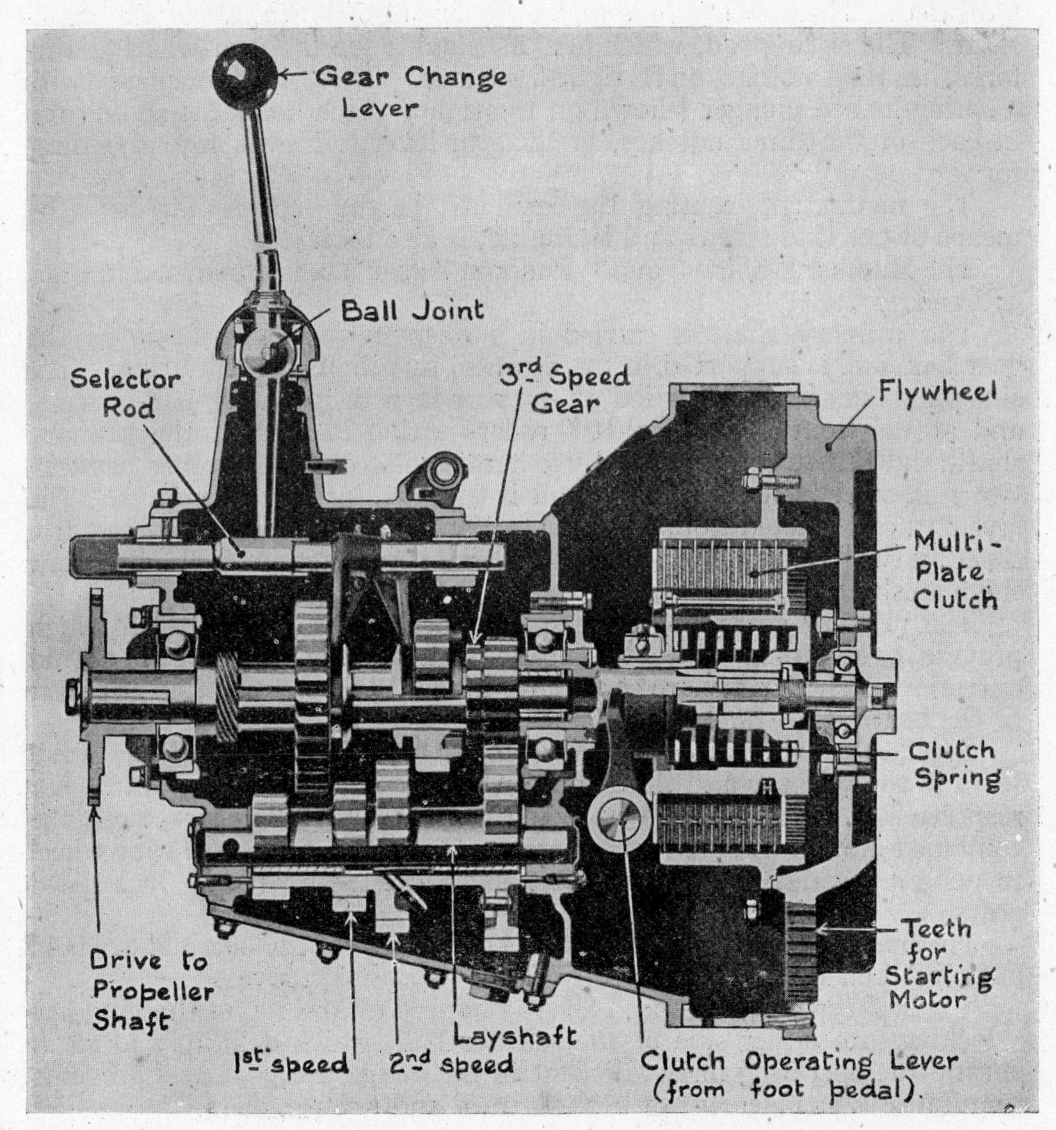

Fig. 374.—A Typical Three-speed American Type of Gear Box and Multiple-disc Clutch.

so that further explanation is unnecessary. It may, however, be pointed out that in this case the gears are shifted by means of a centrally placed lever, which pivots about the ball joint shown in the upper part of the casing, and therefore requires no gate. The positions of the knob of the gear-change lever corresponding to the engagement of the first, second, and third speeds, and also the reverse speed, are the same, generally speaking, as for the gate-change system.

The Meadows three-speed gear box and single dry-plate clutch assembly is illustrated in Fig. 375. The various members of the gear box, the ball and roller bearings, gears, and the main- and layshafts are clearly indicated. The striking rods and forks are also shown, above the mainshaft. The sliding rod, which acts as a guide for the gear-wheel sliding forks, has three notches on its right-hand side. These, in turn, engage with a spring-loaded plunger (shown on the right) which holds the sliding rod in each of the three notches, as the gear lever is moved into the three forward gears.

The method of locating the layshaft, in the endwise direction, by means of external screws and lock nuts, is also indicated.

The Humber " Snipe " and " Pullman " gear box is illustrated in Figs. 376 and 377.

The primary shaft is carried in a deep-groove ball-bearing in the gear box, and is supported in the flywheel by a ball spigot bearing. The six-spline mainshaft is carried at the rear in a deep-groove ball-bearing, and at the front in a " Hyatt " roller-bearing located in the primary shaft, end thrust being taken by a hardened-steel ball running between two cast-steel buttons to which oil is supplied by helical grooves. The layshaft, constructed from a single steel forging, is supported on a central shaft by two " Hyatt " roller-bearings, and is situated immediately below the mainshaft.

The primary gears and third-speed wheels have helical teeth which provide overlapping of tooth engagement, with consequent silence in operation. These gears are constantly in mesh and are mounted adjacent to the bearings to further ensure silence.

Special-type toothed dogs, splined to the mainshaft, mesh with internal teeth in the primary and third-speed wheel, to engage top and third gear respectively, the two low gears being engaged by sliding into mesh the combined first- and second-speed wheel. To obtain reverse, a wide wheel (which remains idle when not in use) slides into mesh with the first-speed gears.

The operating forks are mounted at the offside of the box and are held in position on the shaft by spring-loaded balls and grooves.

The ball-type change-speed lever, mounted on the top of the box, has a locking arm either side of the selector ball, which definitely locks in neutral the operating forks adjacent to the one in use, and also prevents simultaneous engagement of both forward and reverse gears.

The speedometer is positively driven by helical gears from the rear of the mainshaft.

Fig. 378 shows a typical American type of three-speed gear box and control lever.

The gear-box casing is so designed that it bolts on to the engine casing, a machined ring (marked " transmission case," on the lower right corner, in Fig. 378) being arranged for this purpose. This ring bolts on to a corre-

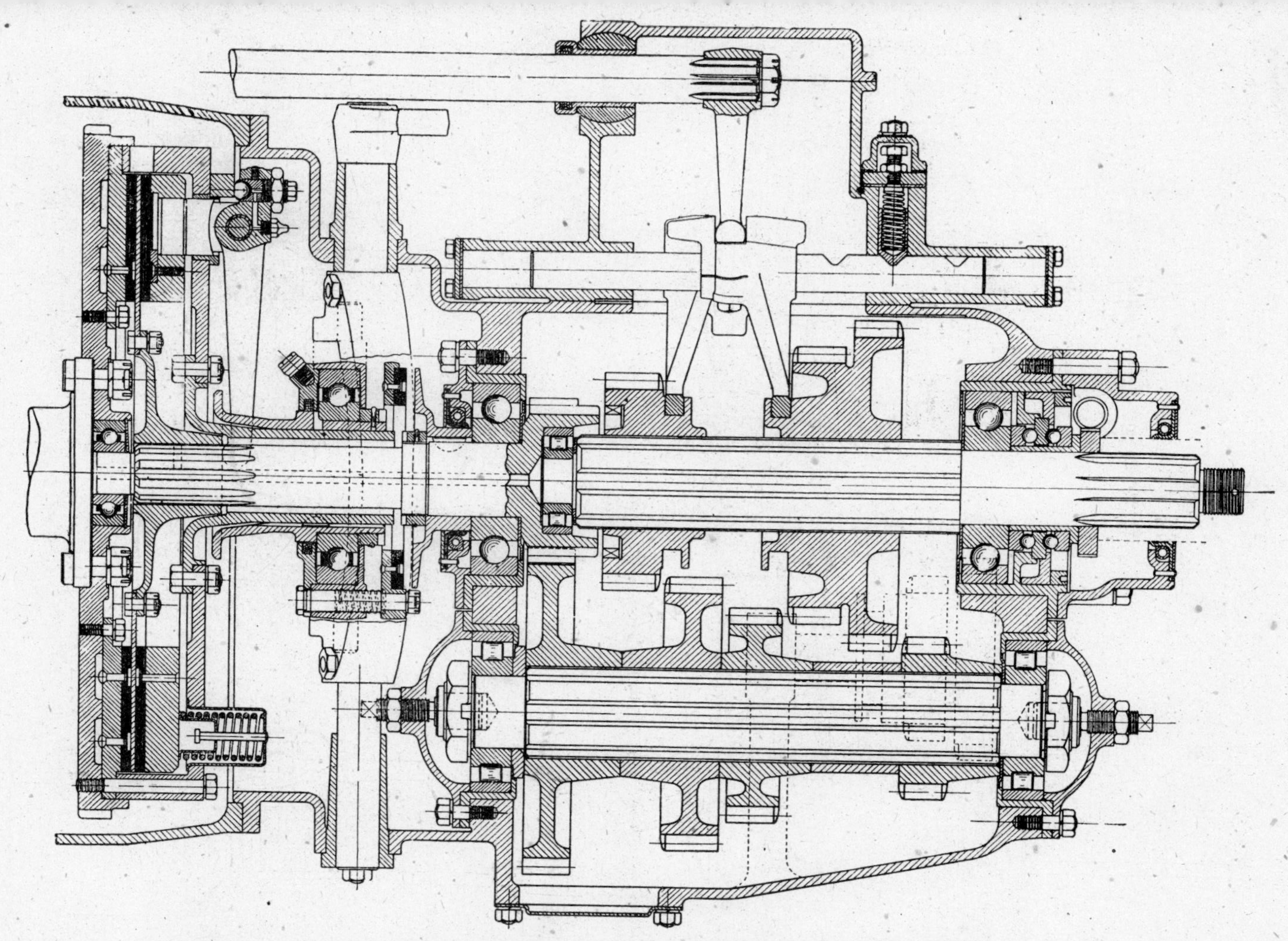

Fig. 375.—The Meadows Three-speed Gear Box and Single-plate Clutch.

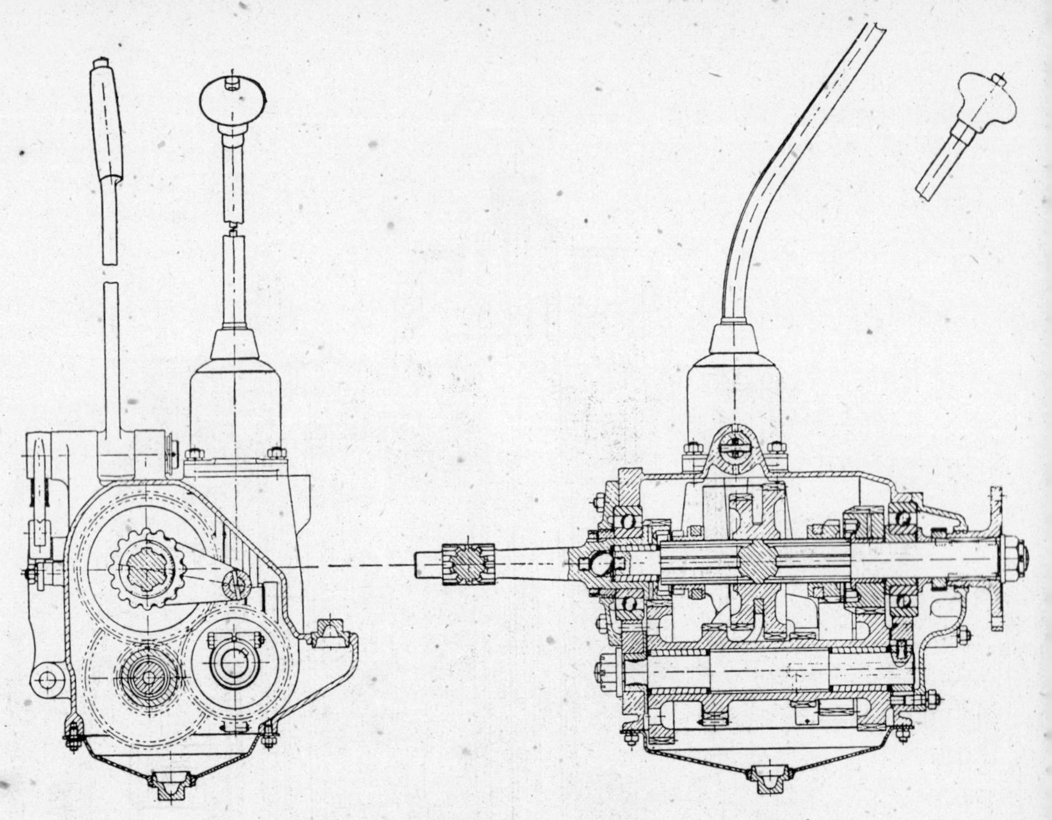

Fig. 376.—The Humber " Snipe " and " Pullman " Gear Box.

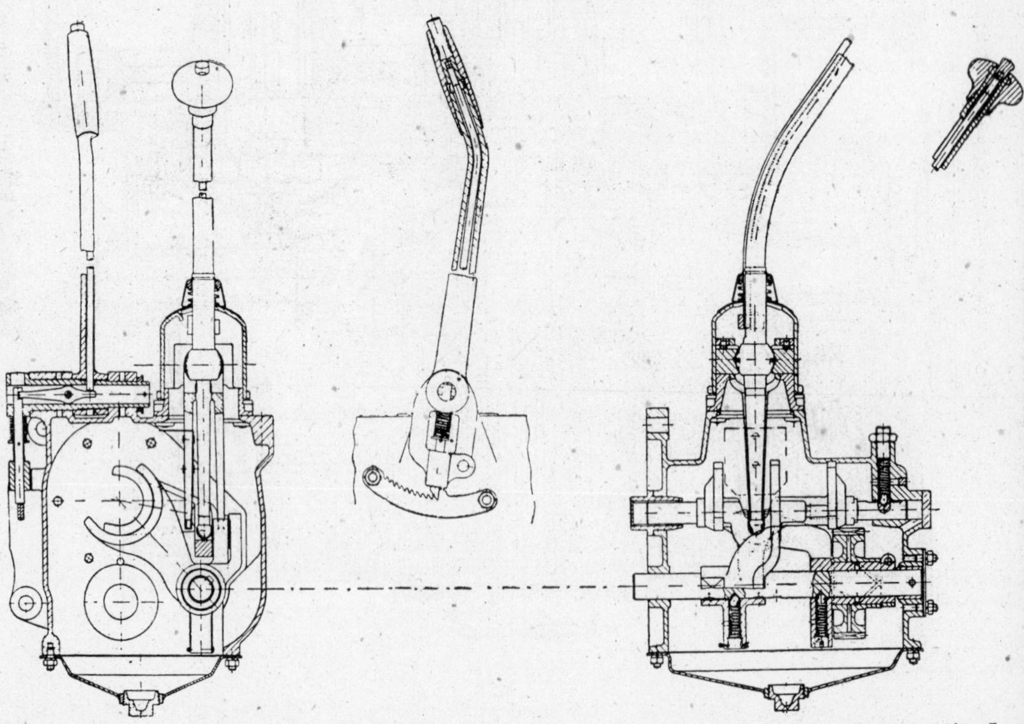

Fig. 377.–Other Views of the Humber Gear Box, showing Selector Fork, Hand Brake, and Gear-operating Leve

sponding one on the engine crankcase. An inspection door is arranged in the top of the clutch casing formed between the gear box and the engine register ring; there is also a drain hole in the lower part.

The various gears on the mainshaft, and the layshaft—here designated "countershaft"—are clearly shown and annotated in the illustration given.

It will be observed that the mainshaft runs on a ball-bearing at its

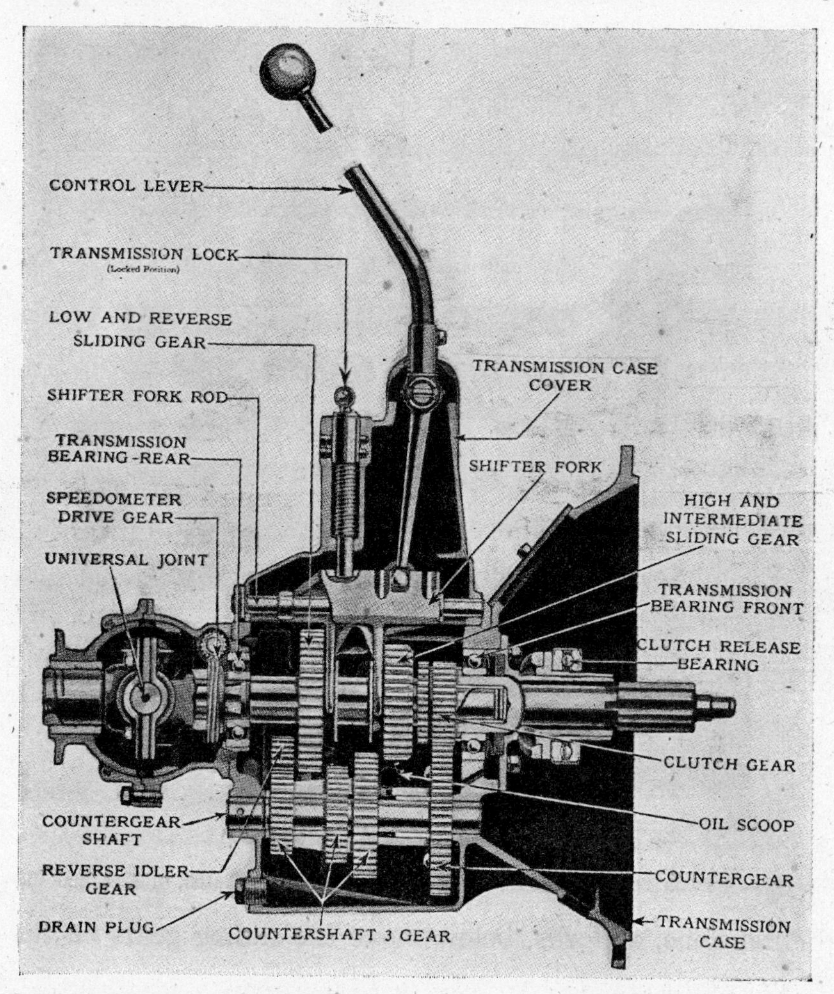

Fig. 378.—Another Typical American Three-speed Gear Box.

rear end and in a bronze bearing at the front, or clutch end. The layshaft is stationary and the gears revolve on it. The reverse idler gear is mounted on a separate shaft to one side of the layshaft, and is in constant mesh with one of the gears on the layshaft. The sliding gears are mounted on the mainshaft in such a manner that they can be moved along to engage with one or the other of the layshaft gears. The high and intermediate sliding gear are provided with internal teeth on their forward side so that they can be moved over the clutch gear to lock the mainshaft and clutch gear together.

The shifter fork operation can readily be followed from the illustration, for it slides along the shifter fork rod—which acts as a guide—and its

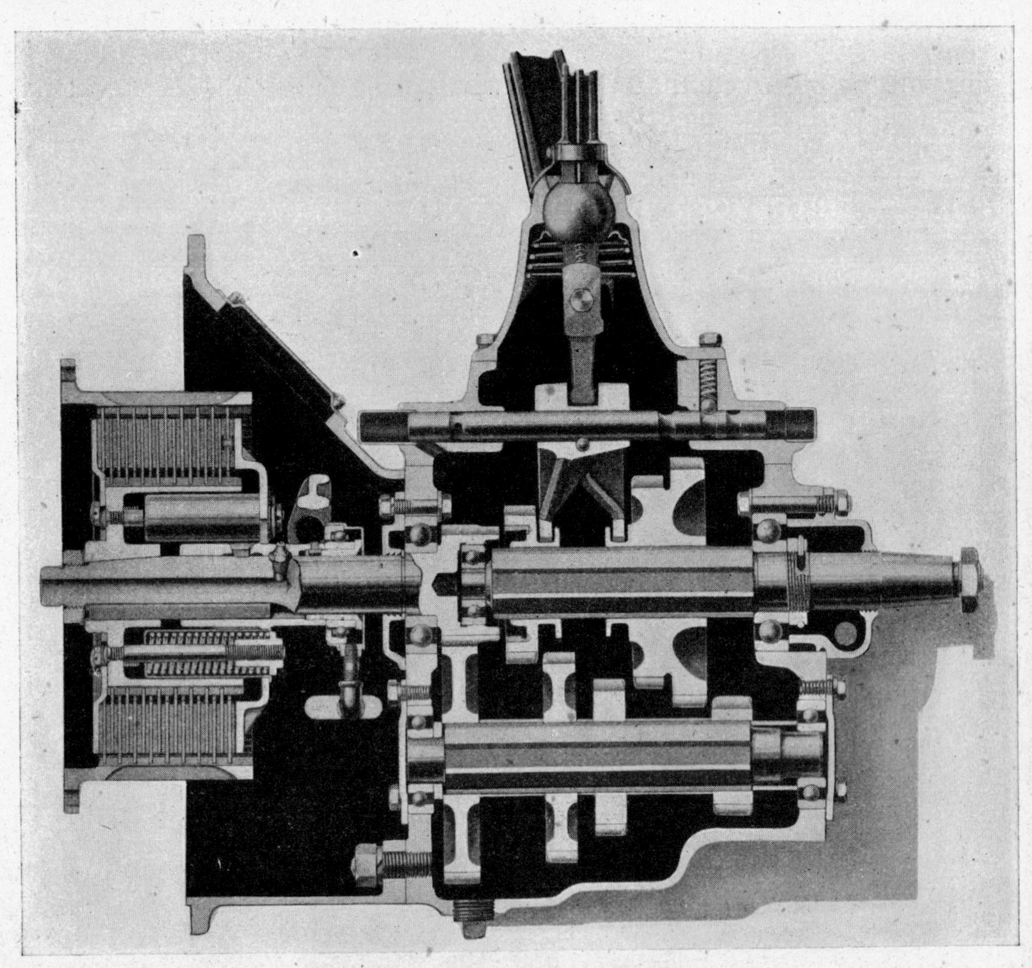

Fig. 379.—A Plain Three-speed Gear Box and Multiple-plate Clutch, in Sectional View.

vertical extensions, or forks, below move the sliding gears on the mainshaft.

The universal joint shown on the left of the illustration transmits the power to the propeller shaft and thence to the back axle.

This illustration shows three interesting details—namely (1) the *oil scoop* on the layshaft for ensuring adequate lubrication of the upper gears; (2) *the speedometer drive,* which consists of a helical gear on the rear end of mainshaft extension; and (3) *the gear lock.* The last is a Yale-key-operated device for locking the gear lever in *neutral* gear. To lock the gear, see that the gear lever is in neutral, insert the key, turn a quarter of a turn to the right, then *press the lock down* level with the lock casing, against the spring shown (many people forget to do this, and in some cases break the key in the lock), and holding in that position, turn key back to original position, when it can be withdrawn. *To unlock*, insert key as before, turn a quarter revolution back to right, when the lock is released.

A good example of a commercial-vehicle gear box is given in Fig. 380 in the case of a commercial car. This is a four-speed model, built for hard work. The mainshaft and layshaft run on large-diameter ball-bearings, and it will be observed that the separate pinion shaft C runs on its own ball-bearings. The gear-striker rod is shown at D.

At the rear end (right) of the mainshaft there is a double ball thrust

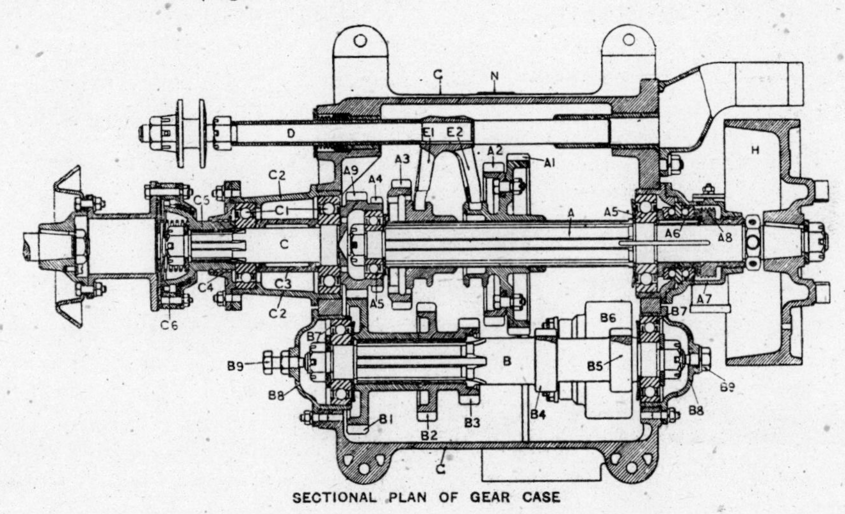

Fig. 380.—A Commercial-vehicle Gear Box (Four-speed).

bearing and an oil-retaining casing. The large drum H on the mainshaft is for the foot brake.

The following is a key to the various parts lettered in Fig. 380:

A, Gear Box Mainshaft
A1, First- and Reverse-speed Wheel on Mainshaft
A2, Second-speed Wheel on Mainshaft
A3, Fourth-speed Clutch and Third-speed Wheel on Mainshaft
A4, Fourth-speed Wheel and Permanent-mesh Wheel on Pinion Shaft
A5, Ball-bearings for Mainshaft
A6, Ball Thrust Washers on Mainshaft
A7, Housing for Ball-bearing and Ball Thrust Washers
A8, Mileage Recorder Worm
A9, Permanent-mesh Wheel on Mainshaft
B, Gear Box Countershaft
B1, Permanent-mesh Wheel on Countershaft
B2, Third-speed Wheel on Countershaft
B3, Second-speed Wheel on Countershaft
B4, First-speed Wheel on Countershaft

B5, Reverse-speed Wheel on Countershaft, gearing with B6
B6, Reverse-speed Wheel on Reverse Shaft, gearing with A
B7, Ball-bearings for Countershaft
B8, Housing for Countershaft Ball-bearings
B9, Set-pins for locating Countershaft
C, Pinion Shaft
C1, Ball-bearings for Pinion Shaft
C2, Housing for ball-bearings
C3, Distance Piece
C4, Cover for Oil-return Screw
C5, Coupling for Pinion Shaft
C6, Internal Toothed Ring
D, Spindle for Change-speed Fork
E1, Third and Fourth Change-speed Fork
E2, First, Second, and Reverse Change-speed Fork
G, Gear-box Casing
H, Foot-brake Drum
N, Position of Level Cock

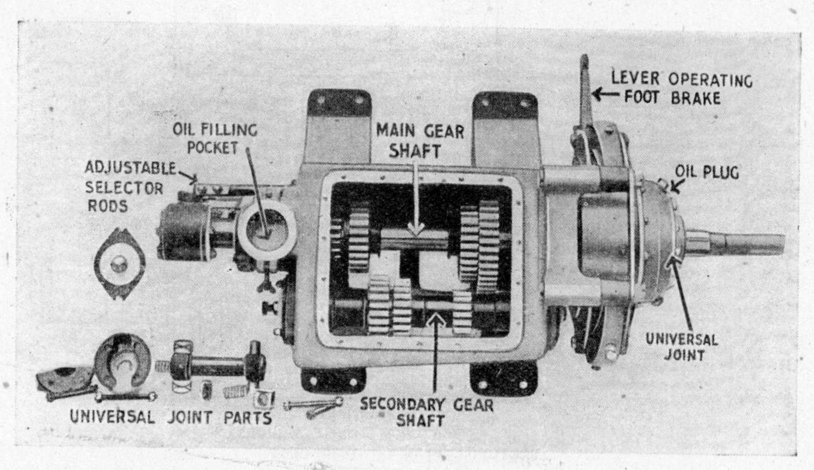

Fig. 381.—Commercial-type Gear Box, with Cover Removed.

Fig. 381 is a photographic illustration of a commercial-type gear box, and universal joint, at the rear of the gear box.

The oil-filling pocket is also shown.

The gear-box cover has been removed, in order to show the gear shafts. The same view shows also the adjustable gear-selector rod, the universal-joint components, and transmission brake.

The side-sectional and end views of the Morris commercial-vehicle (15 cwt. and 1 ton) gear box, given in Fig. 382, should be useful to the service engineer, as showing the construction the gear box and general arrangement of the gears, shafts, and bearings. The plate clutch, gear-selector mechanism, and universal joint are also shown in these illustrations.

LUBRICATION OF THE GEARS

The gear box seldom requires attention, but it is of great importance to maintain the level of the lubricant about constant, not only from the point of view of absence of wear, but also from that of silence of operation.

The usual rule is to examine the level of the lubricant in the gear box once every 500 to 1,000 miles of running in the case of newer cars, and every 250 to 500 miles after a car has had a good deal of use. The instructions of the makers of different cars differ on this point to a certain

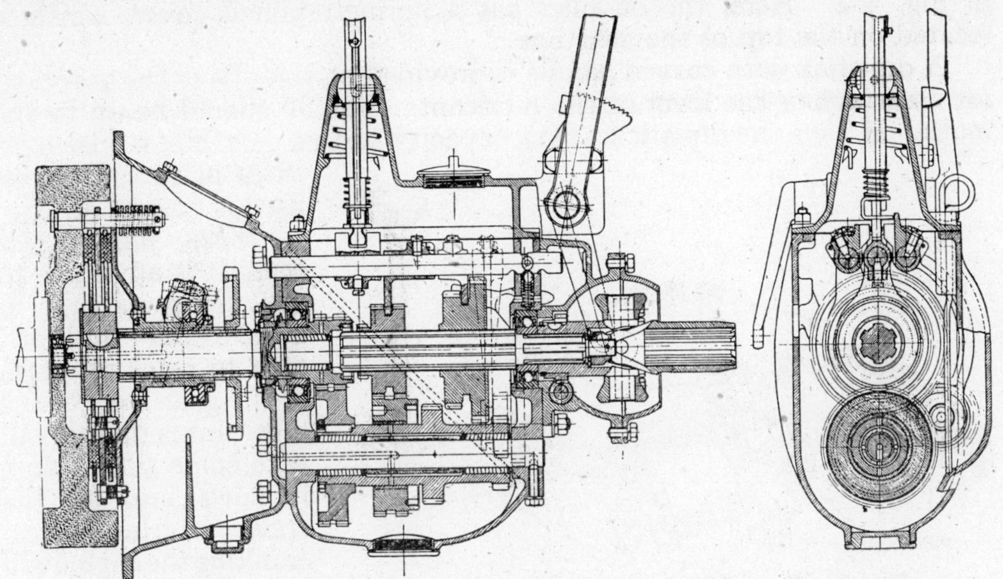

Fig. 382.—Morris Commercial-pattern Gear Box, Clutch, and Metal Universal Joint.

extent, some advocating the weekly replenishment of the lubricant, others recommending the practice every 2,000 miles.

To be on the safe side, however, it is best to examine the level of the lubricant every 500 miles or so, more particularly in cases of leaking gear boxes.

Practically all cars are provided with proper filling orifices to their gear boxes; a short examination will soon reveal the position of the filler plug on any car.

There is also a level indicator, which is usually in the form of a tapered screw plug, about one-third way up the casing from the bottom, and the lubricant is poured in through the filler until it commences to overflow through this plug hole—the plug having been removed, of course, for the purpose.

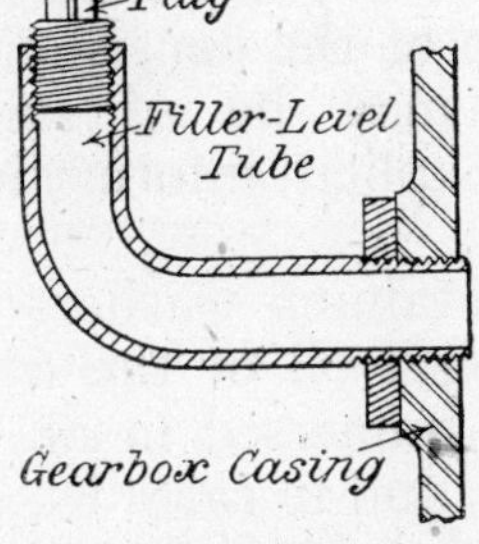

Plug
Filler-Level Tube
Gearbox Casing

Fig. 383.

In many modern cars special lubricant-level gauges of the dipper or float type are fitted to the gear box.

On some American and other type of gear boxes the filler and oil-level gauge are combined, and consist simply of a short piece of tubing bent at right angles, one end being screwed into the gear box and the other, which is arranged vertically, is provided with a screw plug, as shown in Fig. 383. Lubricant is poured into the vertical branch until the level of that in the gear box is the same as about the top of the filler tube. Usually this type takes a long time to fill, as the bore is small and there is no air vent.

The method of lubricating the Rover Sixteen gear box is illustrated in Fig. 384. Here, the oil filler has a spring-retained cover, which is located on the top of the gear box.

A dip-stick with curved handle is provided on the side of the gear box, for ascertaining the level of the lubricant. The oil should be up to the mark " H " on the dip-stick. The capacity of this gear box is just over three pints and the oil used is Castrol XXL.

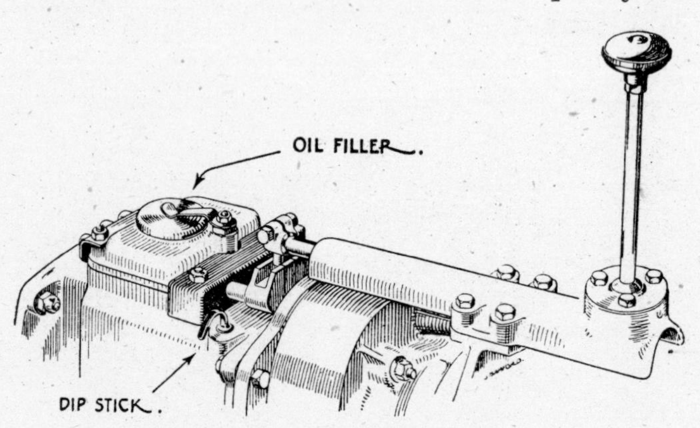

Fig. 384.—Rover Sixteen Gear-box Lubrication.

When filling gear boxes it is advisable to wait for some time in order to allow the lubricant to reach all parts of the gear box; if the lubricant is thick it will take some time before it flows into all the crevices and interstices; cranking the engine will help the lubricant to settle sooner.

It is better when replenishing the gear box with thicker lubricants such as Ambroleum, Sternol Gear Oil, and similar products to *first heat these* in a tin, or pourer, until they are quite fluid, when they can be poured into the gear box readily and quickly. It is best to use a small funnel for filling purposes.

In the event of absence of a gear-box level gauge, the lubricant should be sufficient to just immerse the layshaft—assuming, as is almost invariably the case, that this is below the mainshaft.

As regards *the type of lubricant* to employ for any particular car, it is quite impossible to lay down a definite rule, since each design of gear box requires its own special grade. Some makers recommend ordinary engine oil, whilst others stipulate a lubricating grease of the consistency of vaseline. The following notes on lubricants may be of some assistance in cases where there is no other more explicit information available:

(1) A well-designed gear box, with proper felt retaining washers or oil glands, should always be lubricated with a mineral oil of the consistence of engine oil. The layshaft should just be immersed in oil.

(2) For gear boxes inclined to be on the noisy side, and in cases where there is leakage along the mainshaft bearings, a thicker lubricant should be employed. Ambroleum, a gear lubricant of vaseline consistency when cold, is an excellent remedy for noisy gears and leaky shafts.

(3) For normal types of gear box use one of the gear-box lubricants

sold by the motor-oil manufacturers, such as Sternol, Wakefield's, Price's, Vacuum Mobiloil, or Shell-Mex.

Most motor garages have a list of leading makes of cars with the gear oils recommended for all these.

(4) Once every 3,000 miles or so, the lubricant in the gear box should be emptied out, by removing the lower and upper plugs; some motor

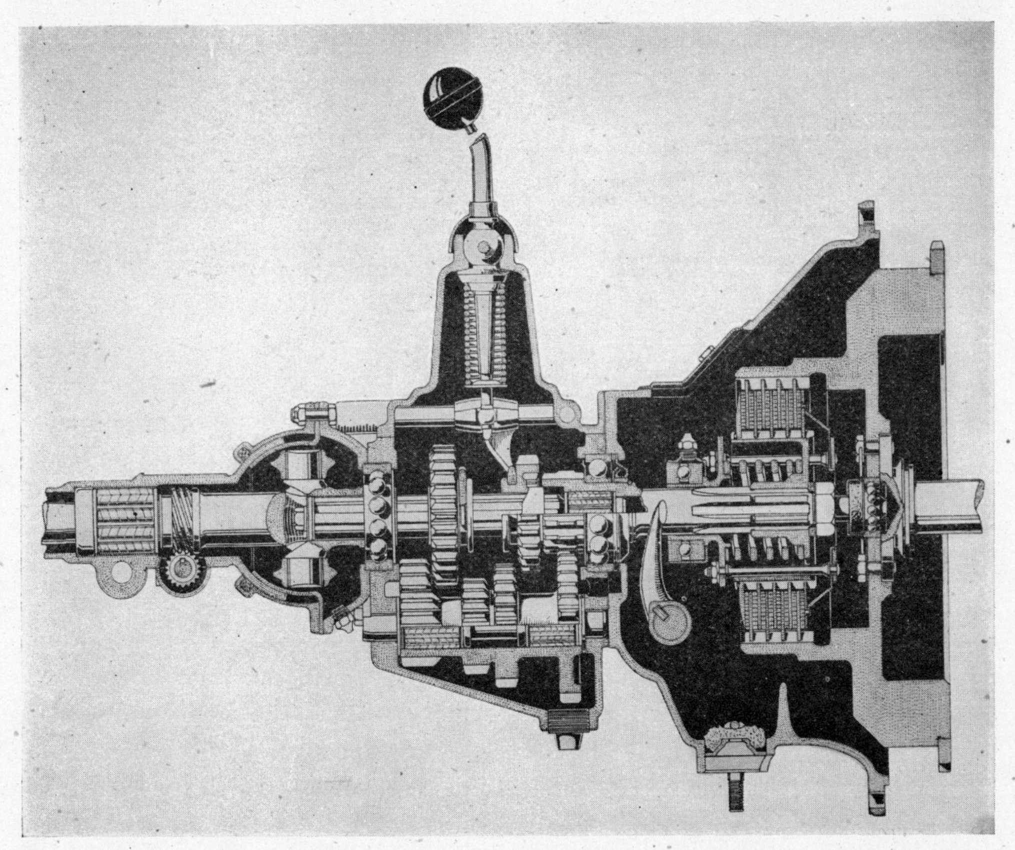

Fig. 385.—Typical Three-speed Gear Box, with Multiple-plate Clutch and Universal Joint. The Speedometer Drive is shown to the rear of the latter.

engineers heat the gear box with a small blow-lamp to accelerate this process.

When the lubricant has been drained out, the lower plug should be replaced, and about *a quart of paraffin poured into the gear box.* The upper plug should now be replaced and the engine started up and allowed to run slowly for a few minutes. This will thoroughly clean the gears and at the same time dislodge any small particles of metal or dirt, causing them to sink to the bottom, and to flow out with the paraffin when the latter is drained off.

(5) If the gear-box cover is taken off, as it should be, on these occasions, to inspect the gears, it may be possible *to repack the ball- or roller-bearings* with a fairly thick acid-proof grease, which will protect the bearings

from the abrasive action of the small particles of metal which often come from the gears—due to the gear-changing action.

(6) *Too much oil* will result in a definite loss of power, due to the churning action. Tests made at the National Physical Laboratory have conclusively shown this, and we need only add that a well-known power-testing brake absorbs the whole of the power of the large aeroplane engine under test by virtue of this churning action. The golden rule is, therefore, use as thin a lubricant as possible under the

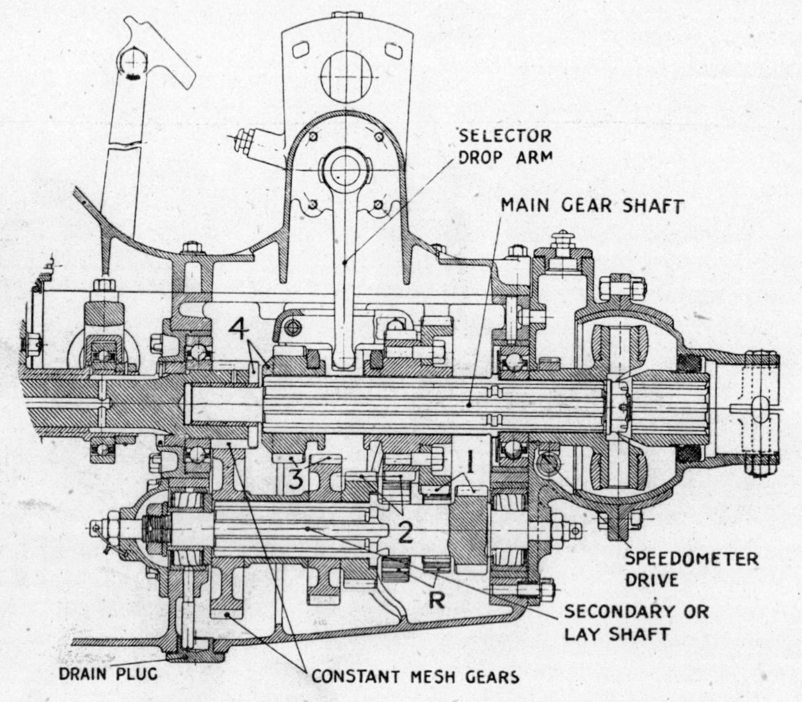

Fig. 386.—Showing Principal Components of Four-speed Commercial-vehicle Gear Box.

circumstances, and replenish often, but keep as low a level in the gear box as possible.

In many cases, the effect of putting in *too much lubricant* is merely to increase the frictional resistance and promote leakage.

(7) *In the case of commercial vehicles* in regular service, the lubricant should be drained out at least two or three times yearly, the inspection cover removed, and the gears carefully cleansed with a brush to remove any foreign matter. The whole gear box should be flushed out with paraffin and refilled with new lubricant; old lubricant will have lost part of its lubricating value and will contain particles of metal and dirt, which are very detrimental to gears and ball-races.

(8) In the case of the gear box (illustrated in Fig. 374) the makers recommend the use of a good grade of steam cylinder oil, but at *the beginning of the winter season* they state that it is advisable *to thin the lubricant,* by adding engine oil; usually a " half-and-half " mixture will

meet winter driving conditions. The oil should be changed after the first 2,000 miles of running, and thereafter twice a year.

(9) When cars are used in *very hot weather, or in tropical climates*, it is advisable to use a much thicker lubricant. The addition of a quantity of good-quality gear grease will often effect this, when the ordinary gear oils have been used ; the resulting mixture should, however, be quite liquid under running conditions. If the lubricating oil becomes too thin under tropical conditions, not only will the ball-bearings suffer, but there will be an increased consumption of gear-box lubricant due to the leakage of the thin oil past the mainshaft bearings ; the gears also may tend to work more noisily.

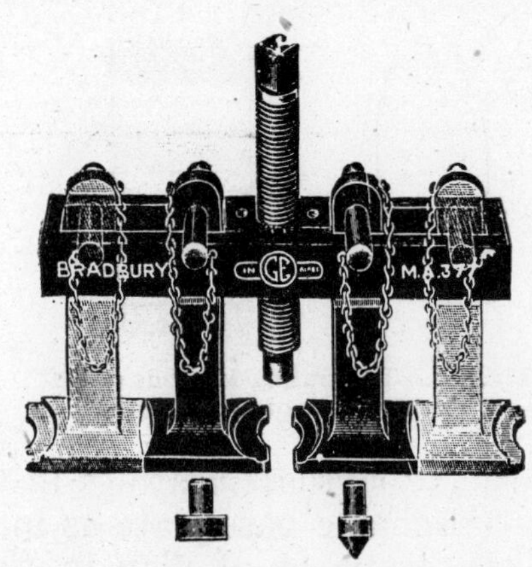

Fig. 387.—The G.E. Gear Wheel Removal Tool.

Fig. 387 illustrates the G.E. universal gear wheel and sprocket withdrawal tool, which is particularly applicable to gear box and engine timing gears, magneto and dynamo couplings ; also to transmission couplings. It is readily adjustable. The jaws are made from heat-treated 40-ton steel. The arms are reversible, one side being recessed for extracting magneto, dynamo, and pump drives where space is limited. The jaws on the other side are heavier, being suitable for larger driving gears. The arms can be locked in any position on the beam with hardened-steel wedges and it is impossible for the jaws to spread from the work when in use. Two detachable nose pieces are provided as shown in the illustration. It has a 10-in. cross-beam, the length of the chain under the beam being 4 in. ; it weighs 10 lb.

EXAMINATION OF THE GEARS

The correct procedure in connection with the periodical examination of a gear box is as follows : First remove the floorboards, and brush all dirt away from the gear-box cover, its holding-down bolts and nuts. Similarly, clean thoroughly with paraffin and a brush the gear-lever housing in gear box—if of the central type. The object of this is to ensure that when the gear-box cover is removed no dirt or grit will get into the gear box accidentally.

It is advisable, also, to brush all dirt and dust away from the footboard ledges and frame channels, so that there is no possibility of one's clothes brushing dirt into the gear box when leaning over the latter.

Having drained out the lubricant, and cleaned the gears with paraffin, in the manner previously described, drain out the paraffin, and remove the gear-box cover, taking care, as we have mentioned, not to allow any dirt to enter. The gear lever being in neutral, it will be possible to rotate some of the gears by hand, and to examine their teeth.

The sides of the teeth on the slider engagement sides should be examined for wear, or burring. Any appreciable wear is evident by a want of symmetry between the two faces of any tooth (as indicated in Fig. 388 (A)), when viewed from the side. If the teeth have not been meshing properly there will be a lack of parallelism on the crowns of the teeth as shown in Fig. 388 (B). The worn portions of the tooth surfaces will be indicated by a high polish—sometimes with slight surface markings due to the breaking down of the case-hardened layer—whilst on the unworn parts the original grinding or machining marks will be visible.

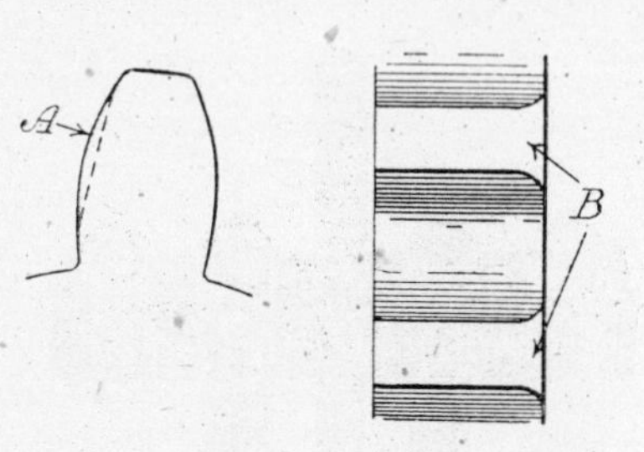

Fig. 388.—Illustrating Methods of Detecting Wear of Gear Teeth.

Test the mesh of the gears for backlash; one of the rear wheels should be jacked up in order to test all of the gear wheels.

Next, take hold of each sliding gear wheel, bodily, and test it for excessive wear on its castellated or keyed shaft; any undue shake or noise will provide an indication of wear in this respect.

Next, take hold of the mainshaft and see if you can detect any end or side play in its bearings; it will not be possible to test the layshaft bearings in this manner, unless the gear-box casing has a detachable base-plate as in some designs. If there are signs of badly worn teeth, or of play in the shaft bearings, the gear box should be dismantled.

This can be accomplished by first disconnecting the clutch coupling shaft—the exact method will, of course, depend upon the type of gear box and clutch—and then the propeller shaft universal. It may also be necessary to disconnect the hand-brake connections, and the gear lever and gate, if the latter is on the right-hand side, away from the gear box.

The gear-box holding-down bolts can then be removed, and the former lifted out of the frame.

The dismantling of the gear box is not a difficult matter as a rule, once it is on the bench, although a certain amount of care is necessary in removing the ball or roller bearings, and the plain bearings (when fitted). Special bearing-extracting tools can be made or purchased for this purpose. It is generally necessary to remove the bearings before the gear shafts can be extracted. In removing ball-bearings note which is the press-fit member—usually the outer race—and force this part out. Do not hammer a ball-race with a hard steel drift; if it is impossible to force the race out by any other method, use a copper drift and apply the blows as evenly as possible around the race. Once a race has been started, it can often be levered out by a suitably improvised device.

All external bearing caps, or adjustment screws on the gear box, should be removed before attempting to get the gear shafts out.

THE ART OF GEAR CHANGING

Gear changing, with the almost universal designs of three- and four-speed gear boxes, is undoubtedly the most difficult operation concerned in the control or driving of motor vehicles.

Bad gear changing not only results in noise, and the attraction of public attention, but it may result in fairly rapid wear of the gear teeth. Too much attention cannot be given to the matter of obtaining adequate experience of gear changing, by frequent practice on the road.

Each design of car has its own gear-changing procedure, depending principally upon the gear box and back-axle ratios, so that the operation of gear changing on one car may not be quite the same as on another.

The beginner is advised to spend at least half an hour daily practising gear changing both up and down, on the level road, until a perfectly silent change can be made in any circumstances. He or she should practice changing up, from rest, noting the speedometer readings when each successive gear is engaged. Thus in the case of a three-speed gear change it is not necessary to accelerate the engine (on the level) to a high speed in each gear before changing up to the next higher one—a procedure frequently followed by those who like to hear their engines hum—but merely sufficiently to enable the next gear to be engaged. In the case of the majority of medium-speed cars, starting from rest in bottom (or 1st) speed, it is only necessary to accelerate to a speed of 4 or 5 miles an hour, before declutching and pushing the gear lever into its second-speed position. Then accelerate to 9 to 12 miles an hour and declutch to engage top (or 3rd) speed. After each lower speed is engaged, let in the clutch gently, and accelerate.

The slower the speeds of the car at which the gears can be changed up, the better; the quicker the operation, as a rule, the better also, for little loss of speed of the car occurs in the operation.

When a car is started from rest do not accelerate violently, but gradually, and when the clutch pedal is depressed for moving the gear lever over, *take the foot off the accelerator*.

In the case of many cars a better change from second to top can be made by accelerating rather more than usual, declutching, and placing the gear lever in neutral, hold it there for several seconds before pushing it into the top-gear position; this pause gives the clutch a chance of stopping its spin and allows the main and layshaft gears to mesh at their proper speeds.

In *cases of difficult gear changing*, the cause may be found in the incorrect adjustment of the clutch stop, or in the clutch plates being "sticky," so as to tend to remain together, or to drag when the clutch pedal is depressed. The clutch stop should come against the spinning (or gear-box side) clutch member immediately the clutch pedal is depressed so as to prevent its spinning. The method of dealing with sticky clutches is dealt with in the chapter on clutches, and so will not be considered further here.

To summarise the operations of changing up, these are as follows:

(1) Accelerate engine, to certain road speed found by trial to be the best, and declutch.

(2) Push gear lever over through neutral, pausing in the latter position in the case of some cars, and then into next higher gear.

(3) Re-engage clutch gently, and accelerate.

It is a more difficult operation to change down, principally because one has not always the choice of suitable road speeds when changing down. Changing down has usually to be done on hills, when it is undesirable to lose road speed if one is to climb the hill satisfactorily. Further, when in traffic one has to reduce speed, changing down must be done expeditiously.

Changing down should be practised, firstly at slow speeds, say from 15 to 10 miles an hour on top gear, and secondly at higher speeds, namely, from 30 to 20 miles an hour, for it is at the latter speeds gear changes from top must be made on hills.

At the slower speeds, it is usually possible to make a quiet change down by declutching, and moving the gear lever right through neutral into the next lower gear, and then re-engaging the clutch; the foot should be removed from the accelerator whilst the engine is declutched. It is often possible to make a good change down by simply accelerating the car to, say, 15 m.p.h., and then decelerating the engine by taking the foot off accelerator and, before the car has had a chance to slow down, suddenly moving the gear lever into neutral, and over into second gear; the car tends to overrun the engine and thus enables the gear lever to be moved into neutral without force.

In many cases it is only necessary to give the clutch a slight depression at the moment of moving the gear lever over.

When changing down at the higher speeds, *double declutching* is usually necessary.

The method of double declutching should be practised on the level a good many times before attempting it on a hill; it will result in a noiseless change down without loss of road speed. The method is as follows:

(1) Depress clutch pedal and move gear lever into neutral.

(2) With gear lever still in neutral re-engage clutch and accelerate engine an appreciable amount.

(3) Depress clutch pedal again and smartly move gear lever into next lower gear.

(4) Re-engage clutch gradually and gradually depress accelerator. Quickness is the keynote of success in the operation of double declutching, and for this reason much practice is necessary in order to perform the above operations as quickly as possible. If carried out slowly, a noisy change will be experienced, due to loss of road speed and consequent incorrect gear speeds for meshing.

If you find the gears grate or fail to mesh noiselessly, *at once declutch*, and, holding the clutch out, place the gear lever in neutral, and apply the brakes.

Whenever you make a mistake, do not attempt to force the gears into mesh, or you will undoubtedly shorten their life, but at once declutch, stop the car and commence over again.

If it is a case of making a mistake in gear changing when attempting to climb a hill, stop and start again on bottom gear—if necessary continuing on this gear to the top of the hill.

When climbing a hill do not allow the car to slow down too much on top gear, but make an early change to the next gear, thus maintaining the engine speed and rendering a much quicker and better climb possible. Most beginners make the mistake of hesitating too long before changing down.

In some cases *a quick change down* can be made by keeping the throttle open (or accelerator depressed) and then slipping the clutch just sufficient to enable the gear lever to be pulled straight through to the next lower gear position.

ADJUSTMENT OF GEAR-BOX BEARINGS

Fig. 389 illustrates a typical design of gear box fitted with Timken roller-bearings ; a special feature of the latter is their ability to take end thrust as well as radial loads.

When the car has seen a fair amount of service, an examination of the main and layshafts will frequently show that a small amount of end play has developed in their bearings. This clearance can be taken up in cases where Timken roller bearings are fitted.

Referring to Fig. 389, the following is the method of taking up wear in the bearings:

To adjust the Timken bearings remove the two locking pieces which lock adjustments from the front and rear of the gear box, then *unscrew* the nut A by turning it anti-clockwise until there is an appreciable resistance. The bearings of the first motion shaft and the shaft itself will now be

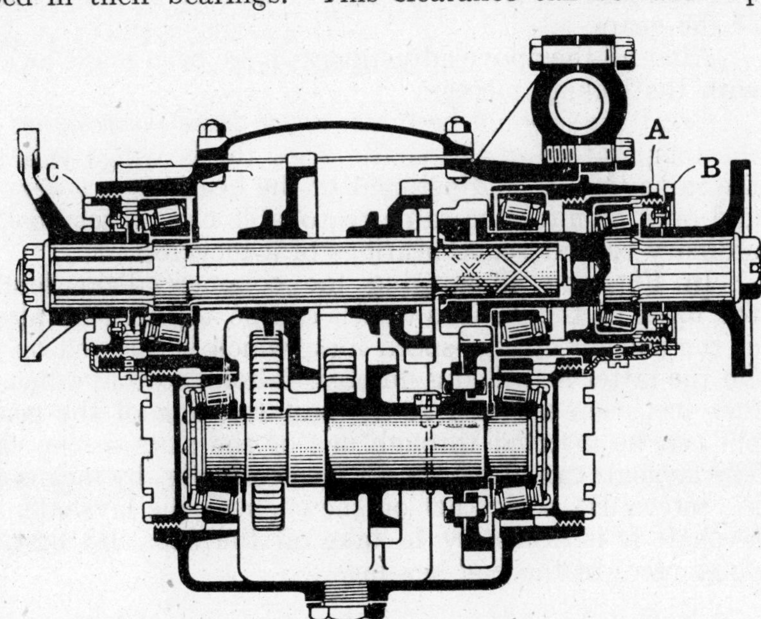

Fig. 389.—Illustrating the Adjustment of Gear-box Bearings.

tight. The same nut A must then be turned in the reverse direction (clockwise) until the shaft just rotates freely and at the same time the slot in the nut comes opposite the locking tongue. This adjustment should allow the shaft to rotate freely without perceptible end play. It will generally be found, on screwing the adjustment nut until a resistance is felt, that backing it in the reverse direction one notch will give the required adjustment. The nut B only retains the front bearing and no adjustment for wear can be made with this nut.

After adjusting the front bearings it may be necessary to adjust the rear bearing, as this bearing may become slack after the adjustment of the former. Screw up clockwise the adjustment nut C at the rear of the gear box where the motion shaft comes through, until resistance is felt to further tightening, then unscrew until the shaft rotates freely without perceptible end play. It will generally be found on screwing the adjustment nut until a resistance is felt, that turning it in the reverse direction one notch will give the required adjustment.

The bearings of the countershaft are adjusted by screwing up the front and rear castellated nuts provided for this shaft. Screw up both the nuts the same amount each until they are just tight and then back off sufficient to allow the shaft to rotate freely but without noticeable end play. Do not make all the adjustment to one nut only, or the shaft will be moved endwise, possibly sufficient to affect the correct meshing of the gears.

After all the above adjustments have been made lock the nuts securely with the locking pieces.

Great care should be taken *not to leave the bearings too tight,* or when the temperature of the shafts rises the bearings will be damaged. At the same time the adjustment of the bearings is a very simple operation and only requires the same reasonable care observed as when adjusting ordinary cup-and-cone bearings of a bicycle.

In Fig. 380, illustrating the commercial-car four-speed gear box, the mesh of the various wheels can be adjusted by altering the position of the end for change-speed fork, which is screwed on to the spindle D. On the latter is drilled a number of holes so that when the change-speed fork has been set to give the best meshing of the gear wheels, a split-pin can be inserted through one of the slots in the change-speed fork. The layshaft can also be positioned correctly, by means of the two adjusting screws B9, which act on the ends of the layshaft. To remove the layshaft it is necessary to take off the caps B8 first, which carry the outer races of the ball-bearings.

THE ROVER GEAR BOX WITH FREE-WHEEL

The Rover 14-h.p. and 16-h.p. cars employ four-speed gear boxes in conjunction with built-in free-wheels. Central gear-change levers are employed. The gears used are of the double-helical constant-mesh kind with a silent second and third gear. A sectional view of the gear box is given in Fig. 390; the free-wheel unit, shown in detail in Fig. 391, is situated at the rear, or propeller shaft end.

The free-wheel device can be locked by means of a control situated on the instrument board. When this is turned clockwise, as far as possible, the free-wheel is locked and the gear box behaves as an ordinary non-synchromesh type.

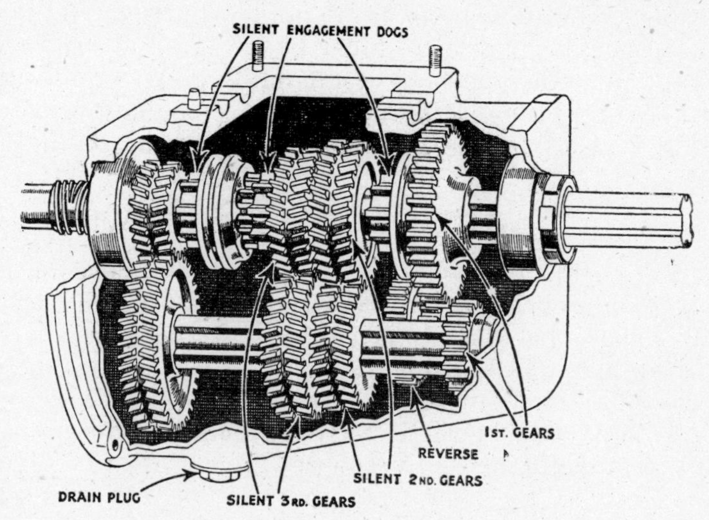

Fig. 390.—The Rover Gear Box with Free-wheel.

The use of the free-wheel greatly simplifies gear changing, the procedure being as follows:

CHANGING UP

As long as the free-wheel is in use, it is not necessary to use the clutch once the car has been set in motion. After having set the car in motion, proceed on first gear, speeding up the engine until about 5 m.p.h. is attained and then proceed as follows to change to a higher gear:

(1) Take your foot off the accelerator pedal.

(2) Pause sufficiently long for the engine " revs " to die down. This will take from one to three seconds, according to speed attained.

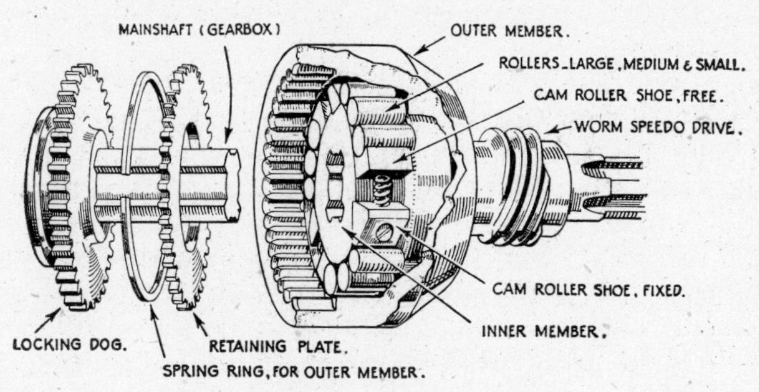

Fig. 391.—The Rover Free-wheel Device.

(3) Move gear lever gently, but firmly, into second position.

(4) Continue with acceleration.

Note.—The pause before changing up is most essential. A long pause will not matter; if too short, a noisy gear change will be the result.

Repeat this procedure from second to third gear, and from third to top gear.

If this method is adopted and strictly followed out, it does away with any necessity for using the clutch once the car is in motion, *but only applies when the free-wheel is in use.*

CHANGING DOWN (With Free-wheel in Operation)

To change down from top to third gear or from any gear to a lower gear, proceed as follows :

Lift your foot off the accelerator pedal and at the same time move the gear lever from the top to the third position, and continue with acceleration. The movement need not be hurried, but it is impossible to do it too quickly, and there must be *no pause in neutral.*

The same method of changing down applies in changing from third to second gear. If a very rapid " change down " is required on a steep hill, it is advisable to use the clutch in the normal manner.

ADJUSTING THE FREE-WHEEL DEVICE

After the free-wheel control has been in use for a certain length of time, it becomes necessary to take up any " backlash " that may have developed.

The " backlash " is caused by the Bowden wire free-wheel control stretching, and adjustment usually becomes necessary after the first 500 miles (800 km.) or even less, according to the amount of use the control has had in that period. After the initial stretch has been taken out of the cable, no further adjustments are necessary. This condition is usually reached by the time 1,000 miles (1,600 km.) have been covered.

When adjustment has been delayed too long a " grating " noise will be heard when " free-wheeling " and the noise obviously comes from the direction of the gear box. When this noise is heard the adjustment should be made at the first opportunity or damage will be caused to the free-wheel. The adjustment is quite simple and takes only a few minutes to carry out.

To adjust the free-wheel control :

(1) Place the free-wheel in the fixed position by turning the control fully in an anti-clockwise direction.

(2) Put the gear lever in the first gear position, release the hand brake and rock the car backwards and forwards several times, a few inches in each direction. This is done to make sure that the free-wheel has fully engaged the fixed position, and if it is done on level ground it will present no difficulties.

(3) Grasp the free-wheel control and move it very gently alternately " left " and " right " the distance required to take up any " backlash " present ; if this is done very lightly, the " backlash " is easily felt. Whatever " backlash " is present (it will probably be as much as ½ in. (13 mm.) measured at the rim of the control knob) will have to be reduced to the smallest perceptible amount. To do this, proceed as follows : Lift up the off-side of the bonnet and remove the scuttle cover ; the back of the instrument board will then be exposed ; the Bowden cable leading to the freewheel control will be seen passing through the bulkhead. At the point where the cable goes through the top of the glove box two small nuts will

be found, a short lock nut and a long adjusting nut. With a spanner release the lock nut by turning it in an anti-clockwise direction, and adjust the cable by rotating the long nut in the required direction (anti-clockwise to reduce " backlash " and clockwise to increase " backlash "). This should be done until the smallest perceptible amount of " backlash " remains at the control knob. It is essential that this small amount be left or only partial engagement of the " fixed " position is possible, with consequent risk of damage to the free-wheel device. Do not forget to retighten the lock nut when the adjustment is correct.

The backlash is measured at the outer edge of the freewheel control knob ; the maximum " free " movement should be ½ in. (13 mm.) and the minimum ⅛ in. (3 mm.).

GEAR BOX WITH OVERDRIVE DEVICE

In view of the popularity of this type of gear box, more especially on American cars used in this country, an account of a typical assembly, with notes on its adjustment and maintenance, will be given, selecting the Chrysler design as a typical example.

The gear box is of the selective type with three forward speeds and one reverse. The second-speed gear on the mainshaft is in constant mesh with the second-speed gear in the countershaft gear set, and both being of the helical type, are quiet in operation. The low and reverse gears are of the sliding type, changing into second, and direct drive is accomplished by a sliding clutch sleeve, which in conjunction with the synchroniser results in easy and quiet changing of gears. The top and second sliding clutch sleeve is designed to synchronise with the top and second-speed gear so as to avoid clashing of gears due to improper declutching and gear changing.

Fig. 392 illustrates the complete gear box and overdrive assembly, with the various items indicated by the figure numbers ; the key being given on page 367.

Referring, first to the gear-box unit, if it should be necessary to remove the gears, *care should be taken to keep the assembly in alignment* with the engine and thus prevent distortion of the clutch shaft and clutch driving disc. This is done by installing two pilot studs, one on each side of the gear-box case in place of two of the cap screws holding the gear box to the clutch housing. These studs will carry the weight of the gear box. The latter is removable without disturbing the clutch assembly except that it is necessary to remove the clutch-release bearing pull-back spring.

The gear box should be filled to the level of the filling plug with gear oil of the recommended type (Motorine, Battersea A). The level should be inspected every 2,000 miles and entirely replaced every 5,000 miles. *The overdrive device* is provided to reduce the ratio of the engine speed to car speed above 40 m.p.h. without manual changing of the gears. When the overdrive is in operation the engine speed is slower than the propeller-shaft speed, whereas in direct drive, that is without using overdrive, the engine speed and propeller-shaft speed are the same. The overdrive unit consists of a planetary gear set, an automatic clutching (engagement) unit and a free-wheeling unit. The engagement of the overdrive is controlled by the engine speed and the free-wheeling unit. The automatic operation of the overdrive can only take place when the free-wheeling unit is in operation. A control button on the instrument panel is provided which may be set in either of two positions. When the control is pulled out all the way to its stop, the overdrive or free-wheeling does not operate at any speed. However, when the control is pushed in, the overdrive and free-wheeling units are in position ready for operation.

Fig. 392.—The Chrysler Gear Box and Overdrive Unit.

When changing the control from one position to another it is necessary to have the engine driving the car ; the clutch pedal must be depressed while pulling out the control. When changing from overdrive to conventional drive, do not exert any more pressure than absolutely necessary on the controls to accomplish the change. Gently, but rapidly, pull out the control, but do not force engagement. *The overdrive control must not be changed at speeds above* 40 to 45 miles per hour (64 to 72 km.).

When the overdrive control is pushed in to the limit of its travel and the car is travelling at a speed of more than 40 to 45 miles (64 to 72 km.) per hour the foot accelerator must be released for at least $1\frac{1}{2}$ seconds in order to bring the overdrive mechanism into operation. Overdrive engagement cannot take place unless the car is operating at a speed in excess of the overdrive cut-in speed, and the engine is running at a speed at least 25 per cent. slower than the car speed. The control should be pushed in to unlock the overdrive and free-wheel, and in this position, at car speeds lower than the overdrive cut-in speed, the drive is taken to the mainshaft through the rear clutch teeth, and the free-wheel cam and rollers. The clutch core and pawls are revolving faster than the clutch shell, but at the same speed as the overdrive clutch, consequently, when the car speed exceeds the overdrive cut-in speed, centrifugal force, acting on the pawls, overcomes the tension of the pawl-adjusting springs and causes the pawls to fly outward into engagement with the slots in the clutch shell. However, as long as the pawls are rotating at a higher speed than the shell, engagement cannot occur due to the design of the pawls, until the foot accelerator is released for the length of time necessary to allow the engine speed to drop sufficiently so that the clutch pawls are turning at the same relative speed as the shell. When this occurs, engagement will take place so that the pawls will lock the clutch core to the shell. The overdrive set is now in operation, reducing the engine speed without reducing the car speed. The power is transmitted to the clutch, the pawls, the shell, and then to the planetary gear set. From this point, finally through the pinion to the ring-gear internal teeth and to the mainshaft. The free-wheeling unit is not in operation when in overdrive. Due to the engaging properties of the overdrive clutch, it is possible to accelerate from low car speeds up to maximum speed in direct drive without the overdrive functioning, because the overdrive clutch will not engage (due to the difference in rotating speed of the clutch pawls and shell) unless the throttle is completely closed for $1\frac{1}{2}$ seconds after the cut-in speed (40 to 45 miles) (64 to 72 km. per hour) has been reached. It is important that all accelerator control rods and the accelerator pedal operate freely without lagging or sticking, and these parts should receive periodic inspections at all points, and be lubricated with light engine oil.

Key to Fig. 392.—The Chrysler Gear Box with Overdrive Device.

1, Gearshift Housing.
2, Gearshift Rail and Fork—First and Reverse.
3, Gearshift Lever Thrust Spring and Cup.
4, Gearshift Lever Thrust-spring Ball.
5, Gearshift Lever.
6, Gearshift Lever Locating Pin.
7, Gearshift Lever Friction-plate Spring.
8, Gearshift Lever Friction Plate.
9, Gearshift Lever Friction-plate Support.
10, Gearshift Rail and Fork—Direct and Second.
11, Transmission Drive Pinion-bearing Retainer Gasket.
12, Gearshift Rail-selector Ball.
13, Gearshift Rail-retainer Oil Seal.
14, Gearshift Rail-selector Ball Spring.
15, Transmission Clutch Gear and Facings.
16, Transmission Clutch-gear Ball.
17, Transmission Shaft Second-speed Gear-thrust Washer.
18, Transmission Shaft Second-speed Gear-thrust Washer Pin.
19, Gearshift Rail Retainer—Rear.
20, Gearshift Rail-retainer Screw.
21, Overdrive Reverse Lock-up Plunger.
22, Overdrive Shift Rail.
23, Gearshift Housing Gasket.
24, Overdrive Housing Adapter.
25, Transmission Shaft-bearing Snap Ring.
26, Transmission Shaft.
27, Overdrive Shift Fork.
28, Overdrive Retractor Spring.
29, Overdrive Shift-rail "C" Washer.
30, Overdrive Shift-rail Expansion Plug.
31, Overdrive Control-shaft Oil Seal.
32, Overdrive Control-shaft Lock Screw.
33, Overdrive Control Lever.
34, Overdrive Shift-rail Poppet Spring Seat.
35, Overdrive Control Shaft.
36, Transmission Drive-pinion Bearing Retainer.
37, Transmission Drive-pinion Bearing Snap Ring.
38, Transmission Drive-pinion Bearing Snap-ring Washer.
39, Transmission Drive-pinion Bearing.
40, Transmission Countershaft.
41, Transmission Shaft Pilot-bearing Roller.
42, Transmission Drive Pinion.
43, Transmission Case Drain Plug.
44, Transmission Countershaft Gear.
45, Transmission Shaft Pilot-bearing Snap Ring.
46, Transmission Countershaft-bearing Spacer.

47, Transmission Clutch-gear Sleeve.
48, Transmission Clutch-gear Ball Spring.
49, Transmission Shaft Second-speed Gear-thrust Washer Spring.
50, Transmission Shaft Second-speed Gear.
51, Transmission Case.
52, Transmission Countershaft Bearing Roller.
53, Transmission Countershaft Gear-thrust Washer.
54, Transmission Countershaft Gear-thrust Washer.
55, Transmission Case Gasket.
56, Overdrive Housing Gasket.
57, Transmission Sliding Gear—First and Reverse.
58, Transmission Shaft Bearing.
59, Overdrive Case Drain Plug.
60, Transmission Shaft Bearing Washer.
61, Transmission Shaft Bearing Washer Snap Ring.
62, Overdrive Ring Gear.
63, Overdrive Stationary Gear.
64, Overdrive Stationary Gear Snap Ring.
65, Overdrive Clutch Sleeve.
66, Overdrive Housing.
67, Overdrive Pinion-cage Snap Ring.
68, Overdrive Clutch-core Hub Bushing.
69, Speedometer Drive Pinion.
70, Freewheeling Cam-retaining Washer.
71, Overdrive Shift-rail Poppet Spring.
72, Overdrive Shifter Head Lock Screw.
73, Overdrive Shifter Head.
74, Overdrive Adjusting Hole Plug.
75, Overdrive Ring Gear Snap Ring.
76, Overdrive Clutch Core.
77, Overdrive Pinion Cage.
78, Overdrive Pinion.
79, Free-wheeling Cam.
80, Overdrive Clutch Pawl.
81, Overdrive Clutch-core Thrust Washer—Front.
82, Overdrive Main Shaft.
83, Overdrive Clutch-core Thrust Washer—Rear.
84, Free-wheeling Roller.
85, Free-wheeling Roller Retainer.
86, Overdrive Clutch Core.
87, Overdrive Clutch-pawl Adjusting Screw—Plain.
88, Overdrive Clutch-pawl Adjusting Spring.
89, Overdrive Mainshaft Bearing Snap Rings.
90, Overdrive Mainshaft Bearing.
91, Free-wheeling Retainer Snap Ring.
92, Overdrive Adjusting-screw Lock Washer.
93, Overdrive Clutch-pawl Adjusting Screw—Slotted.
94, Overdrive Clutch Pawls.
95, Overdrive Mainshaft Nut.
96, Overdrive Mainshaft Companion Flange.
97, Overdrive Mainshaft Oil Seal.
98, Transmission Mainshaft Pilot.
99, Transmission Mainshaft Pilot Bushing.
100, Overdrive Clutch-core Hub.

THE SYNCHRO-MESH GEAR BOX

In this gear box, which is now almost universal, there is a clever device, of American origin, for synchronising the speeds of the driving gear and that of the gear to be engaged, by means of cone clutches, so that these gears may be engaged noiselessly and without effort.

The principle underlying the synchro-mesh gear is to speed up the gear to be engaged until it is running at the same speed as that of the gear with which it is to be meshed, when it will slide into mesh smoothly and without noise. The manner in which this is accomplished can be explained with reference to Fig. 393 which shows two clutch units. In this example the left-hand gear wheel is free to move on the shaft, whilst the right-hand one can slide along the splined shaft, so that when it is moved sufficiently to the left the two clutch members will engage and drive as one. Fig. 394 shows the pair of these clutch members and also two sliding-gear wheels, each of which engages in an internally cut gear inside the driven-shaft gear wheel. In effect, this arrangement is equivalent to a double dog clutch as a means of connecting the drive and driven shaft. In this sketch the outer cones are not shown. Fig. 394 shows the complete double cone members in

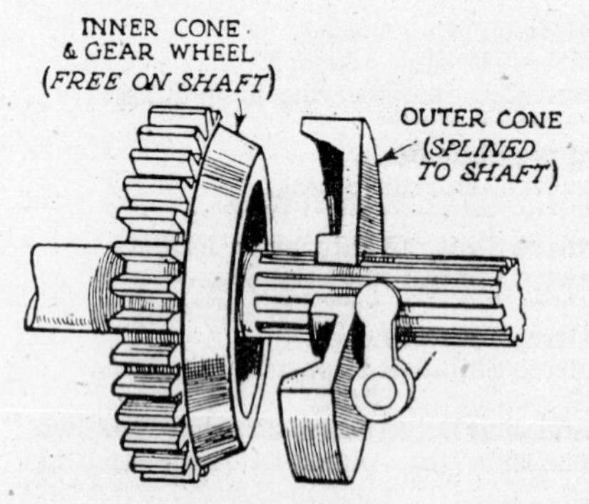

Fig. 393.—Synchro-mesh Gear Unit.

section. During the operation of gear-changing the gear lever moves the outer cone running with the shaft into contact with the inner cone on the gear wheel, thus speeding it up or reducing its speed, as the case may be. In the centre illustration in Fig. 394 the clutch is shown engaged with the internal and external gears locked in place, so that the two revolve solid. In the right-hand diagram of Fig. 394 the gear is shown locked to the left, but with the clutch again quite free. Having fulfilled its purpose in speeding up the left-hand gear member to the speed of the outer cone, the latter is automatically released.

It will be observed that this arrangement applies to the position of two gears, whereas there are actually three different ratios in the gear box. As the lowest gear is merely for emergency, it is not so important to study the gear changing in this case; indeed, in the cars to which this device is fitted it is an easy matter to start off on second gear.

It should be added that in addition to the cone-clutch units there are also oil dashpots for simplifying the action of the cones.

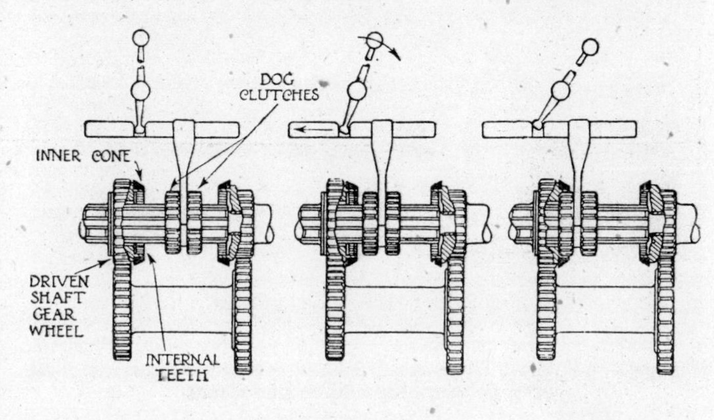

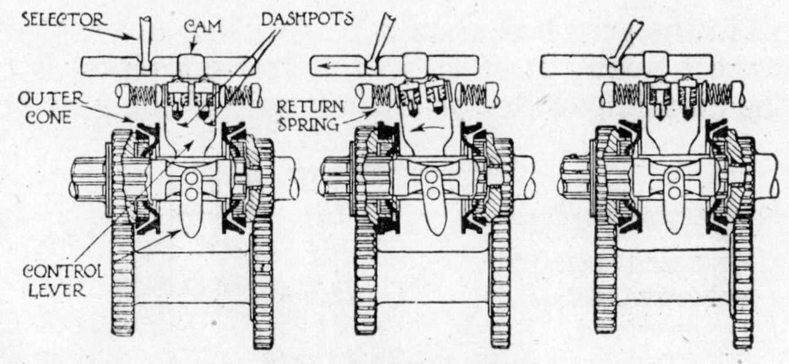

Fig. 394.—Showing Principle of Synchro-mesh Gears.
(Courtesy "*The Autocar.*")

Summarising the above remarks, it can be said that movement of the gear lever from top speed to second engages first the outer cone with the inner, so as to bring the two sets of teeth to approximately the same speed, then it meshes the two sets of teeth so as to run the gear to the shaft. When this is done an operating plunger releases the cone, thus setting the mechanism for the next gear-changing.

The design of the synchro-mesh gears, controls, and damping device is complicated; their adjustment or repair is outside the scope of the ordinary motor mechanic, so that it is necessary to return it to the service station of the makers of the car to which it is fitted. Briefly, the synchro-mesh is obtained by the use of a cone clutch which synchronises the speed of the gear wheels just prior to engagement. Fig. 396 is a cross-section through the gear box of 1935–6 Vauxhall car. This model has silent-mesh second-speed gears.

Fig. 395.—A Typical Three-speed Gear Box with Synchro-mesh Unit at S, between Top and Second Gears.

The silent second speed is obtained by helical gears which are in constant mesh.

The first reduction pinion gears and second-speed gears have helical teeth, while the first and reverse gears are of straight-tooth design.

The speedometer drive is taken from the rear end of the gear-box mainshaft by means of spiral gears, from which it is transmitted to the instrument through a flexible cable.

Lubrication.—At intervals, the level of oil in the gear box should be checked and replenished if necessary. The correct quantity of oil in the box ($2\frac{1}{2}$ pints) is governed by the level of the oil-filling orifice on the left side of the gear-box casing.

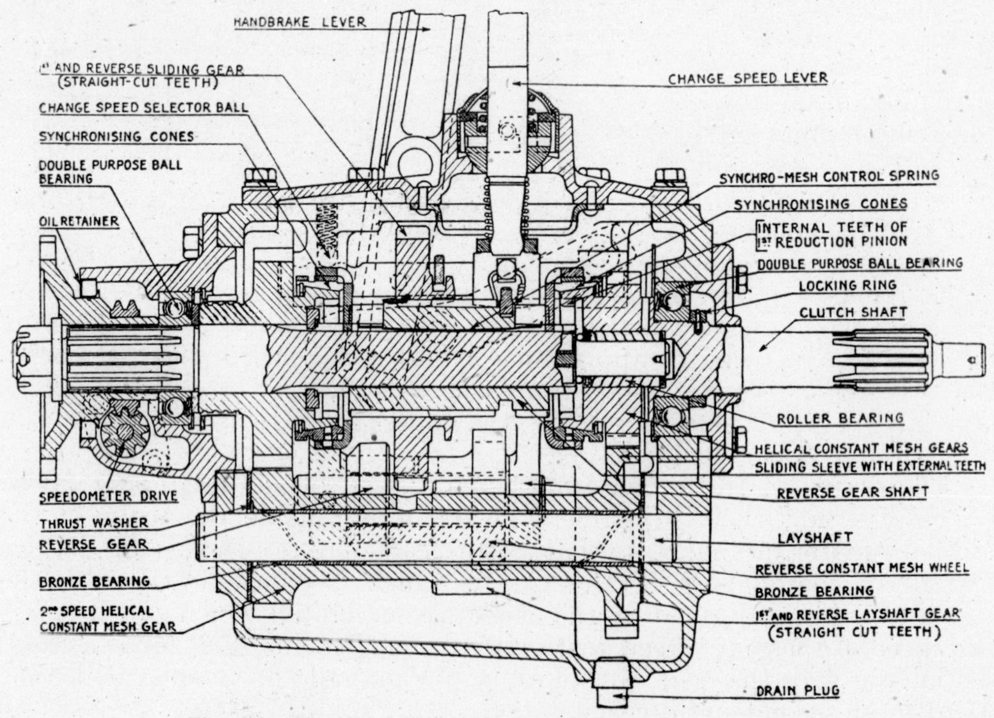

Fig. 396.—The Vauxhall Synchro-mesh Three-speed Gear Box.

To lubricate the speedometer driving cable, slacken the clamping screws of the outer casing guide situated at the top end. Release the clip holding the cable to the dashboard and the top of clutch housing. Remove the two large finger-nuts which hold the speedometer head in position in the instrument board. These nuts are located at the back of the board immediately behind the speedometer head and a little to the left of the cable. One nut is approximately in line with the cable and the other three inches above it. The speedometer head can then be withdrawn through the front of the instrument board together with cable, sufficiently to enable the outer casing clamping ring to be released, after which the outer casing should be pushed back and heavy-grade gear oil forced down by means of an oilcan.

THE AUSTIN GEAR BOX

The Austin cars are now all fitted with synchro-mesh gear boxes and a sectional view of the 7-h.p. and 10-h.p. model is shown in Plate facing p. 372. These are four-speed gear boxes giving synchro-mesh engagement on second, third, and top gears, with ordinary first "crash" change and the usual reverse gear.

The synchro-mesh mechanism is governed by a series of spring-loaded balls as shown in Fig. 397. The inner cone on the inner member C makes contact with the gear cone in order to bring the speeds of the two members to the same value, i.e. to synchronise them, before the dog-clutch member B, overcoming the resistance of the ball A, moves on to give positive gear engagement.

Fig. 397.—The Austin Synchro-mesh Gear Box.

In the Austin cars gear changing may be slightly stiff in the new car until the new parts have eased in use. *Gear changing should, therefore, not be done hurriedly* and no attempt should be made to force the gear lever if engagement is not made at the first attempt. Should difficulty be experienced in engaging a gear when the car is standing, release the clutch for a moment and repeat the procedure.

THE FORD 8- AND 10-H.P. GEAR BOXES

This gear box has three forward speeds and reverse, with silent-running constant-mesh intermediate gears having helical teeth. Direct drive is on top gear. There is a synchro-mesh gear between top and second. A sectional view of the gear box is given in Plate facing p. 374. This also shows the engine flywheel, single-plate clutch, and front-end universal joint of the propeller shaft. The device consists of a conical clutch operating in conjunction with a positive tooth clutch in such a way that synchronisation of the toothed clutch members is brought about by the action of the conical clutch before meshing takes place as previously explained. It is made up of an inner hub and an outer ring. Teeth on the inside of the ring mesh with teeth on the outside of the hub at all times. In neutral position, the central location of the ring on the hub is maintained by six steel balls, held in a groove in the ring by springs. The hub has an internal bronze section at each end which fits the conical steel flange on either intermediate or top gear. When a change is made to either top or intermediate speed, the synchronising device moves as a unit until the bronze section of the hub engages with the conical flange of the gear ; the speed of the two is synchronised or made uniform, and as the change is completed, the internal gear or ring of the synchroniser unit is released from its centrally located position

Fig. 398.—The Alvis Four-speed Synchro-mesh Gear Box.

on the hub, and the internal teeth engage in the teeth of the top or intermediate-speed gear. As the two are rotating at the same speed, the meshing of these gears is effected without clashing of the teeth.

It is important to note that, if the gear-box cover is removed at any time, the outer ring of *the synchroniser should not be moved* forward on its inner hub. If this outer rings travels forward beyond its normal position (which is determined by selector in gear-box cover assembly), the six steel balls which locate the central position of the ring on the hub will, on account of the spring pressure exerted, fly outwards with considerable force. In order to replace them, it would then be necessary to dismantle the gear box ; moreover, special equipment would be needed in order to replace the balls.

THE AUSTIN TEN-FOUR AND SEVEN SYNCHROMESH GEAR BOX IN SECTIONAL VIEW.

Description : This gear box provides for the easy-change synchromesh principle to the second, third, and fourth gear ratios. The second-speed synchromesh unit is embodied in the sliding first-speed gear. The third and fourth synchromesh mechanism is incorporated in the gear coupling.

Fig. 398 illustrates a four-speed gear box having synchro-mesh on all four forward speeds. The gear ratios are 1, 1·43, 2·03, 3·15, and, for reverse, 3·5. These ratios must, of course, be multiplied by the back-axle ratio to obtain the overall ratio for each of the gears.

The gears are of the silent helical pattern. The gear box is mounted at three places on thick rubber washers, and universal joints are provided at each end of the mainshaft. The engine drive is through a short intermediate shaft having fabric universal or flexible joints.

LUBRICATION

It is important to remember that only a fluid lubricant should be used in the gear box, the level of which should be maintained at the height of the filler hole, located on the off-side of the gear-box casing.

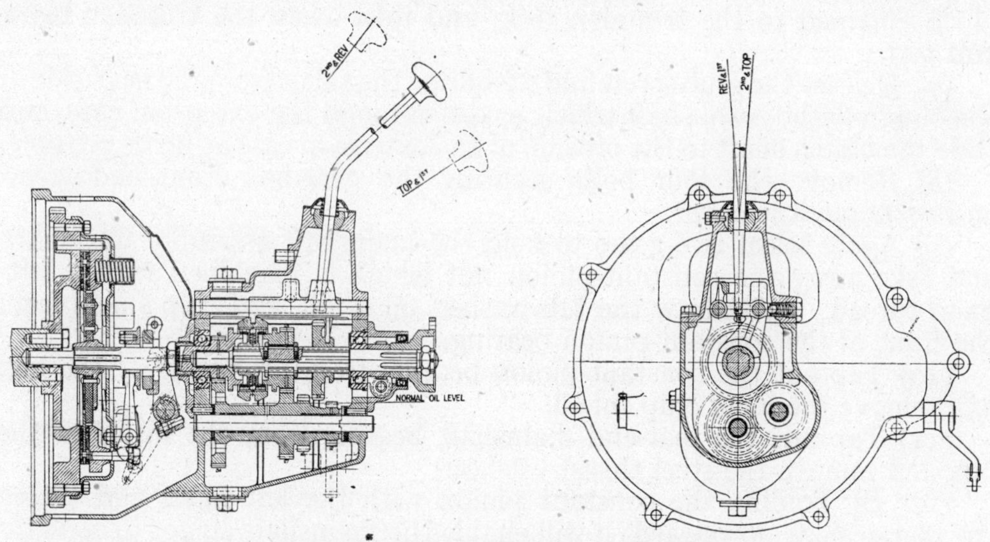

Fig. 399.—The Singer Three-speed Gear Box.

THE SINGER 9-H.P. GEAR BOX

This gear box is of the three-speed and reverse type with synchro-mesh gears for top and second. The gears are of the silent-mesh pattern and lubrication to all gears is provided by splash from the oil reservoir in the base of the casing The working parts of the selector mechanism are lubricated by the oil mist existing inside the casing when the gears are working.

Sectional views (side and end elevations) of this gear box are given in Fig. 399.

DISMANTLING SYNCHRO-MESH GEAR BOX

The general method of taking down a synchro-mesh gear box is well illustrated in the example shown in Fig. 396, the detailed procedure being as follows :

Remove gear box from chassis, and after having drained the oil from the gear box, hold this unit in a vice by means of the drain plug. To dismantle the gear box proceed as follows :

(1) Remove six bolts securing the gear-box lid and control tower to the box.

(2) Select two gears to hold the mainshaft assembly stationary and remove the nut and split-pin from the rear end of the mainshaft in order to allow the front universal joint flange to be withdrawn.

(3) Take out one bolt and withdraw the speedometer-drive bracket complete.

(4) Remove four nuts securing the gear-box end cover and take away the cover.

(5) Slide the speedometer-drive gear from the mainshaft.

(6) Remove the two spring locking rings securing the clutch trunnion block and pad to the trunnion fork, and take away the trunnion block and pad.

(7) Release the grub screw and withdraw the collar from the near-side of the clutch-withdrawal shaft which passes through the extension case, and slide the clutch shaft to the off-side of the extension case as far as possible.

(8) Remove the four bolts securing the gear-box front end cover and withdraw the cover.

(9) Again select two gears to hold the mainshaft assembly stationary and take away the constant-pinion nut which is machined with a left-hand thread. Withdraw the tab washer, oil scroll, and chip shield from the front of the constant-pinion bearing.

(10) Tap out the constant-pinion bearing from the inside of the box and remove the inner chip shield.

(11) Tap out the rear-end mainshaft bearing from the inside of the box and remove the steel thrust washer.

(12) By holding the constant pinion with the left hand and tilting the pinion shaft downwards it will enable the mainshaft spigot to be withdrawn from the bush of the constant pinion, and the mainshaft assembly can now be passed through the top of the gear box. Withdraw the constant pinion backwards through the top of the gear box.

(13) Remove the set-pin and shake-proof washer which secures the lock plate for the reverse shaft and layshaft.

(14) Tap out the layshaft from the front through the rear of the gear box.

(15) Remove the layshaft gear cluster from the top of the box, taking special care of the one bronze thrust washer at the front end of the assembly, and the one steel and one bronze thrust washers at the rear end of the assembly. The slotted steel washer registers in the reverse gear.

(16) Tap out the reverse shaft and remove the reverse gear.

TO DISMANTLE THE MAINSHAFT ASSEMBLY

(1) Slide first-speed gear from mainshaft.

(2) Remove synchro-mesh assembly complete from mainshaft.

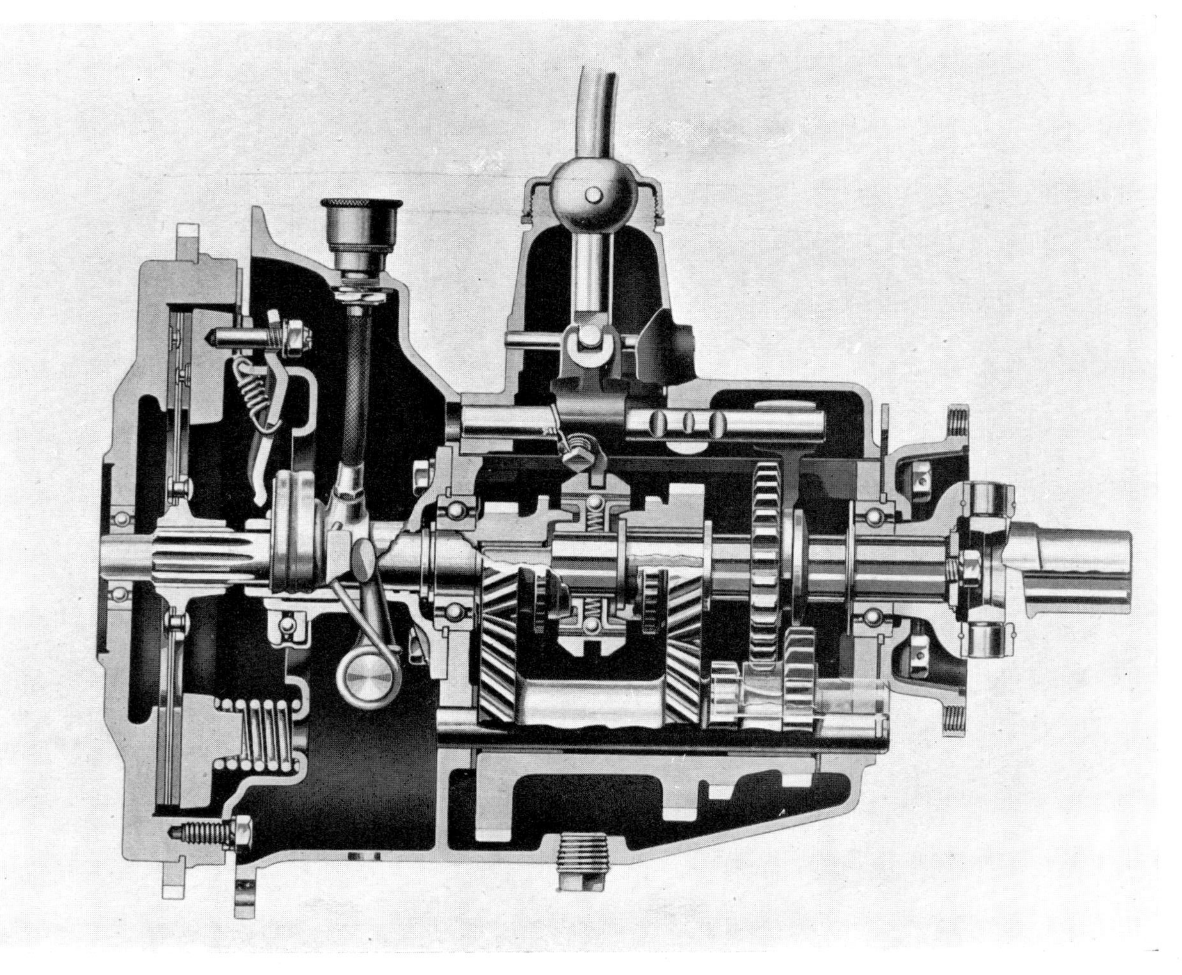

8-H.P. FORD POPULAR AND 10-H.P. DE LUXE GEAR BOX.

(3) To remove the second mainshaft gear, depress one small spring-loaded plunger which secures the splined locking washer at the rear of the second gear. Turn the washer in order to clear the splines and slide this off the shaft. It is then possible to withdraw the second-speed gear, leaving bush on mainshaft, but great care must be taken to avoid losing the plunger and spring.

(4) The synchro-mesh assembly comprises the third and second sliding dog, inside which slides the synchro-sleeve carrying two serrated synchro-cones made of brass, and also contains six balls and springs which in effect lock the top and second sliding dog in the selected position. To dismantle the synchro-mesh assembly, slide it back on to the mainshaft until it butts against the second-speed gear bush. Then depress the third and second sliding dog to its limit, great care being taken to avoid the six balls and springs being lost. Then, withdraw the synchro-sleeve from the mainshaft. No further dismantling is necessary.

THE BEDFORD GEAR BOX

The synchro-mesh gear box employed on the Bedford 19·8-h.p. and 26·3-h.p. goods vehicles (light delivery) is shown in Fig. 400. This has four speeds forward and reverse with synchro-mesh on top and third, with silent-mesh third speed and central ball change. The various parts of the gear box are shown in the key below, Fig. 400.

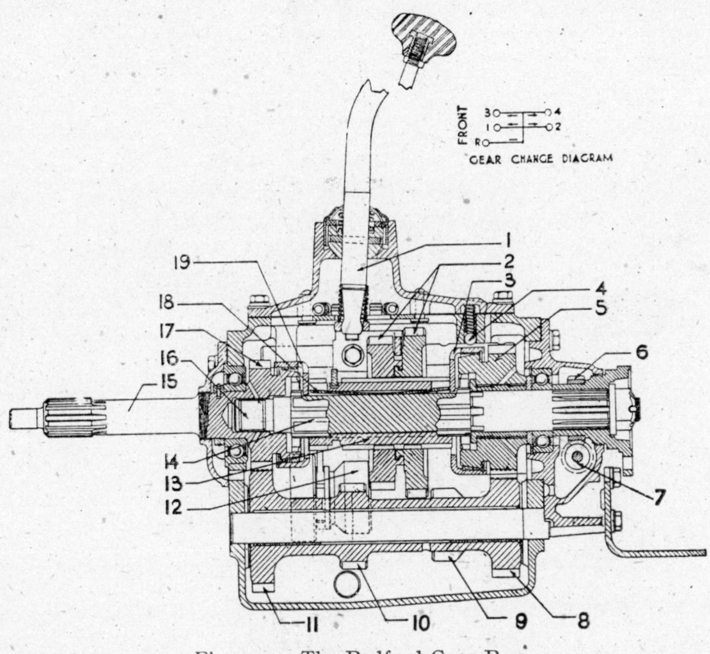

Fig. 400.—The Bedford Gear Box.

Key to Fig. 400.—Section through Bedford Gear Box.

1, Change-speed Lever.
2, First and Second Sliding Gears.
3, Third-speed Synchronising Drum.
4, Selector Ball and Spring.
5, Third-speed Constant-mesh Gear.
6, Speedometer Drive.
7, Speedometer Driven Gear.
8, Layshaft Third-speed Gear.
9, First-speed Layshaft Gear.
10, Second-speed Layshaft Gear.
11, Layshaft Constant-mesh Gear.
12, Reverse Sliding Gear.
13, Sliding Sleeve.
14, Mainshaft.
15, Clutch Shaft.
16, Mainshaft Spigot.
17, First Reduction Pinion.
18, Detent Spring.
19, Top-gear Synchronising Drum.

THE VAUXHALL GEAR BOX

The 1937 Vauxhall 12-h.p. and 14-h.p. gear box is illustrated sectionally in Fig. 401. This has synchro-mesh on top and third. The silent third gear is obtained by helical gears which are in constant mesh. The first reduction pinion gears and third-speed gears have helical teeth, whilst the first, second, and reserve gears are of straight-tooth design. The speedometer drive is taken from the rear end of the gear-box mainshaft by means of spiral gears.

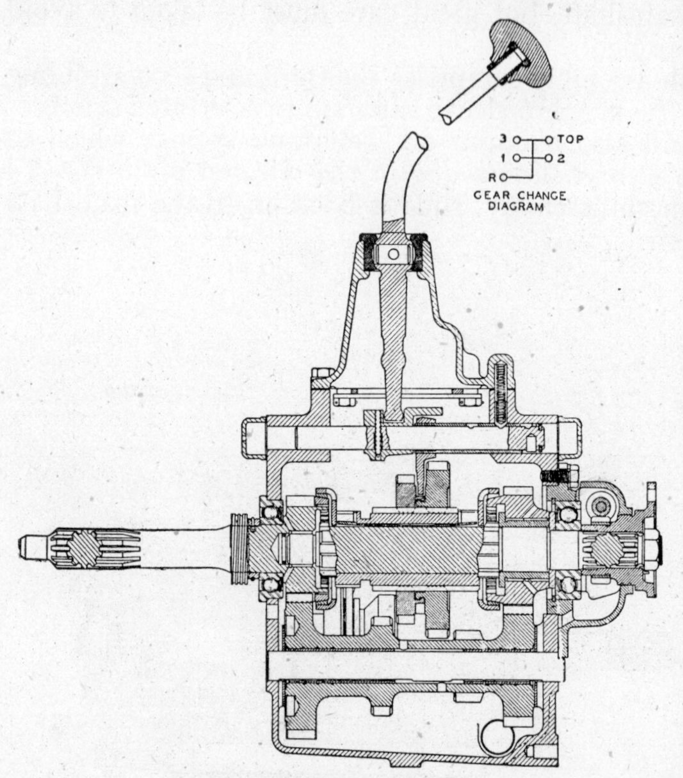

Fig. 401.—The Vauxhall Gear Box.

The Vaxhall gear box should have its lubricant replenished every 1,000 miles. The gear box holds $1\frac{3}{4}$ pints of oil, when the level reaches the mark on the dipper rod which is located on the left-hand rear corner of the top cover. The hole through which the dipper rod passes is also the oil filling orifice.

THE PRE-SELECTIVE GEAR BOX

The Wilson pre-selective gear box which is fitted to Daimler, Lanchester, and Armstrong-Siddeley cars allows the driver to select the gear he wishes to change (up or down) to at any period before actually changing gear, by the simple operation of placing the small gear-indicator lever opposite the gear position required, which is marked on a quadrant mounted under the steering wheel. When it is required to change gear the driver depresses a foot pedal ; on releasing this pedal the gear is changed automatically to the one marked on the steering-wheel indicator, previously mentioned. The gear is thus pre-selected (i.e. selected previously) by means of the steering-column lever, and is changed automatically and without effort or noise, merely by depressing and releasing the gear-change pedal. It is not possible, here, to give full constructional details of this somewhat complicated gear-box mechanism,

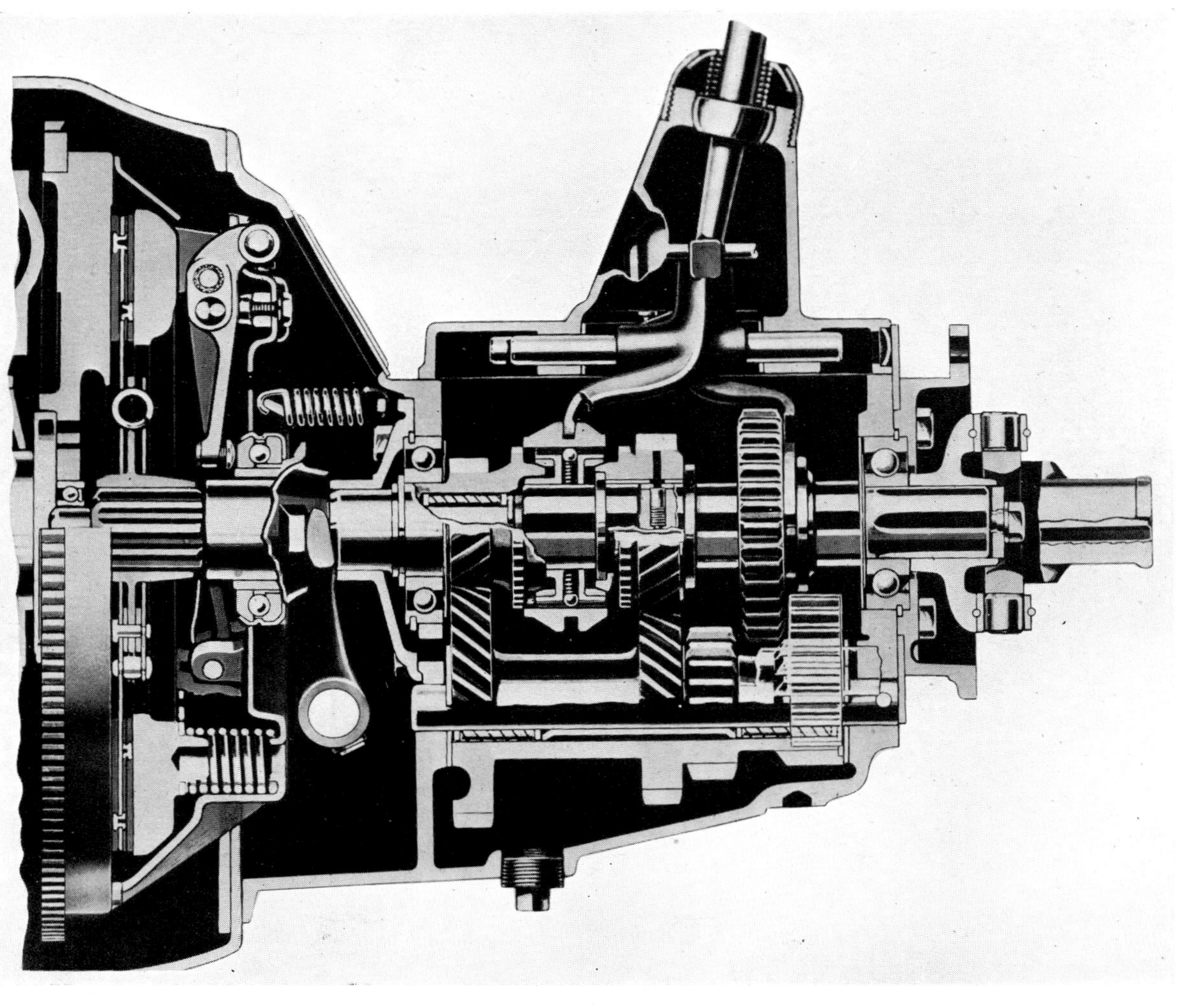

THE FORD V-EIGHT SEMI-CENTRIFUGAL CLUTCH AND THREE-SPEED GEAR BOX.

but only to give an outline of its principle, and to explain its maintenance and lubrication.

The gears used in the gear box in question belong to the sun-and-planet, or epicyclic, type.

The running gear consists of four simple epicyclic trains, interconnected so that combinations can be obtained. The differences of ratio are obtained by compounding the various trains.

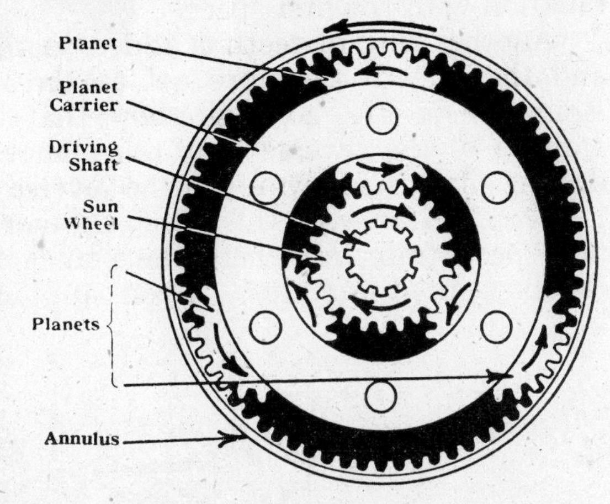

Fig. 402.—Showing Outer Drum Free, the Planet Carrier being Stationary.

Fig. 402 shows diagrammatically a simple epicyclic train. The centre sun wheel is splined on the driving shaft, and meshing with the sun wheel are three planet wheels equally spaced on a carrier ring. The planets are able to rotate upon their own axes, and also are in mesh with the annulus, in which is combined the brake drum.

With the brake off, as shown in Fig. 402, it will be seen that the sun wheel drives the planets, and they, revolving on their own axes, drive the annulus; the directions are indicated by arrows. The planet carrier in this instance will therefore remain stationary and the gear is then idling.

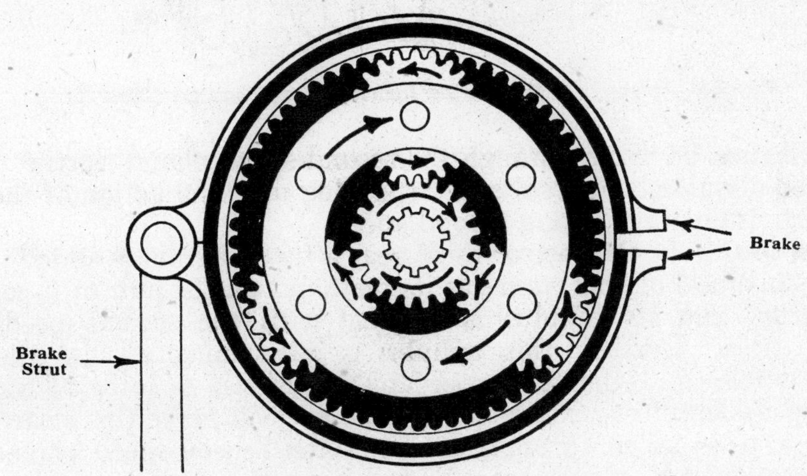

Fig. 403.—In this case the Outer Annulus is Fixed and the Planet Carrier Revolves.

When the brake is applied (Fig. 403) the annulus is prevented from revolving and the planets must revolve around the annulus, taking with them the planet carrier at a slower speed. As the planet carrier is connected to the driven shaft, this will also revolve at a slower speed than the driving shaft; thus a reduction of speed takes place.

This is the action of the first-speed gear.

Fig. 404 shows a perspective section of the running gear and Fig. 405 comprises five views illustrating how the various gears are obtained and the direction of rotation of the various parts.

Reverse Gear.—This is obtained by another epicyclic train in combination with the first speed.

Another ring of teeth is added to the hub of the first-speed annulus, and these teeth therefore act as the sun wheel for the reverse train. Reference to Fig. 405 will show that when the brake is applied to the annulus of the reverse gear the planet carrier, which is splined to the driving shaft, will revolve in the reverse direction.

Second Gear.—In this case another epicyclic train is added to the first-speed train, and here the planet carrier is positively connected to the first-speed annulus. Upon applying the second-speed brake the

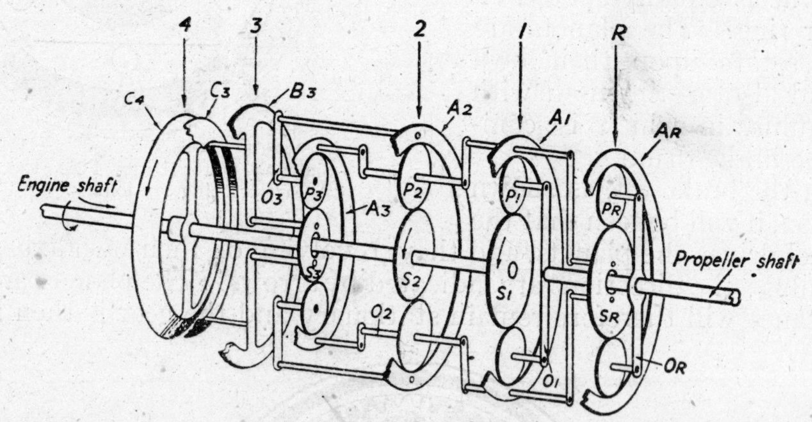

Fig. 404.—Perspective View of the Running Gear (Four-speed Gear Box).

drive will then be taken through the second-speed planet carrier to the first-speed annulus, and results in "speeding up" the action of the first-speed gear train, thus giving second speed.

Third Gear.—In the case of third gear a further train is added.

The sun wheel of this train has its teeth cut on the hub of a separate brake drum and its annulus is integral with the second-speed train planet carrier. Further, this annulus is interconnected with the first-speed annulus, and the third-speed planet carrier is integral with the second-speed annulus. Reference to Fig. 405 will make this clear.

The drive is taken through the first- and second-speed planets and carriers, the speeds of which are governed by the relative speeds of the two annuli. The speeds of these annuli are in their turn governed by the third-speed train, due to the third-speed sun wheel being held by the brake. The result is a further addition to the speed of the first- and second-gear trains, thence to the driven shaft.

Top Gear.—The essential feature of the fourth speed is a cone clutch, the outer member of which is formed within the separate brake drum

The four-speed pre-selective gear box with the cover removed to show the drum-band adjusting screws, and part of the pre-selector mechanism.

The four-speed pre-selective gear box, with the box removed, showing the drum bands and springs in detail.

Showing the various epicyclic gear components of one of the gear-ratio units, for a three-speed gear box.

The three-speed pre-selective gear box running unit, showing the three drums of the epicyclic gear units and final drive shaft.

THE ARMSTRONG-SIDDELEY PRE-SELECTIVE GEAR BOX, SHOWING THE PRINCIPAL COMPONENTS.

and sun wheel for the third speed (see Figs. 404 and 405). The inner member is splined to the driving shaft. To obtain top gear the clutch is engaged and the driving shaft is then connected to the third-speed train. This locks

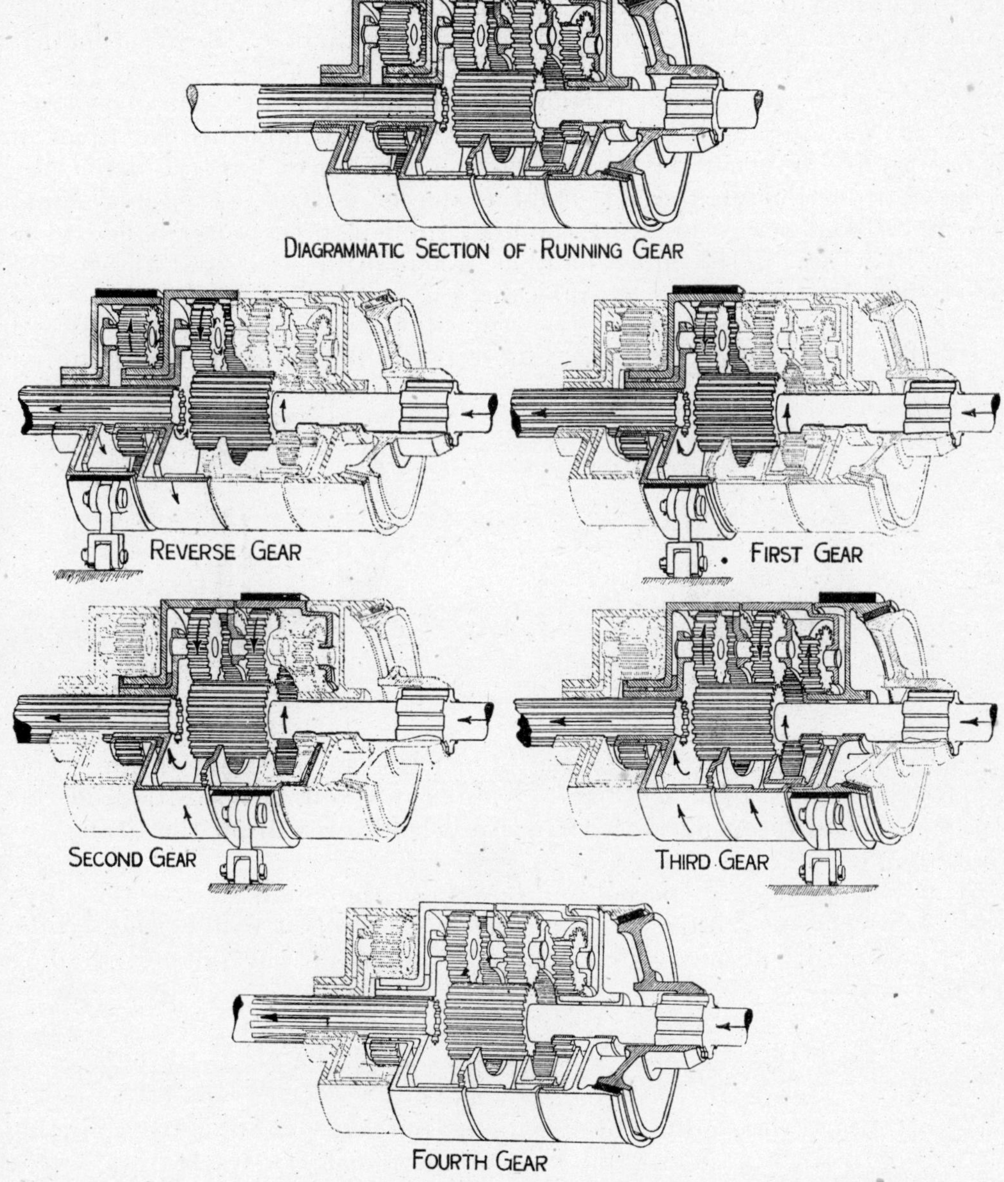

Fig. 405.—Showing the Various Gear-engagement Positions (Armstrong-Siddeley Gear Box)

up all the gear trains so that they revolve as a solid drum, the drive, therefore, being direct. The clutch is of small diameter, as, due to the method of engagement through the epicyclic trains, only one-third of the engine torque is taken through the friction surfaces.

ENGAGING THE SELECTED GEAR

The method of selecting and engaging the gears will next be considered, by reference to the illustrations which follow. In this connection the diagrams are not intended to illustrate any definite model, for the constructional details vary in the different gears made by Messrs. Daimler, Armstrong-Siddeley, etc.

In order to engage any particular train or trains of gears one of the brake drums must be held stationary. This is accomplished by a pair of bands so disposed that the torque reaction is balanced and the mainshaft relieved from loading. Each band is made in two pieces (Fig. 406), the inner band being closed by the load applied to the outer band. The torque reaction of the inner band is taken by a strut and the torque reaction of the outer band by links (see Fig. 406).

In the application of the brakes it will be seen that on the forward drive the bands are self-wrapping, thus greatly reducing the load required

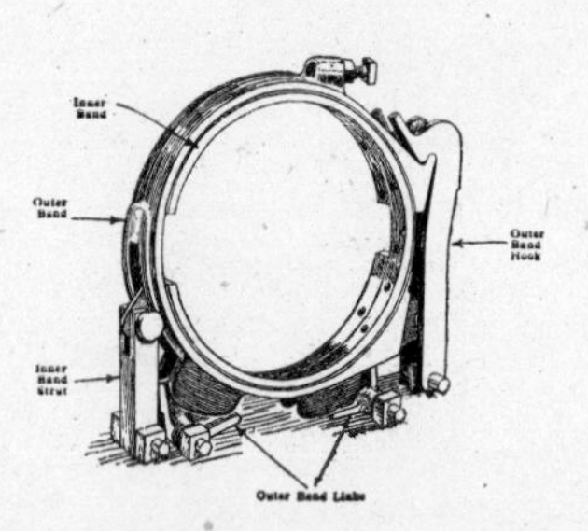

Fig. 406.—The Brake-band Unit.

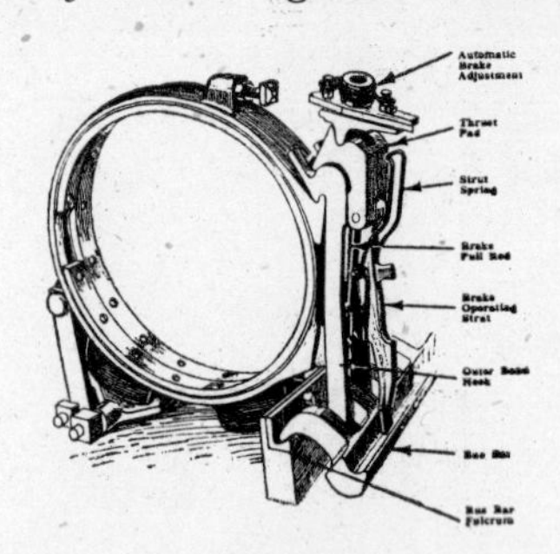

Fig. 407.—Brake Mechanism.

in the pull rod to hold a given torque reaction in the brake drum. The reaction members allow the bands to take up their own position on the drums. When disengaged the bands are held away from the drums by centralisers.

Further to increase the holding powers of the bands on the low gears and to prevent the bands creeping sideways, the reverse, first, and second speed drums are formed with angular grooves on the outside circumference.

THE BRAKE-ACTUATING MECHANISM

The load is applied to the band by means of a spring which operates a bus bar through the medium of a swinging bucket. The bus bar runs the whole length of the gears and pivots on a fulcrum cast on the bottom cover.

When the gear-engaging pedal is depressed the bus bar descends; on releasing the pedal the bus bar rises under spring pressure and lifts the appropriate brake-operating strut.

This mechanism is so arranged that an increasing load is applied to the bus bar as it rises. This is necessary, due to the different torque reactions required on the various gears.

Fig. 407 illustrates the brake-actuating mechanism, and reference to this diagram will assist in identifying the various parts mentioned.

The load from the bus bar is applied to the bands through a strut which is held in the bus-bar knife edge. The strut operates on to a thrust pad, one knife edge resting on the top of the outer band hooks, the other knife edge arranged so as to apply a load on to the pull rod.

It will be seen, therefore, that the toggle action of the thrust pad in rising lifts the pull rod and so contracts the brake.

TOP-GEAR ENGAGEMENT

The top gear, as previously explained, is engaged by means of a cone clutch. The primary actuating mechanism is similar to that of any of the other forward speeds, by means of a pull rod. This pull has to be converted to an end thrust and is obtained through a ball pin working in a cup at the bottom of the pull rod and at its other end in a cup on the inner ball-track member (see Fig. 408). This radial movement of the inner track member is again converted into an axial movement of the same member by means of a number of balls moving in diagonal tracks between the inner and outer members, this movement being transmitted to the inner clutch member through the thrust race. The effect is, therefore, that the upward pull of the pull rod is converted into a backward movement of the inner clutch member into engagement with the outer clutch member.

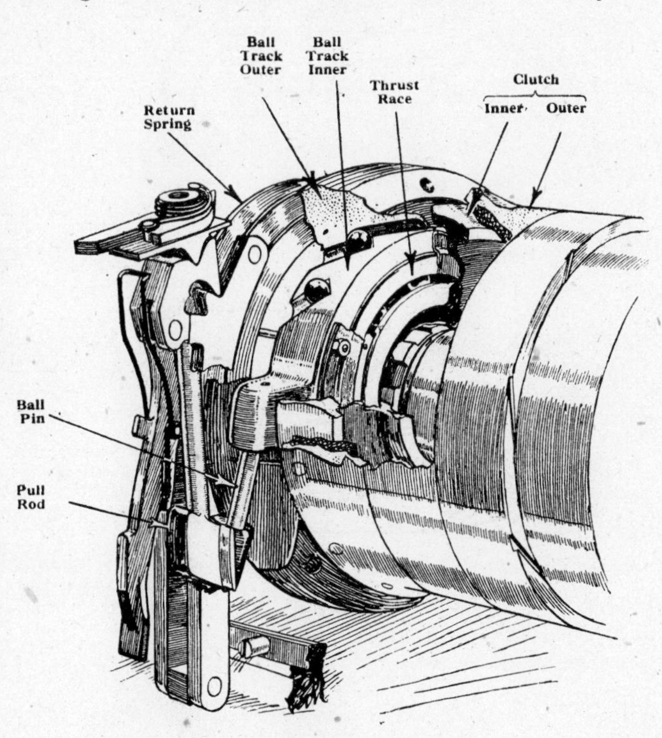

Fig. 408.—Top-gear Engagement.

When top gear is disengaged the clutch inner member is returned to its original position by means of a light spring in front of the track members and attached to the clutch thrust race.

THE BRAKE ADJUSTMENT

To maintain the correct loading on the brake bands it is necessary that the bands are kept correctly compensated for wear. This is achieved by an automatic adjusting device which operates immediately wear takes place.

As the brake band wears the movement of the toggle link increases. The automatic adjustment provides that when this movement exceeds a predetermined amount the pull rod is shortened by means of the automatic adjuster. The adjuster mechanism is shown in Fig. 409. The pull rod screws into a round nut, the base of which is chamfered to register in a table, the table being drilled to allow the pull rod to pass through it. Resting on the table is a ring, which is able to turn freely round the nut. Two pins, one on the table and the other on the ring, hold the two ends of the adjuster spring, and this spring is wound round the nut in such a way that when the ring is rotated clockwise the spring coils will grip the nut and turn it. Anti-clockwise rotation of the ring will cause the spring coils to slip round the nut without turning it. When the brake is "off" the adjuster ring rests against a tail pin, as shown in Fig. 409. The action of the adjuster is as follows. When the brake is applied the adjuster ring is carried forward and strikes the chamfered screw head situated on the brake bands. This causes the ring to partly rotate, the adjusting spring being partly unwound and by this rotation slips on the nut. When the pedal is next depressed and the bus bar again lowered the back end of the ring strikes the tail pin and is rotated back to its original position, the adjuster spring gripping the nut and rotating it in the table and so shortening the pull rod. It will be seen, therefore, that the depression and release of the gear-engaging pedal automatically maintains a constant brake clearance.

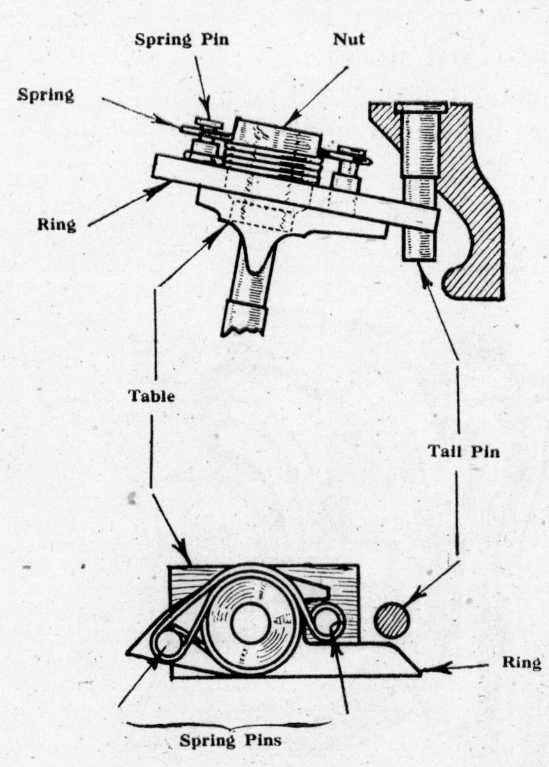

Fig. 409.—Brake Adjustment.

Should slip occur on the bands, the "pumping" of the pedal a few times in each gear will restore the adjustment to its original pitch.

GEAR SELECTION

The gears are selected by means of a camshaft operated by a lever below the steering wheel. Reference to A, Fig. 410 and Fig. 411, will show that this camshaft runs parallel with the bus bar and is adjacent to the brake-operating struts.

With any gear out of engagement the curve of the cam supports a strut guide which is sprung against it and so holds the strut out of the path of the bus bar.

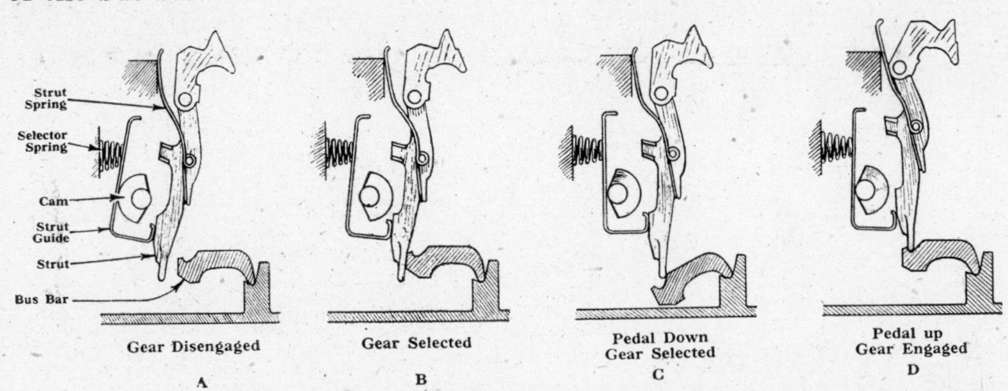

Fig. 410.—Illustrating Gear Selection.

On selecting a gear the cam is turned so that the flat face is supporting the strut guide; the strut guide therefore moves inwards under the pressure of a spring and so places the strut in position against the bus bar, the resistance of the strut spring being overcome by the guide spring (B, Fig. 410). As this selective pressure on the struts is entirely provided by springs, a strut may be selected and pushed over even whilst the bus bar is up and another gear engaged, thus giving preselection. When the gear-engaging pedal is depressed and the bus bar is lowered the newly selected strut is pushed back against the spring by the bus bar and is sprung again into the bus-bar path as soon as the latter reaches its lowest point and allows the strut to pass above it (C, Fig. 411). At the same time the strut used on the previous gear swings back out of the bus-bar path. When the gear-engaging pedal is released the bus bar again rises, carrying with it the new strut and so applies the brake to the appropriate gear train.

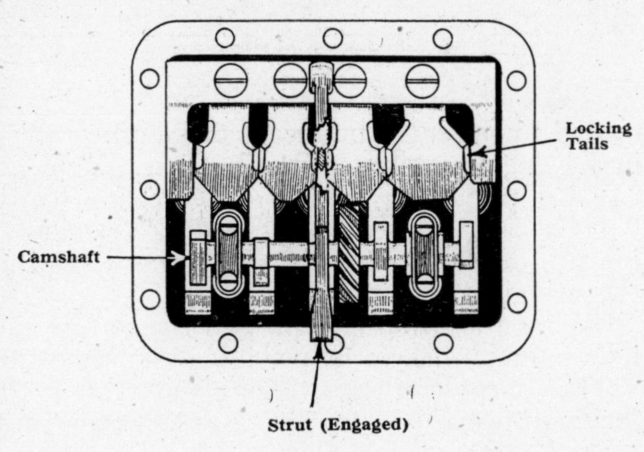

Fig. 411.

To prevent two gears engaging at the same time, a series of locking tails are arranged on the side of the box, and before any strut can rise a small arm formed on the strut has to pass between these tails (see Fig.

411). These locking tails are so arranged that only one strut can pass at a time. Advantage is taken of this to provide neutral, thus an additional flat is provided on the first and reverse cams, each in the same relation to each other on the camshaft. When neutral is selected both the first and reverse struts are unable to pass through the locking tails, thus no gear can be engaged and the mechanism is locked. On the gear box fitted to the 20/25 model a difference is found in the design, in that the strut has to pass through plungers in place of locking tails and also the strut spring is embodied in the strut itself instead of a separate spring bearing against it.

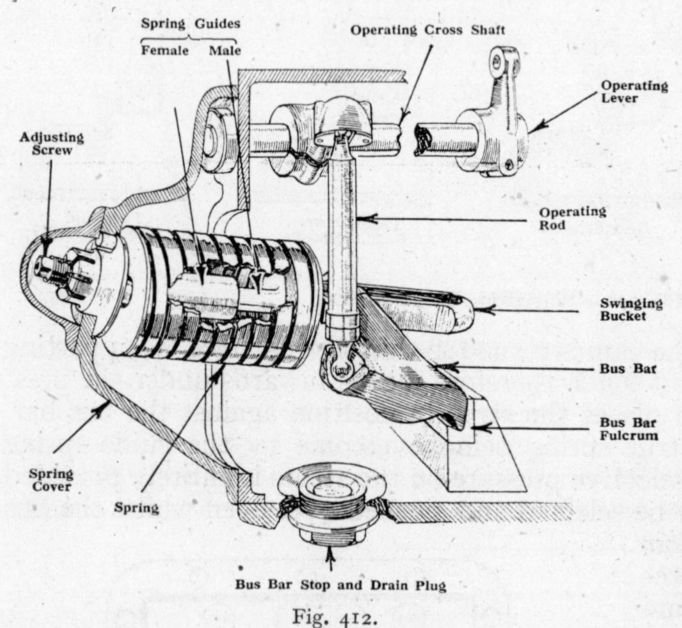

Fig. 412.

THE OPERATING GEAR

This is a separate set of mechanism for operating the bus bar and is situated at the rear end of the box.

A mainspring is provided for loading the bus bar and is situated wthin a cover on the near-side of the box (see Fig. 412).

The spring is anchored in the cover by means of an adjustable ball screw at one end and in a swinging bucket on the bus bar.

The spring gear is so arranged that when the gear-engaging pedal is depressed it actuates a cross shaft at the side of the spring gear, which in its turn depresses the bus bar against the spring through the medium of the swinging bucket (see Fig. 412).

When the pedal is depressed the torque exerted on the bus bar is at its minimum, hence the pedal load is lightest at the bottom of its stroke.

The purpose of the swinging bucket is (1) to ensure the correct loading for the top gear ; (2) to increase the torque on the bus bar by providing a much larger leverage when the pedal is released, thus giving the greatest torque for operating the remaining gears.

In some cases an extra bucket is provided in order to give a much lighter load on the pedal at the bottom of its stroke.

LUBRICATION

The gear box is filled to the level of the top of the filler and circulation is by means of an oscillating pump which is located on the driving shaft at the front end of the box. Oil is sucked from the rear end of the gear case and is forced through the pump plunger into the centre of all driving and driven shafts. The bearings and gears are lubricated through channels from the driving and driven shafts. In addition the whole of the moving gear is running in oil, and the selector brake and operating gear are in the oil bath. An *oil drain plug* is provided, and as the top face of this plug forms a stop for the bus bar in its "down" position, care should be taken not to alter the thickness of the washer.

MAINTENANCE

In regard to replenishment of the lubricant in the gear box the latter should be kept filled to the level of the filler spout with Daimler S.C. oil. The use of the correct grade of oil is important, and Daimler S.C. oil is specially supplied for this purpose. The gear box should be drained, washed out with paraffin, and refilled to the level of the filler spout after the first 500 miles, after which it should be inspected and refilled every 1,000 to 1,500 miles. Wash out and refill about every 5,000 miles.

BRAKE ADJUSTMENT

The brake bands in the gear box are self-adjusting, but it is advisable occasionally to "pump" the gear-engaging pedal ten or a dozen times with the engine stationary. This should be repeated with the selector lever in each of the four forward and reverse speed notches, thus keeping the adjustment of the bands at "concert pitch." It is important that the "pumping" should be done with the *full stroke* of the pedal. Any sign of slipping on the lower gears will almost certainly be due to the gear-engaging pedal *not* having been pumped up.

Note.—On bus and coach chassis fitted with this gear box it is recommended that this "pumping" up should be done regularly in the routine maintenance.

It is important to remember that the gear-engaging pedal *must not be used in any way as an ordinary clutch pedal.* Such use causes *excessive wear* of the brake bands.

DRIVING HINTS FOR PRE-SELECTIVE GEAR BOXES

The following notes are based upon the recommendations of the manufacturers, for users of vehicles equipped with their gear boxes.

1. The gears are selected by means of the small lever situated immediately beneath the steering wheel and are brought into operation when required by depressing and releasing the gear-engaging pedal which takes the place of the usual clutch pedal.

2. *To Start.*

(*a*) Switch on and start the engine.

(*b*) Move the selector lever from "neutral" to "first" or "second" position as required.

(*c*) With the engine idling (the hand-throttle lever should be opened just far enough to preserve a moderate idling speed with the gear engaged), depress the gear-engaging pedal fully and then release it completely. The vehicle is now in gear, but as long as the brake is on will remain stationary.

(*d*) Release the brake.

(*e*) Accelerate the engine, when the vehicle will move away with perfect smoothness.

N.B.—It is most important to observe the above sequence exactly under all circumstances.

3. *To Change Up.*

(*a*) Move the selector lever to the desired position as marked on the dial. This does not change the gear but only pre-selects it.

(*b*) Release the accelerator pedal.

(*c*) Depress the gear-engaging pedal fully and then release it completely when the gear will immediately engage. At low speeds no pause is necessary between depressing and releasing the pedal, but at high speeds a pause should be made in the depressed position, the length of such pause being proportioned to the speed.

4. *To Change Down.*

Observe the same procedure as in 3 above, but *do not* alter the position of the accelerator pedal—keep it in the same position as it was when running in the previous gear.

5. *To Reverse.*

(*a*) To select reverse, it is necessary to lift the selector lever over a catch.

(*b*) Observe the same general procedure as in 3 and 4 above, but remember that reverse is a very low gear and the vehicle will be found to be very sensitive to the control of the accelerator. It will, therefore, be found better to use the hand throttle—barely opened—instead of the accelerator and to control the vehicle by means of the foot brake.

6. *To Stop.*

(*a*) Merely apply the brakes and the vehicle will come to rest in gear with the engine idling.

(*b*) If leaving the vehicle stationary, select " neutral " on the dial; depress the gear-engaging pedal fully and then release it completely. Then switch off.

7. *General.*

(*a*) It is most important that the gear-engaging pedal should not be used in any way as a clutch, and should at all times be operated with a " clean " motion (i.e. pressed down fully and then released completely).

(*b*) There are several ways in which the Daimler transmission system may be used as an emergency safety device, such as braking by engaging first or reverse gear while still going forward, holding the vehicle on steep gradients by means of the throttle, and the like. It is *most important*, however, to remember that *repeated* use of these practices places abnormal strains on the brake bands in the gear box and may also damage the fluid flywheel by generating excessive heat. They should, therefore, only be carried out in *actual emergency*.

ADJUSTMENT OF PRE-SELECTIVE GEAR TOGGLE ACTION

The only adjustment that is necessary on the pre-selective gear box concerns the toggle action which controls the adjustment of the brakes. *If the gears tend to slip* more toggle action is required.

The gear box should first be given a preliminary inspection. To do this the cover should be removed from the top of the gear box. Before commencing the adjustment, set the selection lever to the gear that is about to be adjusted and make a mark on the brake-adjusting nut with an indelible pencil. Pump up the gear-engaging pedal until it is seen that the mark on the brake-adjusting nut has ceased to revolve.

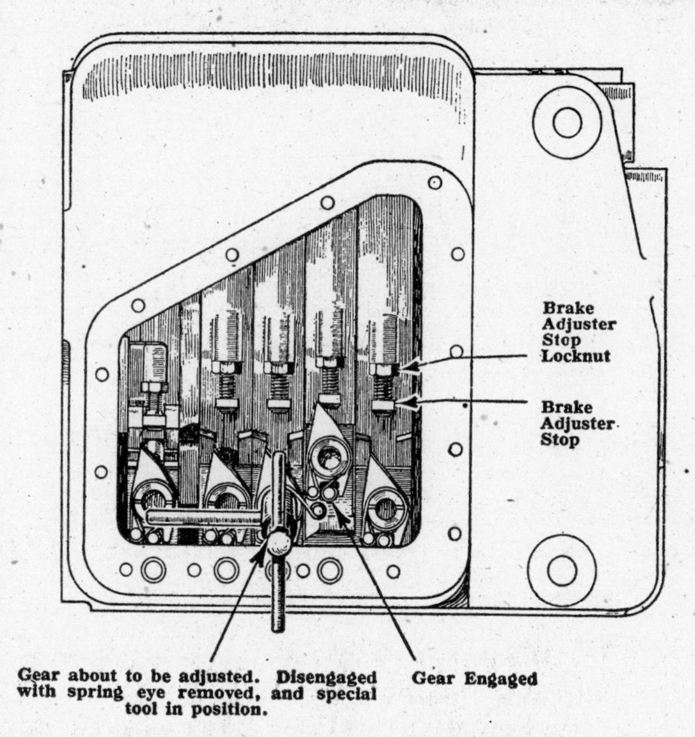

Fig. 413.—Adjusting the Toggle Action.

Presuming the adjusting nut remains stationary, see that there is freedom of travel on the bus-bar operating lever, as shown in Fig. 413. If the gear still slips after the above conditions have been fulfilled and if the free movement is greater than that shown for the specified type of gear box, increased toggle action can be given to this particular gear by proceeding as follows :

TO INCREASE TOGGLE ACTION

1. Make sure that the gear about to be adjusted is disengaged.

Note.—When adjusting reverse and first gears, neutral must not be selected, as these two are partly engaged when neutral is selected.

2. Loosen the lock nut on the brake-adjuster stop situated on the brake band, screw in the brake-adjuster stop a half-turn, and lock up.

3. Remove one spring eye from the pillar—there is no necessity to remove the spring completely.

4. Slack back by half a turn the tapped automatic adjuster nut.
5. Replace the spring on the spring pillar.
6. Select the gear which has just been adjusted.
7. Pump up until automatic adjuster nut stops turning. A suitable tool is provided by the makers for turning this nut.

If the gear still slips after adjusting, as directed, the toggle action can be further increased by repeating the procedure. *It is important to observe,* however, that the amount of free travel "A" (Fig. 410) on any gear must not be less than that given for the first and reverse gears.

Top-gear Adjustment.—Slack back the top-gear automatic adjuster nut and pump up until the point is reached where the travel of the mechanism suddenly decreases. Mark the adjuster nut and continue to pump up. The adjuster nut should cease to move after a quarter of a turn from the marked position. *This is the correct setting.* Check this adjustment before altering the adjuster nut.

To Decrease Toggle Action.—Should it be necessary to decrease the toggle action first loosen the lock nut on the brake-adjuster stop and screw out the adjuster stop half a turn. Then pump up until the automatic adjuster nut stops turning.

For *all plate-clutch types of gear box* it should be observed that the adjuster nut should cease to move *after it has completed three-quarters of a turn from the marked position.*

When checking this adjustment make certain that the travel of the front clutch plate is not less than $\frac{1}{10}$ in. Reduction of toggle action below this point may cause excessive drag in neutral.

SERVICING THE PRE-SELECTIVE GEAR BOX

The servicing of this type of gear box is a matter for the expert mechanic trained in pre-selective gear-box overhaul. It involves a knowledge of the dismantling, relining of the brakes, reassembling, adjusting and checking the assembly.

Space limitations will not allow us to describe the somewhat lengthy servicing procedure, but it may be mentioned that the Daimler Company, Ltd., Coventry, publish a small booklet on the *Fluid Flywheel Self-changing Transmission,* giving detailed instructions concerning the servicing of the pre-selective gear box.

THE HAYES SELF-SELECTOR TRANSMISSION

This automatically operated variable-speed mechanism is fitted as an alternative to the standard Austin gear box on the 16-h.p. and 20-h.p. models. It replaces the ordinary gear box and automatically selects the best gear ratio to suit the engine speed and road resistance. It retains the ordinary clutch for starting and stopping, but dispenses with the usual gear-change lever, although a lever is provided for selecting the forward and reverse positions.

The principle of the Hayes transmission can readily be understood from a consideration of the ordinary ball type of thrust race shown in Fig. 414 *a*. Normally the central race B is kept fixed, whilst the races A rotate in the same directions ; the ball-race cages C also rotate.

If, however, the central race is left free and the cages C are fixed, then the two outer races will, as before, revolve in the same direction, and the balls will be rotated in their fixed cages C, thus imparting, by frictional action, a rotating effect to the race B ; the latter will therefore rotate in the reverse direction to the races A. Fig. 414 *b* shows one of the balls between two races A and B, the arrows indicating the directions of movement of the outer and inner races as well as that of the ball in the case of a journal-type ball-bearing having the cage fixed.

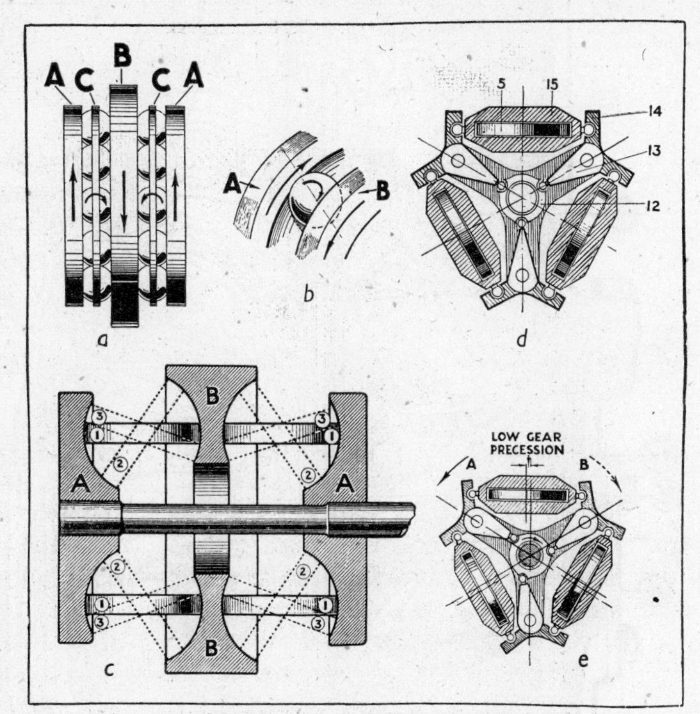

Fig. 414.

In the case of the Hayes transmission (Fig. 414 *c*) the same principle is employed, but instead of having flat races and balls, as in *a*, specially contoured races A and B are employed, in conjunction with narrow rollers 1. The curvature of the two outer races has been increased so as to give " toroidal " surfaces.

With the rollers in position 1, able to rotate on their own axes, yet unable to travel around the race, as they are anchored to an outside object, the transmission from the two outer races A to the double-centre race B will be exactly the same as in the case of the double ball thrust bearing shown in *a*.

As the rollers when in position 1 rotate on tracks of the same diameter on both A and B, the speeds of A and B will be the same, although in opposite directions. If, however, the rollers are tilted to occupy position 2, they will be driven by a smaller diameter of A on to a larger diameter of B. If the diameter of contact of A is one-third that of B the race B will revolve at one-third of the speed of A ; the gear ratio will then be 3 : 1. This tilting of the rollers is the means employed for varying the gear ratio. It is merely a matter of rocking or precessing the rollers to engage with the races A and B on different diameters.

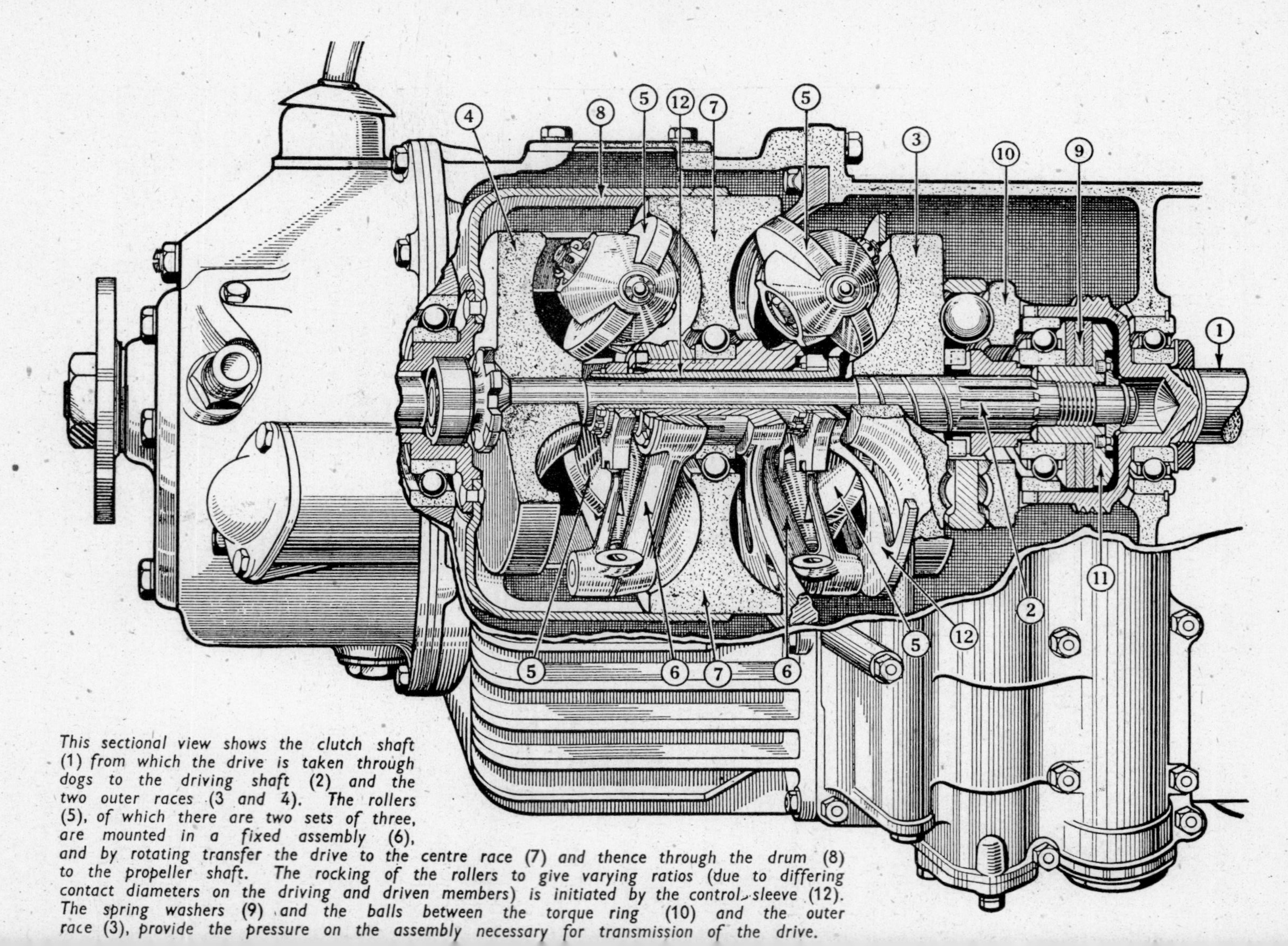

This sectional view shows the clutch shaft (1) from which the drive is taken through dogs to the driving shaft (2) and the two outer races (3 and 4). The rollers (5), of which there are two sets of three, are mounted in a fixed assembly (6), and by rotating transfer the drive to the centre race (7) and thence through the drum (8) to the propeller shaft. The rocking of the rollers to give varying ratios (due to differing contact diameters on the driving and driven members) is initiated by the control sleeve (12). The spring washers (9) and the balls between the torque ring (10) and the outer race (3), provide the pressure on the assembly necessary for transmission of the drive.

Given a gradual form of control an infinite variation of ratio is possible between the limits of the angular rotation of the rollers. This, as Fig. 414 *c* shows, is an extensive one, and in practice ranges from a low gear of about 4 : 1 to an over-gear position (corresponding to position 3 in Fig. 414 *c*) of 1 : 1·7 ; the engine in the latter cases rotates once for every 1·7 revolutions of the propeller shaft ; the range of gear ratios is much greater than that given by any normal gear box.

The complete gear is shown in Fig. 415. The drive is transmitted by the clutch shaft 1 through dogs to the driving shaft 2.

Floating on this shaft are the two outer races (3 and 4), being only connected by dogs for the drive. The steel rollers 5 are supported in the fixed roller assembly 6 which bolts between the two outer casings. The assembly consists of two sets of three rollers (Fig. 414 *e*) which can rotate on their own axes and, being mounted in carriers 15, can rock to various ratio positions.

These transmit the drive from the two steel outer races (3 and 4) to the steel double inner race 7, from which it is conveyed by the large drum 8 to the propeller shaft. As the rollers and races reverse the direction of motion the final drive in the rear axle has to be reversed also, by placing the crown wheel on the off-side instead of on the near-side, of the bevel pinion.

To transmit any given power a certain pressure must exist between the two sets of rollers and their four races. The initial pressure is obtained by three spring washers 9, giving about 1,400 lb. load on the rollers ; additional pressure is provided in a loading device incorporated in

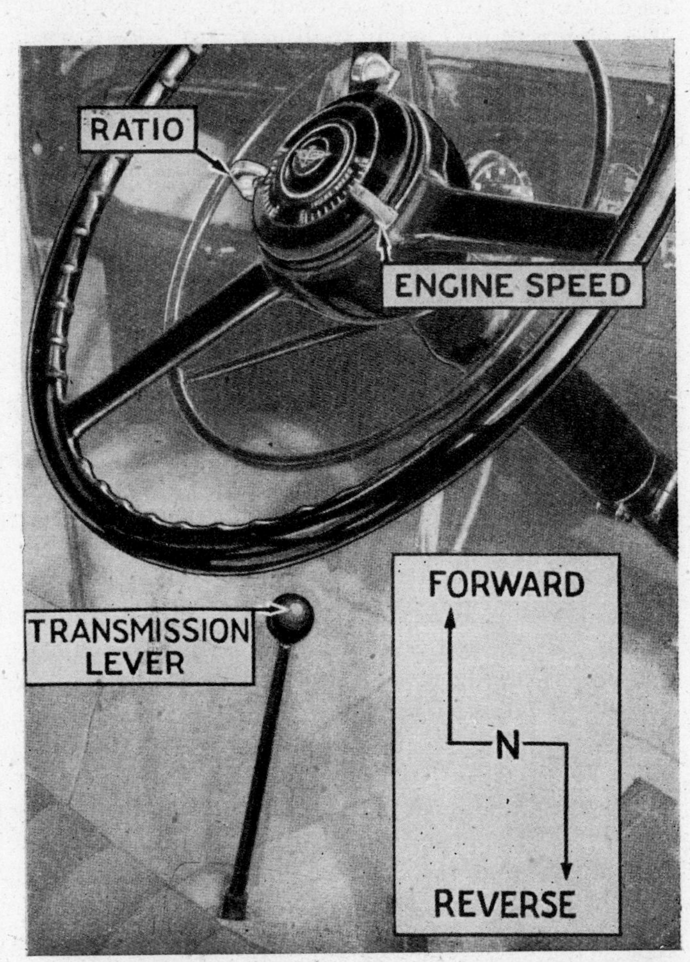

Fig. 416.—Above are shown the Three Controls for the Hayes Self-selector Transmission, namely, the Transmission Lever, and the "Engine Speed" and "Ratio" Levers above the Steering Wheel. The diagram in the right-hand bottom corner shows the movement of the transmission lever for engaging forward or reverse.

the drive. The clutch shaft is dogged to a floating torque ring 10 and the outer race 3, as previously mentioned, also floats, but engages by means of dogs with the drive shaft 2. Grooves in the opposing faces of the torque ring and outer race form inclines for three balls carried between the two members. These balls provide the drive by reason of their wedging action between the inclines. This action further serves to apply an end thrust on the entire roller mechanism towards the rear outer race 4, which is supported by the spring washers 9.

The pressure exerted on the rollers renders it impracticable to change the drive ratio by directly rocking them, so that the alternative method used is to alter slightly the axial position of each roller, thus allowing it to "precess" or roll of its own accord (Fig. 414 *e*) into a new path of contact. Referring to Fig. 415, the control sleeve 12 is linked by special levers to an hydraulic control unit. This sleeve rotates to move the lever 13 (shown more clearly in Fig. 414 *d*); here, 12 is the control sleeve round the mainshaft which operates the three rockers 14. These support the carriers 15 in which the rollers 5 are mounted. These roller carriers have ball ends to provide a universal mounting in the rocker arms; the rollers can therefore rock to any ratio position. Rotation of the sleeve 12 transmitted to the main rocker levers 13 causes the rollers to assume (for instance) the position shown in Fig. 414 *e*, and this displacement of the roller axes initiates precession of the rollers which sends them to the new ratio position over a spiral path on the races.

The hydraulic control unit comprises a pump, driven at half engine speed, to create oil pressure in the control cylinder on top of the control piston. As the oil pressure increases with the engine speed, movement is imparted to the piston which is communicated to the control sleeve to initiate precession of the rollers so as to give a higher ratio.

The driver's controls consist of two small levers above the steering wheel and a transmission lever to engage the forward or reverse drive (Fig. 416).

The control lever on the right works on a scale marked "Engine Speed," whilst the left one operates on a scale marked "Ratio." With the forward drive engaged by the transmission lever, the setting of the two control levers determines the automatic performance of the transmission.

THE LEYLAND HYDRAULIC TORQUE CONVERTER

Many of the Leyland commercial and passenger-vehicle chassis are fitted with a patent hydraulic torque converter in place of the usual clutch and gear box. The device in question incorporates the Lysholm-Smith patent.

The only controls fitted are the accelerator, brakes, and a direct-drive device for top-gear work. *No clutch* is necessary and is therefore not fitted. Moreover, there is *no gear-changing*, for the gear ratio is altered automatically by the torque converter. The driver has only to accelerate the vehicle to increase its speed or power output; when a hill is reached the converter automatically changes the gear ratio to a higher value in order to obtain a greater torque.

No gears are used for the forward motion, the drive through the converter being hydraulic; as a result, the unit is extremely quiet in action. The vehicle glides off, from rest, when the brakes are released and the accelerator pedal depressed. It may even be permitted to run backwards down a hill and then checked by pressing on the accelerator, stopped and propelled forward without any shock.

The converter gives a smooth and rapid acceleration and relieves the driver of any physical or mental exhaustion. Another point in its favour

Fig. 417.—The Race and Roller Assembly of the new Hayes Self-selector Transmission for the Austin Sixteen.

is the interposition of the hydraulic unit between the engine and the rear wheels, so that an excellent oil-damping effect is obtained to eliminate shocks and vibration.

The complete converter unit,[1] with reverse gearing, is housed in a casing similar in size, shape, and weight to the standard Leyland gear box and clutch; this casing is bolted to the rear end of the engine crankcase. It contains, in order from the engine end:

(1) A double-acting clutch for connecting the engine either to the torque converter or directly to the rear axle as required.

(2) The hydraulic system of the converter.

[1] Fully described in *Modern Motor Cars and Commercial Vehicles* (The Caxton Publishing Co., Ltd., London).

(3) A free-wheel device to relieve the converter from over-run effects on the road.

(4) The reverse gear.

The object of the torque converter is to multiply the engine torque in much the same way as by the ordinary gear box. Whilst it is quite possible to drive through the converter at all times, there are definite advantages in providing a direct drive for use on level roads at cruising speeds; an additional drive of this type is therefore provided. The drive from the engine is taken through one or other of the two friction clutches, a single lever in the driver's cab being used to operate both through a simple toggle mechanism. The clutch disc nearest the engine is mounted on a shaft passing through the centre of the converter to the rear axle; this provides the direct "top" drive. The second clutch is mounted on a hollow shaft, the other end of which is connected to the impeller inside the converter casing. These clutches, it should be remembered, are couplings, not clutches as used on ordinary gear-box vehicles.

THE HYDRAULIC SYSTEM

The torque converter consists essentially of a centrifugal pump mounted in a single casing with a three-stage hydraulic turbine. The pump member, which is coupled to the engine fly-wheel by means of the clutch mentioned above, is similar in form to the impeller of the familiar water-circulating pump. The turbine, which is connected to the rear axle through the free-wheel described later, consists of a bladed rotor on which three separate rows of blades are fixed in such a position that they are divided by two rings of stationary blades fixed to the casing. The casing is completely filled with fluid so that when power from the engine is transmitted to the pump the fluid is driven from the pump on to the first set of rotor blades R1 (Fig. 418), then through the stationary blades S1, where its flow is redirected on to the second set of rotating blades R2, through the stationary blades S2, where its direction is again changed on to the third set of moving blades, R3, and so back to the pump. Owing to the shape of the blading and the fact that the fluid impinges on three sets of blades coupled in series, torque can be increased up to the ratio of 4·8 to 1.

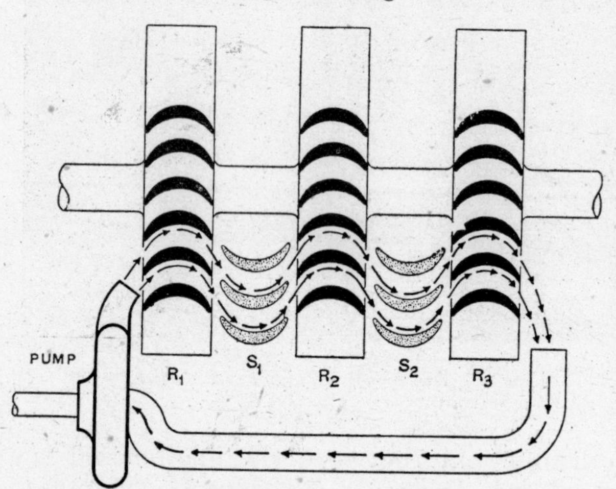

Fig. 418.—Showing Principle of the Hydraulic System.

Labyrinth seals are used in the design to prevent short-circuiting of the fluid between the rotor and casing. Other seals are included to prevent loss of fluid. Slight leakage through these seals is encouraged, however, for the purpose of lubrication, but the fluid thus passing is collected in a small sump and returned to the reserve tank by an ejector fitted in the tank.

Referring to the sectional illustration of the actual torque converter, shown in Fig. 419,[1] the clutch disc A nearest the engine is a shaft passing through the centre of the converter to the rear axle and provides the direct drive. A second clutch disc B is mounted on a hollow shaft C, the other end of which is connected to the impeller inside the converter

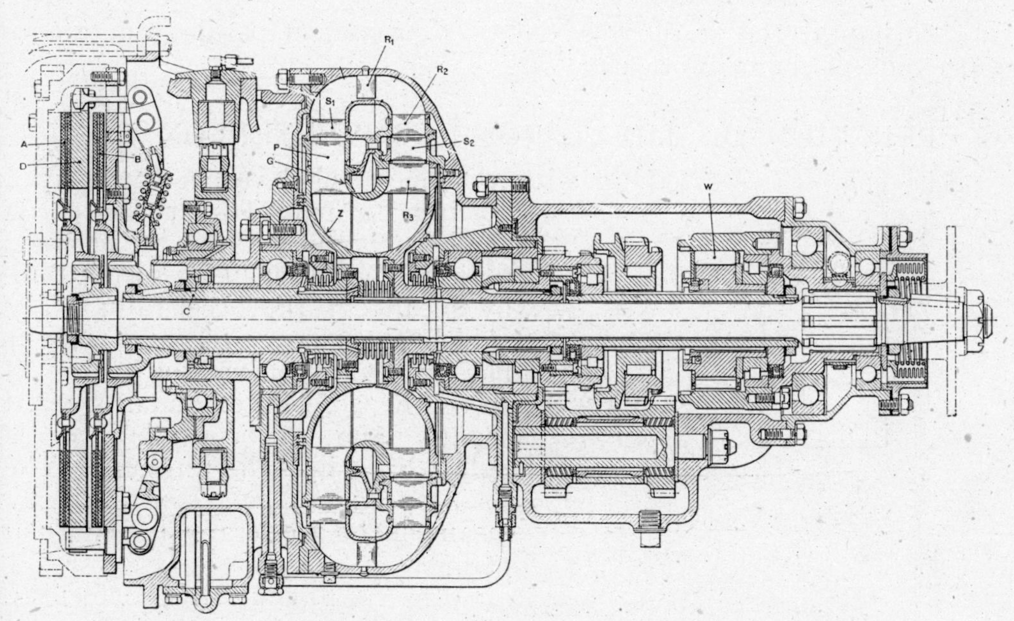

Fig. 419.—A Sectional View of the Leyland Hydraulic Converter Unit.

casing, so forming the drive to the converter. As the clutches are used as couplings only and do not take up the drive as in the conventional clutch, they are subject to little wear. Although not strictly necessary, an intermediate position is provided for the drive plate D, in which position both clutches are disengaged for safety in starting the engine.

It should be noted that the various blades are given the same reference numbers in Fig. 419 as in the diagrammatic sketch in Fig. 418. The pump blades are marked P; the centre carrier ring G; the pump centre Z; and the free-wheel member W. The latter is provided on the shaft driven by the turbine rotor. Thus the converter is completely isolated and comes to rest immediately its clutch is disengaged, so permitting a direct drive in which there can be neither slip nor hydraulic loss. Also it makes coasting possible with absolute safety when the vehicle is being driven through the converter, for should the engine be stopped

[1] Courtesy of *Machinery*.

inadvertently it can be restarted immediately by engaging the direct-drive clutch.

The free-wheel is of the well-tried mechanical type in which a number of rollers, positioned in recesses round the inner or driving member, are used to lock the forward motion. The inner member is driven by the converter and the outer is coupled directly to the propeller shaft. The free-wheel unit is of ample proportions and, taking its drive only through the hydraulic system, works under ideal conditions.

LIQUID USED IN CONVERTER

The liquid used to fill the converter consists of paraffin containing 5 per cent. of engine lubricating oil.

OPERATION OF THE TORQUE CONVERTER ON ROAD

The engine is started up with the operating lever in the neutral position as usual. To start the vehicle the lever is pushed into the forward position and the engine is speeded up, by means of the accelerator. The vehicle then moves off, and when it has reached the usual top-gear road speed the accelerator pedal is eased slightly and the control lever is pulled back into the top gear. The road speed is then controlled by means of the accelerator in the usual manner.

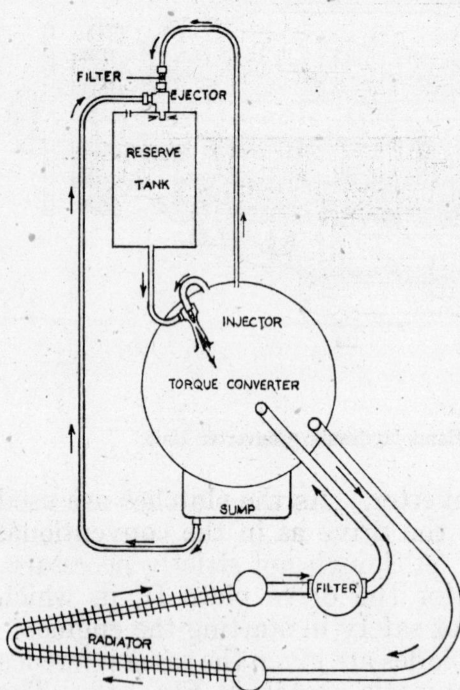

Fig. 420.—Circulation Diagram for Torque Converter.

When approaching stopping places, the control lever is pushed forward, the accelerator released, and the vehicle then glides to rest under the control of its brakes. To restart, the driver merely releases the hand brake, presses the accelerator pedal until top speed is attained, when the lever is pulled back again.

For hilly country the direct or top speed is disengaged and the engine output is controlled by the accelerator only, when the gear ratio is adjusted, automatically, to suit the gradient or load.

MAINTENANCE NOTES

In order to understand the maintenance of the Leyland converter it is necessary to know how the fluid circulates. The circulation diagram is given in Fig. 420. In regard to the leakage of fluid, previously referred to, the fluid is evacuated from this sump and returned to the reserve tank by means of a small ejector situated on top of the reserve tank. The operation of this ejector, shown in Fig. 421, is automatic and is as follows: A pressure pipe from the converter is connected to the ejector nozzle A. The fluid in the converter, being under pressure, is forced along this pipe through the nozzle, thus increasing its velocity, which causes a vacuum to be established in the annular space around the nozzle. This annular passage is in communication with the sump by way of a pipe, and fluid which has leaked into the sump is lifted to the reserve tank (see Fig. 420). A gauze filter B, Fig. 421, protects the nozzle from dirt.

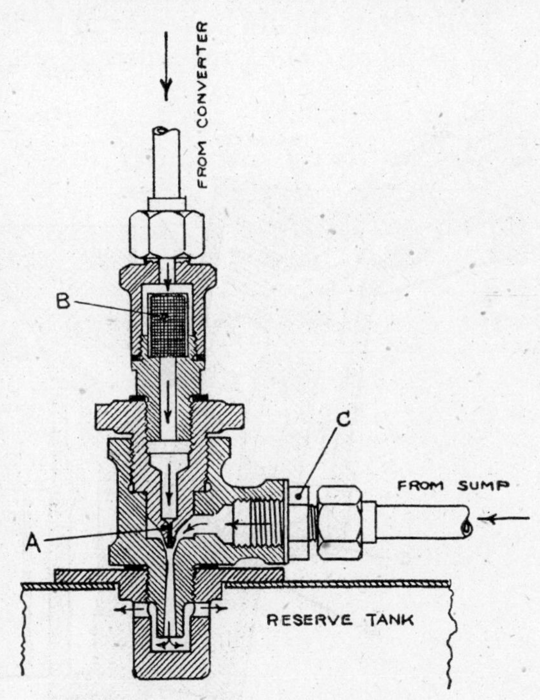

Fig. 421.—The Ejector Device.

In the event of more fluid passing the seals than the ejector can evacuate, the surplus fluid is allowed to escape to the road by means of a stand pipe in the sump.

To keep the converter casing full of fluid, an injector is provided, shown in Fig. 423. This operates by utilising the difference in pressure in the converter casing to cause a flow of fluid through the venturi nozzle D. A vacuum is thus created around the annulus and fluid from the reserve tank is drawn in at E and delivered under pressure to the converter at a point where the pressure is low.

The pressure in the converter is limited by the pressure-relief valve F, which cuts off the supply by by-passing fluid when the casing is full.

Under extreme conditions of operation the fluid heats up somewhat and is liable to gasify. To prevent the temperature becoming excessive, a small radiator is carried on the frame side-member and connected by pipes to the high- and low-pressure sides of the converter. An efficient felt filter is provided in the return pipe between the radiator and converter.

The clutch-withdrawal race, operating fork bushes, and converter-shaft front bearings are lubricated from three Tecalemit nipples on the near-side front lubrication battery. These points should receive weekly attention, a small quantity of gear oil only being given so that excess does not reach the clutches.

The reverse gear box is lubricated with engine oil. Gear oil or grease must not be used. Remove the filler plug weekly and inspect the level, which should be just up to the lowest thread in the filler-plug hole (or ½ in. below outlet). Replenish if necessary, but do not fill beyond this level.

CONVERTER FLUID

The fluid used in the converter is high-boiling-point paraffin to which is added 5 per cent. of engine oil.

The reserve-tank level should be checked daily and replenished if necessary. Great care must be taken when filling the reserve tank to ensure that the fluid is perfectly clean. A petrol strainer, or preferably a cloth, should be used when filling up.

Both filters should be removed periodically and washed thoroughly in clean paraffin. The gauze filter B, Fig. 418, is removed by disconnecting the pressure pipe and unscrewing the filter. This should be done once a week.

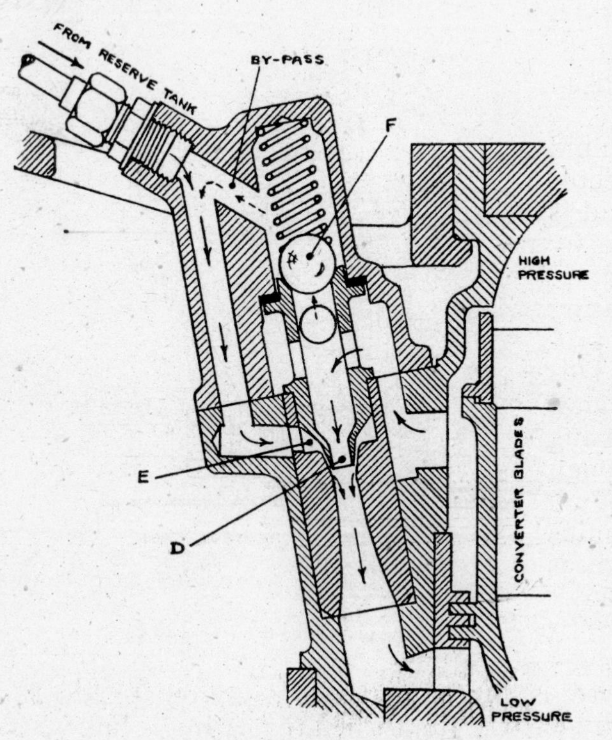

Fig. 422.—The Injector Device for Keeping Converter Casing Full of Fluid.

The felt filter on the frame member in front of the fluid radiator can be removed by detaching the bottom plate from the filter casing. When replacing, make sure that the joint is secure or leakage will result. This filter should be cleaned once a month.

Check over all pipe unions periodically for tightness.

POSSIBLE FAULTS

In regard to the possible faults, these include *poor performance* and *overheating*.

Loss of performance may be due to *gas in the converter casing* or a *choked injector*.

Other possible faults are those of *engine revolutions higher than the normal in converter drive*; *stiffness of the control lever*; *failure of control to act*; and *failure of the free-wheel*.

These faults and the methods of curing them are dealt with fully, with the aid of explanatory diagrams, in *The Leyland Service Manual for Torque Converter*.

THE SINGER "FLUIDRIVE" TRANSMISSION

The Singer 11- and 16-h.p. cars are fitted with an original form of transmission having several advantageous features.

The lay-out of the transmission is shown in Fig. 423. The engine crankshaft rear-end is at A; the "fluidrive" unit at B; clutch at C; clutch-withdrawal fork at D, and gear box at E. There is also a free-wheel device F at the rear of the gear box to facilitate gear-changing and to give higher road mileages for a given fuel consumption, owing to the free-wheeling operation. The "fluidrive" unit, one part of which is attached to the engine crankshaft and the other to the clutch shaft, is a kind of hydraulic clutch or fluid flywheel.

The following are details of the Singer transmission:

The "fluidrive" coupling results in an extremely smooth transmission

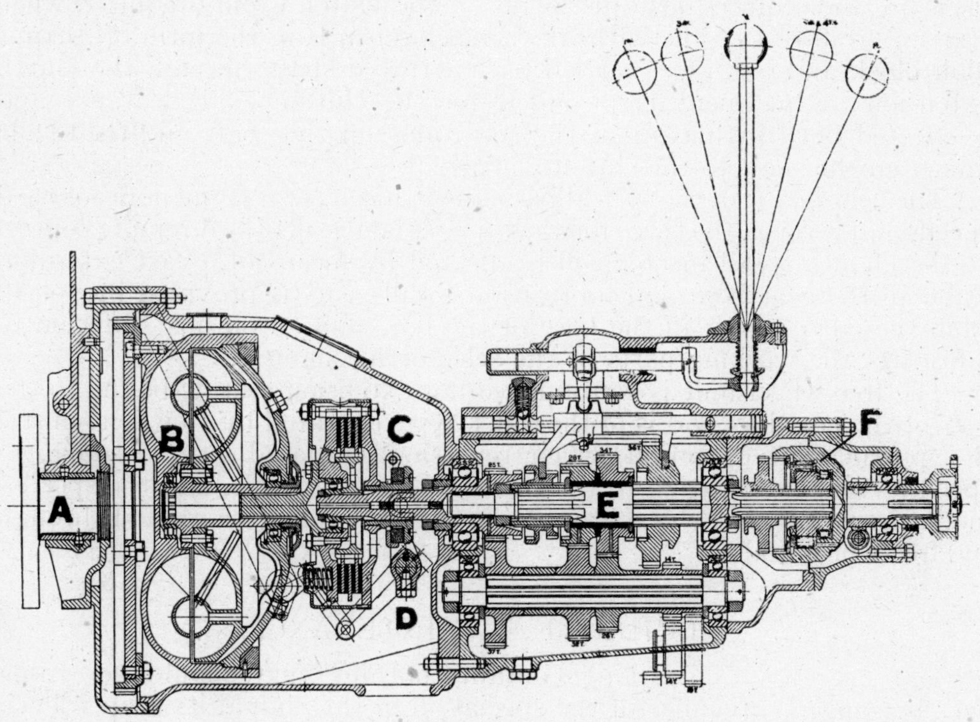

Fig. 423.—The Singer "Fluidrive" Transmission System.

with flexibility of drive on all gears, very low-speed pulling, rapid acceleration, and very easy gear changing.

The "fluidrive" coupling in appearance is very similar to an enclosed dry-plate clutch, but actually consists of two parts only—the driving and driven members (Fig. 423). The driving member is bolted to the flywheel and the driven member free to revolve on a centre sleeve carried on two ball-races in the flywheel casing. The centre sleeve is splined to carry the clutch driving shaft and is also fitted with an oil-retaining ring to prevent loss of fluid.

It will be noted from Fig. 423 that the driven and driving members carry cup-shaped cells, and a small gap separates the driving member from the driven member. The fluid flywheel transmits power in the following manner. Assuming the car to be stationary and the engine running, the rotation of the driving member by the engine causes the oil in its cells to flow towards their outside periphery, and as the driven member is motionless the oil flows past the outside periphery of its cells, through them, and past their inside periphery to the inside periphery of the driving-member cells, and from there back again. In passing from the cells of the driving to those of the driven members, the oil is retarded in velocity and therefore imparts some of its momentum to the driven member, thereby setting it in motion.

The clutch is of the automatic multi-plate type, using low pedal pressure, and requires no adjustmenlt. The clutch is only required when starting from rest. The withdrawa mechanism is in the form of a trunnion block and ball-race, carried on a serrated shaft through the clutch extension; adjustment is provided for the clutch-pedal clearance and is effected both by means of the serrations on the shaft and the toggle link from the shaft to the clutch foot pedal.

The gear box is of the helical permanent-mesh type, giving four forward speeds and reverse, the three forward speeds being silent. A remote control of the change-speed mechanism is effected by means of a cast extension fitted to the gear box, and lubrication to all gears is provided by splash from the oil reservoir in the base of the box, and an oil mist sufficiently lubricates the working parts of the selector mechanism.

The free-wheel unit is contained in an extension casting bolted to the rear of the gear box and is of the roller type, operated by Bowden control (for putting out of action, when reversing), situated near the change-speed lever. Lubrication to the free-wheel is automatic, and the speedometer drive is by skew gear from the mainshaft extension carried through the free-wheel body.

"FLUIDRIVE" MAINTENANCE

The "fluidrive" coupling contains nothing that should go wrong and, beyond maintenance of the special oil in this unit at its proper level, there is no further attention required.

The "fluidrive" coupling contains approximately 5½ pints of Singer "Special" Fluidrive oil. This oil can be procured in pint tins from any of the service depots or dealers, and this oil only should be used.

It is necessary about every 6,000 miles, to inspect the level of oil in the "fluidrive" coupling and this is best carried out after a run when the oil is warm. It is necessary to remove the inspection plate from the clutch housing and turn the coupling until one of the two filler plugs is in a position equivalent to the figure ten on a clock face. This position is, of course, shown from the rear of the engine, that is, looking from the driver's seat. The filler plug should then be removed and oil poured into the coupling until the level of the plug is reached. Under no circumstances must the coupling be filled with the filler plug in any position other than that described above, as this, of course will alter the level of oil contained in the coupling.